# Biology Today and Tomorrow with Physiology

3rd Edition

Cecie Starr | Christine Evers | Lisa Starr

CENGAGE
Learning™

Australia • Brazil • Japan • Korea • Mexico • Singapore • Spain • United Kingdom • United States

## CENGAGE
Learning™

**Biology Today and Tomorrow with Physiology: 3rd Edition**

Cecie Starr | Christine Evers | Lisa Starr

Executive Editor:
 Maureen Staudt
 Michael Stranz

Senior Project Development Manager:
 Linda de Stefano

Marketing Specialist:
 Sara Mercurio
 Lindsay Shapiro

Production/Manufacturing Manager:
 Donna M. Brown

PreMedia Supervisor:
 Joel Brennecke

Rights & Permissions Specialist:
 Kalina Hintz
 Todd Osborne

Cover Image:
 Getty Images*

For product information and technology assistance, contact us at
**Cengage Learning Customer & Sales Support, 1-800-354-9706**

For permission to use material from this text or product,
submit all requests online at **cengage.com/permissions**
Further permissions questions can be emailed to
**permissionrequest@cengage.com**

ISBN-13: 978-1-4240-8068-7

ISBN-10: 1-4240-8068-1

**Cengage Learning**
5191 Natorp Boulevard
Mason, Ohio 45040
USA

Cengage Learning is a leading provider of customized learning solutions with office locations around the globe, including Singapore, the United Kingdom, Australia, Mexico, Brazil, and Japan. Locate your local office at: **international.cengage.com/region**

Cengage Learning products are represented in Canada by Nelson Education, Ltd.

For your lifelong learning solutions, visit **www.cengage.com/custom**

Visit our corporate website at **www.cengage.com**

Printed in the United States of America
1 2 3 4 5 6 7 12 11 10 09 08

# Brief Contents

# Preface

Throughout our lives, we are called upon to make important decisions based on our understanding of science, whatever that understanding may be. This book was designed and written specifically for students who do not intend to become biologists and may never again take another science course. It is an accessible and engaging introduction to biology that provides future decision-makers with a basic understanding of biology and the process of science.

**Accessible Text** Understanding stems mainly from making connections between concepts and details, so a text with too little detail reads as a series of facts that beg to be memorized. However, too much detail overwhelms the introductory student. Thus, we authors are constantly trying to strike the perfect balance between level of detail and accessibility. We revised every page of this edition to pare detail to the minimum level we felt was necessary for the student to be able to make connections. We also know that English is a second language for many students, so we wrote in a clear and straightforward style.

This edition includes many analogies to familiar objects and phenomena that will help students understand abstract concepts. For example, in the discussion of covalent bonding in Chapter 2 (Molecules of Life), we explain that sharing electrons links two atoms, just as sharing earphones links two friends. A graphic of linked listeners (*right*) reinforces the explanation in the text.

**A Wealth of Applications** This book is packed with examples of applications that are relevant to a student's daily life (as marked by red squares in the index). At every opportunity, discussions of biological processes are enlivened by references to their effects on human health and the environment. Each chapter begins with an **IMPACTS/ISSUES** section

that explores a current event or controversy directly related to the chapter's content. For example, in Chapter 2, a discussion of *trans* fats and their effects on health introduces the structure–function relationship of molecules. The introductory topic is integrated into the chapter material and the new **IMPACTS/ ISSUES REVISITED** section that ends each

chapter. This ending section uses chapter content to reinforce and expand the topic presented in the opening essay. In chapter 2, for example, we link the function of hydrolysis enzymes to the unhealthy effects of *trans* fats. We also pose an associated **HOW-WOULD-YOU-VOTE QUESTION** that gives students the opportunity to practice making an informed choice about a science-related controversy. The student web site provides access to articles and other material that the student can use when considering the question.

**Emphasis on the Process of Science** Throughout the book, descriptions of current research and photos of the scientists who do it drive home the message that science is an ongoing endeavor carried out by a diverse community of people. For example, Chapter 5 (Capturing and Releasing Energy) discusses the biofuels research of two young scientists at North Carolina State University (*right*). Research topics include not only what researchers have already discovered, but also how discoveries were made, how our understanding has changed over time, and what remains under investigation.

To strengthen a student's analytical skills and offer further insight into contemporary research, each chapter now includes an exercise on **DIGGING INTO DATA**. The exercise consists of a short text passage—usually about a published scientific experiment—and a table, chart, or other graphic that presents experimental data. The student can use information in the text and graphic to answer a series of questions.

**In-Text Learning Tools** To facilitate learning, each chapter consists of several numbered sections that contain a manageable chunk of information. Every section ends with a boxed **TAKE-HOME MESSAGE** in which we pose a question that reflects the critical content of the section, and then answer the question in bulleted list format. Every chapter has at least one **FIGURE IT OUT QUESTION** with an answer immediately following. These questions allow students to quickly check their understanding as they read. Mastering scientific vocabulary challenges many students, so we have included an **ON-PAGE GLOSSARY** of key terms introduced in each two-page spread, in addition to a complete glossary at the book's end. The end-of-chapter material features a **VISUAL SUMMARY** that reinforces each chapter's key concepts. A **SELF-QUIZ** poses multiple choice and other short answer questions for self-assessment (answers are in Appendix I). A set of more challenging **CRITICAL THINKING QUESTIONS** provides thought-provoking exercises for the motivated student.

**Design and Content Revisions** Previous adopters of *Biology: Today and Tomorrow* will notice that this edition features a dramatically different design. Each chapter now opens with a stunning piece of art designed to encourage student interest in the chapter's topic. The art is also used to illustrate one of the concepts within the chapter. A one-column design gives this book a simple look, and it allows placement of the on-page glossary. The following list highlights some of the revisions to each chapter. A page-by-page guide to revised content and figures is available upon request from your sales representative.

Introduction - Chapter 1 has a new Impacts/Issues section about the discovery of new species, and a new section on critical thinking. Expanded discussions of philosophy and process of science.

Unit I How Cells Work
• Chapter 2 has a new Impacts/Issues section about *trans* fats.
• Chapter 3 has a new Impacts/Issues section about foodborne *E. coli* O157:H7.
• Chapter 4 sections on energy and metabolism have been reorganized and rewritten. The new Impacts/Issues Revisited section covers alcohol metabolism and alcoholic liver disease.
• Chapter 5 now has integrated coverage of photosynthesis and energy-releasing pathways. A new Impacts/Issues about biofuels opens the chapter, and the Impacts/Issues Revisited section introduces the problem of rising atmospheric carbon dioxide.

Unit II Genetics - Material within this unit has been rearranged.
• Chapters 6 describes the structure of chromosomes, and discusses the structure and function of DNA.
• Chapter 7 covers gene expression. Gene control material reworked to focus on human examples such as breast cancer.
• Chapter 8 covers mitosis and meiosis. Revised mitosis spread juxtaposes photos of mitosis in animal and plant cells.
• Chapter 9 covers inheritance. Revised Impacts/Issues section shows a panel of young victims of cystic fibrosis. Tracking traits section has a new essay about human skin color.
• Chapter 10 covers genetic engineering. Content has been simplified and updated with current information and examples.

Unit III Evolution and Diversity - Material within this unit has been rearranged.
• Chapter 11 covers Darwin's theory and evidence of evolution. Transitional fossils and comparative embryology photo series added. New spread visually correlates sedimentary rock layers in the Grand Canyon with periods in the geologic time scale.
• Chapter 12 covers processes of evolution (microevolution, speciation, macroevolution) and classification systems. Revised and expanded coverage of reproductive isolation, cladistics.
• Chapter 13 covers prokaryotes, protists, and viruses. Impacts/Issues section now focuses on the causes of AIDS and malaria.
• Chapter 14 now covers plants and fungi. It opens with an Issues/Impacts section about Nobel Prize winner Wangari Maathai's efforts to replant trees and slow deforestation.
• Chapter 15 has a revised Impacts/Issues section that includes information about additional early bird fossils. New material added about placazoans. Birds are now discussed under the Reptile subhead. Human evolution has been updated to include a discussion of *H. floresiensis*.

• The chapter comparing plants and animals has been deleted.

Unit IV Ecology - The order of material within this unit has been altered and the chapter about animal behavior has been deleted.
• Chapter 16 covers population ecology and has a new Impacts/Issues about population explosions of Canada geese.
• Chapter 17 covers communities and ecosystems, previously covered in two separate chapters.
• Chapter 18 covers the biosphere and human effects. It opens with a new Impacts/Issues about threats to the Arctic and includes increased coverage of global climate change.

Unit V How Animals Work
• Chapter 19 has an updated Impacts/Issues section about stem cells. Homeostasis and thermoregulation now covered here.
• Chapter 20 has a new Impacts/Issues section about myostatin and muscle bulk. Improved coverage of joint, muscle disorders.
• Chapter 21 has more concise coverage of circulation and respiration.
• Chapter 22 has simplified coverage of immunology and a new Impacts/Issues section about the HPV vaccine.
• Chapter 23 has simplified coverage of urine formation.
• Chapter 24 discussion of the spinal cord now includes reflex pathways. Discussion of memory deleted.
• Chapter 25 includes information about role of thymus in AIDS, melatonin's cancer-suppressing effects, effects of phthalates.
• Chapter 26 has expanded and updated coverage of pregnancy, fertility, and sexually transmitted diseases.

Unit VI How Plants Work
• Chapter 27 has a new Impacts/Issues section about phytoremediation.
• Chapter 28 has a new Impacts/Issues section about colony collapse disorder. Expanded, revised asexual reproduction section.

# Acknowledgments

No list can convey our thanks to the team of dedicated people who made this book happen, including our academic advisors listed on the following page. We could not have done this book without Grace Davidson, whose heroic contribution coordinated our efforts and kept us on schedule. Paul Forkner's tenacious photo research helped us achieve our creative vision. At Cengage Learning, Yolanda Cossio and Peggy Williams unwaveringly supported us and our ideals. Andy Marinkovich guided the production effort, Stacy Best helped us learn what works best for instructors, Kristina Razmara continues to refine our amazing technology package, Samantha Arvin helped us stay organized, Alexis Glubka organized and tracked our review feedback, and Elizabeth Momb managed all of the print ancillaries.

LISA STARR, CHRISTINE EVERS, AND CECIE STARR *November, 2008*

# Academic Advisors

We owe a special debt to the members of our advisory board, listed below. They helped us shape the book's design and to choose appropriate content. We appreciate their guidance.

Andrew Baldwin, Mesa Community College
Charlotte Borgeson, University of Nevada, Reno
Gregory A. Dahlem, Northern Kentucky University
Gregory Forbes, Grand Rapids Community College
Hinrich Kaiser, Victor Valley Community College
Lyn Koller, Pierce College
Terry Richardson, University of North Alabama

We also wish to thank the reviewers listed below. Special thanks to Barbara Boss for taking the time to discuss with us how best to improve upon the prior edition.

Meghan Andrikanich, Lorain County Community College
Lena Ballard, Rock Valley College
Barbara D. Boss, Keiser University, Sarasota
Susan L. Bower, Pasadena City College
James R. Bray Jr., Blackburn College
Mimi Bres, Prince George's Community College
Randy Brewton, University of Tennessee
Evelyn K. Bruce, University of North Alabama
Steven G. Brumbaugh, Green River Community College
Chantae M. Calhoun, Lawson State Community College
Thomas F. Chubb, Villanova University
Julie A. Clements, Keiser University, Melbourne
Francisco Delgado, Pima Community College
Elizabeth A. Desy, Southwest Minnesota State University
Brian Dingmann, University of Minnesota, Crookston
Josh Dobkins, Keiser University, online
Pamela K. Elf, University of Minnesota, Crookston
Johnny El-Rady, University of South Florida
Patrick James Enderle, East Carolina University
Jean Engohang-Ndong, BYU Hawaii
Ted W. Fleming, Bradley University
Edison R. Fowlks, Hampton University
Martin Jose Garcia Ramos, Los Angeles City College
J. Phil Gibson, University of Oklahoma
Judith A. Guinan, Radford University
Carla Guthridge, Cameron University
Robert H. Inan, Inver Hills Community College
Dianne Jennings, Virginia Commonwealth University
Ross S. Johnson, Chicago State University
Paul Kaseloo, Virginia State University
Ronald R. Keiper, Valencia Community College West
Dawn G. Keller, Hawkeye Community College
Ruhul H. Kuddus, Utah Valley State College
Vic Landrum, Washburn University
Lisa Maranto, Prince George's Community College
Kevin C. McGarry, Keiser University, Melbourne
Timothy Metz, Campbell University
Alexander E. Olvido, John Tyler Community College
Joshua M. Parke, Community College of Southern Nevada
Elena Pravosudova, Sierra College
Nathan S. Reyna, Howard Payne University
Carol Rhodes, Cañada College
Todd A. Rimkus, Marymount University
Laura H. Ritt, Burlington County College
Lynette Rushton, South Puget Sound Community College
Erik P. Scully, Towson University
Marilyn Shopper, Johnson County Community College
Jennifer J. Skillen, Community College of Southern Nevada
Jo Ann Wilson, Florida Gulf Coast University

We were also fortunate to have conversations with the following workshop attendees. The insights they shared proved invaluable.

Robert Bailey, Central Michigan University
Brian J. Baumgartner, Trinity Valley Community College
Michael Bell, Richland College
Lois Borek, Georgia State University
Heidi Borgeas, University of Tampa
Charlotte Borgenson, University of Nevada
Denise Chung, Long Island University
Sehoya Cotner, University of Minnesota
Heather Collins, Greenville Techincal College
Joe Conner, Pasadena Community College
Gregory A. Dahlem, Northern Kentucky University
Juville Dario-Becker, Central Virginia Community College
Jean DeSaix, University of North Carolina
Carolyn Dodson, Chattanooga State Technical Community College
Kathleen Duncan, Foothill College, California
Dave Eakin, Eastern Kentucky University
Lee Edwards, Greenville Technical College
Linda Fergusson-Kolmes, Portland Community College
Kathy Ferrell, Greenville Technical College
April Ann Fong, Portland Community College
Kendra Hill, South Dakota State University
Adam W. Hrincevich, Louisiana State University
David Huffman, Texas State University, San Marcos
Peter Ingmire, San Francisco State
Ross S. Johnson, Chicago State University
Rose Jones, NW-Shoals Community College
Thomas Justice, McLennan Community College
Jerome Krueger, South Dakota State University
Dean Kruse, Portland Community College
Dale Lambert, Tarrant County College
Debabrata Majumdar, Norfolk State University
Vicki Martin, Appalachian State University
Mary Mayhew, Gainesville State College
Roy Mason, Mt. San Jacinto College
Alexie McNerthney, Portland Community College
Brenda Moore, Truman State University
Alex Olvido, John Tyler Community College
Molly Perry, Keiser University
Michael Plotkin, Mt. San Jacinto College
Amanda Poffinbarger, Eastern Illinois University
Johanna Porter-Kelley, Winston-Salem State University
Sarah Pugh, Shelton State Community College
Larry A. Reichard, Metropolitan Community College
Darryl Ritter, Okaloosa-Walton College
Sharon Rogers, University of Las Vegas
Lori Rose, Sam Houston State University
Matthew Rowe, Sam Houston State University
Cara Shillington, Eastern Michigan University
Denise Signorelli, Community College of Southern Nevada
Jennifer Skillen, Community College of Southern Nevada
Jim Stegge, Rochester Community and Technical College
Andrew Swanson, Manatee Community College
Megan Thomas, University of Las Vegas
Kip Thompson, Ozarks Technical Community College
Steve White, Ozarks Technical Community College
Virginia White, Riverside Community College
Lawrence Williams, University of Houston
Michael L. Womack, Macon State College

# 1 Invitation to Biology

> Ironically, the more we learn about nature,
> the more we realize we have yet to learn.

## 1.1 Impacts/Issues: The Secret Life of Earth

In this era of satellites and global positioning systems, submarines and sonar, could there possibly be any more places on Earth that we have not explored? Well, yes, actually. In 2005, for instance, helicopters dropped a team of explorers into the middle of a vast and otherwise inaccessible Indonesian cloud forest. Within minutes, the explorers realized that their landing site, a dripping, moss-covered swamp, was home to plants and animals that had been unknown to science. Over the next month, they discovered dozens of new species there, including a giant treetop rhododendron with flowers the size of plates and a frog the size of a pea. They also came across hundreds of species that are on the brink of extinction in other parts of the world, some that supposedly were extinct, and one that had not been seen in so long it had been forgotten.

The animals in the forest had never learned to be afraid of humans, so they could be approached and even picked up (Figure 1.1). A few new species were discovered as they casually wandered through the campsite. Team member Bruce Beehler remarked, "Everywhere we looked, we saw amazing things we had never seen before. I was shouting. This trip was a once-in-a-lifetime series of shouting experiences."

**FIGURE 1.1** Biologist Kris Helgen holds a rare golden-mantled tree kangaroo he and his colleagues found in a cloud forest in the Foja Mountains of New Guinea.

How do we know whether a particular organism belongs to a new species? What is a species, anyway, and why should discovering a new one matter to anyone other than a scientist? You will find the answers to such questions in this book. They are part of the scientific study of life, **biology**, which is one of many ways we humans try to make sense of the world around us.

Trying to understand the immense scope of life on Earth gives us some perspective on where we fit into it. For example, we routinely discover hundreds of species every year, but about 20 species become extinct *every minute* in rain forests alone. The current rate of extinctions is about 1,000 times faster than normal, and human activities are responsible for the acceleration. At this rate, we will never know about most of the species that are alive on Earth today. Does that matter? Biologists think so.

Whether or not we are aware of it, we humans are intimately connected with the world around us. We are profoundly changing the entire fabric of life on Earth. The changes are, in turn, affecting us in ways we are just beginning to fathom. Ironically, the more we learn about nature, the more we realize we have yet to learn.

But don't take our word for it. Find out what biologists know, and what they do not, and you will have a solid foundation upon which to base your own opinions about our place in this world. By reading this book, you are choosing to learn about the human connection—your connection—with all life on Earth.

# 1.2 Life's Levels of Organization

If you are reading this book, you are starting to explore how a subset of scientists—biologists—think about nature. **Nature** is every substance and energy in the universe except what humans have manufactured. It includes flowers, water, animals, rocks, thunder, and so on. Biologists study the parts of nature that have to do with life, past and present. Through their work, we glimpse a great pattern of organization (Figure 1.2). The pattern starts with **atoms**, which are basic building blocks of all matter ❶. At the next level of organization, atoms join as **molecules** ❷. Only living cells make the molecules of life—complex carbohydrates and lipids, proteins, and nucleic acids—in nature. The pattern crosses the threshold to life when many molecules organize as a cell ❸. A **cell** is the smallest unit of life that can survive and reproduce on its own, given information in its DNA, energy, and raw materials. An **organism** is an individual that consists of one or more cells. In larger multicelled organisms, trillions of cells may be organized as tissues, organs, and organ systems that interact to keep the individual's body working properly ❹. At the next level of organization, a **population** is a group of individuals of the same type, or species, living in a given area ❺. An example would be all of the lake trout living in Lake Tahoe, California. At the next level, a **community** consists of all populations of all species in a given area ❻. An underwater ocean community, for example, may include many kinds of organisms that make their home in or on a particular reef. The next level of organization is the **ecosystem**: a community interacting with its environment ❼. The most inclusive level, the **biosphere**, encompasses all regions of Earth's crust, waters, and atmosphere in which organisms live ❽.

Remember that life is more than the sum of its individual parts. In other words, some emergent property occurs at each successive level of life's organization. An **emergent property** is a characteristic of a system that does not appear in any of a system's component parts. For example, the molecules of life are themselves not alive. Considering them separately, no one would be able to predict that a particular arrangement of molecules would form a living cell. Life—an emergent property—appears first at the level of the cell.

**FIGURE 1.2 Animated!**
Levels of organization in nature, from simpler to more complex.

❶ Atoms
❷ Molecules
❸ Cells
❹ Organisms
❺ Populations
❻ Communities
❼ Ecosystems
❽ The biosphere

## Take-Home Message  How does "life" differ from "nonlife"?

- The building blocks—atoms—that make up all living things are the same ones that make up all nonliving things.
- Atoms join as molecules. The unique properties of life emerge as certain kinds of molecules become organized into cells.
- Higher levels of organization include multicelled organisms, populations, communities, ecosystems, and the biosphere.

**atom** Fundamental building block of all matter.
**biology** Systematic study of life.
**biosphere** All regions of Earth where organisms live.
**cell** Smallest unit of life.
**community** All populations of all species in a given area.
**ecosystem** A community interacting with its environment.
**emergent property** A characteristic of a system that does not appear in any of a system's component parts.
**molecule** An association of two or more atoms.
**nature** Everything in the universe except what humans have manufactured.
**organism** Individual that consists of one or more cells.
**population** Group of individuals of the same species that live in a given area.

# Overview of Life's Unity

"Life" is not easy to define: It is just too big, and it has been changing for billions of years. Even so, we know that all living things have similar characteristics. All living things require energy and raw materials; they sense and respond to change; and they reproduce with the help of DNA.

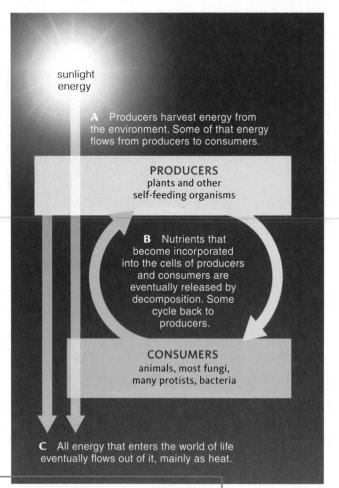

sunlight energy

**A** Producers harvest energy from the environment. Some of that energy flows from producers to consumers.

**PRODUCERS**
plants and other
self-feeding organisms

**B** Nutrients that become incorporated into the cells of producers and consumers are eventually released by decomposition. Some cycle back to producers.

**CONSUMERS**
animals, most fungi,
many protists, bacteria

**C** All energy that enters the world of life eventually flows out of it, mainly as heat.

**FIGURE 1.3 Animated!** The one-way flow of energy and the cycling of materials in the world of life. *Below,* a consumer eating a producer.

**Energy Sustains Life's Organization** Eating supplies your body with energy and nutrients that keep it organized and functioning. **Energy** is the capacity to do work. A **nutrient** is a substance that an organism needs for growth and survival, but cannot make for itself.

All organisms spend a lot of time acquiring energy and nutrients, although different species get them from different sources. The differences allow us to classify organisms into one of two broad categories: producers and consumers. **Producers** make their own food using energy and simple raw materials they get directly from their environment. Plants are producers that use the energy of sunlight to make sugars from water and carbon dioxide (a gas in air). **Consumers** cannot make their own food; they get energy and nutrients indirectly—by feeding on other organisms. Animals are consumers. So are decomposers, which feed on the wastes or remains of other organisms. The leftovers of their meals end up in the environment, where they serve as nutrients for producers. Said another way, nutrients cycle between producers and consumers.

Energy, however, is not cycled. It flows through the world of life in one direction: from the environment to organisms. This flow maintains the organization of individual organisms. It is also the basis of how organisms interact with one another and their environment. The flow is one-way, because with each transfer, some energy escapes as heat. Cells do not use heat to do work. Thus, the energy that enters the world of life eventually leaves it, permanently (Figure 1.3).

**Organisms Sense and Respond to Change** An organism senses and responds to change both inside and outside of its body by way of receptors. A **receptor** is a molecule or cellular structure that responds to a specific form of stimulation (Figure 1.4).

A receptor that has been stimulated can trigger changes in an organism's activities. For example, after you eat, the sugars from your meal enter your bloodstream. The added sugars in your blood bind to molecular receptors on cells of the pancreas (an organ). Binding sets in motion a series of events that causes cells throughout the body to take up sugar faster, so the sugar level in your blood quickly falls. The interplay of processes keeps your blood sugar level within a certain range, which in turn helps keep your cells alive and your body functioning.

The fluid in your blood is part of your body's internal environment, which consists of all body fluids outside of cells. Unless the internal environment is kept within certain ranges of composition, temperature, and other conditions, your body cells will die. By sensing and adjusting to change, you and all other organisms keep conditions in the internal environment within a range that

**FIGURE 1.4** Organisms have receptors that allow them to sense and respond to stimuli such as the mechanical energy of a bite.

favors cell survival. **Homeostasis** is the name for this process, and it is a defining feature of life.

**Organisms Grow and Reproduce** Individuals of every natural population are alike in certain aspects of their body form, function, and behavior, but the details of such traits often differ from one individual to the next. For example, humans characteristically have two eyes, but those eyes occur in a range of color among individuals. Eye color and most other traits are the outcome of information encoded in **DNA**, or deoxyribonucleic acid. DNA is the signature molecule of life. It carries information that guides **growth**—increases in cell number, size, and volume—and **development**, the process by which the first cell of a new individual becomes a multicelled adult.

Only multicelled species undergo development, but all organisms inherit DNA from parents. Lions look like lions and not like peas because they inherited lion DNA, which differs from pea DNA in the information it carries. **Inheritance** refers to the transmission of DNA from parents to offspring. Such transmission occurs by processes of **reproduction**, which produce new individuals.

## Take-Home Message How are all living things alike?

- A one-way flow of energy and a cycling of nutrients sustain life's organization.
- Organisms sense and respond to change. They make adjustments that keep conditions in their internal environment within a range that favors cell survival, a process called homeostasis.
- Organisms grow, develop, and reproduce based on information encoded in their DNA, which they inherit from their parents.

**consumer** Organism that gets energy and carbon by feeding on tissues, wastes, or remains of other organisms.

**development** Multistep process by which the first cell of a new individual becomes a multicelled adult.

**DNA** Deoxyribonucleic acid; molecule that carries hereditary information about traits.

**energy** The capacity to do work.

**growth** Increases in the number, size, and volume of cells in multicelled species.

**homeostasis** Set of processes by which an organism keeps its internal conditions within tolerable ranges.

**inheritance** Transmission of DNA from parents to offspring.

**nutrient** Substance that an organism needs for growth and survival, but cannot make for itself.

**producer** Organism that makes its own food using energy and simple raw materials from the environment.

**receptor** Molecule or structure that responds to a specific form of stimulation.

**reproduction** Process by which parents produce offspring.

# Introduction to Life's Diversity

Each time we discover a new **species**, or kind of organism, we give it a two-part name. The first part of the name specifies the **genus** (plural, genera), which is a group of species that share a unique set of features. It designates one species when combined with the second part, the species name. Individuals of a species share one or more heritable traits, and they can interbreed successfully if the species is a sexually reproducing one. Genus and species names are always italicized. For example, *Panthera* is a genus of big cats. The lions in Figure 1.4 are of the species *Panthera leo*. Tigers, or *P. tigris*, are a different species in the same genus. Note that the genus name may be abbreviated after it has been spelled out once.

We use various classification systems to organize and retrieve information about species. Most systems sort species into groups on the basis of their traits. Figure 1.5 shows a common system in which all species are grouped into three domains: Bacteria, Archaea, and Eukarya. Protists, plants, fungi, and animals make up domain Eukarya. We return to systems of naming and grouping organisms in more detail in Chapter 12.

All **bacteria** (singular, bacterium) and **archaeans** are single-celled organisms. All of them are **prokaryotes**, which means that their DNA is not contained within a nucleus. A nucleus is a membrane-enclosed sac that protects a cell's DNA. As a group, prokaryotes are the most diverse organisms. Different kinds are producers or consumers that inhabit nearly all of the biosphere, including extreme environments such as frozen desert rocks, boiling sulfur-clogged lakes, and nuclear reactor waste. The first cells on Earth may have faced similarly hostile challenges to survival.

Cells of **eukaryotes** have a nucleus. Structurally, **protists** are the simplest kind of eukaryote. Different protist species are producers or consumers. Many are single cells that are larger and more complex than prokaryotes. Some of them are tree-sized, multicelled seaweeds. Cells of fungi, plants, and animals are also eukaryotic. Most **fungi** (singular, fungus), such as the types that form mushrooms, are multicelled. Many are decomposers, and all secrete enzymes that digest food outside the body. Their cells then absorb the released nutrients.

**Plants** are multicelled species that live on land or in freshwater environments. Most are producers. By a process called photosynthesis, they harness the energy of sunlight to drive the production of sugars from carbon dioxide and water. Besides feeding themselves, plants and other photosynthesizers serve as food for most of the other organisms in the biosphere.

**Animals** are multicelled consumers that ingest tissues or juices of other organisms. Herbivores graze, carnivores eat meat, scavengers eat remains of other organisms, and parasites withdraw nutrients from the tissues of a host. Animals grow and develop through a series of stages that lead to the adult form, and most kinds actively move about during at least part of their lives.

Bacteria          Archaea

Eukarya

**FIGURE 1.5 Animated!** Three-domain classification system with a few representatives of life's diversity.

## Take-Home Message

**How do living things differ from one another?**

- Organisms differ in their details; they show tremendous variation in traits.
- Classification systems by which species are grouped according to traits help us organize information about species. One common system sorts all species into three domains: Bacteria, Archaea, and Eukarya.

# The Nature of Scientific Inquiry

Most of us assume that we do our own thinking—but do we, really? You might be surprised to find out just how often we let others think for us. For instance, a school's job, which is to impart as much information as possible to students, meshes with a student's job, which is to acquire as much knowledge as possible. In this rapid-fire exchange of information, it is easy to forget about the quality of what is being exchanged. If you accept information without question, you allow someone else to think for you.

**Critical thinking** means judging information before accepting it. "Critical" comes from the Greek *kriticos* (discerning judgment). When you think this way, you move beyond the content of information. You look for underlying assumptions, evaluate the supporting statements, and think of possible alternatives.

How does the busy student manage this? Be aware of what you intend to learn from new information. Be conscious of bias or underlying agendas in books, lectures, or online. Decide whether ideas are based on opinion or evidence. Question authority figures (respectfully). Consider what you want to believe, and realize that those biases influence your learning. Such practices will help you decide whether to accept or reject information.

### The Scope—and the Limits—of Science

Because each of us is unique, there are as many ways to think about the natural world as there are people. **Science**, the systematic study of nature, is one way. It helps us be objective about our observations of nature, in part because of its limitations. We limit science to a subset of the world: only that which is observable.

Science does not address some questions, such as "Why do I exist?" Most answers to such questions are subjective—they come from within as an integration of the personal experiences and mental connections that shape our consciousness. This is not to say subjective answers have no value, because no human society can function for long unless its individuals share standards for making judgments, even if they are subjective. Moral, aesthetic, and philosophical standards vary from one society to the next, but all help people decide what is important and good. All give meaning to what we do.

Also, science does not address the supernatural, or anything that is "beyond nature." Science does not assume or deny that supernatural phenomena occur, but scientists may still cause controversy when they discover a natural explanation for something that was thought to be supernatural. Such controversy often arises when a society's moral standards have become interwoven with its understanding of nature.

For example, Nicolaus Copernicus studied the planets centuries ago in Europe, and concluded that Earth orbits the sun. Today his conclusion seems obvious, but at the time it was heresy. The prevailing belief was that the Creator made Earth—and, by extension, humans—as the center of the universe. Galileo Galilei, another scholar, found evidence for the Copernican model of the solar system and published his findings. He was forced to publicly recant his publication, and to put Earth back at the center of the universe.

Exploring a traditional view of the natural world from a scientific perspective might be misinterpreted as questioning morality even though the two are not the same. As a group, scientists are no less moral, less lawful, or less spiritual than anyone else. As you will see in the next section, however, their work follows a particular standard: Their explanations must be testable in ways that others can repeat.

**animal** Multicelled consumer that develops through a series of embryonic stages and moves about during part or all of the life cycle.

**archaean** A member of the prokaryotic domain Archaea.

**bacterium** A member of the prokaryotic domain Bacteria.

**critical thinking** Mental process of judging information before accepting it.

**eukaryote** Organism whose cells characteristically have a nucleus.

**fungus** Type of eukaryotic consumer that obtains nutrients by digestion and absorption outside the body.

**genus** A group of species that share a unique set of traits.

**plant** A multicelled, typically photosynthetic producer.

**prokaryote** Single-celled organism in which the DNA is not contained in a nucleus.

**protist** Diverse group of simple eukaryotes.

**science** Systematic study of nature.

**species** A type of organism.

Science helps us communicate our experiences without bias, so it may be as close as we can get to a universal language. We are fairly sure, for example, that laws of gravity apply everywhere in the universe. Intelligent beings on a distant planet would likely understand the concept of gravity. We might well use gravity or another scientific concept to communicate with them, or anyone, anywhere. The point of science, however, is not to communicate with aliens. It is to find common ground here on Earth.

## Take-Home Message  What is science?

- Science is the study of the observable—those objects or events for which objective evidence can be gathered. It does not address the supernatural.

## Science helps us communicate our experiences without bias.

# 1.6  How Science Works

**Observations, Hypotheses, and Tests** To get a sense of how science works, consider this list of common research practices:

1. Observe some aspect of nature.

2. Frame a question about your observation.

3. Read what others have discovered concerning the subject, then propose a **hypothesis**, a testable answer to your question.

4. Using the hypothesis as a guide, make a **prediction**—a statement of some condition that should exist if the hypothesis is not wrong. Making predictions is called the if–then process: "if" is the hypothesis, and "then" is the prediction.

5. Devise ways to test the accuracy of the prediction by conducting experiments or gathering information. Tests may be performed on a **model**, or similar system, if testing an object or event directly is not possible.

6. Assess the results of the tests or observations—the data. Data that confirm the prediction are evidence in support of the hypothesis. Data that disprove the prediction are evidence that the hypothesis may be flawed.

7. Report all the steps of your work, along with any conclusions you drew, to the scientific community.

You might hear someone refer to these practices as "the scientific method," as if all scientists march to the drumbeat of a fixed procedure. They do not. There are different ways to do research, particularly in biology (Figure 1.6). Some biologists survey and observe without making hypotheses. Others make hypotheses and leave the testing to others. A few stumble onto valuable information they are not even looking for. Regardless of the variation, one thing is constant: Scientists do not accept information simply because someone says it is true. They evaluate the supporting evidence and find alternative explanations. Does this practice sound familiar? It should—it is critical thinking.

**Theories and Laws** Suppose a hypothesis has not been disproven even after years of tests. It is consistent with all evidence gathered to date, and it has helped us to make successful predictions about other phenomena. When a hypothesis meets these criteria, it is considered a **scientific theory** (Table 1.1). For

FIGURE 1.6 Making observations for a field study is one of many ways of doing science.

example, scientists no longer spend time testing the hypothesis that all matter is composed of atoms, for the compelling reason that no one has ever detected matter composed of anything else. This hypothesis is now called atomic theory.

A **law of nature** describes a phenomenon that has been observed to occur in every circumstance without fail, but for which we currently do not have a complete scientific explanation. The laws of thermodynamics, which describe energy, are examples. We know how energy behaves, but not why it behaves the way it does.

Most scientists carefully avoid the word "truth" when discussing science, preferring instead to use "accurate" in reference to data. In science, there is only evidence that supports a hypothesis because an infinite number of tests would be necessary to confirm that a theory holds under every possible circumstance. A single observation or result that is not consistent with a theory would open it to revision. For example, if someone discovered a type of matter not composed of atoms, the atomic theory would be revised. The theory of evolution, which states that change occurs in a line of descent over time, still holds after a century of testing and scrutiny. As with all other scientific theories, we cannot be sure that it will hold under all possible conditions, but we can say it has a very high probability of not being wrong. If evidence turns up that is inconsistent with evolution, biologists will revise the theory.

You may hear people apply the word "theory" to a speculative idea, as in the phrase "It's just a theory." Speculation is opinion or belief, a personal conviction that is not necessarily supported by evidence. A scientific theory is not an opinion: By definition, it must be supported by a large body of evidence.

Unlike theories, many beliefs and opinions cannot be tested. Ideas that cannot be tested cannot be disproven. Personal conviction has tremendous value in our lives, but it is not the same as scientific theory.

## Take-Home Message  How does science work?

■ Scientific inquiry involves making observations and asking questions about some aspect of nature; formulating hypotheses; making predictions and testing them using real or model systems; and reporting the results and conclusions.

| Table 1.1 | Examples of Scientific Theories |
|-----------|----------------------------------|
| Theory | Main Premises |
| Cell theory | All organisms consist of one or more cells, the cell is the basic unit of life, and all cells arise from existing cells. |
| Atomic theory | All substances consist of atoms. |
| Evolution | Change occurs in inherited traits of a population over generations. |
| Germ theory | Microorganisms cause many diseases. |
| Global warming | Human activities are causing Earth's average temperature to increase. |
| Plate tectonics | Earth's crust is cracked into pieces that move in relation to one another. |
| Big Bang | The universe originated with an explosion and continues to expand. |

**hypothesis** Testable explanation of a natural phenomenon.
**law of nature** Generalization that describes a consistent natural phenomenon for which there is incomplete scientific explanation.
**model** System similar to an object or event that cannot itself be tested directly.
**prediction** A statement, based on a hypothesis, about a condition that should exist if the hypothesis is not wrong.
**scientific theory** Hypothesis that has not been disproven after many years of rigorous testing, and is useful for making predictions about other phenomena.

# The Power of Experiments

Careful observations are one way to test predictions that flow from a hypothesis. So are experiments. **Experiments** are tests that can support or falsify a prediction. They are usually designed to determine the effects of a single **variable**, which is a characteristic or event that differs among individuals. Biological systems are complex, with many interacting variables. It can be difficult to study one variable separately from the rest. Thus, biology researchers often test two groups of individuals, side by side. An **experimental group** is a set of individuals that have a certain characteristic or receive a certain treatment. This group is tested side by side with a **control group**, which is identical to the experimental group except for one variable—the characteristic or the treatment being tested. Thus, any differences in experimental results between the two groups should be an effect of changing the variable. We will look at two different experiments to see how these groups are used.

**Potato Chips and Stomachaches** In 1996 the FDA approved Olestra®, a fat replacement manufactured from sugar and vegetable oil, as a food additive. Potato chips were the first Olestra-containing food product on the market in the United States. Controversy soon raged. Some people complained of intestinal problems after eating the chips and concluded that the Olestra was at fault. Two years later, researchers at Johns Hopkins University School of Medicine designed an experiment to test the hypothesis that this food additive causes cramps. They predicted that *if* Olestra causes cramps, *then* people who eat Olestra will be more likely to get cramps than people who do not.

To test the prediction, they used a Chicago theater as a "laboratory." They asked 1,100 people between the ages of thirteen and thirty-eight to watch a movie and eat their fill of potato chips. Each person got an unmarked bag that contained 13 ounces of chips. The individuals who got Olestra-containing potato chips were the experimental group, and individuals who got regular chips were the control group. The variable consisted of the presence of Olestra in the chips. Afterward, the researchers contacted all of the people and tabulated any reports of gastrointestinal problems. Of 563 people making up the experimental group, 89 (15.8 percent) complained about cramps. However, so did 93 of the 529 people (17.6 percent) making up the control group—who had munched on the regular chips! This experiment disproved the prediction that people who eat Olestra are more likely to get cramps than people who do not (Figure 1.7).

**A  Hypothesis**
Olestra® causes intestinal cramps.

↓

**B  Prediction**
People who eat potato chips made with Olestra will be more likely to get intestinal cramps than those who eat potato chips made without Olestra.

↓

| C  Experiment | Control Group<br>Eats regular<br>potato chips | Experimental Group<br>Eats Olestra<br>potato chips |
|---|---|---|
| | ↓ | ↓ |
| D  Results | 93 of 529 people<br>get cramps later<br>(17.6%) | 89 of 563 people<br>get cramps later<br>(15.8%) |

↓

**E  Conclusion**
Percentages are about equal. People who eat potato chips made with Olestra are just as likely to get intestinal cramps as those who eat potato chips made without Olestra. These results do not support the hypothesis.

**FIGURE 1.7 Animated!** The steps in a scientific experiment to determine if Olestra causes cramps. A report of this study was published in the *Journal of the American Medical Association* in January of 1998.

**Butterflies and Birds** Consider the peacock butterfly, a winged insect that was named for the large, colorful spots on its wings. In 2005, researchers published a report on their tests to identify factors that help peacock butterflies defend themselves against insect-eating birds. The researchers made two observations. First, when a peacock butterfly rests, it folds its wings, so only the dark underside shows. Second, when a butterfly sees a predator approaching, it repeatedly flicks its paired forewings and hindwings open and closed. At the same time, each forewing slides over the hindwing, which produces a hissing sound and a series of clicks.

| Table 1.2 | Results of Peacock Butterfly Experiment* | | | | |
|---|---|---|---|---|---|
| Wing Spots | Wing Sound | Total Number of Butterflies | Number Eaten | Number Survived |
| Spots | Sound | 9 | 0 | 9 (100%) |
| No spots | Sound | 10 | 5 | 5 (50%) |
| Spots | No sound | 8 | 0 | 8 (100%) |
| No spots | No sound | 10 | 8 | 2 (20%) |

*\* Proceedings of the Royal Society of London, Series B (2005) 272: 1203–1207.*

**FIGURE 1.8** Peacock butterfly defenses.

**A** When a bird approaches, this butterfly repeatedly flicks its wings open and closed, which exposes brilliant spots and produces hissing and clicking sounds.

The researchers tested whether the behavior deters blue tits **B**. They painted over the spots of some butterflies, cut the sound-making part of the wings on others, and did both to a third group; then the biologists exposed each butterfly to a hungry bird. The results are listed *above*, in Table 1.2.

**Figure It Out:** What percentage of butterflies with no spots and no sound survived the test?

*Answer: 20 percent*

The researchers asked the question, "Why does a peacock butterfly flick its wings?" After they reviewed earlier studies, they came up with two hypotheses that might explain the wing-flicking behavior:

1. Although the wing-flicking probably attracts predatory birds, it also exposes brilliant spots that resemble owl eyes (Figure 1.8**A**). Anything that looks like owl eyes is known to startle small, butterfly-eating birds, so exposing the wing spots might scare off predators.

2. The hissing and clicking sounds produced when the peacock butterfly rubs the sections of its wings together may deter predatory birds.

The researchers used their hypotheses to make the following predictions:

1. *If* brilliant wing spots of peacock butterflies deter predatory birds, *then* individuals with no wing spots will be more likely to get eaten by predatory birds than individuals with wing spots.

2. *If* the sounds that peacock butterflies produce deter predatory birds, *then* individuals that do not make the sounds will be more likely to be eaten by predatory birds than individuals that make the sounds.

The next step was the experiment. The researchers painted the wing spots of some butterflies black, cut off the sound-making part of the hindwings of others, and did both to a third group. They put each butterfly into a large cage with a hungry blue tit (Figure 1.8**B**) and then watched the pair for thirty minutes.

Table 1.2 lists the results of the experiment. All of the butterflies with unmodified wing spots survived, regardless of whether they made sounds. By contrast, only half of the butterflies that had spots painted out but could make sounds survived. Most of the butterflies with neither spots nor sound structures were eaten quickly. The test results confirmed both predictions, so they support the hypotheses. Birds are deterred by peacock butterfly sounds, and even more so by wing spots.

**control group** A group of objects or individuals that is identical to an experimental group except for one variable.

**experiment** A test designed to support or falsify a prediction.

**experimental group** A group of objects or individuals that display or are exposed to a variable under investigation.

**variable** A characteristic or event that differs among individuals.

**FIGURE 1.9** Example of error bars in a graph. This particular graph was adapted from the peacock butterfly research described on the previous page.

The researchers recorded the number of times each butterfly flicked its wings in response to an attack by a bird.

The *orange* squares represent the average frequency of wing flicking for each sample set of butterflies. *Black* error bars that extend above and below the squares indicate the range of values—the sampling error—for each set of butterflies.

## Sampling Error

Researchers can rarely observe all individuals of a group. For example, the explorers you read about in Section 1.1 did not—and could not—survey every uninhabited part of New Guinea. The cloud forest itself cloaks more than 2 million acres of the Foja Mountains. Surveying all of it would take unrealistic amounts of time and effort. Besides, tromping about even in a small area can damage delicate forest ecosystems.

Given such limitations, researchers often look at subsets of an area, a population, event, or some other aspect of nature. They test or survey the subset, then use the results to make generalizations. However, generalizing from a subset is risky because a subset may not be representative of the whole.

For example, the golden-mantled tree kangaroo pictured in Figure 1.1 was first discovered in 1993 on a single forested mountaintop in New Guinea. For more than a decade the species was never seen outside of that habitat, which is getting smaller every year because of human activities. Thus, the golden-mantled tree kangaroo was considered to be one of the most endangered animals on the planet. Then, in 2005, the explorers featured in Section 1.1 discovered that this kangaroo species is fairly common in the Foja Mountain cloud forest. As a result, biologists now believe its future is secure, at least for the moment.

**Sampling error** is a difference between results from a subset and results from the whole. It happens most often when a sample size is small. Starting with a large sample or repeating an experiment many times helps minimize sampling error. Sampling error is an important consideration in the design of most experiments. However, it is sometimes unavoidable, as illustrated by the example of the golden-mantled tree kangaroo. Error bars on a graph may indicate sampling error or other variation in experimental results. For example, the error bars in Figure 1.9 show the range of results for each sample set of butterflies.

## Probability

Probability is a measure of the chance that a particular outcome will occur. That chance depends on the total number of possible outcomes. We usually express probability as a percentage. For instance, if 10 million people enter a drawing, each has the same probability of winning: 1 in 10 million, or a very improbable 0.00001 percent.

Sample size is important in probability. To understand why, imagine flipping a coin. There are two possible outcomes: The coin lands heads up, or it lands tails up. Every time you flip the coin, the chance that it will land, say, heads up, is one in two (1/2)—a probability of 50 percent. However, when you actually flip the coin, it often lands heads up, or tails up, several times in a row. With just 10 flips, the proportion of times that heads actually land up may be very far from 50 percent. With 1,000 flips, that proportion is more likely to be near 50 percent.

An experimental result is said to be **statistically significant** if it is unlikely to have occurred by chance. In this context, the word "significant" does not refer to the result's importance. It means that the result has been subjected to a rigorous statistical analysis that shows it has a very low probability (usually 5 percent or less) of being skewed by sampling error.

Variation in data is often shown as error bars on a graph. Depending on the graph, error bars may indicate variation around an average for one sample set (Figure 1.9), or the difference between two sample sets.

**Asking Useful Questions** Researchers try to design experiments that have a single variable and that will yield counts or some other data that can be measured or otherwise gathered objectively. Even so, they risk designing experiments and interpreting results in terms of what they want to find out. Particularly when studying humans, isolating a single variable is not often possible. For example, by thinking critically, we may realize that the people who participated in the Olestra experiment were chosen randomly. That means the study was not controlled for gender, age, weight, medications taken, and so on. Such variables may well have influenced the results.

Scientists expect one another to put aside bias. If one individual does not, others will, because science is both cooperative and competitive.

## Take-Home Message  What is the purpose of experiments?

- Natural processes are often influenced by many interacting variables.
- Experiments help researchers unravel causes of complex natural processes by focusing on the effects of changing a single variable.
- Researchers try to design experiments carefully in order to minimize sampling error and the potential for bias.

**FIGURE 1.10** Discovered in Madagascar in 2005, this tiny mouse lemur was named *Microcebus lehilahytsara* in honor of primatologist Steve Goodman (lehilahytsara is a combination of the Malagasy words for "good" and "man"). Lemurs are evolutionary cousins of monkeys and apes.

# 1.8

# Impacts/Issues Revisited:
# The Secret Life of Earth

Just since 2002, biologists have discovered many hundreds of species that had been previously unknown to science. A return expedition to New Guinea's Foja Mountains turned up a mouse-sized opossum and a cat-sized rat. Expeditions elsewhere revealed lemurs (Figure 1.10) and sucker-footed bats in Madagascar; birds in the Philippines; monkeys in Tanzania, Brazil, and India; cave-dwelling spiders and insects in two of California's national parks; carnivorous sponges near Antarctica; whales, sharks, giant jellylike animals, fishes, and other aquatic wildlife; and scores of plants and single-celled organisms. Most were discovered by biologists who were simply trying to find out what lives where.

Biologists make discoveries every day, though we may never hear of them. Each new species they discover is another reminder that we do not yet know all of the organisms on our own planet. We don't even know how many to look for. The vast information about the 1.8 million species we do know about changes so quickly that collating it has been impossible—until now. A new web site, titled the Encyclopedia of Life, is intended to be an online reference source and database of species information that is maintained by collaborative effort. See it at www.eol.org.

## How Would
# YOU
## ☑ Vote?

There is a possibility that substantial populations of some species currently listed as endangered may exist in unexplored areas. Should we wait to protect endangered species until all of Earth has been surveyed? See CengageNow for details, then vote online (cengagenow.com).

**sampling error** Difference between results derived from testing an entire group of events or individuals, and results derived from testing a subset of the group.
**statistically significant** Refers to a result that is statistically unlikely to have occurred by chance.

# Summary

**Section 1.1** Biology is the systematic study of life. New species are discovered on a continuing basis. We have encountered only a fraction of the organisms that live on Earth, in part because we have explored only a fraction of its habitable regions.

**Section 1.2** Biologists think about nature at different levels of organization. All matter consists of atoms, which combine as molecules. Organisms consist of one or more cells, the smallest units of life. A population is a group of individuals of a species in a given area; a community is all populations of all species in a given area. An ecosystem is a community interacting with its environment. The biosphere includes all regions of Earth that hold life.

CENGAGENOW™ Explore life's levels of organization with the interaction on CengageNow.

**Section 1.3** Life has underlying unity in that all living things have similar features. All organisms require energy and nutrients to sustain themselves. Producers such as plants make their own food; animals and other consumers eat other organisms, or their wastes and remains. Receptors help organisms keep the conditions in their internal environment within ranges that their cells tolerate—a process called homeostasis. DNA, which is inherited from parents, contains information that is the source of an individual's traits.

A one-way flow of energy through the biosphere and the cycling of nutrients among organisms sustains life, and life's organization.

CENGAGENOW™ See energy flow and materials cycling with the animation on CengageNow.

**Section 1.4** The millions of species (types of organisms) that currently exist on Earth show tremendous diversity in that they differ greatly in details of body form and function. Each species is given a unique two-part name that includes genus and species name. Various classification systems sort species into groups on the basis of subsets of shared traits. One system categorizes all organisms into three domains: Bacteria, Archaea, and Eukarya. Plants, protists, fungi, and animals are the eukaryotes.

CENGAGENOW™ Explore characteristics of the three domains of life with the interaction on CengageNow.

**Section 1.5** Critical thinking means judging the quality of information before deciding whether or not to accept it. Science is one of many ways of looking at the natural world. It helps us to communicate our experiences without bias by focusing on only testable ideas about observable phenomena. Science does not address the supernatural.

**Section 1.6** Researchers make and test potentially falsifiable predictions about how the natural world works. Generally, scientific inquiry involves forming a hypothesis (a testable assumption) about an observation, then making and testing predictions based on the hypothesis. A hypothesis that is not consistent with the results of scientific tests (evidence) is modified or discarded.

A scientific theory is a long-standing hypothesis that is useful for making predictions about other phenomena. A law of nature describes a consistent and universal phenomenon (such as gravity) for which we do not yet have a complete scientific explanation.

**Section 1.7** Natural processes are often influenced by many interacting variables. Experiments simplify interpretations of complex biological systems by focusing on the effect of one variable at a time. Biology researchers necessarily experiment on subsets of a group, which may result in sampling error.

CENGAGENOW™ See the steps in an experiment and how sample size affects accuracy with the interactions on CengageNow.

## Self-Quiz    Answers in Appendix I

1. _____ are fundamental building blocks of all matter.
   a. Cells                    c. Nutrients
   b. Atoms                    d. Molecules

2. The smallest unit of life is the _____ .
   a. atom                     c. cell
   b. molecule                 d. organism

3. _____ move around for at least part of their life.
   a. Organisms                c. Animals
   b. Plants                   d. Prokaryotes

4. Organisms require _____ and _____ to maintain themselves, grow, and reproduce.

5. _____ is a process that maintains conditions in the internal environment within ranges that cells can tolerate.
   a. Sampling error           c. Homeostasis
   b. Development              d. Critical thinking

6. Bacteria, Archaea, and Eukarya are three _____ .
   a. organisms                c. consumers
   b. domains                  d. producers

7. DNA _____ .
   a. guides growth            c. is transmitted from
      and development             parents to offspring
   b. is a nucleic acid        d. all of the above

8. An animal is a(n) _____ (choose all that apply).
   a. organism                 e. consumer
   b. domain                   f. producer
   c. species                  g. prokaryote
   d. eukaryote                h. trait

9. Plants are _____ (choose all that apply).
   a. organisms
   b. a domain
   c. a species
   d. eukaryotes
   e. consumers
   f. producers
   g. prokaryotes
   h. traits

10. _____ is the transmission of DNA to offspring.
    a. Reproduction
    b. Development
    c. Homeostasis
    d. Inheritance

11. A process by which an organism produces offspring is called _____ .
    a. reproduction
    b. inheritance
    c. development
    d. homeostasis

12. Science only addresses that which is _____ .
    a. alive
    b. observable
    c. variable
    d. indisputable

13. A control group is _____ .
    a. a set of individuals that have a certain characteristic or receive a certain treatment
    b. the standard against which an experimental group is compared
    c. the experiment that gives conclusive results

14. Match the terms with the most suitable description.
    _____ emergent property
    _____ species
    _____ scientific theory
    _____ hypothesis
    _____ prediction

    a. statement of what a hypothesis leads you to expect to see
    b. type of organism
    c. occurs at a higher organizational level in nature, not at levels below it
    d. time-tested hypothesis
    e. testable explanation

Additional questions are available on CENGAGENOW™

# Critical Thinking

1. Why would you think twice about ordering from a restaurant menu that lists only the second part of the species name (not the genus) of its offerings? *Hint:* Look up *Ursus americanus, Ceanothus americanus, Bufo americanus, Homarus americanus, Lepus americanus,* and *Nicrophorus americanus.*

2. Witnesses in a court of law are often asked to "swear to tell the truth, the whole truth, and nothing but the truth." Can you think of a less subjective alternative for this oath?

3. Procter & Gamble makes Olestra and financed the study described in Section 1.7. The main researcher was a consultant to Procter & Gamble during the study. What do you think about scientific information that comes from tests financed by companies with a vested interest in the outcome?

4. Suppose an outcome of some event has been observed to happen with great regularity. Can we predict that the same outcome will always occur? Not really, if there is no way to test all of the variables that affect the outcome. To illustrate the point, Garvin McCain and Erwin Segal offer the following parable.

# Digging Into Data

## Peacock Butterfly Predator Defenses

The photographs *below* represent experimental and control groups used in the peacock butterfly experiment that was discussed in Section 1.7.

See if you can identify the experimental groups, and match them up with the relevant control group(s). *Hint:* Identify which variable is being tested in each group (each variable has a control).

 **A** Wing spots painted out

 **D** Wings painted but spots visible

 **B** Wing spots visible; wings silenced

 **E** Wings cut but not silenced

 **C** Wing spots painted out; wings silenced

 **F** Wings painted but spots visible; wings cut but not silenced

Once there was a highly intelligent turkey that lived in a pen and was attended by a kind, thoughtful master. The turkey had nothing to do but reflect on the world's wonders and regularities. It observed some major regularities. Morning always started out with the sky turning light, followed by the master's footsteps, which was always followed by the appearance of food. Other things varied—sometimes the morning was warm and sometimes it was cold, for example—but food always followed footsteps. The sequence of events was so predictable that it eventually became the basis of the turkey's theory about the goodness of the world. One morning, after more than 100 confirmations of the goodness theory, the turkey listened for the master's footsteps, heard them, and had its head chopped off.

Any scientific theory is modified or discarded when contradictory evidence becomes available. The absence of absolute certainty has led some people to conclude that "facts are irrelevant—facts change." If that is so, should we stop doing scientific research? Why or why not?

5. In 2005 a South Korean scientist, Woo-suk Hwang, reported that he had made immortal stem cells from eleven human patients. His research was hailed as a breakthrough for people affected by currently incurable degenerative diseases, because such stem cells might be used to repair a person's own damaged tissues. Hwang published his results in a respected scientific journal. In 2006, the journal retracted his paper after other scientists discovered that Hwang and his colleagues had faked their results. Does the incident show that the results of scientific studies cannot be trusted? Or does it confirm the usefulness of a scientific approach, because other scientists quickly discovered and exposed the fraud?

# 2 Molecules of Life

# Small differences in the way molecules are put together can have big effects in a living organism.

## Impacts/Issues: Fear of Frying

The human body requires only about a tablespoon of fat each day to stay healthy, but most people in developed countries eat far more than that. The average American consumes the equivalent of one stick of butter per day—about 100 pounds of fat per year—which may be part of the reason why the average American is overweight. Being overweight increases one's risk for many health conditions. However, the total quantity of fat we eat may be of less importance to health than the *kinds* of fats we eat. Fats are more than just inert molecules that accumulate in strategic areas of our bodies. They are major constituents of cell membranes, and as such they have powerful effects on cell function.

The typical fat molecule has three fatty acids, which have long chains of carbon atoms. Different fats consist of different fatty acids. Fats with a certain arrangement of hydrogen atoms around that carbon chain are called *trans* fats. Small amounts of *trans* fats occur naturally in red meat and dairy products, but most of the *trans* fats that humans eat come from partially hydrogenated vegetable oil, an artificial food product.

Hydrogenation, a manufacturing process that adds hydrogen atoms to a substance, changes liquid vegetable oils into solid fats. Procter & Gamble Co. developed partially hydrogenated soybean oil in 1908 as a substitute for the more expensive solid animal fats they had been using to make candles. However, the demand for candles began to wane as more households in the United States became wired for electricity, and P & G began to look for another way to sell its proprietary fat. Partially hydrogenated vegetable oil looks a lot like lard, so in 1911 the company began aggressively marketing it as a revolutionary new food: a solid cooking fat with a long shelf life, mild flavor, and lower cost than lard or butter. By the mid-1950s, hydrogenated vegetable oil had become a major part of the American diet. It was (and still is) found in a tremendous number of manufactured and fast foods (Figure 2.1).

For decades, hydrogenated vegetable oil was considered more healthy than animal fats because it was made from plants. We now know otherwise. The *trans* fats in hydrogenated vegetable oils raise the level of cholesterol in our blood more than any other fat, and they directly alter the function of our arteries and veins. The effects of such changes are quite serious. Eating as little as 2 grams a day of hydrogenated vegetable oils increases a person's risk of atherosclerosis (hardening of the arteries), heart attack, and diabetes. A small serving of french fries made with hydrogenated vegetable oil contains about 5 grams of *trans* fats.

All organisms consist of the same kinds of molecules, but small differences in the way those molecules are put together can have big effects in a living organism. With this concept, we introduce you to the chemistry of life. This is your chemistry. It makes you far more than the sum of your body's molecules.

*trans* fatty acid

**FIGURE 2.1** *Trans* fats. *Left*, the particular arrangement of hydrogen atoms around two carbon atoms (*yellow* box) makes a *trans* fat very unhealthy as a food. *Right*, french fries and other fast foods are often cooked with *trans* fats.

an atom

| proton |
| neutron |
| electron |

**FIGURE 2.2** Atoms consist of electrons moving around a core, or nucleus, of protons and neutrons. Models cannot show what atoms really look like. Electrons zoom around in fuzzy, three-dimensional spaces about 10,000 times bigger than a nucleus.

# 2.2 Start With Atoms

Life's unique characteristics start with the properties of different **atoms**, tiny particles that are building blocks of all substances. Even though they are about 20 million times smaller than a grain of sand, atoms consist of even smaller subatomic particles: positively charged **protons** ($p^+$), uncharged **neutrons**, and negatively charged **electrons** ($e^-$). **Charge** is an electrical property: Opposite charges attract, and like charges repel. Protons and neutrons cluster in an atom's central core, or **nucleus**, and electrons move around the nucleus (Figure 2.2).

Atoms differ in the number of subatomic particles. The number of protons in an atom's nucleus is called the **atomic number**, and it determines the type of atom, or element. **Elements** are pure substances, each consisting only of atoms that have the same number of protons in their nucleus. For example, the atomic number of carbon is 6, so all atoms with six protons in their nucleus are carbon atoms, no matter how many electrons or neutrons they have. A chunk of carbon consists only of carbon atoms, and all of those atoms have six protons. Each of the 118 known elements has a symbol that is an abbreviation of its Latin name (Appendix VI shows a periodic table of the elements). Carbon's symbol, C, is from *carbo*, the Latin word for coal. Coal is mostly carbon.

The same elements that make up a living body also occur in, say, dirt or seawater, but the proportions of different elements differ between living and nonliving things. For example, a human body contains a lot of carbon, but seawater and Earth's crust contain very little. Why? A body contains a greater proportion of carbon atoms because only living things make the molecules of life, which have a greater proportion of carbon atoms than other molecules do.

Carbon and all other elements occur in different forms, or **isotopes**, that differ in their number of neutrons. We refer to an isotope by its total number of protons and neutrons, which is the isotope's **mass number**. Mass number is shown as a superscript to the left of an element's symbol. For example, atoms of the most common carbon isotope, $^{12}C$, have six protons and six neutrons; those of $^{14}C$ have six protons and eight neutrons ($6 + 8 = 14$).

$^{14}C$ (carbon 14) is a radioactive isotope, or **radioisotope**, which means that the nucleus of a $^{14}C$ atom is unstable. Many isotopes are like this. Atoms of radioisotopes emit subatomic particles and energy when their nucleus spontaneously disintegrates. This process, **radioactive decay**, can transform one element into another. For example, $^{14}C$ decays when one of its neutrons splits into a

**atom** Particle that is a fundamental building block of matter.
**atomic number** Number of protons in the atomic nucleus; determines the element.
**charge** Electrical property of some subatomic particles. Opposite charges attract; like charges repel.
**electron** Negatively charged subatomic particle that occupies orbitals around the atomic nucleus.
**element** A pure substance that consists only of atoms with the same number of protons.
**isotopes** Forms of an element that differ in the number of neutrons their atoms carry.
**mass number** Total number of protons and neutrons in the nucleus of an element's atoms.
**neutron** Uncharged subatomic particle in the atomic nucleus.
**nucleus** Core of an atom; occupied by protons and neutrons.
**proton** Positively charged subatomic particle that occurs in the nucleus of all atoms.
**radioactive decay** Process by which atoms of a radioisotope spontaneously emit energy and subatomic particles when their nucleus disintegrates.
**radioisotope** Isotope with an unstable nucleus.

vacancy

no
vacancy

**FIGURE 2.3 Animated!** Shell models. Each circle (shell) represents all orbitals at one energy level. Atoms with vacancies in their outermost shell can interact with other atoms.

proton and an electron. The proton stays in the nucleus, and the electron is emitted. Thus, an atom of $^{14}C$ (with six protons and eight neutrons) becomes an atom of $^{14}N$, which is nitrogen (with seven protons and seven neutrons).

An atomic nucleus cannot be altered by heat or any other ordinary means. Thus, a radioisotope decays at a constant rate into predictable products, independently of external factors such as temperature, pressure, or whether the atoms are part of molecules. For example, we know that half of the $^{14}C$ atoms in any sample will be $^{14}N$ atoms after 5,730 years. This predictability can be used to estimate the age of rocks and fossils (we return to this topic in Section 11.4).

Researchers and clinicians also introduce radioisotopes into living organisms. All isotopes of an element generally have the same chemical properties. This consistency means that organisms use atoms of one isotope (such as $^{14}C$) the same way that they use atoms of another (such as $^{12}C$). Thus, radioisotopes are often used in **tracers**, which are molecules with a detectable substance attached. Typically, a radioactive tracer is a molecule in which radioisotopes have been swapped for one or more atoms. Researchers deliver radioactive tracers into a biological system such as a cell or a body, then use an instrument that can detect radioactivity to follow the tracer as it moves through the system.

**Why Electrons Matter** Electrons are really, really small. How small are they? If they were as big as apples, you would be about 3.5 times taller than our solar system is wide. Simple physics explains the motion of, say, an apple falling from a tree, but electrons are so tiny that such everyday physics cannot explain their behavior. However, that behavior underlies atomic interactions.

A typical atom has about as many electrons as protons, so a lot of electrons may be zipping around one nucleus. Those electrons never collide, despite moving at nearly the speed of light (300,000 kilometers per second, or 670 million miles per hour). Why not? They avoid one another because they travel in different orbitals, which are defined volumes of space around the nucleus.

**A** The first shell corresponds to the first energy level, and it can hold up to 2 electrons. Hydrogen has one proton, so it has one vacancy. A helium atom has 2 protons, and no vacancies. The number of protons in each shell model is shown.

first shell

1 proton
1 electron
hydrogen (H)

helium (He)

**B** The second shell corresponds to the second energy level, and it can hold up to 8 electrons. Carbon has 6 protons, so its first shell is full. Its second shell has 4 electrons, and four vacancies. Oxygen has 8 protons and two vacancies. Neon has 10 protons and no vacancies.

second shell

carbon (C)

oxygen (O)

neon (Ne)

**C** The third shell, which corresponds to the third energy level, can hold up to 8 electrons, for a total of 18. A sodium atom has 11 protons, so its first two shells are full; the third shell has one electron. Thus, sodium has seven vacancies. Chlorine has 17 protons and one vacancy. Argon has 18 protons and no vacancies.

third shell

sodium (Na)

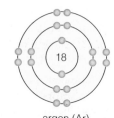
chlorine (Cl)

argon (Ar)

Imagine that an atom is a multilevel apartment building, with rooms available for rent by electrons. The nucleus is in the basement, and each "room" is an orbital. No more than two electrons can share a room at the same time. Each "floor" of the building corresponds to one energy level, and each has a certain number of rooms available to rent to electrons. Electrons fill orbitals from lower to higher energy levels. In other words, they populate rooms from the ground floor up. The farther an electron is from the basement, the greater its energy. An electron can move to a room on a higher floor if an energy input gives it a boost, but it immediately emits its extra energy and moves back down.

We use a **shell model** to visualize how electrons populate an atom. In this model, nested "shells" correspond to successively higher energy levels. Thus, each shell includes all rooms on one floor of our atomic apartment building. We draw a shell model of an atom by filling its shells with electrons (represented as balls or dots), from the innermost shell out, until there are as many electrons as the atom has protons. For example, there is only one room on the first floor, one orbital at the lowest energy level. It fills up first. In hydrogen, the simplest atom, a single electron occupies that room (Figure 2.3**A**). Helium has two electrons that fill its first shell. In larger atoms, more electrons rent the second-floor rooms (Figure 2.3**B**). When the second floor fills, more electrons rent third-floor rooms (Figure 2.3**C**), and so on.

If an atom's outermost shell is full of electrons, we say that it has no vacancies. Helium is an example. Atoms of such elements are chemically inactive, which means they are most stable as single atoms. By contrast, if an atom's outermost shell has room for another electron, it has a vacancy. Hydrogen has one vacancy. Atoms with vacancies tend to interact with other atoms: They give up, acquire, or share electrons until they have no vacancies in their outermost shell. Any atom is in its most stable state when it has no vacancies.

**Ions** The negative charge of an electron is the same magnitude as the positive charge of a proton, so the two charges cancel one another. Thus, an atom that has as many electrons as protons has no charge. An atom with different numbers of electrons and protons is called an **ion**. An ion carries a charge; either it acquired a positive charge by losing an electron, or it acquired a negative charge by pulling an electron away from another atom (Figure 2.4). For example, an uncharged chlorine atom has 17 protons and 17 electrons. Seven electrons are in its outermost (third) shell, which can hold eight, so it has one vacancy. Chlorine tends to pull an electron away from another atom to fill that vacancy. When that happens, the atom becomes a chloride ion (Cl⁻) with 17 protons, 18 electrons, and a net negative charge (Figure 2.4**A**). As another example, an uncharged sodium atom has 11 protons and 11 electrons. This atom has one electron in its outer (third) shell, which can hold eight, so it has seven vacancies. A sodium atom tends to lose the single electron in its third shell. When that happens, the atom has two full shells and no vacancies. It is a sodium ion (Na⁺), with 11 protons, 10 electrons, and a net positive charge (Figure 2.4**B**).

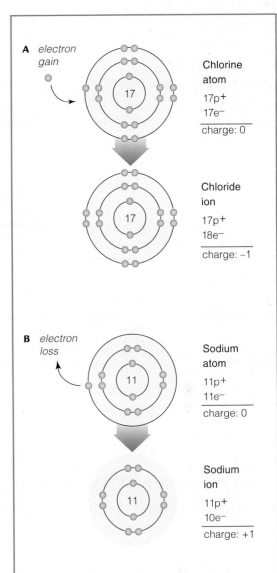

**A** electron gain

Chlorine atom
17p+
17e⁻
_____
charge: 0

Chloride ion
17p+
18e⁻
_____
charge: –1

**B** electron loss

Sodium atom
11p+
11e⁻
_____
charge: 0

Sodium ion
11p+
10e⁻
_____
charge: +1

**FIGURE 2.4 Animated!** Ion formation.

**A** A chlorine atom becomes a negatively charged chloride ion (Cl⁻) when it gains an electron and fills the vacancy in its third, outermost shell.

**B** A sodium atom becomes a positively charged sodium ion (Na⁺) when it loses the electron in its third shell. The atom's full second shell is now its outermost, so it has no vacancies.

## Take-Home Message
**What are the basic building blocks of all matter?**

- Tiny particles called atoms are the building blocks of all substances. Atoms consist of electrons moving around a nucleus of protons and neutrons.

- An element is a pure substance that consists only of atoms with the same number of protons.

- Atoms tend to get rid of vacancies by gaining or losing electrons (thereby becoming ions), or by sharing electrons with other atoms.

**ion** Atom that carries a charge because it has an unequal number of protons and electrons.
**shell model** Model of electron distribution in an atom.
**tracer** A molecule with a detectable label.

# From Atoms to Molecules

| Table 2.1 | Different Ways of Referring to a Molecule | |
|---|---|---|
| Common name | Water | Familiar term. |
| Chemical name | Dihydrogen monoxide | Systematically describes elemental composition. |
| Chemical formula | $H_2O$ | Indicates unvarying proportions of elements. Subscripts show number of atoms of an element per molecule. The absence of a subscript means one atom. |
| Structural formula | H—O—H | Represents each covalent bond as a single line between atoms. |
| Structural model | 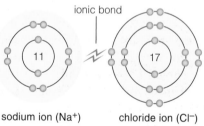 | Shows the positions and relative sizes of atoms. |
| Shell model | | Shows how pairs of electrons are shared in covalent bonds. |

Two atoms with vacancies can join in a **chemical bond**, which is an attractive force that arises when their electrons interact. The result is a **molecule**, a union of two or more atoms joined by a chemical bond. Molecules that consist of two or more different elements are called **compounds**. Table 2.1 lists some of the ways we represent molecules.

The same atoms bonded together in different ways make up different molecules. For example, carbon atoms bonded one way form a soft, slippery mineral called graphite. Carbon atoms bonded a different way make the hardest mineral, diamond. Carbon atoms bonded to oxygen and hydrogen atoms make sugar. The idea that different structures can be assembled from the same basic building blocks is a recurring theme in our world, and also in biology (Figure 2.5).

Although bonding applies to a range of interactions among atoms, we can categorize most bonds into distinct types based on their different properties. Which type forms—an ionic, covalent, or hydrogen bond—depends on the atoms that take part in it.

**Ionic Bonds** An **ionic bond** is a strong mutual attraction of two oppositely charged ions. Such bonds do not usually form by the direct transfer of an electron from one atom to another. Instead, atoms that have already become ions stay close together because of their opposite charges. Table salt (sodium chloride, or NaCl) is an example of an ionic solid. Ionic bonds hold sodium and chloride ions together in salt crystals:

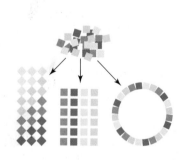

ionic bond

sodium ion (Na⁺)          chloride ion (Cl⁻)

**Covalent Bonds** In a **covalent bond**, two atoms share a pair of electrons, so each atom's vacancy becomes partially filled. Sharing electrons links the two atoms, just as sharing a pair of earphones links two friends (Figure 2.6). Covalent bonds can be stronger than ionic bonds, but they are not always so. Structural formulas show how covalent bonds connect atoms. A line between two atoms represents a single covalent bond, in which two atoms share one pair of electrons. An example is molecular hydrogen ($H_2$), with a single covalent bond between two hydrogen atoms (H—H, *right*).

Two lines between atoms represent a double covalent bond, in which two atoms share two pairs of electrons. A double covalent bond links two oxygen atoms in molecular oxygen (O=O, *right*). Three lines indicate a triple covalent bond, in which two

molecular hydrogen ($H_2$)

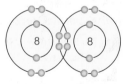

molecular oxygen ($O_2$)

atoms share three pairs of electrons. A triple covalent bond links two nitrogen atoms in molecular nitrogen (N≡N, or $N_2$).

Some covalent bonds are **nonpolar**, meaning that the atoms participating in the bond are sharing electrons equally. There is no difference in charge between the two ends of such bonds. The bonds in molecular hydrogen ($H_2$), oxygen ($O_2$), and nitrogen ($N_2$) mentioned earlier are examples. These molecules are some of the gases that make up air. The bonds in methane ($CH_3$), another gas, are also nonpolar.

Atoms participating in **polar** covalent bonds do not share electrons equally. One atom pulls the electrons a little more toward its "end" of the bond, so that atom bears a slightly negative charge. The atom at the other end of the bond bears a slightly positive charge. For example, a water molecule (H—O—H, *right*) has two covalent bonds; both are polar. The oxygen atom in a water molecule carries a slight negative charge, and each of the hydrogen atoms carries a slight positive charge. Any separation of charge into distinct positive and negative regions is called **polarity**. As you will see in the next section, the polarity of the water molecule is important for the world of life.

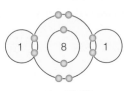

water ($H_2O$)

**Hydrogen Bonds** Hydrogen bonds form between polar regions of two molecules, or between two regions of the same molecule. A **hydrogen bond** is a weak attraction between a hydrogen atom and another atom taking part in a separate polar covalent bond. Hydrogen bonds form between water molecules:

hydrogen bond

Like ionic bonds, hydrogen bonds form by the mutual attraction of opposite charges: The hydrogen atom has a slight positive charge and the other atom has a slight negative charge. However, unlike ionic bonds, hydrogen bonds do not make molecules out of atoms, so they are not chemical bonds.

Hydrogen bonds form and break much more easily than covalent or ionic bonds do. Even so, many of them form. Their collective strength imparts unique properties to many substances such as water. Hydrogen bonds that form among the atoms of biological molecules such as DNA hold these molecules in their characteristic shapes.

## Take-Home Message    **How do atoms interact?**

- A chemical bond forms when the electrons of two atoms interact. Depending on the atoms, the bond may be ionic or covalent.
- An ionic bond is a strong mutual attraction between ions of opposite charge.
- Atoms share a pair of electrons in a covalent bond. When the atoms share electrons equally, the bond is nonpolar; when they share unequally, it is polar.
- A hydrogen bond is an attraction between a hydrogen atom and another atom taking part in a different polar covalent bond.

**FIGURE 2.6** Sharing electrons links two atoms just as sharing earphones links two friends.

**chemical bond** An attractive force that arises between two atoms when their electrons interact.

**compound** Type of molecule that has atoms of more than one element.

**covalent bond** Chemical bond in which two atoms share a pair of electrons.

**hydrogen bond** Attraction that forms between a covalently bonded hydrogen atom and another atom taking part in a separate covalent bond.

**ionic bond** Type of chemical bond in which a strong mutual attraction forms between ions of opposite charge.

**molecule** Group of two or more atoms joined by chemical bonds.

**nonpolar** Having an even distribution of charge.

**polar** Having an uneven distribution of charge.

**polarity** Any separation of charge into distinct positive and negative regions.

**FIGURE 2.7 Animated!** Water. **A** Polarity of a water molecule: Each of the hydrogen atoms has a slight positive charge, and the oxygen atom has a slight negative charge. **B** The many hydrogen bonds (dashed lines) that keep water molecules clustered together impart special properties to liquid water. **C** Visible effect of cohesion: a wasp drinking (not sinking). Cohesion imparts surface tension to liquid water, which means that the surface of liquid water behaves a bit like a sheet of elastic.

**FIGURE 2.8 Animated!**
Water molecules that surround an ionic solid pull its atoms apart, thereby dissolving them.

**cohesion** Tendency of molecules to stick together.

**evaporation** Transition of a liquid to a gas.

**hydrophilic** Describes a substance that dissolves easily in water.

**hydrophobic** Describes a substance that resists dissolving in water.

**pH** Measure of the number of hydrogen ions in a fluid.

**salt** Compound that dissolves easily in water and releases ions other than $H^+$ and $OH^-$.

**solute** A dissolved substance.

**solvent** Liquid that can dissolve other substances.

**temperature** Measure of molecular motion.

# 2.4 Water

Life evolved in water. All living organisms are mostly water, many of them still live in it, and all of the chemical reactions of life are carried out in water. What makes water so fundamentally important for life?

Water's special properties as a liquid begin with the two polar covalent bonds in each water molecule. Overall, the molecule has no charge, but the oxygen pulls the shared electrons a bit more than the hydrogen atoms do. Thus, each of the atoms in a water molecule carries a slight charge: The oxygen atom is slightly negative, and the hydrogen atoms are slightly positive (Figure 2.7**A**). The separation of charge means that the water molecule itself is polar. The polarity is very attractive to other water molecules, and hydrogen bonds form between them in tremendous numbers (Figure 2.7**B**). Extensive hydrogen bonding between water molecules imparts unique properties to liquid water, and those properties make life possible.

First, water is an excellent solvent. A **solvent** is a liquid that can dissolve other substances. When a substance dissolves, its individual molecules or ions become **solutes** as they disperse. Salts, sugars, and many other compounds that dissolve easily in water are polar, so many hydrogen bonds form between them and water molecules. A **salt** is a compound that dissolves easily in water and releases ions other than $H^+$ and $OH^-$ when it does. Hydrogen bonding with water dissolves such **hydrophilic** (water-loving) substances by pulling their individual molecules away from one another and keeping them apart (Figure 2.8).

You can see how water interacts with **hydrophobic** (water-dreading) substances if you shake a bottle filled with water and salad oil, then set it on a table and watch what happens. Salad oil consists of nonpolar molecules, and water molecules do not form many hydrogen bonds with nonpolar molecules. Shaking breaks some of the hydrogen bonds that keep water molecules together. However, the water quickly begins to cluster into drops as new hydrogen bonds form among its molecules. The bonding excludes molecules of oil and pushes them together into droplets that rise to the surface of the water. The same interaction occurs at the thin, oily membrane that separates the water inside of cells from the water outside of them. The organization of membranes—and of life—starts with such interactions (you will read more about membranes in Chapter 3).

A second property of water is temperature stability. **Temperature** is a way to measure the energy of molecular motion: All molecules jiggle nonstop, and they jiggle faster as they absorb heat. However, extensive hydrogen bonding restricts the movement of water molecules—it keeps them from jiggling as much as they would otherwise. Thus, compared with other liquids, water absorbs much more heat before its temperature rises. Temperature stability is an important component of homeostasis, because most of the molecules of life function properly only within a certain range of temperature.

Below 0°C (32°F), water molecules do not jiggle enough to break hydrogen bonds, and they become locked in the rigid, lattice-like bonding pattern of ice. Individual water molecules pack less densely in ice than they do in water, so ice floats on water. During cold winters, ice sheets may form near the surface of ponds, lakes, and streams. Such ice "blankets" insulate liquid water under them, so they help keep fish and other aquatic organisms from freezing.

A third life-sustaining property of liquid water is **cohesion**, which means that water molecules resist separating from one another (Figure 2.7**C**). This property is important in many processes that sustain multicelled bodies. As one example, water molecules constantly escape from the surface of liquid water as vapor, a process called **evaporation**. Evaporation is resisted by the hydrogen bonding that keeps water molecules together. In other words, overcoming water's cohesion takes energy. Thus, evaporation sucks energy in the form of heat from liquid water, which decreases its surface temperature. Evaporative water loss can help you and some other mammals cool off when you sweat in hot, dry weather. Sweat, which is about 99 percent water, cools the skin as it evaporates.

## Take-Home Message  **Why is water essential to life?**

- Being polar, water molecules hydrogen-bond to one another and to other polar (hydrophilic) substances, and repel nonpolar (hydrophobic) substances.

- Extensive hydrogen bonding between water molecules gives water unique properties that make life possible: cohesion, temperature stability, and a capacity to dissolve many substances.

# 2.5 Acids and Bases

In liquid water, some water molecules spontaneously separate into hydrogen ions ($H^+$) and hydroxide ions ($OH^-$). These ions combine again to form water:

$$H_2O \longrightarrow H^+ + OH^- \longrightarrow H_2O$$

water      hydrogen  hydroxide      water
             ions      ions

**pH** is a measure of the number of hydrogen ions in water or any other liquid. When the number of $H^+$ ions is the same as the number of $OH^-$ ions, the pH of the solution is 7, or neutral. The pH of pure water (not rainwater or seawater) is like this. The more hydrogen ions, the lower the pH. A one-unit decrease in pH corresponds to a tenfold increase in the amount of $H^+$ ions, and a one-unit increase corresponds to a tenfold decrease in the amount of $H^+$ ions (Figure 2.9). One way to get a sense of the scale is to taste dissolved baking soda (pH 9),

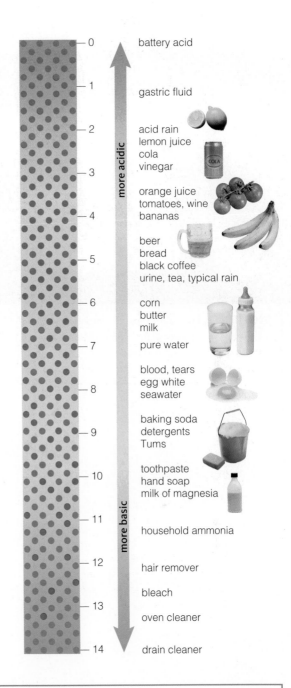

more acidic

0 — battery acid

1 — gastric fluid

2 — acid rain
lemon juice
cola
vinegar

3 —

orange juice
tomatoes, wine
bananas

4 —

beer
bread
black coffee
urine, tea, typical rain

5 —

6 — corn
butter
milk

7 — pure water

8 — blood, tears
egg white
seawater

9 — baking soda
detergents
Tums

10 — toothpaste
hand soap
milk of magnesia

more basic

11 — household ammonia

12 — hair remover

bleach

13 — oven cleaner

14 — drain cleaner

**FIGURE 2.9 Animated!** A pH scale. Here, *red* dots signify hydrogen ions ($H^+$) and *blue* dots signify hydroxyl ions ($OH^-$). Also shown are approximate pH values for some common solutions. This pH scale ranges from 0 (most acidic) to 14 (most basic). A change of one unit on the scale corresponds to a tenfold change in the amount of $H^+$ ions.

Figure It Out: What is the approximate pH of cola?

Answer: 2.5

distilled water (pH 7), and lemon juice (pH 2). Nearly all of life's chemistry occurs near pH 7. Most of your body's internal environment (tissue fluids and blood) is between pH 7.3 and 7.5.

Substances called **acids** give up hydrogen ions when they dissolve in water, so they lower the pH of fluids and make them acidic (below pH 7). **Bases** accept hydrogen ions, so they can raise the pH of fluids and make them basic, or alkaline (above pH 7). Acids or bases that accumulate in the environment can be harmful to organisms because they change the pH of fluids in an ecosystem. For instance, fossil fuel emissions and nitrogen-containing fertilizers release strong acids into the atmosphere (Figure 2.10). The acids make rain acidic, which in turn can drastically change the pH of water and soil (we return to this topic in Section 18.5). Such changes are harmful because most enzymes and other biological molecules function properly only within a narrow range of pH. Even a slight deviation from that range can halt cellular processes.

Under normal circumstances, fluids in cells and bodies stay within a consistent range of pH because they are buffered. A **buffer** is a set of chemicals, often a weak acid or base and a salt, that can keep the pH of a solution stable. It works because the two chemicals can alternately donate and accept ions that contribute to pH changes. For example, when a base is added to an unbuffered fluid, the number of OH⁻ ions increases, so the pH rises. However, if the fluid is buffered, the addition of base causes the buffer to release H⁺ ions. These combine with OH⁻ ions to form water, which does not affect pH. So, the buffered fluid's pH stays the same even when base is added.

For example, carbon dioxide gas takes part in an important buffer system. It becomes carbonic acid when it dissolves in human blood:

$$H_2O \ + \ CO_2 \ \longrightarrow \ H_2CO_3$$
$$\text{carbon dioxide} \qquad \text{carbonic acid}$$

The carbonic acid can separate into hydrogen ions and bicarbonate ions, which can turn around and recombine to form carbonic acid:

$$H_2CO_3 \ \longrightarrow \ H^+ \ + \ HCO_3^- \ \longrightarrow \ H_2CO_3$$
$$\text{carbonic acid} \qquad\qquad \text{bicarbonate} \qquad \text{carbonic acid}$$

Together, carbonic acid and bicarbonate constitute a buffer. Any excess OH⁻ in blood combines with the H⁺ to form water, which does not contribute to pH. Any excess H⁺ in blood combines with the bicarbonate. Thus bonded, the hydrogen does not affect pH. The exchange of ions keeps the blood pH between 7.3 and 7.5, but only up to a point. A buffer can neutralize only so many ions. Even slightly more than that limit and the pH of the fluid changes dramatically. Buffer failure can be catastrophic in a biological system. For example, too much carbonic acid forms in blood when breathing is impaired suddenly. The resulting decline in blood pH may cause an individual to enter a coma, which is a dangerous level of unconsciousness. Hyperventilation (sustained rapid breathing) causes the body to lose too much $CO_2$. The loss can result in a rise in blood pH. Prolonged muscle spasm (tetany) or coma may result.

**FIGURE 2.10** Sulfur dioxide emissions from a coal-burning power plant. Some airborne pollutants, including sulfur dioxide, dissolve in water vapor to form acids that end up in rain.

**acid** Substance that releases hydrogen ions in water.

**base** Substance that accepts hydrogen ions in water.

**buffer** Set of chemicals that can keep the pH of a solution stable by alternately donating and accepting ions that contribute to pH.

**organic** Type of molecule that consists primarily of carbon and hydrogen atoms.

# Take-Home Message  Why are hydrogen ions important to life?

- Hydrogen ions contribute to pH. Acids release hydrogen ions in water; bases accept them. Salts release ions other than H⁺ and OH⁻.

- Buffers keep the pH of body fluids stable. They are part of homeostasis.

# 2.6 Organic Molecules

Living things consist mainly of hydrogen, oxygen, and carbon atoms (Table 2.2). Most of the oxygen and hydrogen are in the form of water. Put water aside, and carbon makes up more than half of what is left. The carbon in living organisms is part of the molecules of life: complex carbohydrates, lipids, proteins, and nucleic acids. These molecules consist primarily of hydrogen and carbon atoms, so they are **organic**. The term is a holdover from a time when such molecules were thought to be made only by living things, as opposed to the "inorganic" molecules that formed by nonliving processes. The term persists, even though we now know that organic compounds were present on Earth long before organisms were, and we can also make them in laboratories.

Carbon's importance to life starts with its versatile bonding behavior. Each carbon atom can form covalent bonds with up to four other atoms. Depending on the other elements in the resulting molecule, such bonds may be polar or nonpolar. Many organic compounds have a backbone—a chain of carbon atoms—to which other atoms attach. The ends of a backbone may join so that the carbon chain forms one or more ring structures. The versatility means that carbon atoms can be assembled into a variety of organic molecules.

Using different kinds of models to represent the structure of organic compounds allows us to focus on different characteristics of a particular molecule. For example, structural formulas show how all the atoms in a molecule connect to one another (Figure 2.11**A**). In such models, each line indicates one covalent bond. A double line (=) indicates a double bond; a triple line (≡) indicates a triple bond. Some of the atoms or bonds in a molecule may be implied but not shown (Figure 2.11**B**). Hydrogen atoms bonded to a carbon backbone may also be omitted, and other atoms as well.

For simplicity, carbon ring structures such as the ones that occur in glucose and other sugars are often represented as polygons that imply carbon atoms at their corners (Figure 2.11**C**). Ball-and-stick models show the positions of the atoms in three dimensions (Figure 2.11**D**). Single, double, and triple covalent bonds are all shown as one stick connecting two balls, which represent atoms. Ball size reflects relative size of the atoms. Space-filling models show the overall shape of a molecule (Figure 2.11**E**). Note that the elements in ball-and-stick and space-filling models are typically coded using the same color scheme.

| Table 2.2 | Some Elemental Abundances* | | |
|---|---|---|---|
| Element | Human | Earth | Seawater |
| Hydrogen | 62.0% | 3.1% | 66.0% |
| Oxygen | 24.0 | 60.0 | 33.0 |
| Carbon | 12.0 | 0.3 | <0.1 |
| Nitrogen | 1.2 | <0.1 | <0.1 |
| Phosphorus | 0.2 | <0.1 | <0.1 |
| Calcium | <0.1 | <0.1 | <0.1 |
| Sodium | <0.1 | <0.1 | 0.3 |
| Potassium | <0.1 | 0.8 | <0.1 |
| Chlorine | <0.1 | <0.1 | 0.3 |

\* As a percentage of the total number of atoms in each source

**A** glucose  **B** glucose  **C** glucose  **D** glucose  **E** glucose

carbon  hydrogen  oxygen  nitrogen  phosphorus

**FIGURE 2.11** Modeling an organic molecule. **A** A structural formula shows atoms and bonds. **B,C** Structural formulas are often abbreviated to omit labels for some atoms such as the carbons at the corners of ring structures. **D** A ball-and-stick model shows the arrangement of atoms in three dimensions. **E** A space-filling model shows a molecule's overall shape. *Right*, typical color code for elements in molecular models.

**A** Condensation. Cells build large molecules from smaller ones by this reaction. An enzyme removes a hydroxyl group from one molecule and a hydrogen atom from another. Water forms as a covalent bond forms between the two molecules.

**B** Hydrolysis. Cells split molecules into smaller ones by this water-requiring reaction. An enzyme splits a molecule by attaching a hydroxyl group and a hydrogen atom (both from water) to each half.

**FIGURE 2.12 Animated!**
Two common metabolic processes by which cells build and break down organic molecules.

**From Structure to Function** All biological systems are based on the same organic molecules, a similarity that is a legacy of life's common origin. However, the details of those molecules differ among organisms. Just as atoms bonded in different numbers and arrangements form different molecules, so do simple organic building blocks bonded in different numbers and arrangements form different versions of the molecules of life.

Cells maintain pools of small organic molecules that they assemble into complex carbohydrates, lipids, proteins, and nucleic acids. When used as sub-units of larger molecules, the small organic molecules (simple sugars, fatty acids, amino acids, and nucleotides) are called **monomers**. Molecules that consist of multiple monomers are called **polymers**.

Cells build polymers from monomers, and break down polymers to release monomers. **Metabolism** refers to activities by which cells acquire and use energy as they make and break apart organic compounds. These activities help cells stay alive, grow, and reproduce. Metabolism also requires enzymes, which are molecules that make reactions proceed faster than they would on their own.

Cells commonly construct large molecules from smaller ones by **condensation**, a process in which an enzyme covalently bonds two molecules together. Water usually forms as a product of condensation when a hydroxyl group (—OH) from one of the molecules combines with a hydrogen atom from the other molecule (Figure 2.12**A**). Large molecules are typically broken down into smaller ones by **hydrolysis**, which is the reverse of condensation (Figure 2.12**B**). Enzymes break a bond by attaching a hydroxyl group to one atom and a hydrogen atom to the other. The —OH and —H are derived from a water molecule.

## Take-Home Message How are all of the molecules of life alike?

- Carbohydrates, lipids, proteins, and nucleic acids are all organic molecules, which consist mainly of carbon and hydrogen atoms.
- Cells assemble large polymers from smaller monomers of simple sugars, fatty acids, amino acids, and nucleotides. They also break apart polymers into their component monomers.

# 2.7 Carbohydrates

**Carbohydrates** consist of carbon, hydrogen, and oxygen atoms in a 1:2:1 ratio. Cells use different kinds of carbohydrates as structural materials and for energy. With one sugar unit, monosaccharides are the simplest carbohydrates. "Saccharide" is from a Greek word that means sugar. Common monosaccharides have a backbone of five or six carbon atoms. Most are water soluble, so they are easily transported through the internal fluids of all organisms. The sugars that are part of nucleic acids are five-carbon monosaccharides. Cells use six-carbon glucose as an energy source or as a monomer of larger molecules.

An oligosaccharide is a short chain of covalently bonded monosaccharides (*oligo*– means a few). Disaccharides consist of two sugar monomers. Sucrose, the most plentiful sugar in nature, has one unit of glucose and one of fructose, another monosaccharide. Sucrose extracted from sugarcane or sugar beets is our table sugar (*left*). Oligosaccharides with three or more sugar units are often attached to lipids or proteins that have important functions in immunity.

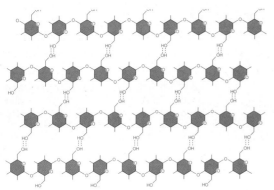

**A** Cellulose, a structural component of plants. Chains of glucose units stretch side by side and hydrogen-bond at many —OH groups. The hydrogen bonds stabilize the chains in tight bundles that form long fibers. Very few types of organisms can digest this tough, insoluble material.

**B** In starch, a series of glucose units form a chain that coils. Starch is the main energy reserve in plants, which store it in their roots, stems, leaves, fruits, and seeds (such as coconuts).

**C** Glycogen. In animals, this polysaccharide functions as an energy reservoir. It is especially abundant in the liver and muscles of active animals, including people.

**FIGURE 2.13** Three of the most common complex carbohydrates and their locations in a few organisms. Each polysaccharide consists only of glucose units, but different bonding patterns that link the subunits result in substances with very different properties.

"Complex" carbohydrates, or polysaccharides, are straight or branched chains of hundreds or thousands of sugar monomers. The most common polysaccharides (cellulose, starch, and glycogen) consist only of glucose monomers, but as substances their properties are very different. Why? The answer begins with differences in patterns of covalent bonding that link their glucose units. Cellulose, the major structural material of plants, may be the most abundant organic molecule in the biosphere. Glucose chains that stretch side by side are linked by hydrogen bonds that stabilize them in tight, sturdy bundles (Figure 2.13**A**). By contrast, the covalent bonding pattern of starch makes the molecule coil like a spiral staircase (Figure 2.13**B**). Starch does not dissolve easily in water, so it resists hydrolysis. This stability is a reason why starch is used to store chemical energy in the watery, enzyme-filled interior of plant cells. In animals, the long, branched chains of glycogen are the energy-storage equivalent of starch in plants (Figure 2.13**C**). Muscle and liver cells make and store glycogen. When the glucose level in blood falls, liver cells break glycogen into its component glucose monomers by hydrolysis. The released glucose enters the bloodstream, and the blood glucose level rises again.

## Take-Home Message  What are carbohydrates?

- Subunits of simple carbohydrates (sugars), arranged in different ways, form various types of complex carbohydrates.
- Cells use carbohydrates for energy or as structural materials.

**carbohydrate** Molecule that consists primarily of carbon, hydrogen, and oxygen atoms in a 1:2:1 ratio.

**condensation** Process by which enzymes build large molecules from smaller subunits; water also forms.

**hydrolysis** Process by which an enzyme breaks a molecule into smaller subunits by attaching a hydroxyl group to one part and a hydrogen atom to the other.

**metabolism** All the enzyme-mediated chemical reactions by which cells acquire and use energy as they build and break down organic molecules.

**monomer** Molecule that is a subunit of polymers.

**polymer** Molecule that consists of multiple monomers.

## FIGURE 2.14 Fatty acids.

**A** The backbone of stearic acid is fully saturated with hydrogen atoms.

**B** The backbone of linolenic acid, with three double bonds, is unsaturated. The first double bond occurs at the third carbon from the end, so linoleic acid is called an omega-3 fatty acid. Omega-3 and omega-6 fatty acids are "essential fatty acids." Your body does not make them, so they must come from food.

The only difference between oleic acid **C**, a *cis* fatty acid, and elaidic acid **D**, a *trans* fatty acid, is the arrangement of hydrogens around the one double bond in the backbone.

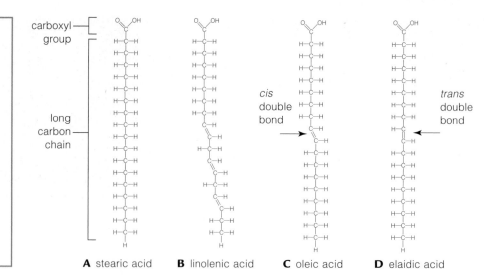

**A** stearic acid    **B** linolenic acid    **C** oleic acid    **D** elaidic acid

# 2.8 Lipids

**Lipids** are fatty, oily, or waxy organic compounds. Many lipids incorporate **fatty acids**, small organic compounds that consist of a long carbon chain with an acidic carboxyl group at one end (Figure 2.14). **Fats** are lipids with one, two, or three fatty acids that dangle like tails from a small alcohol called glycerol. Most neutral fats, including butter and vegetable oils, have three fatty acid tails, so they are called **triglycerides**. Triglycerides are the most abundant and richest energy source in vertebrate bodies. They are concentrated in adipose tissue that insulates and cushions body parts.

The fatty acid tails of **saturated fats** have only single bonds (Figure 2.14**A**). Animal fats tend to remain solid at room temperature because their saturated fatty acid tails can pack tightly. By contrast, the fatty acid tails of **unsaturated fats** have one or more double bonds that kink their carbon chains (Figure 2.14**B**). Kinky tails keep unsaturated fats from packing tightly. Most vegetable oils are liquid at room temperature because they are unsaturated (Figure 2.14**C**). The partially hydrogenated vegetable oils that you learned about in Section 2.1 are an exception. The double bond in these *trans* fatty acids keeps them straight. *Trans* fats pack tightly, so they are solid at room temperature (Figure 2.14**D**).

A **phospholipid** has two fatty acid tails attached to a phosphate-containing head (Figure 2.15**A**). The tails are hydrophobic, but the phosphate makes the head hydrophilic. Phospholipids are the most abundant lipids in cell membranes, which have two layers of lipids (Figure 2.15**B**). The heads of one layer are dissolved in the cell's watery interior, and the heads of the other layer are dissolved in the cell's fluid surroundings. All of the hydrophobic tails are sandwiched between the heads.

**Waxes** are complex, varying mixtures of lipids with long fatty acid tails bonded to long-chain alcohols or carbon rings. The molecules pack tightly, so the resulting substance is firm and water-repellent. A layer of secreted waxes that covers the exposed surfaces of plants helps restrict water loss and keep out parasites and other pests. Other types of waxes protect, lubricate, and soften skin and hair. Waxes, together with fats and fatty acids, make feathers waterproof. Bees store honey and raise new generations of bees inside honeycomb, which they make from beeswax.

hydrophilic head

two hydrophobic tails

**A**

one layer of lipids

one layer of lipids

**B** a lipid bilayer

**FIGURE 2.15** Phospholipids. **A** Each phospholipid has a hydrophilic head and two hydrophobic tails. **B** A double layer of phospholipids is the structural foundation of all cell membranes.

**FIGURE 2.16** Estrogen and testosterone, steroid hormones that cause different traits to arise in males and females of many species such as wood ducks (*Aix sponsa*).

**Steroids** are lipids with a rigid backbone of four carbon rings and no fatty acid tails. All eukaryotic cell membranes contain them. Cholesterol, the most common steroid in animal tissue, is also a starting material that cells remodel into many molecules, such as bile salts (which help digest fats) and vitamin D (required to keep teeth and bones strong). Steroid hormones are also derived from cholesterol. Estrogens and testosterone, hormones that govern reproduction and secondary sexual traits, are steroid hormones (Figure 2.16).

## Take-Home Message  **What are lipids?**

- Lipids are fatty, waxy, or oily organic compounds.
- Triglycerides are lipids that serve as energy reservoirs in vertebrate animals.
- Phospholipids are the main lipid component of cell membranes.
- Waxes are lipid components of water-repelling and lubricating secretions.
- Steroids are lipids that occur in cell membranes. Some are remodeled into other molecules.

# 2.9  Proteins

A **protein** is an organic compound composed of one or more chains of amino acids. An **amino acid** is a small organic compound with an amine group, a carboxyl group (the acid), and one or more atoms called an "R group." Typically, these groups are all attached to the same carbon atom:

Of all biological molecules, proteins are the most diverse. Structural proteins support cell parts and multicelled bodies. Spiderwebs, feathers, hooves, and hair, as well as bones and other body parts consist mainly of structural proteins. Foods such as seeds and eggs are nutritious in part because they are high in protein. Most enzymes are proteins. Proteins move substances, help cells communicate, and defend the body. Amazingly, cells can make thousands of different kinds of proteins from only twenty kinds of amino acids.

**amino acid**  Small organic compound with a carboxyl group, an amine group, and a characteristic side group (R).

**fat**  Lipid with one, two, or three fatty acid tails.

**fatty acid**  Organic compound that consists of a long chain of carbon atoms with an acidic carboxyl group at one end.

**lipid**  Fatty, oily, or waxy organic compound.

**phospholipid**  A lipid with a phosphate group in its hydrophilic head, and two nonpolar fatty acid tails.

**protein**  Organic compound that consists of one or more chains of amino acids.

**saturated fat**  Fatty acid with no double bonds in its carbon tail.

**steroid**  A type of lipid with four carbon rings and no fatty acid tails.

**triglyceride**  A lipid with three fatty acid tails attached to a glycerol backbone.

**unsaturated fat**  Lipid with at least one double bond in a fatty acid tail.

**wax**  Water-repellent lipid with long fatty acid tails bonded to long-chain alcohols or carbon rings.

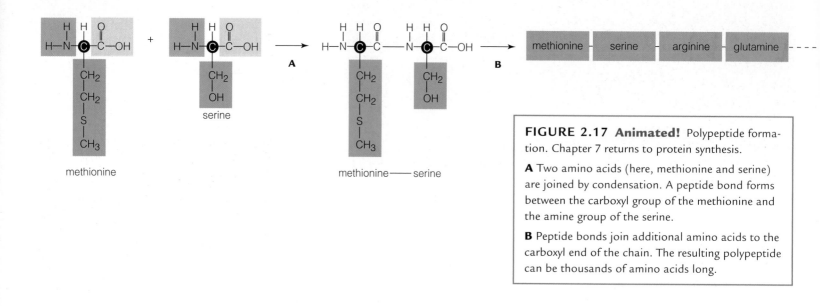

FIGURE 2.17 **Animated!** Polypeptide formation. Chapter 7 returns to protein synthesis.

**A** Two amino acids (here, methionine and serine)
are joined by condensation. A peptide bond forms
between the carboxyl group of the methionine and
the amine group of the serine.

**B** Peptide bonds join additional amino acids to the
carboxyl end of the chain. The resulting polypeptide
can be thousands of amino acids long.

# The shape of each protein defines its biological activity.

Protein synthesis involves covalently bonding amino acids into a chain.
For each type of protein, instructions coded in DNA specify the order in which
any of the twenty kinds of amino acids will occur at every place in the chain.
By condensation, an enzyme joins the amine group of an amino acid with the
carboxyl group of the next in a bond called a **peptide bond** (Figure 2.17). The
process is repeated hundreds or thousands of times, so a long chain of amino
acids called a **polypeptide** forms (Figure 2.18). The linear sequence of amino
acids in each type of protein is unique. The amino acid sequence is the protein's
primary structure ❶. Enzymes may attach linear or branched oligosaccharides to
polypeptide chains, thus forming sugar-proteins such as those that allow a tissue
or a body to recognize its own cells.

Even before a polypeptide is finished, it begins to acquire secondary structure
by twisting and folding. Hydrogen bonds that form between amino acids may
hold parts of the polypeptide chain in flat sheets, or in coils (helices) that are
a bit like spiral staircases ❷. Similar patterns of sheets and coils occur in most
types of proteins.

Much as an overly twisted rubber band coils back on itself, the sheets and
coils of a protein can fold up even more into compact domains. A "domain" is
a part of a protein that is organized as a structurally stable unit. Such units constitute a protein's third level of organization, its tertiary structure ❸. Tertiary
structure is what makes a protein a working molecule. As an example, the barrel-
shaped domains of some proteins function as tunnels through which ions cross
cell membranes.

Many proteins also have a fourth level of organization, or quaternary structure: They consist of two or more polypeptide chains bonded together or in
close association ❹. Most enzymes and many other proteins are globular, with
several polypeptide chains folded into shapes that are roughly spherical.

Some proteins aggregate by many thousands into much larger structures,
with their polypeptide chains organized into strands or sheets. The keratin in
your hair is an example ❺. Some fibrous proteins contribute to the structure
and organization of cells and tissues. Others, such as the actin and myosin that
form filaments in muscle cells, are part of the mechanisms that help cells and
cell parts move.

| lysine | - | glycine | - | glycine | - | arginine |

① ② ③ ④

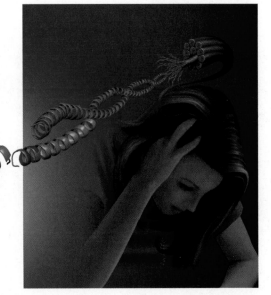

**FIGURE 2.18 Animated!** Protein structure.

① A protein's primary structure consists of a linear sequence of amino acids (a polypeptide chain).

② Secondary structure arises when a polypeptide chain twists into a coil (helix) or sheet held in place by hydrogen bonds between different parts of the molecule. The same patterns of secondary structure occur in many different proteins.

③ Tertiary structure occurs when a chain's coils and sheets fold up into a functional domain such as a barrel or pocket. In this example, the coils of a globin chain form a pocket.

④ Some proteins have quaternary structure, in which two or more polypeptide chains associate as one molecule. Hemoglobin, shown here, consists of four globin chains (*green* and *blue*). Each globin pocket now holds a heme group (*red*).

⑤ Many proteins aggregate by the thousands into larger structures, such as the keratin filaments that make up hair.

**The Importance of Protein Structure**  An enzyme speeds up a process, a receptor protein receives an energy signal, hemoglobin molecules in your blood carry oxygen—you and all other organisms consist of and depend on protein function. However, a protein only functions properly if it stays coiled, folded, and packed in a particular way, because the shape of each protein defines its biological activity. That shape depends on many hydrogen bonds and other interactions that heat, shifts in pH, or detergents can disrupt. At such times, proteins **denature**, which means they unwind and otherwise lose their three-dimensional shape. Once a protein's shape unravels, so does its function.

You can see denaturation in action when you cook an egg. A protein called albumin is a major component of egg white. Heat does not disrupt the covalent bonds of albumin's primary structure, but it does destroy the weaker hydrogen bonds that maintain the protein's shape. When a translucent egg white turns opaque, the albumin has been denatured. For very few proteins, denaturation is reversible if normal conditions return, but albumin is not one of them. There is no way to uncook an egg.

Prion diseases, including mad cow disease (bovine spongiform encephalitis, or BSE) in cattle, Creutzfeldt–Jakob disease in humans, and scrapie in sheep, are the dire aftermath of a misfolded protein. These infectious diseases may be inherited, but more often they arise spontaneously. All are characterized by relentless deterioration of mental and physical abilities that eventually causes death of the individual.

All prion diseases begin with a protein that occurs normally in mammals. One, PrP$^C$, is found in cell membranes throughout the body. This copper-binding protein is especially abundant in brain cells, but we still know very little about what it does. Very rarely, a PrP$^C$ protein spontaneously misfolds so that it loses some of its coiled character. In itself, a single misfolded protein molecule

**denature**  To unravel the shape of a protein or other large biological molecule.
**peptide bond**  A bond between the amine group of one amino acid and the carboxyl group of another.
**polypeptide**  Chain of amino acids linked by peptide bonds.

PrP^C
protein

Conformational
change

?

prion
protein

A

B

C

**FIGURE 2.19** Variant Creutzfeldt–Jakob disease (vCJD).

**A** The PrP^C protein becomes a prion when it misfolds into an as-yet unknown conformation. Prions cause other PrP^C proteins to misfold, and the misfolded proteins aggregate into long fibers.

**B** Slice of brain tissue from a person with vCJD. Characteristic holes and prion protein fibers radiating from several deposits are visible.

**C** Charlene Singh, here being cared for by her mother, was one of three people who developed symptoms of the disease while living in the United States. Like the others, Singh most likely contracted the disease elsewhere; she spent her childhood in Britain. She was diagnosed in 2001, and she died in 2004.

would not pose much of a threat. However, when this particular protein misfolds, it becomes a **prion**, or infectious protein (Figure 2.19**A**). The altered shape of a misfolded PrP^C protein somehow causes normally folded PrP^C proteins to misfold too. Because each misfolded protein becomes infectious, the number of prions increases exponentially.

The shape of misfolded PrP^C proteins allows them to align tightly into long fibers. Fibers composed of prion protein begin to accumulate in the brain as large, water-repellent patches. The patches grow as more prions form, and they begin to disrupt brain cell function, an effect that is the source of prion disease symptoms. Tiny holes form in the brain as its cells die (Figure 2.19**B**). Eventually, the brain becomes so riddled with holes that it looks like a sponge.

In the mid-1980s, an epidemic of mad cow disease in Britain was followed by an outbreak of a new variant of Creutzfeldt–Jakob disease (vCJD) in humans. Researchers isolated a prion similar to the one in scrapie-infected sheep from cows with BSE, and also from humans affected by the new type of Creutzfeldt–Jakob disease (Figure 2.19**C**). How did the prion get from sheep to cattle to people? Prions are not denatured by cooking or typical treatments that inactivate other types of infectious agents. The cattle became infected by the prion after eating feed prepared from the remains of scrapie-infected sheep, and people became infected by eating beef from the infected cattle.

Two hundred people have died from vCJD since 1990. The use of animal parts in livestock feed is now banned, and the number of cases of BSE and vCJD has since declined. Cattle with BSE still turn up, but so rarely that they pose little threat to the general human population.

## Take-Home Message  Why is protein structure important?

- A protein's function depends on its structure, which consists of chains of amino acids that twist and fold into functional domains.
- Changes in a protein's structure may also alter its function.

# 2.10 Nucleic Acids

**Nucleotides** are small organic molecules, various kinds of which function as energy carriers, enzyme helpers, chemical messengers, and subunits of DNA and RNA. Each nucleotide consists of a sugar with a five-carbon ring, bonded to a nitrogen-containing base and one or more phosphate groups. The nucleotide **ATP** (adenosine triphosphate) has a row of three phosphate groups attached to a ribose sugar (Figure 2.20**A**). When ATP transfers the outermost phosphate group to other molecules, it also transfers energy. You will read about such phosphate-group transfers and their important metabolic role in Chapter 5.

**Nucleic acids** are chains of nucleotides in which the sugar of one nucleotide is joined to the phosphate group of the next. An example is **RNA**, or ribonucleic acid, named after the ribose sugar of its component nucleotides. RNA consists of four kinds of nucleotide monomers, one of which is ATP. RNA molecules carry out protein synthesis, which we discuss in Chapter 7.

**DNA**, or deoxyribonucleic acid, is a nucleic acid named after the deoxyribose sugar of its component nucleotides. A DNA molecule consists of two nucleotide chains twisted into a double helix (Figure 2.20**B**). Hydrogen bonds between the nucleotides hold the two strands of DNA together. Each cell starts out life with DNA inherited from a parent cell. That DNA contains all of the information necessary to build a new cell and, in the case of multicelled organisms, an entire individual. The cell uses DNA's information to make RNA and proteins. Parts of a DNA molecule are identical or nearly so in all organisms, but most is unique to a species or an individual (Chapter 6 returns to DNA structure and function).

## Take-Home Message  **What are nucleotides and nucleic acids?**

- Nucleotides are monomers of the nucleic acids DNA and RNA, coenzymes, energy carriers, and messengers.
- DNA's nucleotide sequence encodes heritable information.
- Different types of RNA have roles in the processes by which a cell uses the information in its DNA.

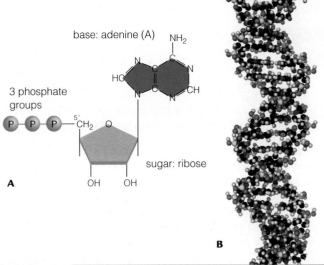

base: adenine (A)

3 phosphate groups

sugar: ribose

**A**

**B**

**FIGURE 2.20 Animated!** A nucleotide and a nucleic acid. **A** The nucleotide ATP. **B** DNA consists of two chains of nucleotides, twisted into a double helix held together by hydrogen bonds.

# 2.11 Impacts/Issues Revisited:
# Fear of Frying

*Trans* fatty acids are relatively rare in unprocessed foods, so it makes sense from an evolutionary standpoint that our bodies may not have enzymes to deal with them efficiently. The enzymes that hydrolyze *cis* fatty acids have difficulty breaking down *trans* fatty acids, a problem that may be a factor in the ill effects of *trans* fats. Several countries have already restricted the use of *trans* fats in food. In 2004, Denmark passed a law prohibiting importation of foods that contain partially hydrogenated vegetable oils. French fries and chicken nuggets that the Danish import from the United States contain almost no *trans* fats; the same foods sold to consumers in the United States contain 5 to 10 grams of *trans* fats per serving.

**ATP** Nucleotide that consists of an adenine base, five-carbon ribose sugar, and three phosphate groups. Also functions as an energy carrier.

**DNA** Nucleic acid that carries hereditary material; consists of two nucleotide chains twisted in a double helix.

**nucleic acid** Chain of nucleotides joined by sugar–phosphate bonds.

**nucleotide** Monomer of nucleic acids; has five-carbon sugar, nitrogen-containing base, and phosphate groups.

**prion** Infectious protein.

**RNA** Typically single-stranded nucleic acid; roles in protein synthesis.

# Summary

**Section 2.1** All living things consist of the same kinds of molecules, put together in slightly different ways.

**Section 2.2** All substances consist of atoms. Atoms are composed of electrons traveling around a nucleus of protons and neutrons. Elements are pure substances that consist only of atoms with the same number of protons. Researchers make tracers with detectable substances such as radioisotopes, which emit subatomic particles and energy as they decay spontaneously.

carbon (C)

CENGAGENOW™ Study electron distribution and the shell model, and learn how radioisotopes are used in a clinical setting, with the animations and interaction on CengageNow.

**Section 2.3** Atoms tend to fill their vacancies by gaining or losing electrons, or by sharing electrons with other atoms. Ions are atoms with unequal numbers of protons and electrons.

Ionic and covalent bonds are chemical bonds, which join atoms in molecules. An ionic bond is a strong mutual attraction of oppositely charged ions. Atoms share a pair of electrons in a covalent bond, which is polar if the electrons are not shared equally, and nonpolar if the sharing is equal. Hydrogen bonds form between a hydrogen atom and another atom taking part in a separate polar covalent bond.

CENGAGENOW™ See how different objects are assembled from the same materials, and compare the types of bonds in biological molecules with the animations on CengageNow.

**Section 2.4** Polar covalent bonds join two hydrogen atoms to one oxygen atom in each water molecule. The molecule's polarity invites extensive hydrogen bonding between water molecules, and this bonding is the basis of unique properties that make life possible: cohesion, temperature stability, and a capacity to dissolve many substances.

CENGAGENOW™ Learn how water's structure gives rise to its unique properties with animation on CengageNow.

**Section 2.5** pH reflects the number of hydrogen ions ($H^+$) in a solution. At neutral pH (7), the amounts of $H^+$ and $OH^-$ ions are the same. Salts release ions other than $H^+$ and $OH^-$ in water. Acids release $H^+$; bases accept $H^+$. A buffer keeps a solution within a consistent range of pH. Most cell and body fluids are buffered because the molecules of life work only within a narrow range of pH.

CENGAGENOW™ Discover the pH of common substances with the interaction on CengageNow.

**Section 2.6** Carbohydrates, proteins, lipids, and nucleic acids are organic molecules, which consist primarily of carbon and hydrogen atoms. Carbon atoms bond covalently with up to four other atoms, often forming long chains or rings. Enzyme-driven reactions construct large molecules from smaller subunits, and break large molecules into smaller ones.

glucose

CENGAGENOW™ Use the animation on CengageNow to see how sucrose forms by a condensation reaction.

**Section 2.7** Enzymes assemble complex carbohydrates such as cellulose, glycogen, and starch from simple carbohydrate (sugar) subunits. Cells use carbohydrates for energy, and as structural materials.

**Section 2.8** Lipids are greasy or oily nonpolar molecules, often with one or more fatty acid tails. Phospholipids are the main structural component of cell membranes. Waxes are lipids that are part of water-repellent and lubricating secretions. Steroids are lipids that occur in cell membranes, and some are remodeled into other molecules.

CENGAGENOW™ See a triglyceride form with animation on CengageNow.

**Sections 2.9** Protein structure begins as a linear sequence of amino acids called a polypeptide chain (primary structure). The chains form sheets and coils (secondary structure), which may pack into functional domains (tertiary structure). Many proteins, including most enzymes, consist of two or more polypeptides (quaternary structure). Fibrous proteins aggregate into large chains or sheets. A protein's structure dictates its function, so changes in a protein's structure may alter its function.

CENGAGENOW™ Explore amino acid structure and peptide bond formation with the animations on CengageNow.

**Section 2.10** Nucleotides consist of a sugar, a nitrogen-containing base, and phosphate groups. Nucleic acids DNA and RNA are polymers of nucleotide monomers. DNA encodes heritable information about a cell's proteins and RNAs. Different RNAs interact with DNA and with one another to carry out protein synthesis.

CENGAGENOW™ Explore DNA structure with the animation on CengageNow.

# Self-Quiz   Answers in Appendix I

1. A(n) _____ is a molecule into which a radioisotope has been incorporated.

2. A(n) _____ forms when atoms of two or more elements bond covalently.

3. Atoms share electrons unequally in a(n) _____ bond.

4. A(n) _____ substance repels water.

5. Hydrogen ions ($H^+$) are _____ .
   a. indicated by pH          c. in blood
   b. protons                  d. all of the above

6. When dissolved in water, a(n) _____ donates $H^+$.

7. A(n) _____ is a chemical partnership between a weak acid or base and its salt.

8. Each carbon atom can share pairs of electrons with up to _____ other atom(s).

# Digging Into Data

## Effects of Dietary Fats on Lipoprotein Levels

Cholesterol does not dissolve in blood, so it is carried through the bloodstream by lipid–protein aggregates called lipoproteins. Lipoproteins vary in structure. Low-density lipoprotein (LDL) carries cholesterol to body tissues such as artery walls, where it can form deposits associated with cardiovascular disease. LDL is often called "bad" cholesterol. High-density lipoprotein (HDL) carries cholesterol away from tissues to the liver for disposal, so HDL is often called "good" cholesterol.

In 1990, Ronald Mensink and Martijn Katan published a study that tested the effects of different dietary fats on blood lipoprotein levels. Their results are shown in Figure 2.21.

1. In which group was the level of LDL ("bad" cholesterol) highest?

2. In which group was the level of HDL ("good" cholesterol) lowest?

3. An elevated risk of heart disease has been correlated with increasing LDL-to-HDL ratios. In which group was the LDL:HDL ratio highest? Rank the three diets according to their potential effect on cardiovascular health.

protein    lipid

an HDL particle

|  | Main Dietary Fats | | | |
|  | *cis*-fatty acids | *trans*-fatty acids | saturated fats | optimal level |
| --- | --- | --- | --- | --- |
| LDL | 103 | 117 | 121 | <100 |
| HDL | 55 | 48 | 55 | >40 |
| ratio | 1.87 | 2.44 | 2.2 | <2 |

**FIGURE 2.21** Effect of diet on lipoprotein levels. Researchers placed 59 men and women on a diet in which 10 percent of their daily energy intake consisted of *cis* fatty acids, *trans* fatty acids, or saturated fats. Blood LDL and HDL levels were measured after three weeks on the diet; averaged results are shown in mg/dL (milligrams per deciliter of blood). All subjects were tested on each of the diets. The ratio of LDL to HDL is also shown.

---

9. _____ is a simple sugar (a monosaccharide).
   a. Glucose    c. Ribose    e. a and c
   b. Sucrose    d. Starch    f. a, b, and c

10. Unlike saturated fats, the fatty acid tails of unsaturated fats incorporate one or more _____ .

11. Is this statement true or false? Unlike saturated fats, all of the unsaturated fats are beneficial to health because their fatty acid tails do not pack tightly together.

12. Which of the following is a class of molecules that encompasses all of the other molecules listed?
   a. triglycerides    c. waxes     e. lipids
   b. fatty acids      d. steroids  f. phospholipids

13. _____ are to proteins as _____ are to nucleic acids.
   a. Sugars; lipids      c. Amino acids; hydrogen bonds
   b. Sugars; proteins    d. Amino acids; nucleotides

14. A denatured protein has lost its _____ .
   a. hydrogen bonds    c. function
   b. shape             d. all of the above

15. _____ consist(s) of nucleotides.
   a. sugars    b. DNA    c. RNA    d. b and c

16. Match each molecule with its most suitable description.
   _____ chain of amino acids            a. polar
   _____ energy carrier in cells         b. phospholipid
   _____ glycerol, fatty acids, phosphate c. temperature
   _____ two strands of nucleotides      d. DNA
   _____ one or more sugar monomers      e. ATP
   _____ richest source of energy        f. triglycerides
   _____ hydrophilic                     g. atomic number
   _____ number of protons in nucleus    h. carbohydrate
   _____ molecular jiggling              i. polypeptide

Additional questions are available on CENGAGENOW™

---

# Critical Thinking

1. Alchemists were medieval scholars and philosophers who were the forerunners of modern-day chemists. Many spent their lives trying to transform lead (atomic number 82) into gold (atomic number 79). Explain why they never did succeed in that endeavor.

2. Draw a shell model of a nitrogen atom, which has 7 protons.

3. In 1976, a team of chemists in the UK was developing new insecticides by modifying sugars with chlorine ($Cl_2$), phosgene ($Cl_2CO$), and other toxic gases. One young member of the team misunderstood his verbal instructions to "test" a new molecule. He thought he had been told to "taste" it. Luckily, the molecule was not toxic, but it was very sweet. It became the food additive sucralose.

Sucralose has three chlorine atoms substituted for three hydroxyl groups of sucrose. It binds so strongly to the sweet-taste receptors on the tongue that the human brain perceives it as 600 times sweeter than sucrose (table sugar). Sucralose was originally marketed as an artificial sweetener called Splenda, but it is now available under several other brand names.

Researchers proved that the body does not recognize sucralose as a carbohydrate by feeding sucralose labeled with $^{14}C$ to volunteers. Analysis of the radioactive molecules in the volunteers' urine and feces showed that 92.8 percent of the sucralose passed through the body without being altered. Many people are worried that the chlorine atoms impart toxicity to sucralose. How would you respond to that concern?

sucrose          sucralose

# 3 Cell Structure

> Cell for cell, bacteria that live in and on a human body outnumber the person's own cells by about ten to one.

# 3.1 Impacts/Issues:    Food for Thought

We find bacteria at the bottom of the ocean, high up in the atmosphere, miles underground—essentially anywhere we look. Mammal intestines typically harbor fantastic numbers of them, but bacteria are not just stowaways there. Intestinal bacteria make vitamins that mammals cannot, and they crowd out more dangerous germs. Cell for cell, bacteria that live in and on a human body outnumber the person's own cells by about ten to one.

*Escherichia coli* is one of the most common intestinal bacteria of warm-blooded animals. Only a few of the hundreds of types, or strains, of *E. coli*, are harmful. One, O157:H7, makes a potent toxin that can severely damage the lining of the human intestine. After ingesting as few as ten O157:H7 cells, a person may become ill with severe cramps and bloody diarrhea that lasts up to ten days. In some people, complications of O157:H7 infection result in kidney failure, blindness, paralysis, and death. About 73,000 people in the United States become infected with *E. coli* O157:H7 each year, and more than 60 of them die.

*E. coli* O157:H7 lives in the intestines of other animals—mainly cattle, deer, goats, and sheep—apparently without sickening them. Humans are exposed to the bacteria when they come into contact with feces of animals that harbor it, for example, by eating contaminated ground beef. During slaughter, meat occasionally comes into contact with feces. Bacteria in the feces stick to the meat, then get thoroughly mixed into it during the grinding process. Unless contaminated meat is cooked to at least 71°C (160°F), live bacteria will enter the digestive tract of whoever eats it.

People also become infected by eating fresh fruits and vegetables that have come into contact with animal feces. For example, in 2006, more than 200 people became ill and 3 died after eating fresh spinach. The spinach was grown in a field close to a cattle pasture, and water contaminated with manure may have been used to irrigate the field. Washing contaminated produce with water does not remove *E. coli* O157:H7, because the bacteria are sticky.

The economic impact of such outbreaks, which occur with some regularity, extends beyond the casualties. Growers lost $50–100 million recalling fresh spinach after the 2006 outbreak. In 2007, about 5.7 million pounds of ground beef were recalled after 14 people were sickened. Food growers and processors are beginning to implement new procedures that they hope will reduce *E. coli* O157:H7 outbreaks. Some meats and produce are now tested for pathogens before sale, and improved documentation should allow a source of contamination to be pinpointed more quickly.

What makes bacteria sticky? Why do people but not cows get sick with *E. coli* O157:H7? You will begin to find answers to these and many more questions that affect your health in this chapter, as you learn about cells and how they work.

**FIGURE 3.1** Examples of cells. Each one of the cells pictured here is an individual organism; all are protists.

# 3.2 What, Exactly, Is a Cell?

There are many different kinds of cells, a few of which are shown in Figure 3.1. Despite their differences, however, all cells have certain organizational and functional features. For example, every cell has an outer membrane, or **plasma membrane**, that separates its metabolic activities from events outside of the cell. At its most basic structural level, a cell membrane consists of a **lipid bilayer**, a double layer of lipids (*right*). In addition to a plasma membrane, many cells also have membranes that divide their interior into compartments with various functions. A cell would die very quickly without continuously exchanging substances such as raw materials and wastes with its environment, so a plasma membrane is necessarily permeable to certain substances. Gases such as oxygen and carbon dioxide freely cross lipid bilayers, as does water. Ions and other substances can only cross with the assistance of proteins embedded in the membrane. Other proteins carry out different functions, as you will see in Section 3.4.

one layer of lipids

one layer of lipids

a lipid bilayer

A plasma membrane encloses a fluid or jellylike mixture of water, sugars, ions, and proteins called **cytoplasm**. An important part of homeostasis consists of maintaining the composition of cytoplasm, which differs—often dramatically—from the composition of fluid outside the cell. Some or all of a cell's metabolism occurs in the cytoplasm, and the cell's internal components, including organelles, are suspended in it. **Organelles** are structures that carry out special metabolic functions inside a cell.

All cells start out life with DNA, although a few types of cells lose it as they mature. We categorize cells into two major categories, prokaryotic and eukaryotic, based on whether their DNA is housed in a nucleus or not. The **nucleus** (plural, nuclei) is an organelle with a double membrane that contains the cell's DNA. Only eukaryotic cells have a nucleus. In most prokaryotic cells, the DNA is suspended directly in the cytoplasm. We call the region of cytoplasm in which prokaryotic DNA is most concentrated a **nucleoid**.

Almost all cells are too small to see with the naked eye. Why? The answer begins with the processes that keep a cell alive. A living cell must exchange substances with its environment at a rate that keeps pace with its metabolism. Nutrients have to enter the cell fast enough to supply its molecule-building activities, and wastes have to exit at a rate that prevents the cell from being poisoned. Both processes occur across the plasma membrane, which can handle

**cytoplasm** Semifluid substance enclosed by a cell's plasma membrane.

**lipid bilayer** Structural foundation of cell membranes; mainly phospholipids arranged tail-to-tail in two layers.

**nucleoid** Region of cytoplasm where the DNA is concentrated inside a prokaryotic cell.

**nucleus** Organelle with two membranes that holds a eukaryotic cell's DNA.

**organelle** Structure that carries out a specialized metabolic function inside a cell.

**plasma membrane** A cell's outermost membrane.

| Diameter (cm) | 2 | 3 | 6 |
|---|---|---|---|
| Surface area (cm$^2$) | 12.6 | 28.2 | 113 |
| Volume (cm$^3$) | 4.2 | 14.1 | 113 |
| Surface-to-volume ratio | 3:1 | 2:1 | 1:1 |

**FIGURE 3.2 Animated!** Examples of surface-to-volume ratio. This physical relationship between increases in volume and surface area limits the size and influences the shape of cells.

only so many exchanges at a time between the cytoplasm and the external environment. Thus, cell size is limited by a physical relationship called the **surface-to-volume ratio**. By this ratio, an object's volume increases with the cube of its diameter, but its surface area increases only with the square.

Apply the surface-to-volume ratio to a round cell. As Figure 3.2 shows, when a cell expands in diameter, its volume increases faster than its surface area does. Imagine that a round cell expands until it is four times its original diameter. The volume of the cell has increased 64 times ($4^3$), but its surface area has increased only 16 times ($4^2$). Each unit of plasma membrane must now handle exchanges with four times as much cytoplasm ($64 \div 16 = 4$). If the cell gets too big, the inward flow of nutrients and the outward flow of wastes across that membrane will not be fast enough to keep the cell alive.

Why not? A cell is filled with cytoplasm, and metabolic activities occur all through it. Molecules disperse themselves through cytoplasm by their own random motions, but this movement occurs only so quickly. Nutrients must cross the plasma membrane and get distributed through the cytoplasm fast enough to satisfy a cell's metabolic needs, and wastes must be removed fast enough to keep the cell from poisoning itself. Nutrients and wastes would not be able to move through the middle of a big, round cell fast enough to keep up with metabolism.

Surface-to-volume limits also affect the body plans of multicelled species. For example, small cells attach end to end to form strandlike algae, so that each can interact directly with its surroundings. Muscle cells in your thighs are as long as the muscle in which they occur, but each is thin, so it exchanges substances efficiently with fluids in the tissue surrounding it.

**The Cell Theory** Hundreds of years of observations of cell structure and function led to the way we now answer the question, What is a cell? A **cell** is the smallest unit that shows the properties of life: It carries out metabolism and homeostasis, and either reproduces on its own or it is part of a larger organism. By this definition, each cell is alive even if it is part of a multicelled body, and all living organisms consist of one or more cells. We also know that cells reproduce themselves by dividing, so it follows that all existing cells must have arisen by division of other cells. Later chapters discuss the processes by which cells divide, but for now all you need to know is that a cell passes its hereditary material—its DNA—to offspring during those processes. Taken together, these four generalizations constitute the **cell theory**, a foundation of modern biology (Table 3.1).

| Table 3.1 | The Cell Theory |
|---|---|

1. Every living organism consists of one or more cells.

2. A cell is the smallest unit of life, individually alive even as part of a multicelled organism.

3. Every living cell came into existence by division of a pre-existing cell.

4. Cells contain hereditary material (DNA) that they pass along to their offspring during processes of cell division.

**cell** Smallest unit of life.
**cell theory** Fundamental theory of biology: All organisms consist of one or more cells; the cell is the smallest unit of life; each new cell arises from another cell; and a cell passes hereditary material to its offspring.
**surface-to-volume ratio** A relationship in which the volume of an object increases with the cube of the diameter, but the surface area increases with the square.

## Take-Home Message
### How are all cells alike?

- The cell is the fundamental unit of all life.
- All cells start life with a plasma membrane, cytoplasm, and a region of DNA, which, in eukaryotic cells only, is enclosed by a nucleus.
- The surface-to-volume ratio limits cell size and influences cell shape.

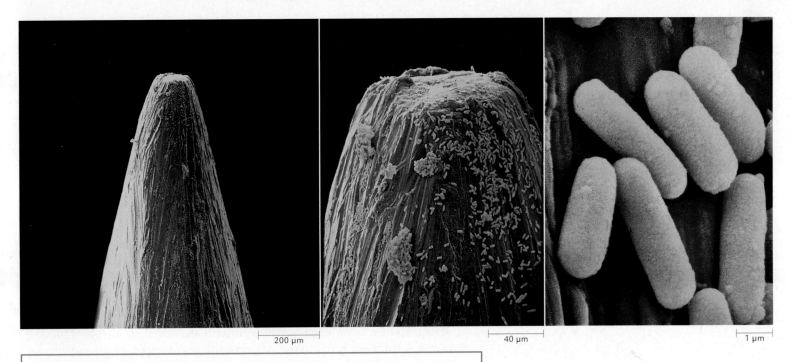

200 μm      40 μm      1 μm

**FIGURE 3.3** Rod-shaped bacterial cells on the tip of a household pin, shown at increasingly higher magnifications (enlargements). The "μm" is an abbreviation for micrometers, or millionths of a meter. **Figure It Out:** About how big are these bacteria?

*Answer: About 1 μm wide and 5 μm long*

# 3.3 Measuring Cells

Do you ever think of yourself as being about 3/2000 of a kilometer (1/1000 of a mile) tall? Probably not, yet that is how we measure cells. Use the scale bars in Figure 3.3 like a ruler and you can see that the cells shown are a few micrometers "tall." One micrometer (μm) is one-thousandth of a millimeter, which is one-thousandth of a meter, which is one-thousandth of a kilometer (0.62 miles). The cells in the photos are bacteria. Bacteria are among the smallest and structurally simplest cells on Earth. The cells that make up your body are generally larger and more complex than bacteria.

**Animalcules and Beasties** No one even knew cells existed until well after the first microscopes were invented. Those microscopes were not very sophisticated. Given the simplicity of their instruments, it is amazing that the pioneers in microscopy observed as much as they did. By the mid-1600s, Antoni van Leeuwenhoek, a Dutch draper, was spying on the microscopic world of rainwater, insects, fabric, sperm, feces—essentially any sample he could fit into his homemade microscope (shown at *right*). He was fascinated by the tiny organisms he saw moving in many of his samples. For example, in scrapings of tartar from his teeth, Leeuwenhoek saw "many very small animalcules, the motions of which were very pleasing to behold." He (incorrectly) assumed that movement defined life, and (correctly) concluded that the moving "beasties" he saw were alive. Perhaps Leeuwenhoek was so pleased to behold his animalcules because he did not understand the implications of what he was seeing: Our world, and our bodies, teem with bacteria and other microbial life.

sample holder    focusing knob

lens

Leeuwenhoek's microscope

molecules of life

small molecules

lipids

DNA (width)

complex carbohydrates

proteins

viruses

mitochondria, chloroplasts

most bacteria

most eukaryotic cells

electron microscopes

light microscopes

0.1 nm    1 nm    10 nm    100 nm    1 µm    10 µm

Robert Hooke, a contemporary of Leeuwenhoek, added another lens that made the instrument easier to use. Many of the microscopes we use today are still based on his design. Hooke magnified a piece of thinly sliced cork from a mature tree and saw tiny compartments (his drawing of them is shown at *right*). Hooke named the compartments cellulae—a Latin word for the small chambers that monks lived in—and thus coined the term "cell." Actually, they were dead plant cell walls, which is what cork consists of, but Hooke did not think of them as being dead because neither he nor anyone else knew cells could be alive. He observed cells "fill'd with juices" in green plant tissues but did not realize they were alive, either.

For nearly 200 years after Hooke discovered them, cells were assumed to be part of a continuous membrane system in multicelled organisms, not separate entities. In the mid-1800s, botanist Matthias Schleiden realized that a plant cell is an independent living unit even when it is part of a plant. Schleiden compared notes with zoologist Theodor Schwann, and together they concluded that the tissues of animals as well as plants are composed of cells and their products. The cell theory, first articulated in 1839 by Schwann and Schleiden and later revised, was a radical new interpretation of nature that underscored life's unity.

**FIGURE 3.4** Different microscopes reveal different characteristics of the same organism, a green alga (*Scenedesmus*).

**A** Light micrograph. A phase-contrast microscope yields high-contrast images of transparent specimens, such as cells.

**B** Light micrograph. A reflected light microscope captures light reflected from opaque specimens.

**C** Fluorescence micrograph. The chlorophyll molecules in these cells emitted red light (they fluoresced) naturally.

**D** A transmission electron micrograph reveals fantastically detailed images of internal structures.

**E** A scanning electron micrograph shows surface details of cells and structures. SEMs may be artificially colored to highlight certain details.

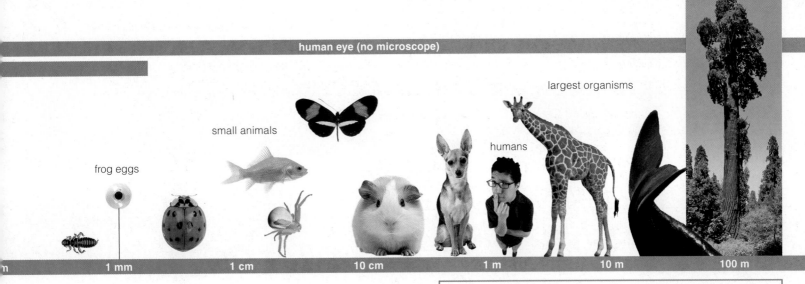

largest organisms

small animals

humans

frog eggs

| 1 mm | 1 cm | 10 cm | 1 m | 10 m | 100 m |

## Modern Microscopes

Like their early predecessors, many modern microscopes rely on visible light to illuminate objects. All light travels in waves, a property that makes it bend when it passes through curved glass lenses. Inside microscopes, such lenses focus light into a magnified image of a specimen. Photographs of images enlarged with any microscope are called micrographs (Figure 3.4). Figure 3.5 compares the resolving power of light and electron microscopes with that of the unaided human eye.

Phase-contrast microscopes shine light through specimens, but most cells are nearly transparent. Their internal details may not be visible unless they are first stained, or exposed to dyes that only some cell parts soak up. Parts that absorb the most dye appear darkest. Staining results in an increase in contrast (the difference between light and dark) that allows us to see a greater range of detail (Figure 3.4**A**). Surface details can be revealed by reflected light (Figure 3.4**B**).

With a fluorescence microscope, a cell or a molecule is the light source; it fluoresces, or emits energy in the form of light, when a laser beam is focused on it. Some molecules fluoresce naturally (Figure 3.4**C**). More typically, researchers attach a light-emitting tracer to the cell or molecule of interest.

Other microscopes can reveal finer details. For example, electron microscopes use electrons instead of visible light to illuminate samples. Transmission electron microscopes beam electrons through a thin specimen. The specimen's internal details appear on the resulting image as shadows (Figure 3.4**D**). Scanning electron microscopes direct a beam of electrons back and forth across a surface of a specimen, which has been coated with a thin layer of gold or another metal. The metal emits both electrons and x-rays, which are converted into an image of the surface (Figure 3.4**E**). Both types of electron microscopes can resolve structures as small as 0.2 nanometers.

**FIGURE 3.5** Relative sizes. *Above*, the diameter of most cells is in the range of 1 to 100 micrometers. *Below*, converting among units of length; see Units of Measure, Appendix V. **Figure It Out:** Which is smallest: a protein, a lipid, or a water molecule?

*Answer: A water molecule*

| | |
|---|---|
| 1 centimeter (cm) | = 1/100 meter, or 0.4 inch |
| 1 millimeter (mm) | = 1/1000 meter, or 0.04 inch |
| 1 micrometer (μm) | = 1/1,000,000 meter, or 0.00004 inch |
| 1 nanometer (nm) | = 1/1,000,000,000 meter, or 0.00000004 inch |
| 1 meter | $= 10^2$ cm $= 10^3$ mm $= 10^6$ μm $= 10^9$ nm |

## Take-Home Message  How do we see cells?

- Most cells are visible only with the help of microscopes.
- Different types of microscopes reveal different aspects of cell structure.

**A** Phospholipids are the most abundant component of eukaryotic cell membranes. Each phospholipid molecule has a hydrophilic head and two hydrophobic tails.

hydrophilic head

two hydrophobic tails

**B** In a watery fluid, phospholipids spontaneously line up into two layers: hydrophobic tails cluster together, and hydrophilic heads face outward, toward the fluid. This lipid bilayer forms the framework of all cell membranes.

**C** A lipid bilayer spontaneously shapes itself into a sheet or bubble. A plasma membrane is basically a lipid bilayer balloon filled with fluid. Many types of proteins intermingle among the lipids in a cell membrane—a few that are typical of plasma membranes are shown *opposite*.

one layer of lipids

one layer of lipids

**FIGURE 3.6 Animated!** Cell membrane structure. **A–C** Organization of lipids in cell membranes. **D–G** Examples of membrane proteins.

## The Structure of Cell Membranes

A cell membrane is a barrier that selectively controls exchanges between the cell and its surroundings. This function emerges when certain lipids—mainly phospholipids—interact. A phospholipid molecule consists of a phosphate-containing head and two fatty acid tails. The polar head is hydrophilic, which means it interacts with water molecules. The nonpolar tails are hydrophobic, so they do not interact with water molecules. The tails do, however, interact with the tails of other phospholipids. When swirled into water, phospholipids spontaneously assemble into two layers, with all of their nonpolar tails sandwiched between all of their polar heads. Such lipid bilayers are the basic framework of all cell membranes (Figure 3.6**A–C**).

Other molecules—including steroids and proteins—are embedded in or associated with the lipid bilayer of a cell membrane. Most of these molecules flow around more or less freely. The fluidity arises from the behavior of the phospholipids, which drift sideways and spin around their long axis in a bilayer. Their tails wiggle too. The **fluid mosaic model** describes a cell membrane as a two-dimensional liquid of mixed composition.

**Membrane Proteins** A cell membrane physically separates an external environment from an internal one, but that is not its only task. Many types of proteins are associated with a cell membrane, and each type adds a specific function to it. Thus, even though every cell membrane consists mainly of a phospholipid bilayer, different cell membranes can have different characteristics depending on which proteins are associated with them. For example, a plasma membrane has proteins that no internal cell membrane has. Many plasma membrane proteins are **enzymes**, which accelerate chemical processes without being changed by them. **Adhesion proteins** fasten cells together in animal tissues. **Recognition proteins** function as unique identity tags for each individual or species (Figure 3.6**D**). Being able to recognize "self" means that foreign cells (harmful ones, in particular) can also be recognized.

A plasma membrane is basically a lipid bilayer balloon filled with fluid.

fluid

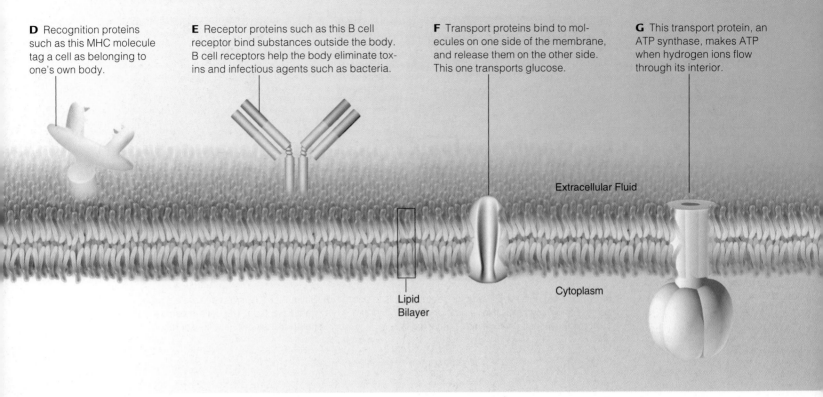

**D** Recognition proteins such as this MHC molecule tag a cell as belonging to one's own body.

**E** Receptor proteins such as this B cell receptor bind substances outside the body. B cell receptors help the body eliminate toxins and infectious agents such as bacteria.

**F** Transport proteins bind to molecules on one side of the membrane, and release them on the other side. This one transports glucose.

**G** This transport protein, an ATP synthase, makes ATP when hydrogen ions flow through its interior.

Extracellular Fluid

Lipid Bilayer

Cytoplasm

**Receptor proteins** bind to a particular substance outside of the cell, such as a hormone or toxin (Figure 3.6**E**). Binding triggers a change in the cell's activities that may involve metabolism, movement, division, or even cell death. Different receptors occur on different cells, but all are critical for homeostasis.

Additional proteins occur on all cell membranes. **Transport proteins** move specific substances across a membrane, typically by forming a channel through it. These proteins are important because lipid bilayers are impermeable to most substances, including ions and polar molecules. Some transport proteins are open channels through which a substance moves on its own across a membrane (Figure 3.6**F**,**G**). Others use energy to actively pump a substance across. We return to the topic of transport across membranes in the next chapter.

## Take-Home Message  **What is a cell membrane?**

■ A cell membrane is a mosaic of different kinds of lipids and proteins.

■ The foundation of cell membranes is the lipid bilayer: two layers of phospholipids, tails sandwiched between heads.

■ Many types of proteins add various functions to lipid bilayers in membranes.

# 3.5
# Introducing Prokaryotic Cells

The word prokaryote means "before the nucleus," a reminder that the first prokaryotes evolved before the first eukaryotes. All prokaryotes are single-celled. As a group, they are the smallest and most metabolically diverse forms of life

**adhesion protein** Membrane protein that helps cells stick together in tissues.

**enzyme** Molecule that speeds a chemical process without being changed by it.

**fluid mosaic model** A cell membrane can be considered a two-dimensional fluid of mixed composition.

**receptor protein** Plasma membrane protein that binds to a particular substance outside of the cell.

**recognition protein** Plasma membrane protein that tags a cell as belonging to self (one's own body).

**transport protein** Protein that passively or actively assists specific ions or molecules across a membrane.

**A** Protein filaments, or pili, anchor bacterial cells to one another and to surfaces. Here, *Salmonella* Typhimurium cells (*red*) use their pili to invade human cells.

**B** Ball-shaped *Nostoc* cells are a type of freshwater photosynthetic bacteria. The cells in each strand stick together in a sheath of their own jellylike secretions.

flagellum

capsule

cell wall

plasma membrane

cytoplasm, with ribosomes

DNA in nucleoid

pilus

**FIGURE 3.8 Animated!** Generalized body plan of a prokaryote.

that we know about. Prokaryotes inhabit nearly all of Earth's environments, including some very hostile places.

Domains Bacteria and Archaea make up the prokaryotes (Section 1.4 and Figure 3.7). The two kinds of cells may be alike in appearance and size, but they differ in structure and metabolic details. Some characteristics of archaeans indicate they are more closely related to eukaryotic cells than they are to bacteria. Chapter 13 revisits prokaryotes in more detail. Here we present a simple overview.

Most prokaryotic cells are not much bigger than a few micrometers. None has a complex internal framework, but protein filaments under the plasma membrane reinforce the cell's shape. Such filaments also act as scaffolding for internal structures.

Figure 3.8 shows a general body plan of a prokaryotic cell. The cytoplasm of these cells contains many **ribosomes** (organelles upon which polypeptides are assembled), and in some species, additional organelles. The cell's single chromosome, a circular DNA molecule, is located in the cytoplasm, in an irregularly shaped region called the nucleoid. Most nucleoids are not enclosed by a membrane. The cytoplasm of many prokaryotes also contains plasmids. These small circles of DNA carry a few genes (units of inheritance) that can provide advantages, such as resistance to antibiotics.

Many prokaryotic cells have one or more flagella projecting from their surface. **Flagella** (singular, flagellum) are long, slender cellular structures used for motion. A bacterial flagellum rotates like a propeller that drives the cell through fluid habitats, such as an animal's body fluids. Some bacteria also have protein filaments called **pili** (singular, pilus) projecting from their surface (Figure 3.7**A**). Pili help cells cling to or move across surfaces. One kind, a "sex" pilus, attaches to another bacterium and then shortens. The attached cell is reeled in, and a plasmid is transferred from one cell to the other through the pilus.

A durable **cell wall** surrounds the plasma membrane of nearly all prokaryotes. Dissolved substances easily cross this permeable layer on the way to and from the plasma membrane. The cell wall of most bacteria consists of a polymer of peptides and polysaccharides. The wall of most archaeans consists of proteins. Sticky polysaccharides form a slime layer, or capsule, around the wall

**C** The archaean *Pyrococcus furiosus* was discovered in ocean sediments near an active volcano. It lives best at 100°C (212°F), and it makes a rare kind of enzyme that contains tungsten atoms.

**D** *Ferroglobus placidus* prefers superheated water spewing from the ocean floor. The durable composition of archaean lipid bilayers (note the gridlike texture) keeps their membranes intact at extreme heat and pH.

**E** *Metallosphaera prunae*, an archaean discovered in a smoking pile of ore at a uranium mine, prefers high temperatures and low pH. (*White* shadows are an artifact of electron microscopy.)

of many types of bacteria. The sticky capsule helps these cells adhere to many types of surfaces (such as spinach leaves and meat), and it also offers some protection against predators and toxins.

The plasma membrane of all bacteria and archaeans selectively controls which substances move into and out of the cell, as it does for eukaryotic cells. The plasma membrane bristles with transporters and receptors, and it also incorporates proteins that carry out important metabolic processes. For example, part of the plasma membrane of cyanobacteria (Figure 3.7**B**) folds into the cytoplasm. Molecules that carry out photosynthesis are embedded in this membrane, just as they are in the inner membrane of chloroplasts, which are organelles specialized for photosynthesis in eukaryotic cells (we return to chloroplasts in Section 3.6).

**Biofilms** Bacterial cells often live so close together that an entire community shares a layer of secreted polysaccharides and proteins. A communal living arrangement in which single-celled organisms live in a shared mass of slime is called a **biofilm**. In nature, a biofilm typically consists of multiple species, all entangled in their own mingled secretions. It may include bacteria, algae, fungi, protists, and archaeans. Participating in a biofilm allows the cells to linger in a favorable spot rather than be swept away by fluid currents, and to reap the benefits of living communally. For example, rigid or netlike secretions of some species serve as permanent scaffolding for others; species that break down toxic chemicals allow more sensitive ones to thrive in polluted habitats that they could not withstand on their own; and waste products of some serve as raw materials for others.

## Take-Home Message  **What do all prokaryotic cells have in common?**

- All prokaryotes are single-celled organisms with no nucleus. Bacteria and archaeans are the only prokaryotes.

- Prokaryotes have a relatively simple structure, but as a group they are the most diverse forms of life. They inhabit nearly all regions of the biosphere.

**biofilm** Community of different types of microorganisms living within a shared mass of slime.

**cell wall** Semirigid but permeable structure that surrounds the plasma membrane of some cells.

**flagellum** Long, slender cellular structure used for motility.

**pilus** A protein filament that projects from the surface of some bacterial cells.

**ribosome** Organelle of protein synthesis.

**FIGURE 3.9 Animated!**

Common components of eukaryotic cells. This is an animal cell.

**1** A plasma membrane controls the kinds and amounts of substances that move into and out of a cell.

**2** The nucleus contains, protects, and controls access to DNA.

**3** Endoplasmic reticulum (ER) modifies new polypeptides and synthesizes lipids; has other tasks.

**4** Different types of vesicles transport, store, or digest substances, among other functions.

**5** Golgi bodies finish, sort, and ship lipids and proteins.

**6** Mitochondria make ATP.

**7** Ribosomes, either attached to ER or free in cytoplasm, assemble polypeptides from amino acids.

**8** Centrioles produce and organize microtubules.

**9** Cytoskeletal elements provide structural support; move cell parts or the whole cell.

# 3.6 A Peek Inside a Eukaryotic Cell

All protists, fungi, plants, and animals are eukaryotes. Some of these organisms are independent, free-living cells (Figure 3.1); others consist of many cells working together as a body.

By definition, a eukaryotic cell starts out life with a nucleus (*eu*– means true; *karyon* means nut, or kernel). Like many other organelles, a nucleus has a membrane. An organelle's outer membrane controls the types and amounts of substances that cross it. Such control maintains a special internal environment that allows the organelle to carry out its particular function. That function may be isolating toxic or sensitive substances from the rest of the cell, transporting substances through cytoplasm, maintaining fluid balance, or providing a favorable environment for a special process.

A typical eukaryotic cell contains a nucleus, an endomembrane system (ER, vesicles, and Golgi bodies), mitochondria, and cytoskeletal elements. Certain cells also have other special structures (Figures 3.9 and 3.10). Much as interactions among organs keep an animal body alive and well, interactions among these components keep a cell alive and well.

**The Nucleus** A nucleus serves two important functions. First, it keeps the cell's genetic material—its one and only copy of DNA—safe and sound. Isolated in its own compartment, DNA stays separated from the bustling activity of the cytoplasm, and from metabolic processes that might damage it **2**.

The second function of a nucleus is to control the passage of certain molecules between the nucleus and the cytoplasm. The nuclear membrane, which is called the **nuclear envelope**, carries out this function. A nuclear envelope consists of two lipid bilayers folded together as a single membrane. Receptors and transporters stud both sides of the bilayer; other proteins cluster to form tiny pores that span it. These molecules and structures work as a system to selectively transport various molecules across the nuclear membrane. Cells access their DNA when they make RNA and proteins, so the molecules involved in this process must pass into the nucleus and out of it. Control over their transport through the nuclear membrane is one way the cell regulates the amount of RNA and proteins it makes.

### The Endomembrane System

The **endomembrane system** is a series of interacting organelles between the nucleus and the plasma membrane. Its main function is to make lipids, enzymes, and proteins for secretion or insertion into cell membranes. It also destroys toxins, recycles wastes, and has other specialized functions. The system's components vary among different types of cells, but here we present the most common ones.

Part of the endomembrane system is an extension of the nuclear envelope called **endoplasmic reticulum**, or **ER** ❸. ER forms a continuous compartment that folds into flattened sacs and tubes. Two kinds of ER, rough and smooth, are named for their appearance in electron micrographs. Thousands of ribosomes attached to the outer surface of rough ER make polypeptides that thread into the interior of the ER as they are assembled. Inside the ER, the polypeptides fold and take on their tertiary structure. Some of them become part of the ER membrane itself.

Smooth ER has no ribosomes, so it does not make protein. Some of the polypeptides made in the rough ER end up as enzymes in the smooth ER. These enzymes make most of the lipids that form the cell's membranes. They also break down carbohydrates, fatty acids, and some drugs and poisons.

Small, membrane-enclosed, saclike **vesicles** form in great numbers, in a variety of types, either on their own or by budding from other organelles or from the plasma membrane ❹. Many vesicles transport substances from one organelle to another, or to and from the plasma membrane. Those called **peroxisomes** contain enzymes that can inactivate toxins. Drink alcohol, and the peroxisomes in your liver and kidney cells break down nearly half of it. Eukaryotic cells also contain **vacuoles**. These vesicles appear empty under a microscope, but they serve an important function. Most are like trash cans: They collect waste, debris, or toxins, and dispose of these materials by fusing with other vesicles called lysosomes. **Lysosomes** contain powerful digestive enzymes that break down the contents of vacuoles.

Some vesicles fuse with and empty their contents into a **Golgi body**. This organelle has a folded membrane that typically looks a bit like a stack of pancakes ❺. Enzymes in a Golgi body put finishing touches on proteins and lipids that have been delivered from the ER. They attach phosphate groups or sugars, and cut certain polypeptides. The finished products (membrane proteins, proteins for secretion, and enzymes) are sorted and packaged into new vesicles that carry them to the plasma membrane or to lysosomes.

### Mitochondria

The **mitochondrion** (plural, mitochondria) is an organelle that specializes in making ATP ❻. A mitochondrion has two membranes, one highly folded inside the other, that form its ATP-making machinery. Nearly all eukaryotic cells have mitochondria, which resemble bacteria in size, form, and

nuclear envelope   mitochondrion   DNA in nucleus   nuclear pore   rough ER with attached ribosomes

0.5 μm

**FIGURE 3.10** Inside a cell taken from a mouse's pancreas.

**endomembrane system** Series of interacting organelles (endoplasmic reticulum, Golgi bodies, vesicles) between nucleus and plasma membrane; produces lipids, proteins.

**endoplasmic reticulum (ER)** Organelle that is a continuous system of sacs and tubes; extension of the nuclear envelope. Rough ER is studded with ribosomes; smooth ER is not.

**Golgi body** Organelle that modifies polypeptides and lipids; also sorts and packages finished products into vesicles.

**lysosome** Enzyme-filled vesicle that functions in intracellular digestion.

**mitochondrion** Double-membraned organelle that produces ATP.

**nuclear envelope** A double membrane that constitutes the outer boundary of the nucleus.

**peroxisome** Enzyme-filled vesicle that breaks down amino acids, fatty acids, and toxic substances.

**vacuole** A fluid-filled organelle that isolates or disposes of waste, debris, or toxic materials.

**vesicle** Small, membrane-enclosed, saclike organelle; different kinds store, transport, or degrade their contents.

outer membrane

outer compartment

inner compartment

inner membrane

0.5 μm

**A**

two outer membranes

stroma

inner membrane

1 μm

**B**

FIGURE 3.11 **Animated!** Bacteria-like organelles. **A** Mitochondrion, specialized for producing large quantities of ATP for eukaryotic cells. **B** Chloroplast, specialized for photosynthesis.

Figure It Out: What organelle is visible to the upper right in the micrograph of the mitochondrion?

*Answer: Rough ER*

**chloroplast** Organelle of photosynthesis.

**cilium** Short, movable structure that projects from the plasma membrane of some eukaryotic cells.

**cytoskeleton** Dynamic framework of protein filaments that support, organize, and move eukaryotic cells and their internal structures.

**intermediate filament** Cytoskeletal element that locks cells and tissues together.

**microfilament** Reinforcing cytoskeletal element; fiber of actin subunits.

**microtubule** Cytoskeletal element involved in movement; hollow filament of tubulin subunits.

**motor protein** Type of energy-using protein that interacts with cytoskeletal elements to move the cell's parts or the whole cell.

**pseudopod** Extendable lobe of membrane-enclosed cytoplasm.

biochemistry (Figure 3.11**A**). They have their own DNA and ribosomes, and they divide independently of the cell. Such clues led to a theory that mitochondria evolved from aerobic bacteria that took up permanent residence inside a host cell. By the theory of endosymbiosis, one cell was engulfed by another cell, or entered it as a parasite, but escaped digestion. That cell kept its plasma membrane and reproduced inside its host. In time, the cell's descendants became permanent residents that offered their hosts the benefit of extra ATP. Structures and functions once required for independent life were no longer needed and were lost over time. Later descendants evolved into mitochondria. We explore evidence for the theory of endosymbiosis in Section 13.3.

**Chloroplasts** Photosynthetic cells of plants and many protists contain **chloroplasts**, which are organelles specialized for photosynthesis. Most chloroplasts have an oval or disk shape formed by two outer membranes enclosing a semifluid interior called the stroma (Figure 3.11**B**). The stroma contains enzymes and the chloroplast's own DNA. Photosynthesis takes place at a third, highly folded membrane inside the stroma (we describe the process of photosynthesis in more detail in Chapter 5). In many ways, chloroplasts resemble photosynthetic bacteria, and, like mitochondria, they may have evolved by endosymbiosis.

**The Cytoskeleton** Between the nucleus and plasma membrane of all eukaryotic cells is a system of interconnected protein filaments collectively called the **cytoskeleton**. Elements of the cytoskeleton reinforce, organize, and move cell structures, and often the whole cell. Some are permanent; others form only at certain times.

**Microtubules** are long, hollow cylinders that consist of subunits of the protein tubulin. They form a dynamic scaffolding for many cellular processes, rapidly assembling when they are needed and then disassembling when they are not. For example, some of the microtubules that assemble before a eukaryotic cell divides separate the cell's duplicated chromosomes, then disassemble. As another example, microtubules that form in the growing end of a young nerve cell support and guide its lengthening in a particular direction (Figure 3.12).

**Microfilaments** are fibers that consist primarily of subunits of the globular protein actin. They strengthen or change the shape of eukaryotic cells. Cross-linked, bundled, or gel-like arrays of them make up the cell cortex, which is a reinforcing mesh under the plasma membrane. Actin microfilaments that form at the edge of a cell drag or extend it in a certain direction. In muscle cells, microfilaments of myosin and actin interact to bring about contraction.

**Intermediate filaments** are the most stable parts of a cell's cytoskeleton. They lock cells and tissues together. For example, some intermediate filaments called lamins form a layer that structurally supports the inner surface of the nuclear envelope.

All eukaryotic cells have similar microtubules and microfilaments. Despite the uniformity, both kinds of elements play diverse roles. How? They interact with accessory proteins, such as **motor proteins** that move cell parts when they

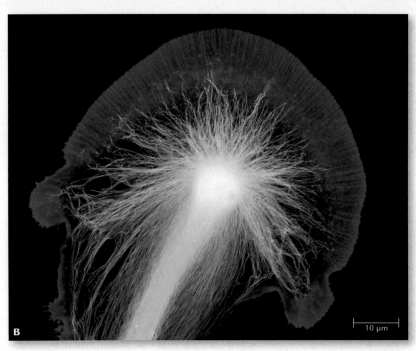

**FIGURE 3.12** Cytoskeletal elements. **A** Tubulin subunits assembling into a microtubule, and actin subunits assembling into a microfilament.

**B** Microtubules (*yellow*) and actin microfilaments (*blue*) in the growing end of a nerve cell support and guide the cell's lengthening in certain directions.

tubulin subunit    actin subunit

A    25 nm    6–7 nm

B    10 μm

are repeatedly energized by ATP. A cell is like a train station during a busy holiday, with molecules being transported through its interior. Microtubules and microfilaments are like dynamically assembled train tracks, and motor proteins are freight engines that move along them (Figure 3.13).

**Cilia, Flagella, and False Feet** Organized arrays of microtubules are the basis of movement in eukaryotic flagella and cilia. Eukaryotic flagella are whiplike structures that propel cells such as sperm (*left*) through fluid. They have a different internal structure and motion than prokaryotic flagella.

**Cilia** (singular, cilium) are short, hairlike structures that project from the surface of some cells. Cilia are usually shorter and more profuse than flagella. Their coordinated beating propels motile cells through fluid, and stirs fluid around stationary cells. For example, the cilia on thousands of cells lining your airways sweep inhaled particles away from your lungs.

Amoebas and other types of eukaryotic cells form **pseudopods**, or "false feet." As these temporary, irregular lobes bulge outward, they move the cell and engulf a target such as prey. Elongating microfilaments force the lobe to advance in a steady direction. Motor proteins that are attached to the microfilaments drag the plasma membrane along with them. An amoeba with multiple pseudopods is shown at the far left in Figure 3.1.

## Take-Home Message    What do all eukaryotic cells have in common?

- All eukaryotic cells start life with a nucleus, ribosomes, and other organelles. The nucleus protects and controls access to a cell's DNA.

- The endomembrane system, which includes ER, vesicles, and Golgi bodies, makes and modifies proteins and lipids.

- Mitochondria are organelles that produce ATP. Some cells also contain chloroplasts, which specialize in photosynthesis.

**FIGURE 3.13 Animated!**
A motor protein (*tan*) drags cellular freight (here, a *pink* vesicle) as it inches along a microtubule.

ECM

**❶ Tight junctions**

Rows of proteins that run parallel with the free surface of a tissue; stop leaks between adjoining cells.

**❷ Adhering junction**

A mass of interconnected proteins that welds one cell to another or to ECM; anchored under the plasma membrane by intermediate filaments.

**❸ Gap junction**

Cylindrical clusters of proteins that span the plasma membrane of adjoining cells; clusters are often paired as channels that open and close.

**FIGURE 3.14 Animated!** Cell junctions in animal tissues.

**adhering junction** Cell junction that anchors cells to each other or to extracellular matrix.

**cell junction** Structure that connects a cell to another cell or to extracellular matrix.

**extracellular matrix (ECM)** Complex mixture of substances secreted by cells; supports cells and tissues; roles in cell signaling.

**gap junction** Cell junction that forms a channel across the plasma membranes of adjoining animal cells.

**tight junctions** Arrays of fibrous proteins; join epithelial cells and collectively prevent fluids from leaking between them.

# 3.7 Cell Surface Specializations

Most cells of multicelled organisms are surrounded and organized by a nonliving, complex mixture of fibrous proteins and polysaccharides called **extracellular matrix**, or **ECM**. Secreted by the cells it surrounds, ECM supports and anchors cells, separates tissues, and functions in cell signaling. Different types of cells secrete different kinds of ECM. For example, a waxy ECM secreted by plant cells forms a cuticle, or covering, that protects the plant's exposed surfaces and limits water loss. The cuticle of crabs, spiders, and other arthropods is mainly chitin, a polysaccharide.

ECM in animals typically consists of various kinds of carbohydrates and proteins; it is the basis of tissue organization, and it provides structural support. Bone is mostly an extracellular matrix composed of collagen, a fibrous protein, hardened by mineral deposits. The cell wall around the plasma membrane of plant cells and many protists and fungi is a type of ECM that is structurally different from a prokaryotic cell wall, but both types protect, support, and impart shape to a cell. Both are also porous: Water and solutes easily cross it on the way to and from the plasma membrane. Cells could not live without exchanging these substances with their environment.

A cell wall or other ECM does not prevent a cell from interacting with other cells or the surroundings. In multicelled species, such interaction occurs by way of **cell junctions**, which are structures that connect a cell to other cells and to the environment. Cells send and receive ions, molecules, or signals through some junctions. Other kinds help cells recognize and stick to each other and to extracellular matrix.

Cells in most animal tissues connect to their neighbors and to ECM by way of one or more types of cell junctions (Figure 3.14). In epithelial tissues that line body surfaces and internal cavities, rows of proteins that form **tight junctions** between plasma membranes prevent body fluids from seeping between adjacent cells ❶. To cross these tissues, fluid must pass directly through the cells. Thus, transport proteins embedded in the cell membranes control which ions and molecules cross the tissue. For example, an abundance of tight junctions in the lining of the stomach normally keeps acidic fluid from leaking out. If a bacterial infection damages this lining, acid and enzymes can erode the underlying layers. The result is a painful peptic ulcer. Figure 3.15 shows how tight junctions seal the linings of ducts and tubes in the kidney.

**Adhering junctions** composed of adhesion proteins snap cells to each other and anchor them to extracellular matrix ❷. Skin and other tissues that are subject to abrasion or stretching have a lot of adhering junctions. These cell junctions also strengthen contractile tissues such as heart muscle.

**Gap junctions** form channels that connect the cytoplasm of adjoining cells, thus permitting ions and small molecules to pass directly from the cytoplasm of one cell to another ❸. By opening or closing, they allow entire regions of cells to respond to a single stimulus. For example, heart muscle and other tissues in which the cells perform some coordinated action have many of these communication channels. A signal passes instantly from cell to cell through gap junctions, so all of the connected cells can respond as a unit.

In plants, open channels called plasmodesmata (singular, plasmodesma) extend across the primary wall of adjoining cells, connecting the cytoplasm of the cells. Substances such as water, nutrients, and signaling molecules can flow quickly from cell to cell through plasmodesmata.

**FIGURE 3.15** In this fluorescence micrograph, a continuous array of tight junctions (*green*) seals the abutting surfaces of kidney cell membranes. DNA is *red*. **Figure It Out:** Why does the DNA appear clumped in each cell?

*Answer: In eukaryotic cells, DNA occurs in the nucleus.*

## Take-Home Message
### What structures form on the outside of eukaryotic cells?

- Many cells secrete extracellular matrix that support and anchor them.
- Cells of many protists, nearly all fungi, and all plants, have a porous wall around the plasma membrane. Animal cells do not have walls.
- Via cell junctions, cells make structural and functional connections with one another and with extracellular matrix in tissues.

## 3.8 Impacts/Issues Revisited:
### Food for Thought

The photo on the *left* shows *E. coli* O157:H7 bacteria (*red*) clustering on intestinal cells of a small child. This type of bacteria can cause a serious intestinal illness in people who eat foods contaminated with it. Meat, poultry, milk, and fruits that have been sterilized by exposure to radiation are now available in supermarkets. By law, irradiated foods must be marked with the symbol on the *right*. Items that bear this symbol have been exposed to radiation, but are not themselves radioactive. Irradiating fresh foods kills bacteria and prolongs shelf life. However, some worry that the irradiation process may alter the food and produce harmful chemicals. Whether health risks are associated with consuming irradiated foods is still unknown.

**How Would YOU Vote?** Some think the safest way to protect consumers from food poisoning is by exposing food to x-rays or other high-energy radiation, which kills bacteria. Others think we should tighten food safety standards instead. Would you choose irradiated food? **See CengageNow for details, then vote online (CengageNow.com).**

# Summary

**Sections 3.1–3.2** All organisms consist of one or more cells. By the cell theory, the cell is the smallest unit of life, and it is the basis of life's continuity. The surface-to-volume ratio limits cell size. All cells start out life with a plasma membrane, cytoplasm in which structures such as ribosomes are suspended, and DNA. The DNA of eukaryotic cells is contained in a nucleus; that of prokaryotes is not. The lipid bilayer is the foundation of all cell membranes.

CENGAGENOW™ Investigate the physical limits on cell size with the interactions on CengageNow.

**Section 3.3** Most cells are too small to see with the naked eye. Different types of microscopes use light or electrons to reveal different details of cells.

**Section 3.4** A cell membrane is a mosaic of lipids (mainly phospholipids) and proteins. It functions as a selectively permeable barrier that separates an internal environment from an external one. The lipids are organized as a double layer in which the nonpolar tails of both layers are sandwiched between the polar heads.

The membranes of most cells can be described as a fluid mosaic. Proteins that are temporarily or permanently associated with a membrane carry out most membrane functions. All membranes have transport proteins. Plasma membranes also incorporate receptor proteins, adhesion proteins, enzymes, and recognition proteins.

CENGAGENOW™ Use the animations on CengageNow to learn about membrane structure and receptor proteins.

**Section 3.5** Bacteria and archaeans are the prokaryotes. Prokaryotes have no nucleus, but many have a cell wall and one or more flagella or pili. Biofilms are shared living arrangements among bacteria and other microbial organisms.

CENGAGENOW™ View prokaryotic cell structure with the animation on CengageNow.

**Section 3.6** Eukaryotic cells start out life with a nucleus and other membrane-enclosed organelles. Pores, receptors, and transport proteins in the nuclear envelope control the movement of molecules into and out of the nucleus.

The endomembrane system includes rough and smooth endoplasmic reticulum, vesicles, and Golgi bodies. This set of organelles functions mainly to make and modify lipids and proteins; it also recycles molecules and particles such as worn-out cell parts, and inactivates toxins. Other eukaryotic organelles include mitochondria (which produce ATP), chloroplasts (which specialize in photosynthesis), peroxisomes, lysosomes, and vacuoles. Eukaryotic cells also have

a cytoskeleton that includes a mesh of microfilaments called the cell cortex. Motor proteins that are the basis of movement interact with microfilaments in pseudopods or microtubules in cilia and eukaryotic flagella.

CENGAGENOW™ Use the interaction and animations on CengageNow to survey the major types of eukaryotic organelles; learn more about cytoskeletal elements; view the nuclear envelope, endomembrane system, and a chloroplast; and study the structure of cell walls and junctions.

**Section 3.7** Cells of most prokaryotes, protists, fungi, and all plant cells have a wall around the plasma membrane. Many eukaryotic cell types also secrete a cuticle. Cell junctions connect animal cells to one another and to extracellular matrix (ECM); plasmodesmata connect plant cells.

## Self-Quiz   Answers in Appendix I

1. The _____ is the smallest unit of life.

2. Every cell is descended from another cell. This idea is called _____ .
   a. evolution
   b. the theory of relativity
   c. the cell theory
   d. cell biology

3. True or false? Some protists are prokaryotes.

4. Cell membranes consist mainly of a _____ .
   a. carbohydrate bilayer and proteins
   b. protein bilayer and phospholipids
   c. lipid bilayer and proteins

5. Unlike eukaryotic cells, prokaryotic cells _____ .
   a. have no plasma membrane     c. have no nucleus
   b. have RNA but not DNA         d. a and c

6. In a lipid bilayer, _____ of all the lipid molecules are sandwiched between all the _____ .
   a. hydrophilic tails; hydrophobic heads
   b. hydrophilic heads; hydrophilic tails
   c. hydrophobic tails; hydrophilic heads
   d. hydrophobic heads; hydrophilic tails

7. Enzymes contained in _____ break down worn-out organelles, bacteria, and other particles.

8. Put the following structures in order according to the pathway of a secreted protein:
   a. plasma membrane           c. endoplasmic reticulum
   b. Golgi bodies              d. post-Golgi vesicles

9. The main function of the endomembrane system is building and modifying _____ and _____ .

10. Is this statement true or false? The plasma membrane is the outermost component of all cells. Explain your answer.

# Digging Into Data

## Organelles and Cystic Fibrosis

CFTR is a transporter in the plasma membrane of epithelial cells. Sheets of these cells line the cavities and ducts of the lungs, liver, pancreas, intestines, reproductive system, and skin. The transporter pumps chloride ions out of these cells, and water follows the ions. A thin, watery film forms on the surface of the epithelial cell sheets. Mucus slides easily over the wet sheets of cells.

In some people, these epithelial cell membranes do not have enough working copies of the CFTR protein, and chloride ion transport is disrupted. Not enough chloride ions leave the cells, and so not enough water leaves them either. The result is thick, dry mucus that sticks to the epithelial cell sheets. In the respiratory tract, the mucus clogs airways to the lungs and makes breathing difficult. The mucus is too thick for the ciliated cells lining the airways to sweep out, and bacteria thrive in it. Low-grade infections occur and may persist for years.

These symptoms characterize cystic fibrosis (CF), the most common fatal genetic disorder in the United States. Even with a lung transplant, most CF patients live no longer than thirty years, at which time their lungs usually fail. There is no cure.

In most individuals with cystic fibrosis, the 508th amino acid of the CFTR protein (a phenylalanine) is missing (Figure 3.16**A**). A CFTR protein with this change is made correctly, and it can transport ions correctly, but it never reaches the plasma membrane to

do its job. In 2000, Sergei Bannykh and his coworkers developed a way to measure the relative amounts of the CFTR protein localized in different areas of a cell. They compared the pattern of distribution of CFTR with and without the CF deletion (Figure 3.16**B**).

1. Which organelle contains the least amount of CFTR protein in normal cells? In cells with the deletion? Which contains the most?

2. In which organelle is the amount of CFTR protein most similar in both types of cells?

3. Where is the CFTR protein with the deletion getting held up?

**FIGURE 3.16** Changes in the CFTR protein affect intracellular transport. **A** Model of CFTR. The parts shown here are ATP-driven motors that widen or narrow a channel (*gray* arrow) across the plasma membrane. The tiny part of the protein that is missing in most people with cystic fibrosis is shown on the ribbon in *green*.

**B** Comparison of the amounts of CFTR protein associated with endoplasmic reticulum, vesicles traveling from ER to Golgi, and Golgi bodies. The patterns of CFTR distribution in normal cells, and cells with the deletion that causes cystic fibrosis, were compared.

---

11. Most membrane functions are carried out by _____ .
    a. proteins
    b. phospholipids
    c. nucleic acids
    d. hormones

12. No animal cell has a _____ .
    a. plasma membrane
    b. flagellum
    c. lysosome
    d. cell wall

13. _____ connect the cytoplasm of plant cells.
    a. Plasmodesmata
    b. Adhering junctions
    c. Tight junctions
    d. a and b

14. Match each cell component with its function.
    _____ mitochondrion
    _____ chloroplast
    _____ ribosome
    _____ smooth ER
    _____ Golgi body
    _____ rough ER
    a. protein synthesis
    b. associates with ribosomes
    c. ATP production
    d. sorts and ships
    e. assembles lipids; other tasks
    f. photosynthesis

Additional questions are available on CENGAGENOW™

## Critical Thinking

1. In a classic episode of *Star Trek*, a titanic amoeba engulfs an entire starship. The crew of the ship blows the cell to bits before it reproduces. Think of at least one problem a biologist would have with this particular scenario.

2. A student is examining different samples with a transmission electron microscope. She discovers a single-celled organism (*below*) swimming in a freshwater pond. Which of this organism's structures can you identify? Is it a prokaryotic or eukaryotic cell? Can you be more specific about the type of cell based on what you know about cell structure? Look ahead to Section 13.5 to check your answers.

> Ethanol is toxic: If you put more of it into your body than your enzymes can deal with, then you will die.

## 4.1 Impacts/Issues: A Toast to Alcohol Dehydrogenase

The next time someone asks you to have a drink, stop for a moment and think about the cells in your body that detoxify alcohol. It makes no difference whether you drink a bottle of beer, a glass of wine, or 1–1/2 ounces of vodka. Each holds the same amount of alcohol or, more precisely, ethanol. Ethanol molecules move quickly from the stomach and small intestine into the bloodstream. Almost all of the ethanol ends up in the liver, a large organ in the abdomen. The liver has impressive numbers of enzymes, and one of them, alcohol dehydrogenase, helps rid the body of ethanol and other toxins (Figure 4.1).

Ethanol is really hard on the liver. For one thing, breaking it down produces molecules that directly damage liver cells, so the more you drink, the fewer liver cells you have left to do the breaking down. Ethanol also interferes with normal processes of metabolism that keep the remaining liver cells—and the rest of the body—alive. For example, oxygen that would normally take part in breaking down fatty acids is diverted to breaking down ethanol, so fats tend to accumulate as large globules in the tissues of heavy drinkers. A common outcome of such processes is alcoholic hepatitis, a disease characterized by inflammation and destruction of liver tissue. Alcoholic cirrhosis, another possibility, leaves the liver permanently scarred. (The word cirrhosis is from the Greek word *kirros*, or orange-colored, after the abnormal skin color of people with the disease.)

Eventually, the liver of a heavy drinker just quits working, with dire health consequences. The liver is the largest gland in the human body, and it has many important functions. In addition to breaking down fats and toxins, it helps regulate the body's blood sugar level, and it makes blood proteins that are essential for blood clotting, immune function, and maintaining the solute balance of body fluids.

**FIGURE 4.1** Alcohol dehydrogenase helps the body break down ethanol and other toxic alcohols. This enzyme makes it possible for humans to drink beer, wine, and other alcoholic beverages.

alcohol dehydrogenase

Binge drinking, a self-destructive behavior that involves consuming large amounts of alcohol in a brief period of time, is currently the most serious drug problem on college campuses in the United States. Tens of thousands of undergraduate students have been polled about their drinking habits in recent surveys. More than half of them reported that they regularly drink five or more alcoholic beverages within a two-hour period.

Binge drinking does far more than damage one's liver. Aside from the related 500,000 injuries from accidents, the 600,000 assaults by intoxicated students, 100,000 cases of date rape, and 400,000 incidences of (whoops) unprotected sex among students, binge drinking is responsible for killing or causing the death of more than 1,700 college students every year. Ethanol is toxic: If you put more of it into your body than your enzymes can deal with, then you will die. With this sobering example, we invite you to learn about how and why your cells break down organic compounds, including toxic molecules like ethanol.

# 4.2 Life Runs on Energy

**Energy**, remember, is the capacity to do work, but this definition is not very satisfying. Even the brilliant physicists who study it cannot say what energy is, exactly. However, even without a perfect definition, we have an intuitive understanding of energy just by thinking about familiar forms of it, such as light, heat, electricity, and motion. We also understand intuitively that one form of energy can be converted to another. Think about how a lightbulb changes electricity into light, or how an automobile changes gasoline into motion.

Thermodynamics, which is the study of heat and other energy (*therm* is a Greek word for heat; *dynam* means energy), tells us that the total amount of energy before and after every conversion is always the same. In other words, energy cannot be created or destroyed—a phenomenon we call the **first law of thermodynamics**. Remember, a law of nature describes something that occurs without fail, but our explanation of why it occurs is incomplete (Section 1.6).

Thermodynamics also tells us that energy tends to disperse until no part of a system holds more than another part. For example, heat flows from a hot pan to air in a cool kitchen until the temperature of both is the same. We never see cool air raising the temperature of a hot pan. Again, this phenomenon is always true, but we do not know exactly why. Thus, we call the tendency of energy to disperse the **second law of thermodynamics**.

Work occurs as a result of an energy transfer. For example, making ATP (Section 2.10) is work, and it requires energy. A plant cell can do this work by transferring energy from the environment (light) to molecules that use the energy to build ATP. This particular transfer involves an energy conversion (light to chemical energy). Most cellular work occurs by transferring chemical energy from one molecule to another. For example, chemical energy transferred from ATP to other molecules is used for cellular work, such as making glucose.

Every time an energy transfer occurs, a bit of energy disperses, usually in the form of heat. For example, a typical incandescent lightbulb converts about 5 percent of the energy of electricity into light. The remaining 95 percent of the energy ends up as heat that radiates from the bulb. Dispersed heat is not very useful for doing work, and it is not easily converted to a more useful form of energy (such as electricity). Because some of the energy in every transfer disperses as heat, and heat is not useful for doing work, we can say that the total amount of energy available for doing work in the universe is always decreasing.

Is life an exception to this depressing flow? An organized body is hardly dispersed. Energy becomes concentrated in each new organism as the molecules of life organize into cells. Even so, living things constantly use energy to grow, to move, to acquire nutrients, to reproduce, and so on. Inevitable losses occur during the energy transfers that maintain life. Unless those losses are replenished with energy from another source, the complex organization of life will end.

Most of the energy that fuels life on Earth is energy from the sun. In our world, energy flows from the sun, through producers, then consumers (Figure 4.2). During this journey, the energy changes form and changes hands many times. Each time, some energy escapes as heat until, eventually, all of it is permanently dispersed. However, the second law of thermodynamics does not say how quickly the dispersal has to happen. Energy's spontaneous dispersal

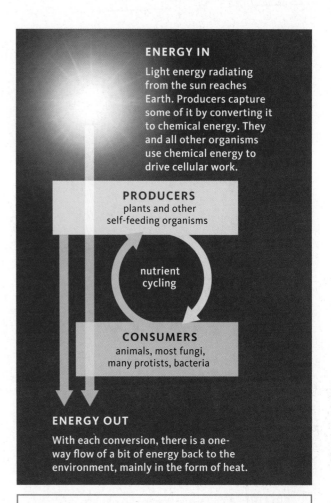

**ENERGY IN**
Light energy radiating from the sun reaches Earth. Producers capture some of it by converting it to chemical energy. They and all other organisms use chemical energy to drive cellular work.

**PRODUCERS**
plants and other self-feeding organisms

nutrient cycling

**CONSUMERS**
animals, most fungi, many protists, bacteria

**ENERGY OUT**
With each conversion, there is a one-way flow of a bit of energy back to the environment, mainly in the form of heat.

**FIGURE 4.2** A one-way flow of energy into living organisms compensates for a one-way flow of energy out of them. Energy inputs drive a cycling of materials among producers and consumers.

**energy** The capacity to do work.
**first law of thermodynamics** Energy cannot be created or destroyed.
**second law of thermodynamics** Energy tends to disperse.

is resisted by chemical bonds. Think of all the bonds in the countless molecules that make up your skin, heart, liver, fluids, and other body parts. Those bonds hold the molecules, and you, together—at least for the time being.

## Take-Home Message  What is energy?

■ Energy is the capacity to do work. It can be converted from one form to another, but it cannot be created or destroyed. It disperses spontaneously.

■ Organisms can maintain their complex organization only as long as they replenish themselves with energy they harvest from someplace else.

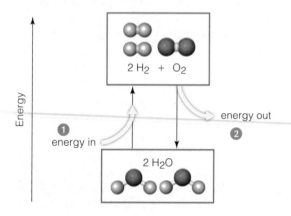

**FIGURE 4.3** Energy inputs and outputs in chemical reactions.

**1** Some reactions convert molecules with lower energy to molecules with higher energy, so they require a net energy input to proceed.

**2** Other reactions convert molecules with higher energy to molecules with lower energy, so they end with a net energy output.

Figure It Out: **Which law of thermodynamics explains energy inputs and outputs in chemical reactions?**

*Answer: The first law*

**activation energy**  Minimum amount of energy required to start a reaction.
**ATP**  Adenosine triphosphate; the main energy carrier between reaction sites in cells.
**phosphorylation**  Phosphate-group transfer.
**product**  A molecule remaining at the end of a reaction.
**reactant**  Molecule that enters a reaction.
**reaction**  Process of chemical change.

# 4.3 Energy in the Molecules of Life

Cells store energy in chemical bonds, and access the energy stored in chemical bonds by breaking them. Both processes change molecules or ions into other molecules or ions (Section 2.3). A process by which a chemical change occurs is called a **reaction**. During a reaction, one or more **reactants** (molecules that enter a reaction) become one or more **products** (molecules that remain at the reaction's end). Intermediate molecules may form between reactants and products. We show a chemical reaction as an equation in which an arrow points from reactants to products:

A number before a formula indicates the number of molecules. You can see that atoms shuffle around, but they never disappear: The same number of atoms that enter a reaction remain at the reaction's end.

Every chemical bond holds energy, and the amount of energy depends on which elements are taking part in the bond. For example, the covalent bond between an oxygen and a hydrogen atom in any water molecule holds a certain amount of energy, which differs from the amount of energy held by a covalent bond between two oxygen atoms in molecular oxygen ($O_2$). Thus, in most reactions, the energy of the reactants differs from the energy of the products (Figure 4.3). Reactions in which the reactants have less energy than the products require a net (or overall) energy input to proceed **1**.

Cells store energy in chemical bonds by running energy-requiring reactions. For example, light energy drives the overall reactions of photosynthesis, which convert carbon dioxide and water to glucose and oxygen. Unlike light, glucose can be stored in a cell. In other reactions, the reactants have greater energy than the products. Such reactions release energy **2**. Cells access the energy held in chemical bonds by running energy-releasing reactions. An example is the overall process of aerobic respiration, which releases the energy of glucose by breaking the bonds between its carbons.

**Why the World Does Not Go Up in Flames** The molecules of life release energy when they combine with oxygen. For example, think of how a spark ignites wood. Wood is mostly cellulose, a carbohydrate with long chains of repeating glucose units (Section 2.7). A spark starts a reaction that converts cellulose and oxygen to water and carbon dioxide. This reaction releases enough energy to start the same reaction with other cellulose and oxygen molecules. That is why wood keeps burning once it has been lit.

Earth is rich in oxygen—and in potential energy-releasing reactions. Why doesn't it burst into flames? Luckily, it takes energy to break the chemical bonds of reactants, even in an energy-releasing reaction. **Activation energy** is the minimum amount of energy that will get a chemical reaction started, a bit like a hill that reactants must climb before they can run down the other side to products (Figure 4.4).

Activation energy varies by the reaction. For example, guncotton, or nitrocellulose, is a highly explosive derivative of cellulose. Christian Schönbein accidentally discovered a way to make it when he used his wife's cotton apron to wipe up a nitric acid spill on his kitchen table, then hung it up to dry next to the oven. The apron promptly exploded. Being a chemist in the 1800s, Schönbein immediately made plans to market guncotton as a firearm explosive, but it turned out to be too unstable. So little activation energy is needed to make guncotton react with oxygen that it explodes spontaneously. After a few manufacturing plants burned down, guncotton was abandoned in favor of gunpowder, which has a higher activation energy for a reaction with oxygen.

**ATP—The Cell's Energy Currency** Cells pair reactions that require energy with reactions that release energy. ATP is part of that process for many reactions in cells. **ATP**, or adenosine triphosphate, is an energy carrier: It accepts energy released by energy-releasing reactions, and delivers energy to energy-requiring reactions. ATP is the main currency in a cell's energy economy, so we use a cartoon coin to symbolize it.

ATP is a nucleotide with three phosphate groups (Figure 4.5). The bonds that link those phosphate groups hold a lot of energy. When a phosphate group is transferred from ATP to another molecule, energy is transferred along with it. That energy contributes to the "energy in" part of an energy-requiring reaction. A phosphate-group transfer is called **phosphorylation**.

Cells constantly use up ATP to drive energy-requiring reactions, so they constantly replenish it. When ATP loses a phosphate, ADP (adenosine diphosphate) forms. ATP forms again when ADP binds phosphate:

ATP forms in energy-requiring reactions
ATP drives energy-requiring reactions
ADP + phosphate

# Take-Home Message   How do cells use energy?

- Cells store and retrieve energy by making and breaking chemical bonds.
- Some reactions require a net input of energy. Others end with a net release of energy.
- ATP and other energy carriers couple energy-releasing reactions with energy-requiring ones.

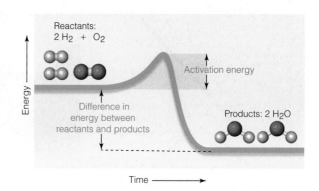

Reactants:
$2 H_2 + O_2$

Activation energy

Difference in energy between reactants and products

Products: $2 H_2O$

Energy

Time

**FIGURE 4.4 Animated!** Activation energy. Most reactions will not proceed without an input of activation energy, which is shown here as a bump in an energy hill. In this example, the reactants have more energy than the products. Activation energy keeps such energy-releasing reactions from running spontaneously.

adenine

three phosphate groups

ribose

**A** Structure of ATP.

adenine    AMP    ADP    ATP

ribose ——— P —— P —— P

**B** After it loses one phosphate group, the nucleotide is ADP (adenosine diphosphate); after losing two phosphate groups, it is AMP (adenosine monophosphate).

**FIGURE 4.5 Animated!** ATP, the energy currency of all cells.

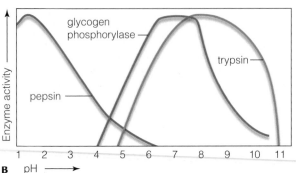

**FIGURE 4.6** Enzymes, temperature, and pH. **A** Tyrosinase is involved in the production of melanin, a black pigment in skin cells. The form of this enzyme in Siamese cats is inactive above about 30°C, so the warmer parts of the cat's body end up with less melanin, and lighter fur. **B** How pH values affect the activity of three enzymes in the human body.

**active site** Pocket in an enzyme where substrates bind and a reaction occurs.
**allosteric** Describes a region of an enzyme other than the active site that can bind regulatory molecules.
**coenzyme** An organic molecule that is a cofactor.
**cofactor** A metal ion or a coenzyme that associates with an enzyme and is necessary for its function.
**enzyme** Protein or RNA that speeds a reaction without being changed by it.
**feedback inhibition** Mechanism by which a change that results from some activity decreases or stops the activity.
**metabolic pathway** Series of enzyme-mediated reactions by which cells build, remodel, or break down an organic molecule.
**substrate** A reactant molecule that is specifically acted upon by an enzyme.

# 4.4 How Enzymes Work

Centuries might pass before sugar would break down to carbon dioxide and water on its own, yet that same conversion takes just moments inside a cell. Enzymes make the difference. **Enzymes** are molecules that make chemical reactions proceed much faster than they would on their own. Most are proteins, but some are RNAs. An enzyme is not consumed or changed by participating in a reaction; it can work again and again. Each kind recognizes and alters specific reactants called **substrates**. For instance, alcohol dehydrogenase removes two hydrogen atoms from an ethanol molecule (the enzyme's substrate), which results in a molecule of acetaldehyde.

Enzymes work because they have one or more **active sites**, which are pockets where substrates bind and where reactions proceed:

An active site is complementary in shape, size, polarity, and charge to the enzyme's substrate. That fit is the reason why each enzyme acts only on specific substrates. An enzyme's active site squeezes substrates close together, redistributes their charge, or causes some other change. The change reduces activation energy, so it lowers the barrier that prevents the reaction from proceeding.

**Factors That Influence Enzyme Activity** Adding heat boosts the energy of a system, which is one reason why molecular motion increases with temperature (Section 2.4). The greater the energy of reactants, the closer a reaction is to its activation energy. Thus, the rate of an enzymatic reaction typically increases with temperature, but only up to a point. Above a certain temperature, the hydrogen bonds that hold an enzyme in its characteristic shape break (Section 2.9). The enzyme stops working when it denatures, so the reaction rate falls sharply (Figure 4.6**A**). Body temperatures above 42°C (107.6°F) adversely affect many of your enzymes, which is why severe fevers are dangerous.

The pH tolerance of enzymes varies. Most enzymes in the human body work best at pH 6–8, but some work outside this typical range (Figure 4.6**B**). For example, pepsin functions only in stomach fluid, where it breaks down proteins in food. The fluid is very acidic, with a pH of about 2. An enzyme's activity is also influenced by the amount of salt in the surrounding fluid, because salt influences the hydrogen bonds that hold an enzyme in its three-dimensional shape.

**Cofactors** are atoms or molecules (other than proteins) that associate with enzymes and are necessary for their function. Some are metal ions. Organic molecules that are cofactors are called **coenzymes**. Some coenzymes must be tightly bound to an enzyme. Others, such as NAD$^+$ (nicotine adenine dinucleotide), participate in enzymatic reactions as separate molecules. Unlike enzymes, many coenzymes are modified by taking part in a reaction. They are typically regenerated in other reactions.

**Organized, Enzyme-Mediated Reactions** Metabolism, remember, refers to the enzyme-mediated chemical reactions by which cells acquire and use energy as they build and break down organic molecules (Section 2.6). Any series of enzyme-mediated reactions by which a cell builds, rearranges, or breaks down an organic substance is called a **metabolic pathway**. Some metabolic pathways build large molecules from smaller ones; others break down large molecules into smaller ones. A pathway may be linear, meaning that the reactions occur in a straight line from reactant to product:

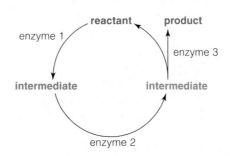

Other pathways are cyclic. In a cyclic pathway, the last step regenerates a reactant for the first step (*right*).

Cells conserve energy and resources by making what they need—no more, no less—at any given moment. How does a cell adjust the types and amounts of molecules it produces? Several mechanisms help a cell maintain, raise, or lower its production of thousands of different substances. For example, reactions do not only run from reactants to products. Many also run in reverse at the same time, with some of the products being converted back to reactants. The rates of the forward and reverse reactions often depend on the concentrations of reactants and products: A high concentration of reactants pushes the reaction in the forward direction, and a high concentration of products pushes it in the reverse direction.

Other mechanisms more actively regulate enzymes. Certain molecules in a cell influence how fast enzyme molecules are made, or influence the activity of enzymes that have already been built. For example, the end product of a series of enzymatic reactions may inhibit one of the enzymes in the series, an effect called **feedback inhibition** (Figure 4.7).

Some regulatory molecules activate or inhibit an enzyme by binding directly to its active site. Others bind to **allosteric** sites, which are regions of an enzyme (other than the active site) where regulatory molecules bind. *Allo*– means other, and *steric* means structure. Binding of an allosteric regulator alters the shape of the enzyme in a way that enhances or inhibits its function (Figure 4.8).

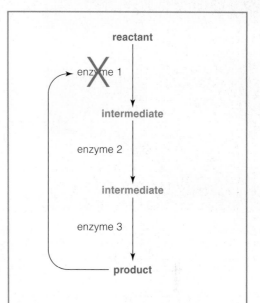

**FIGURE 4.7 Animated!** Feedback inhibition. In this example, three kinds of enzymes act in sequence to convert a substrate to a product, which inhibits the activity of the first enzyme.

**Figure It Out:** Is this an example of a cyclic or a linear metabolic pathway?

*Answer: Linear*

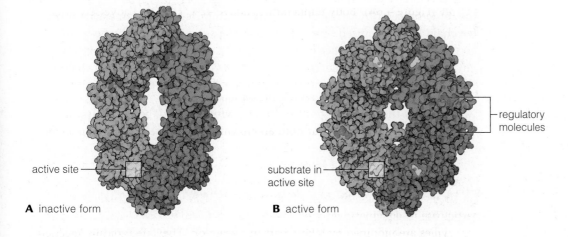

**A** inactive form     **B** active form

**FIGURE 4.8 Animated!** Allosteric effects. **A** Pyruvate kinase is an enzyme that consists of four identical polypeptide chains. Each chain has an active site and a binding site for a regulatory molecule. **B** When regulatory molecules (*magenta*) bind to the allosteric sites, the overall shape of the enzyme changes. The change makes the enzyme functional. Here, substrate molecules (*yellow*) and metal ion cofactors (*green*) are bound to the active sites.

**A** Glucose and oxygen react (burn) when exposed to a spark. Energy is released all at once as light and heat when $CO_2$ and water form.

**B** The same overall reaction occurs in small steps with an electron transfer chain. Energy is released in amounts that cells can harness for cellular work.

1. Energy input splits glucose into carbon dioxide, electrons, and hydrogen ions ($H^+$).
2. Electrons lose energy as they move through an electron transfer chain.
3. Energy released by electrons is harnessed for cellular work.
4. Electrons, hydrogen ions, and oxygen combine to form water.

---

**FIGURE 4.9 Animated!** Comparing uncontrolled and controlled energy release.

**Electron Transfers** As you learned in Section 4.3, the bonds of organic molecules hold a lot of energy that can be released by combustion. Burning an organic substance in the presence of oxygen releases its energy all at once, explosively (Figure 4.9**A**). Cells use oxygen to break the bonds of organic molecules. However, they have no way to harvest an explosive burst of energy, so they break the molecules apart in several steps that release energy in small, manageable increments. Most of these steps are reactions in which a molecule accepts electrons from another molecule.

Coenzymes are among the many types of molecules that accept and donate electrons in electron transfer reactions. In the next chapter, you will learn about the importance of these reactions in electron transfer chains. An **electron transfer chain** is an organized series of reaction steps in which membrane-bound arrays of enzymes and other molecules give up and accept electrons in turn. Electrons are at a higher energy level (Section 2.2) when they enter a chain than when they leave. Electron transfer chains can harvest the energy given off by an electron as it drops to a lower energy level (Figure 4.9**B**).

**concentration** The number of molecules or ions per unit volume of a fluid.
**concentration gradient** Difference in concentration between adjoining regions of fluid.
**diffusion** Net movement of molecules or ions from a region where they are more concentrated to a region where they are less so.
**electron transfer chain** Array of enzymes and other molecules that accept and give up electrons in sequence, thus releasing the energy of the electrons in usable increments.
**selective permeability** Membrane property that allows some substances, but not others, to cross.

## Take-Home Message  What is a metabolic pathway?

- Enzymes greatly enhance the rate of specific reactions. An enzyme's particular substrates bind at its active site, and it works best within certain ranges of temperature, pH, and salt concentration.

- Control mechanisms enhance or inhibit the activity of many enzymes. The adjustments help cells produce only what they require in any given interval.

- A metabolic pathway is a sequence of enzyme-mediated reactions that builds, breaks down, or remodels organic molecules.

- Many metabolic pathways involve electron transfers.

# Movement of Ions and Molecules

Metabolism only works because cells maintain the composition of their cytoplasm and internal fluids within certain ranges. If the composition of those fluids varied a lot, say in pH or the amount of salt, enzymes in the cell would stop working, and so would the cell.

Cells thrive even in environments that offer extreme conditions such as low pH and high salt. How does a cell keep its internal composition stable when that composition differs—often dramatically—from conditions outside of the cell? The answer begins with a property of membranes called **selective permeability**. Selectively permeable membranes allow some substances but not others to cross. This property helps a cell or membrane-enclosed organelle to control which substances and how much of each enter and leave it (Figure 4.10).

Such control is vital, because metabolism depends on the capacity to increase, decrease, and maintain concentrations of specific solutes. That capacity allows a cell or organelle to keep itself stocked with raw materials for reactions, to remove wastes, and to maintain internal fluid volume and pH within tolerable ranges.

Gases (such as oxygen and carbon dioxide), small nonpolar molecules, and water cross a bilayer freely.

Other molecules and ions cannot cross a lipid bilayer on their own.

lipid bilayer

**FIGURE 4.10 Animated!** Selective permeability of cell membranes. Small, nonpolar molecules, gases, and water molecules freely cross the lipid bilayer. Polar molecules and ions only cross with the help of proteins that span the bilayer.

**Diffusion** Selective permeability begins with the behavior of fluids—specifically, the behavior of water and substances dissolved in it. A dissolved substance, remember, is a solute (Section 2.4). How much of it is dissolved in a given amount of fluid is the solute's **concentration**. A difference in solute concentration between two adjacent regions is called a **concentration gradient**. Solute molecules or ions tend to move "down" their concentration gradient, from a region of higher concentration to one of lower concentration. Why? Molecules and ions are always in motion; they collide at random and bounce off one another millions of times each second. The more crowded they are, the more often they collide. Thus, during any interval, more of them get knocked out of a region of higher concentration than get knocked into it.

**Diffusion** is the net (or overall) movement of molecules or ions in response to a concentration gradient. It is an essential way in which substances move into, through, and out of cells. In multicelled species, diffusion also moves substances between cells in different regions of the body or between cells and extracellular fluids. Any substance tends to diffuse in a direction set by its own concentration gradient, not by the gradients of any other solutes that may be sharing the same space in the solution. How quickly a particular solute diffuses through a particular solution depends on five factors:

1. Size. It takes less energy to move a smaller molecule, so smaller molecules diffuse more quickly than larger ones.

2. Temperature. Molecules move faster at higher temperature, so they collide more often. Thus, diffusion is faster at higher temperature.

3. Steepness of the concentration gradient. The rate of diffusion is higher with steeper gradients, because molecules collide more often in a region of greater concentration.

4. Charge. Opposite charges attract, and like charges repel. An overall charge can affect the rate and direction of diffusion of ions between two regions.

5. Pressure. Pressure squeezes molecules together, and molecules that are more crowded collide and rebound more frequently. Thus, diffusion occurs faster at higher pressures.

**Osmosis and Tonicity** Like any other substance, water molecules tend to diffuse in response to their own concentration gradient. How can water be more or less concentrated? Think of water's concentration in terms of relative numbers of water molecules and solute molecules in a solution. The concentration of water depends on the total number of molecules or ions dissolved in it. The higher the solute concentration, the lower the water concentration. For example, if you pour some sugar into a container that is partially filled with water, you increase the total volume of liquid. The number of water molecules is unchanged, but they are now dispersed in a larger total volume. As a result of the added solute (in this case, the sugar molecules), the number of water molecules per unit volume—the water concentration—has decreased:

When water diffuses across a selectively permeable membrane, the diffusion is called **osmosis**. Turgor counters osmosis. **Turgor** is pressure that a volume of fluid exerts against a cell wall, membrane, tube, or other structure that holds it. The amount of turgor that can stop water from diffusing into cytoplasmic fluid or another solution is called **osmotic pressure**.

Think about growing plant cells. Cytoplasm typically contains more solutes than soil water does, so water tends to diffuse from soil water into these cells. The osmosis causes fluid pressure—turgor—to build up inside the cells. The turgor pushes against the cell walls from the inside, so it keeps the cells plump and the plant erect, just as high air pressure in a tire keeps it inflated. If the soil dries out, it loses water but not solutes, so its concentration of solutes increases. If the solutes in soil water become more concentrated than in cytoplasmic fluid, water will tend to diffuse out of the plant's cells and turgor in them will decrease. The plant wilts as the cytoplasm in its cells shrinks.

Tonicity refers to the relative concentrations of solutes in two fluids separated by a selectively permeable membrane. When the solute concentrations differ, the fluid with the lower concentration of solutes is said to be **hypotonic** (*hypo–*, under). The other one, with the higher solute concentration, is **hypertonic** (*hyper–*, over). Fluids that are **isotonic** have the same solute concentration.

Water tends to follow its gradient and diffuse from a hypotonic to a hypertonic fluid (Figures 4.11 and 4.12**A**). If a selectively permeable membrane separates two fluids that are not isotonic, water will cross the membrane, and move from the hypotonic fluid into the hypertonic one ❶. Osmosis will continue until the two fluids are isotonic ❷, or until some pressure against the hypertonic fluid counters the movement.

Cell membranes are selectively permeable, and water crosses them freely. Thus, if a cell's cytoplasm is hypertonic with respect to the fluid outside of its plasma membrane, water will diffuse into it. If its cytoplasm is hypotonic with respect to the fluid on the outside, water will diffuse out of it.

Most free-living cells have built-in mechanisms that compensate for differences in tonicity between cytoplasm and external fluid. Such cells can maintain their cytoplasm at a constant volume by pumping water one way or the other across their plasma membrane. Most cells of multicelled species have no such

selectively permeable membrane

**FIGURE 4.11 Animated!** Osmosis. Water moves across a selectively permeable membrane that separates two fluids of differing solute concentration.

❶ Initially, the volume of fluid is the same in the two compartments, but the solute concentration differs.

❷ The fluid volume in the two compartments changes as water follows its gradient and diffuses across the membrane.

**A**  2% sucrose      10% sucrose      water

**FIGURE 4.12 Animated!** Tonicity.

**A** Tonicity experiment that shows what happens when a selectively permeable membrane bag is immersed in solutions of different tonicity.

**B–D** The micrographs show human red blood cells immersed in fluids of different tonicity.

Figure It Out: Which of the three solutions in **A** is hypertonic with respect to the fluid in the bag?

*Answer: The 10% sucrose solution*

**B** Red blood cells immersed in an isotonic solution do not change in volume. The fluid portion of blood is typically isotonic with cytoplasm.

**C** Red blood cells immersed in a hypertonic solution shrivel up because more water diffuses out of the cells than into them.

**D** Red blood cells immersed in a hypotonic solution swell up because more water diffuses into the cells than out of them.

mechanism, and their volume will change if the external fluid is not isotonic with the cytoplasm. Thus, in multicelled organisms, maintaining the tonicity of extracellular fluids is a critical part of homeostasis. Normally, body fluids are isotonic with fluid inside cells (Figure 4.12**B**). If extracellular fluid were to become hypertonic, the cells would lose water from their cytoplasm, and they would shrivel (Figure 4.12**C**). If the fluid were to become hypotonic, too much water would diffuse into the cells, and they would swell and burst (Figure 4.12**D**).

## Take-Home Message   **What influences the movement of ions and molecules?**

- Molecules or ions tend to diffuse into an adjoining region of fluid in which they are not as concentrated.
- Osmosis is a net diffusion of water between two fluids that differ in water concentration and are separated by a selectively permeable membrane.

# 4.6  Membrane-Crossing Mechanisms

Molecules that can cross a membrane on their own do so by diffusing directly across the lipid bilayer. Other molecules can cross only with the assistance of transport proteins (Section 3.4). Each type of transport protein can move a specific ion or molecule across a membrane. Glucose transporters only transport glucose; calcium pumps only pump calcium; and so on. The specificity of transport protein binding means that the amounts and types of substances that cross a membrane depend on which transport proteins are embedded in it.

**hypertonic** Describes a fluid with a high solute concentration relative to another fluid.

**hypotonic** Describes a fluid with a low solute concentration relative to another fluid.

**isotonic** Describes a fluid with the same solute concentration relative to another fluid.

**osmosis** The diffusion of water across a selectively permeable membrane.

**osmotic pressure** Amount of turgor that prevents osmosis into cytoplasm or other hypertonic fluid.

**turgor** Pressure that a fluid exerts against a wall, membrane, or some other structure that contains it.

Extracellular
Fluid

glucose

①

Cytoplasm    lipid bilayer

②

③

For example, a glucose transporter in a plasma membrane can bind to a molecule of glucose, but not to a molecule of phosphorylated glucose. Enzymes in cytoplasm phosphorylate glucose as soon as it enters the cell. Phosphorylation prevents the molecule from moving back through the glucose transporter and leaving the cell.

**Passive Transport** In **passive transport**, the movement of a solute (and the direction of the movement) through a transport protein is driven entirely by the solute's concentration gradient. For this reason, passive transport is also called facilitated diffusion. The solute simply binds to the passive transport protein, and the protein releases it to the other side of the membrane (Figure 4.13).

A glucose transporter is an example of a passive transport protein ❶. This protein changes shape when it binds to a molecule of glucose ❷. The shape change moves the solute to the opposite side of the membrane, where it detaches. Then, the transporter reverts to its original shape ❸. Some passive transporters do not change shape; they form permanently open channels through a membrane. Others are gated, which means they open and close in response to a stimulus such as a shift in electric charge or binding to a signaling molecule.

**Active Transport** Solute concentrations shift constantly in the cytoplasm and in extracellular fluid. Maintaining a solute's concentration at a certain level often means transporting the solute against its gradient, to the side of a membrane where it is more concentrated. Pumping a solute against its gradient takes energy. In **active transport**, a transport protein uses energy to pump a solute against its gradient across a cell membrane. After a solute binds to an active transporter, an energy input (often in the form of a phosphate-group transfer from ATP) changes the shape of the protein. The change causes the transporter to release the solute to the other side of the membrane.

A calcium pump is an example of an active transporter. This protein moves calcium ions across muscle cell membranes (Figure 4.14). Muscle cells contract when the nervous system causes calcium ions to flood out from a special organelle, the sarcoplasmic reticulum, which is wrapped around the muscle fiber. The

Sarcoplasmic
Reticulum

Cytoplasm

calcium

A

B

C

ATP

**FIGURE 4.14 Animated!** Active transport. This model shows a calcium transporter embedded in a muscle cell membrane. **A** Two calcium ions bind to the transport protein. **B** Energy in the form of a phosphate group is transferred from ATP to the protein. The transfer causes the protein to change shape so that it ejects the calcium ions to the opposite side of the membrane. **C** After it loses the calcium ions, the transport protein resumes its original shape.

flood clears out binding sites on motor proteins (Section 3.6) that make muscles contract. Contraction ends after calcium pumps have moved most of the calcium ions back into the sarcoplasmic reticulum, against their concentration gradient. Calcium pumps keep the concentration of calcium in that compartment 1,000 to 10,000 times higher than it is in muscle cell cytoplasm.

Cotransporters are active transport proteins that move two substances at the same time, in opposite directions across a membrane. Nearly all of the cells in your body have cotransporters called sodium–potassium pumps (Figure 4.15). Sodium ions ($Na^+$) in the cytoplasm diffuse into the pump's open channel and bind to its interior. A phosphate-group transfer from ATP causes the pump to change shape. Its channel opens to extracellular fluid, where it releases the $Na^+$. Then, potassium ions ($K^+$) from extracellular fluid diffuse into the channel and bind to its interior. The transporter releases the phosphate group and reverts to its original shape. The channel opens to the cytoplasm, where it releases the $K^+$.

Bear in mind, the membranes of all cells, not just those of animals, have active transporters. For example, active transporters in plant leaf cells pump sugars into tubes that distribute them throughout the plant body.

**active transport** Energy-requiring mechanism by which a transport protein pumps a solute across a cell membrane against its concentration gradient.
**passive transport** Mechanism by which a concentration gradient drives the movement of a solute across a cell membrane through a transport protein. Requires no energy input.

Extracellular
Fluid

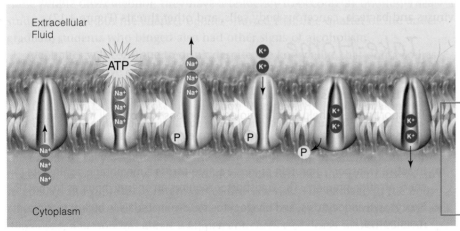

ATP

Cytoplasm

**FIGURE 4.15** Cotransport. This model shows how a sodium–potassium pump transports sodium ions ($Na^+$, *red*) from cytoplasm to extracellular fluid, and potassium ions ($K^+$, *purple*) in the other direction across the plasma membrane. A phosphate-group transfer from ATP provides energy for the transport.

# Summary

**Section 4.1**  Metabolic processes build and break down organic molecules such as ethanol and other toxins. Currently the most serious drug problem on college campuses is binge drinking.

**Section 4.2**  Energy is the capacity to do work. Energy cannot be created or destroyed (first law of thermodynamics), but it can be converted from one form to another and thus transferred between objects or systems. Energy tends to disperse spontaneously (second law of thermodynamics). A bit disperses at each energy transfer, usually in the form of heat.

Living things maintain their organization only as long as they harvest energy from someplace else. Energy flows in one direction through the biosphere, starting mainly from the sun, then into and out of ecosystems. Producers and then consumers use energy to assemble, rearrange, and break down organic molecules that cycle among organisms throughout ecosystems.

**Section 4.3**  Cells store and retrieve energy by making and breaking chemical bonds in metabolic reactions (Table 4.1). ATP is the main energy carrier in cells. Phosphate-group transfers (phosphorylations) to and from ATP couple energy-releasing reactions with energy-requiring ones.

**CENGAGENOW**  Learn about chemical bookkeeping and investigate ATP with the animations on CengageNow.

**Section 4.4**  Enzymes are proteins or RNAs that greatly enhance the rate of a chemical reaction. Each type works best within a characteristic range of temperature, salt concentration, and pH. Controls over enzymes allow cells to conserve energy and resources by producing only what they require. Cells concentrate, convert, and dispose of most substances in enzyme-mediated reaction sequences called metabolic pathways. Electron transfer chains allow cells to harvest energy in manageable increments.

**CENGAGENOW**  Investigate enzymes and activation energy, observe controls over enzymes, and compare the effects of controlled and uncontrolled energy release with the animations on CengageNow.

**Section 4.5**  A concentration gradient is a difference in the concentration of a substance between adjoining regions of fluid. Molecules or ions tend to follow their own gradient and move toward the region where they are less concentrated, a behavior called diffusion.

| Table 4.1 | Key Players in Metabolic Reactions |
|---|---|
| Reactant | Substance that enters a metabolic reaction; also called a substrate of an enzyme |
| Intermediate | Substance that forms in a reaction or pathway between the reactants and products |
| Product | Substance that remains at the end of a reaction |
| Enzyme | Protein or RNA that greatly enhances the rate of a reaction, but is not changed by participating in it |
| Cofactor | Molecule or ion that assists enzymes |
| Energy carrier | Mainly ATP; couples reactions that release energy with reactions that require energy |

**CENGAGENOW**  Investigate diffusion and osmosis with the animation on CengageNow.

**Section 4.6**  Gases, water, and small nonpolar molecules can diffuse across a lipid bilayer. Most other molecules and ions cross only with the help of transport proteins, which move specific solutes across membranes. Transporters allow a cell or membrane-enclosed organelle to control which substances enter and exit. The types of transport proteins in a membrane determine which substances cross it. Active transport proteins use energy, usually from ATP, to pump a solute against its concentration gradient. Passive transport proteins work without an energy input; solute movement is driven by the concentration gradient.

Osmosis is the diffusion of water across a selectively permeable membrane, from the region with a lower solute concentration (hypotonic) toward the region with a higher solute concentration (hypertonic).

**CENGAGENOW**  Compare the processes of passive and active transport with the animation on CengageNow.

## Self-Quiz    Answers in Appendix I

1. _____ is life's primary source of energy.
   a. Food          b. Water          c. Sunlight          d. ATP

2. Energy _____ .
   a. cannot be created or destroyed
   b. can change from one form to another
   c. tends to disperse spontaneously
   d. all of the above

3. If we liken a chemical reaction to an energy hill, then an _____ reaction is an uphill run.
   a. energy-requiring          c. ATP-assisted
   b. energy-releasing          d. both a and c

4. _____ are always changed by participating in a reaction. (Choose all that are correct.)
   a. Enzymes          c. Reactants
   b. Cofactors          d. Intermediates

5. Enzymes _____ .
   a. are proteins, except for a few RNAs
   b. lower the activation energy of a reaction
   c. are changed by the reactions they catalyze
   d. a and b

6. Which of the following statements is not correct? A metabolic pathway _____ .
   a. is a sequence of enzyme-mediated reactions
   b. may build or break down molecules
   c. generates heat
   d. can include an electron transfer chain
   e. none of the above

7. Diffusion is the movement of ions or molecules from a region where they are _____ (more/less) concentrated to another where they are _____ (more/less) concentrated.

8. Name one molecule that can readily diffuse across a lipid bilayer.

9. Some sodium ions cross a cell membrane through transport proteins that first must be activated by an energy boost. This is an example of _____ .
   a. passive transport      c. facilitated diffusion
   b. active transport        d. a and c

10. Immerse a living cell in a hypotonic solution, and water will tend to _____ .
   a. move into the cell      c. show no net movement
   b. move out of the cell    d. move in by endocytosis

11. Fluid pressure against a wall or cell membrane is called _____ .

12. Vesicles form by _____ .
   a. endocytosis      d. phagocytosis
   b. exocytosis       e. all of the above

13. Match each term with its most suitable description.
   _____ reactant            a. assists enzymes
   _____ enzyme              b. there at reaction's end
   _____ first law           c. enters a reaction
   _____ product             d. unchanged by participating
   _____ cofactor               in a reaction
   _____ gradient            e. energy cannot be created
   _____ phospholipid           or destroyed
   _____ active transport    f. basis of diffusion
   _____ phagocytosis        g. important in membranes
                             h. one cell engulfs another
                             i. requires energy boost

Additional questions are available on CENGAGENOW™

# Critical Thinking

1. Beginning physics students are often taught the basic concepts of thermodynamics with two phrases: First, you can't win. Second, you can't break even. Explain.

2. Dixie Bee wanted to make Jell-O shots for her next party, but felt guilty about encouraging her guests to consume alcohol. She tried to compensate for the toxicity of the ethanol by adding healthy fresh pineapple to the shots, but then the Jell-O never set up. What do you think happened? *Hint:* Jell-O consists of sugar and gelatin, a protein manufactured from collagen. Heat dissolves Jell-O because it breaks the hydrogen bonds between its protein molecules. The hydrogen bonds form again and hold the protein molecules together as a solid when the Jell-O cools.

3. Seawater and extracellular fluid contain approximately the same kinds and proportions of salts, which is a legacy of life's probable origin in ocean water. However, those solutes are about four times more concentrated in seawater than in body fluids. On the outer surface of the body, a thick layer of dead, keratin-stuffed cells make skin waterproof. When you take a long bath, your skin wrinkles because the dry keratin molecules in the dead skin cells absorb water and swell up. Is skin wrinkling in water an example of osmosis or does it occur by a different mechanism? Would you predict that skin wrinkles faster in fresh water or salt water? Why?

# Digging Into Data

## Effects of Artichoke Extract on Hangovers

Ethanol is a toxin, so it makes sense that drinking it can cause various symptoms of poisoning—headache, stomachache, nausea, fatigue, impaired memory, dizziness, tremors, and diarrhea, among other ailments. All are symptoms of hangover, the common word for what happens as the body is recovering from a bout of heavy drinking.

The most effective treatment for a hangover is to avoid drinking in the first place. Folk remedies (such as aspirin, coffee, bananas, more alcohol, honey, barley grass, pizza, milkshakes, glutamine, raw eggs, charcoal tablets, or cabbage) abound, but few have been studied scientifically. In 2003, Max Pittler and his colleagues tested one of them. The researchers gave 15 participants an unmarked pill containing either artichoke extract or a placebo (an inactive substance) just before or after drinking enough alcohol to cause a hangover. The results are shown in Figure 4.19.

1. How many participants experienced a hangover that was worse with the placebo than with the artichoke extract?

2. How many participants experienced a worse hangover with the artichoke extract?

3. Calculate the numbers you counted in questions 1 and 2 as a percentage of the total number of participants. How much difference is there between the percentages?

4. Does these results support the hypothesis that artichoke extract is an effective hangover treatment? Why or why not?

| Participant (Age, Gender) | Severity of Hangover | |
|---|---|---|
| | Artichoke Extract | Placebo |
| 1 (34, F) | 1.9 | 3.8 |
| 2 (48, F) | 5.0 | 0.6 |
| 3 (25, F) | 7.7 | 3.2 |
| 4 (57, F) | 2.4 | 4.4 |
| 5 (34, F) | 5.4 | 1.6 |
| 6 (30, F) | 1.5 | 3.9 |
| 7 (33, F) | 1.4 | 0.1 |
| 8 (37, F) | 0.7 | 3.6 |
| 9 (62, M) | 4.5 | 0.9 |
| 10 (36, M) | 3.7 | 5.9 |
| 11 (54, M) | 1.6 | 0.2 |
| 12 (37, M) | 2.6 | 5.6 |
| 13 (53, M) | 4.1 | 6.3 |
| 14 (48, F) | 0.5 | 0.4 |
| 15 (32, F) | 1.3 | 2.5 |

**FIGURE 4.19** Results of a study that tested artichoke extract as a hangover preventive. All participants were tested once with the placebo and once with the extract, with a week interval between. Each rated the severity of 20 hangover symptoms on a scale of 0 (not experienced) to 10 ("as bad as can be imagined"). The 20 ratings were averaged as a single, overall rating, which is listed here.

# 5 Capturing and Releasing Energy

## 5.1 Impacts/Issues: Green Energy

Today, the expression "food is fuel" is not just about eating. With fossil fuel prices soaring, there is an increasing demand for biofuels, which are oils, gases, or alcohols made from organic matter that is not fossilized. Much of the material currently used for biofuel production consists of food crops—mainly corn, soybeans, and sugarcane. Growing these crops in large quantities is typically expensive and damaging to the environment, and using them to make biofuel competes with our food supply. The diversion of food crops to biofuels production is now contributing to a major increase in food prices worldwide.

How did we end up competing with our vehicles for food? We both run on the same fuel: energy that plants have stored in chemical bonds. Petroleum, coal, and natural gas are fossil fuels, which formed from the remains of ancient swamp forests that decayed and compacted over millions of years. They consist mainly of molecules originally assembled by ancient plants. Biofuels—and foods—consist mainly of molecules originally assembled by modern plants.

Plants use the energy of sunlight to assemble carbohydrates from carbon dioxide and water. That process is **photosynthesis**, and it is the way that plants make their own food. Directly or indirectly, photosynthesis also feeds most other life on Earth: We and almost all other organisms sustain ourselves by extracting energy stored in the organic products of photosynthesis. Animals and other **heterotrophs** get energy and carbon by breaking down organic molecules assembled by other organisms (*hetero–* means other; *–troph* refers to nourishment). Plants and other **autotrophs** harvest energy directly from the environment, and they get carbon from inorganic molecules (*auto–* means self).

A lot of energy is locked up in the chemical bonds of molecules made by plants. That energy can fuel heterotrophs, as when an animal cell powers ATP synthesis by breaking the bonds of sugars. It can also fuel our cars, which run on energy released by burning biofuels. Both processes are fundamentally the same: They release energy by breaking the bonds of organic molecules. Both use oxygen to break those bonds, and both produce carbon dioxide.

Plants such as corn and other food crops are typically rich in oils or sugars, molecules that are easily converted to biofuels. For example, we use heterotrophic bacteria to conveniently convert corn sugars to ethanol. Using other plant materials to make biofuels takes an extra step, because they contain a higher proportion of cellulose. Cellulose is a tough and insoluble carbohydrate, and bacteria cannot break it down. Breaking the bonds between cellulose's component sugars is an energy-intensive process that adds cost to the biofuel product. Thus, current biofuels research focuses on finding a cost-effective way to break down the abundant cellulose in fast-growing weeds (Figure 5.1) and agricultural wastes such as wood chips, wheat straw, cotton stalks, and rice hulls—all materials that we now dump in landfills or burn.

**FIGURE 5.1** Switchgrass (*Panicum virgatum*), a fast-growing weed that grows wild in North American prairies. The abundant cellulose in its thick, strong stems holds enough energy to yield more than 1,100 gallons of ethanol biofuel per acre per year.

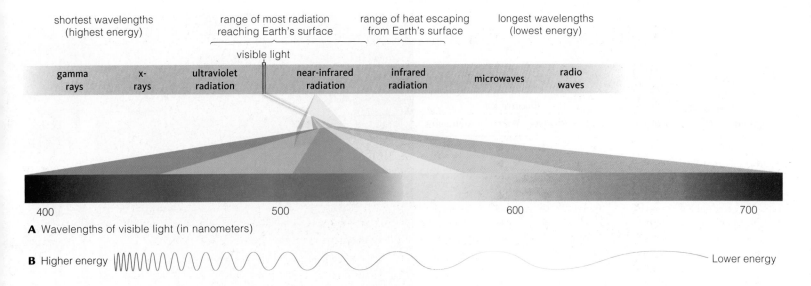

shortest wavelengths
(highest energy)

range of most radiation
reaching Earth's surface

range of heat escaping
from Earth's surface

longest wavelengths
(lowest energy)

visible light

| gamma rays | x-rays | ultraviolet radiation | near-infrared radiation | infrared radiation | microwaves | radio waves |

400   500   600   700

**A** Wavelengths of visible light (in nanometers)

**B** Higher energy                                          Lower energy

**FIGURE 5.2 A** Electromagnetic spectrum of radiant energy, which undulates across space as waves that are measured in nanometers. Visible light makes up a very small part of the electromagnetic spectrum. Raindrops or a prism can separate its different wavelengths, which are visible to us as different colors. **B** Light is organized as packets of energy called photons. The shorter a photon's wavelength, the greater its energy.

# 5.2 Capturing Rainbows

Harnessing the energy of sunlight for work is complicated business, or we would have been able to do it in an economically sustainable way by now. Plants do it by converting light energy to chemical energy, which they and most other organisms use to drive cellular work. The first step involves capturing light. In order to understand how that happens, you have to understand a little about the nature of light.

Most of the energy that reaches Earth's surface is in the form of visible light, so it should not be surprising that visible light is the energy that drives photosynthesis. Visible light is a very small part of a large spectrum of electromagnetic energy radiating from the sun. Light travels in waves, moving through space a bit like waves moving across an ocean. The distance between the crests of two successive waves is the light's **wavelength**, which we measure in nanometers (nm). Humans and many other organisms see particular wavelengths of light in the range of 380 to 750 nanometers as different colors (Figure 5.2**A**).

Light travels in waves, but it is also organized in packets of energy called photons. A photon's energy and its wavelength are related, so all photons traveling at the same wavelength carry the same amount of energy. Photons that carry the least energy travel in longer wavelengths; those that carry the most energy travel in shorter wavelengths (Figure 5.2**B**).

Photosynthesizers use pigments to capture light. A **pigment** is an organic molecule that selectively absorbs light of specific wavelengths. Wavelengths of light that are not absorbed are reflected, and that reflected light gives a pigment its characteristic color. For example, if a pigment absorbs violet, blue, and green light, it reflects the rest of the visible light spectrum, which consists of yellow, orange, and red light. This pigment would appear orange to us.

**Chlorophyll *a*** is by far the most common photosynthetic pigment in plants, and in photosynthetic protists and bacteria. Chlorophyll *a* absorbs purple and

**autotroph** Organism that makes its own food using carbon from inorganic molecules such as $CO_2$, and energy from the environment.

**chlorophyll *a*** Main photosynthetic pigment in plants.

**heterotroph** Organism that obtains energy and carbon from organic compounds assembled by other organisms.

**photosynthesis** Metabolic pathway by which most autotrophs capture light energy and use it to make sugars from $CO_2$ and water.

**pigment** An organic molecule that can absorb light of certain wavelengths.

**wavelength** Distance between the crests of two successive waves of light.

| Table 5.1 | Some Examples of Photosynthetic Pigments | | | | |
|---|---|---|---|---|---|
| | | Occurrence | | | |
| Pigment | Color | Plants | Protists | Bacteria | Archaeans |
| Chlorophyll *a* | green | ● | ● | ● | |
| Other chlorophylls | green | ● | ● | ● | |
| Phycobilins | | | | | |
| phycocyanobilin | blue | | ● | ● | |
| phycoerythrobilin | red | | ● | ● | |
| phycoviolobilin | purple | | ● | ● | |
| Carotenoids | | | | | |
| beta-carotene | orange | ● | ● | ● | |
| lycopene | red | ● | ● | | |
| lutein | yellow | ● | ● | ● | |
| zeaxanthin | yellow | ● | ● | ● | |
| fucoxanthin | orange | ● | ● | | |
| Anthocyanins | purple | ● | ● | ● | |
| Retinal | purple | | | | ● |

red light, so it appears green to us. Accessory pigments, including other chlorophylls, absorb additional colors of light for photosynthesis. A few of the 600 or so known accessory pigments are listed in Table 5.1.

Most photosynthetic organisms use a combination of pigments for photosynthesis. In plants, chlorophylls are usually so abundant that they mask the colors of the other pigments, so leaves are typically green. Green leaves change color during autumn because they stop making pigments as the plant prepares for a period of dormancy. Chlorophyll breaks down faster than other pigments, so the leaves turn red, orange, yellow, or purple as their chlorophyll content declines and the accessory pigments show through. Accessory pigments also color many flowers, fruits, and roots red or orange. For example, the color of a tomato changes from green to red as it is ripening because it starts making carotenoids instead of chlorophylls.

In photosynthesis, pigment molecules are a bit like antennas that are specialized for receiving light energy. When a pigment absorbs a photon, its electrons become excited. The excited electrons return quickly to a lower energy level by emitting the extra energy (Section 2.2). As you will see, molecules in the membranes of photosynthetic cells can capture the energy emitted by an excited electron, and use it to drive ATP synthesis.

## Take-Home Message How do photosynthetic organisms absorb light?

- Energy radiating from the sun travels through space in waves and is organized as packets called photons.

- The spectrum of radiant energy from the sun includes visible light. Humans perceive different wavelengths of visible light as different colors. The shorter the wavelength, the greater the energy.

- Pigments absorb light at specific wavelengths. Photosynthetic species use pigments such as chlorophyll *a* to harvest the energy of light for photosynthesis.

**All life is sustained by inputs of energy, but not all forms of energy can sustain life.**

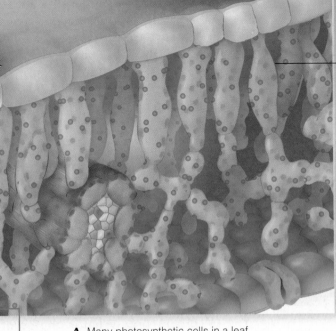

**FIGURE 5.3 Animated!** Zooming in on the sites of photosynthesis in a leaf.

**A** Many photosynthetic cells in a leaf

**B** Many chloroplasts in a photosynthetic cell

**C** Many thylakoids in a chloroplast

# 5.3 Storing Energy in Carbohydrates

All life is sustained by inputs of energy, but not all forms of energy can sustain life. Sunlight, for example, is abundant here on Earth, but it cannot be used to directly power protein synthesis or the other energy-requiring reactions that all organisms must run in order to stay alive. Photosynthesis converts the energy of light into the energy of chemical bonds. Unlike light, chemical energy can power the reactions of life, and it can be stored for use at a later time.

In plants, photosynthesis occurs in certain types of cells (Figure 5.3**A**). Photosynthetic cells contain **chloroplasts**, which are organelles specialized for photosynthesis (Figure 5.3**B**). Plant chloroplasts have two outer membranes, and they are filled with a semifluid substance called **stroma**. Suspended in the stroma are the chloroplast's DNA, some ribosomes, and a third, much-folded **thylakoid membrane**. The folds of a thylakoid membrane typically form stacks of interconnected disks called thylakoids (Figure 5.3**C**). The space enclosed by the thylakoid membrane forms one continuous compartment.

Many clusters of light-harvesting pigments are embedded in a thylakoid membrane. These clusters absorb photons of different energies. The membrane also incorporates **photosystems**, which are groups of hundreds of pigments and other molecules that work as a unit to begin the reactions of photosynthesis.

The overall process of photosynthesis can be summarized this way:

$$6CO_2 + 6H_2O \xrightarrow{\text{light energy}} C_6H_{12}O_6 + 6O_2$$

carbon dioxide    water    glucose    oxygen

The equation means that photosynthesis converts carbon dioxide and water to glucose and oxygen. However, photosynthesis is not one reaction. It is a

**chloroplast** Organelle of photosynthesis in plants and some protists.

**photosystem** Cluster of pigments and proteins that converts light energy to chemical energy in photosynthesis.

**stroma** Semifluid matrix between the thylakoid membrane and the two outer membranes of a chloroplast.

**thylakoid membrane** A chloroplast's highly folded inner membrane system; forms a continuous compartment in the stroma.

metabolic pathway (Section 4.4), a series of many reactions that occur in two stages (Figure 5.4). The first stage occurs at the thylakoid membrane. It is driven by light, so the collective reactions of this stage are called the **light-dependent reactions**. These reactions convert the energy of light to the chemical bond energy of ATP. The coenzyme NADP+ (nicotinamide adenine dinucleotide phosphate) accepts electrons and hydrogen ions. When this coenzyme is carrying electrons and hydrogen, we refer to it as NADPH. Water molecules are broken apart into oxygen and hydrogen atoms. Hydrogen ions stay in the chloroplast and participate in the process of ATP formation, and the oxygen atoms leave the cell as oxygen gas ($O_2$).

The reactions of the second stage of photosynthesis run in the stroma. They are collectively called the **light-independent reactions** because light does not power them. They run on energy delivered by molecules that formed in the first stage—ATP and NADPH. During the second-stage reactions, glucose and other carbohydrates are synthesized from carbon dioxide and water.

**FIGURE 5.4** Summary of the metabolic pathway of photosynthesis as it occurs in plant chloroplasts.

## Take-Home Message  What is photosynthesis and where does it occur?

- In the first stage of photosynthesis, light energy drives the formation of ATP and NADPH, and oxygen is released. These light-dependent reactions occur at the thylakoid membrane in plant chloroplasts.
- In the second stage of photosynthesis, ATP and NADPH drive the synthesis of glucose and other carbohydrates from water and carbon dioxide. These light-independent reactions occur in the stroma.

# 5.4 The Light-Dependent Reactions

The light-dependent reactions of photosynthesis convert light energy to chemical bond energy in the form of ATP, and they also yield NADPH and $O_2$:

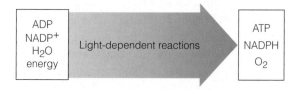

The reactions begin when a pigment in a thylakoid membrane absorbs a photon, and the photon's energy boosts one of the pigment's electrons to a higher energy level (Section 2.2). The electron quickly emits the extra energy and drops back to its unexcited state. That energy would be lost to the environment if nothing else were to happen, but in a thylakoid membrane the energy of excited electrons is kept in play. The pigments in the membrane can hold onto energy by passing it back and forth, a bit like volleyball players hold onto a ball by passing it back and forth among team members.

The reactions of photosynthesis begin when energy being passed among photosynthetic pigments reaches a photosystem (Figure 5.5). At the center of each photosystem is a special pair of chlorophyll *a* molecules. Absorbing energy pops electrons right out of that special pair ❶. The electrons immediately enter an electron transfer chain (Section 4.4) in the thylakoid membrane.

**electron transfer phosphorylation** Metabolic pathway in which electron flow through electron transfer chains sets up a hydrogen ion gradient that drives ATP formation.

**light-dependent reactions** Metabolic pathway of photosynthesis that converts light energy to chemical energy of ATP and NADPH.

**light-independent reactions** Metabolic pathway of photosynthesis that uses ATP and NADPH to assemble sugars from water and $CO_2$.

The Light-Dependent Reactions of Photosynthesis

A photosystem can donate only a few electrons to electron transfer chains before it must be restocked with more. Where do replacements come from? The photosystem gets more electrons by pulling them away from water molecules in the thylakoid compartment ❷. Losing electrons causes the water molecules to break apart into hydrogen ions and oxygen. The oxygen diffuses out of the cell as $O_2$ gas.

The actual conversion of light energy to chemical energy occurs when a photosystem donates electrons to an electron transfer chain ❸. Light does not take part in chemical reactions, but electrons do. In a series of reactions, electrons pass from one molecule of the chain to the next, and they release a bit of energy at each step.

The molecules of the electron transfer chain use the released energy to move hydrogen ions ($H^+$) across the membrane, from the stroma to the thylakoid compartment ❹. Thus, the flow of electrons through electron transfer chains sets up and maintains a hydrogen ion gradient across the thylakoid membrane.

This gradient motivates hydrogen ions in the thylakoid compartment to move back into the stroma. However, ions cannot diffuse through lipid bilayers (Section 4.5). $H^+$ leaves the thylakoid compartment only by flowing through membrane transport proteins called ATP synthases (Section 3.4).

Hydrogen ion flow through an ATP synthase causes this protein to attach a phosphate group to ADP ❼, so ATP forms in the stroma. The process by which the flow of electrons through electron transfer chains drives ATP formation is called **electron transfer phosphorylation**.

After the electrons have moved through the first electron transfer chain, they are accepted by another photosystem. This photosystem absorbs light energy, which causes electrons to pop out of its special pair of chlorophylls ❺. The electrons then enter a second, different electron transfer chain. At the end of this chain, $NADP^+$ accepts the electrons along with $H^+$, so NADPH forms ❻:

$$NADP^+ + 2e^- + H^+ \longrightarrow NADPH$$

ATP and NADPH continue to form as long as electrons continue to flow through transfer chains in the thylakoid membrane, and electrons flow through the

**FIGURE 5.5 Animated!** Light-dependent reactions of photosynthesis in the thylakoid membrane.

❶ Light energy ejects electrons from a photosystem.

❷ The photosystem pulls replacement electrons from water molecules, which break apart into oxygen and hydrogen ions. The oxygen leaves the cell as $O_2$.

❸ The electrons enter an electron transfer chain in the thylakoid membrane.

❹ Energy lost by the electrons as they move through the transfer chain causes hydrogen ions to be pumped from the stroma into the thylakoid compartment. A hydrogen ion gradient forms across the thylakoid membrane.

❺ Light energy pops electrons out of another photosystem. Replacement electrons come from an electron transfer chain.

❻ The electrons move through a second electron transfer chain, then combine with $NADP^+$ and $H^+$, so NADPH forms.

❼ Hydrogen ions in the thylakoid compartment are propelled through the interior of ATP synthases by their gradient across the thylakoid membrane. Hydrogen ion flow causes ATP synthases to attach phosphate to ADP, so ATP forms in the stroma.

chains as long as water and oxygen are plentiful. When water and oxygen are scarce, the flow of electrons slows, and so does ATP and NADPH production.

## Take-Home Message What happens during the light-dependent reactions of photosynthesis?

- In the light-dependent reactions of photosynthesis, chlorophylls and other pigments in the thylakoid membrane transfer the energy of light to photosystems.
- Absorbing energy causes electrons to leave photosystems and enter electron transfer chains in the membrane. The flow of electrons through the transfer chains sets up hydrogen ion gradients that drive ATP formation.
- Oxygen is released and electrons end up in NADPH.

# 5.5 The Light-Independent Reactions

ATP and NADPH that form in the light-dependent reactions power the energy-requiring second stage of photosynthesis, which occurs in the stroma of chloroplasts. The light-independent reactions that make up this stage convert carbon dioxide to glucose and other carbohydrates:

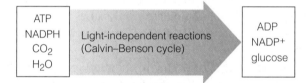

These reactions are also called the **Calvin–Benson cycle**, after the scientists who discovered them. Even though the Calvin–Benson cycle is often shown as a wheel or disk, it is not an object. It is a cyclic pathway, in which the product of the last reaction is the starting material of the first reaction (Section 4.4).

Extracting carbon atoms from an inorganic source and incorporating them into an organic molecule is a process called **carbon fixation**. In the Calvin–Benson cycle, an enzyme with a cumbersome name (ribulose-1,5-bisphosphate carboxylase, or **rubisco** for short) fixes carbon. Rubisco attaches a molecule of carbon dioxide to a molecule of ribulose bisphosphate, or RuBP. The molecule that forms splits at once into two 3-carbon intermediates called PGA, which continue in the cycle (Figure 5.6). It takes six cycles of Calvin–Benson reactions to fix the six carbon atoms necessary to make one glucose molecule.

Plants use the glucose they make in the light-independent reactions as building blocks for other organic molecules, or they break it down to access the energy in its bonds. However, most of the glucose is converted at once to sucrose or starch by other pathways that conclude the light-independent reactions. Excess glucose is stored as starch grains in the stroma of the chloroplast.

**Rascally Rubisco** Several adaptations allow plants to live where water is scarce or sporadically available. For example, a thin, waterproof coating called a cuticle prevents water loss by evaporation from aboveground plant parts. However, the cuticle also prevents gases from crossing through cells on the plant's surface. Gases play a critical role in photosynthesis, so photosynthetic parts are often studded with tiny, closable gaps called **stomata** (singular, stoma). When stomata are open, carbon dioxide for the light-independent reactions can diffuse

**FIGURE 5.6 Animated!** Light-independent reactions of photosynthesis which, in chloroplasts, occur in the stroma. The sketch is a summary of six cycles of the Calvin–Benson reactions and their product, one glucose molecule.

**FIGURE 5.7** Carbon-fixing adaptations. Most plants, including basswood (*Tilia americana* **A**), are C3 plants. **B** Photorespiration in C3 plants makes sugar production inefficient on dry days. Additional reactions minimize photorespiration in C4 plants such as corn (*Zea mays* **C**), and CAM plants such as jade plants (*Crassula argentea* **D**).

from air into the plant's photosynthetic tissues, and oxygen produced by the light-dependent reactions can diffuse from photosynthetic cells into the air.

Plants that use only the Calvin–Benson cycle are called **C3 plants**, because 3-carbon PGA is the first stable intermediate to form in the light-independent reactions. C3 plants typically conserve water on dry days by closing their stomata. However, when stomata are closed, oxygen produced by the light-dependent reactions cannot escape from the plant. Oxygen that accumulates in photosynthetic tissues limits sugar production. Why? At high oxygen levels, rubisco attaches oxygen (instead of carbon) to RuBP. This pathway, **photorespiration**, produces carbon dioxide, so the plant loses carbon instead of fixing it (Figure 5.7**A,B**). In addition, ATP and NADPH are used to shunt the pathway's intermediates back to the Calvin–Benson cycle, so it takes extra energy to make sugars on dry days. C3 plants compensate for rubisco's inefficiency by making a lot of it: Rubisco is the most abundant protein on Earth.

Some plants have adaptations that help them minimize photorespiration. A 4-carbon molecule is the first stable intermediate that forms in the light-independent reactions of corn, bamboo, and other **C4 plants** (Figure 5.7**C**). Such plants fix carbon twice, in two kinds of cells. In the first kind of cell, carbon is fixed by an enzyme that does not use oxygen even at high oxygen levels. An intermediate is transported to another kind of cell and converted to carbon dioxide, which enters the Calvin–Benson cycle. The extra reactions keep the carbon dioxide level high near rubisco, thus minimizing photorespiration. In succulents, cactuses, and other plants, the extra reactions run at a different time rather than in different cells. The C4 reactions run during the day, and the Calvin–Benson cycle runs at night. Such **CAM plants** are named for *Crassulacean Acid Metabolism*, after the family of plants in which this pathway was first studied (Figure 5.7**D**).

## Take-Home Message What happens during the light-independent reactions of photosynthesis?

■ Driven by the energy of ATP and electrons from NADPH, the light-independent reactions of photosynthesis use carbon and oxygen (from $CO_2$) to build sugars.

**C3 plant** Type of plant that uses only the Calvin–Benson cycle to fix carbon.

**C4 plant** Type of plant that minimizes photorespiration by fixing carbon twice, in two cell types.

**Calvin–Benson cycle** Light-independent reactions of photosynthesis; cyclic pathway that forms glucose from $CO_2$.

**CAM plant** Type of C4 plant that conserves water by fixing carbon twice, at different times of day.

**carbon fixation** Process by which carbon from an inorganic source such as carbon dioxide becomes incorporated into an organic molecule.

**photorespiration** Reaction in which rubisco attaches oxygen instead of carbon dioxide to ribulose bisphosphate.

**rubisco** Ribulose bisphosphate carboxylase. Carbon-fixing enzyme of the Calvin–Benson cycle.

**stomata** Gaps that open between guard cells on plant surfaces.

# 5.6 Photosynthesis and Aerobic Respiration: A Global Connection

The first cells on Earth did not tap into sunlight. Like some modern archaeans, these ancient organisms extracted energy and carbon from simple molecules such as methane and hydrogen sulfide—gases that were plentiful in the nasty brew that constituted Earth's early atmosphere (Figure 5.8 ❶).

The first photosynthetic autotrophs evolved about 3.2 billion years ago, probably in shallow ocean waters. Sunlight offered these **photoautotrophs** an essentially unlimited supply of energy, and they were very successful. Oxygen gas ($O_2$) released from uncountable numbers of water molecules began seeping out of uncountable numbers of photosynthesizers, and it accumulated in the ocean and the atmosphere. From that time on, the world of life would never be the same ❷.

Molecular oxygen had been a very small component of Earth's early atmosphere before photosynthesis evolved. The new abundance of atmospheric oxygen exerted tremendous selection pressure on all organisms. Why? Oxygen gas reacts easily with metals such as enzyme cofactors, and free radicals (molecules with unpaired electrons) form during those reactions. Free radicals damage biological molecules, so they are dangerous to life.

The ancient cells had no way to detoxify oxygen radicals, so most of them quickly died out. Only a few lineages persisted in deep water, muddy sediments, and other **anaerobic** (oxygen-free) habitats. New metabolic pathways that detoxified oxygen radicals evolved in the survivors. Organisms with such pathways were the first **aerobic** organisms—they could live in the presence of oxygen. As you will see, one of the pathways, aerobic respiration, put oxygen's reactive properties to good use. **Aerobic respiration** is one of several pathways by which organisms access the energy stored in carbohydrates. This pathway requires oxygen, and it produces carbon dioxide and water—the raw materials from which photosynthesizers make sugars. With this connection, the cycling of carbon, hydrogen, and oxygen through living things came full circle (*right*).

**FIGURE 5.8** Then ❶ and now ❷, a view of how Earth's atmosphere was permanently altered by the evolution of photosynthesis. Photosynthesis is now the main pathway by which energy and carbon enter the web of life.

**Extracting Energy From Carbohydrates** Like those early organisms, photoautotrophs of today's world capture energy from the sun, and store it in the form of carbohydrates. They and most other organisms use energy stored in carbohydrates to run the diverse reactions that sustain life. However, carbohydrates rarely participate in such reactions, so how do cells harness their energy? In order to use the energy stored in carbohydrates, cells must first transfer it to ATP, which does participate in many of the energy-requiring reactions that a cell runs. The transfer occurs by breaking the bonds of carbohydrates, which releases

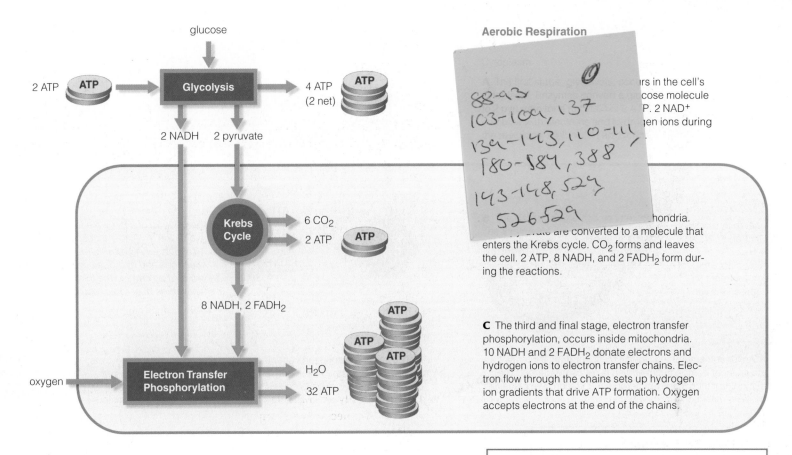

glucose

2 ATP — Glycolysis → 4 ATP (2 net)

2 NADH     2 pyruvate

Krebs Cycle → 6 CO₂
→ 2 ATP

8 NADH, 2 FADH₂

oxygen → Electron Transfer Phosphorylation → H₂O
→ 32 ATP

*(handwritten note):*
88-93
103-109, 137
139-143, 110-111
580-584, 388
143-148, 529
526-529

**Aerobic Respiration**

...urs in the cell's ...cose molecule ...P. 2 NAD⁺ ...gen ions during...

...hondria. ...ate are converted to a molecule that enters the Krebs cycle. CO₂ forms and leaves the cell. 2 ATP, 8 NADH, and 2 FADH₂ form during the reactions.

**C** The third and final stage, electron transfer phosphorylation, occurs inside mitochondria. 10 NADH and 2 FADH₂ donate electrons and hydrogen ions to electron transfer chains. Electron flow through the chains sets up hydrogen ion gradients that drive ATP formation. Oxygen accepts electrons at the end of the chains.

---

**FIGURE 5.9 Animated!** Overview of aerobic respiration. The reactions start in the cytoplasm and end in mitochondria.

Figure It Out: What is aerobic respiration's typical net yield of ATP? *Answer: 38 − 2 = 36 ATP per glucose*

---

energy that drives ATP synthesis. There are a few different kinds of carbohydrate-breakdown pathways, but aerobic respiration is the one that typical eukaryotic cells use at least most of the time. Aerobic respiration yields much more ATP than other carbohydrate breakdown pathways. You and other multicelled organisms could not live without its higher yield.

**Aerobic Respiration Begins** The reactions of aerobic respiration take place in three stages. The first stage, **glycolysis**, converts one 6-carbon molecule of glucose into two 3-carbon molecules of **pyruvate**:

glucose — glycolysis → pyruvate (2)

Glycolysis occurs in cytoplasm (Figure 5.9**A**). Two ATP are invested to begin the reactions, but four ATP form by the end. Thus, we say that the net (overall) yield of glycolysis is two ATP per glucose. Two NAD⁺ (nicotinamide adenine dinucleotide) also combine with electrons and hydrogen ions during the reactions. When this coenzyme is carrying electrons and hydrogen, we refer to it as NADH.

After glycolysis, aerobic respiration continues in two more stages that run inside mitochondria (Figure 5.9**B,C**).

**Aerobic Respiration Continues** The second stage of aerobic respiration occurs inside mitochondria. It includes two sets of reactions, acetyl–CoA formation and the Krebs cycle, that break down the pyruvate from glycolysis. The reactions begin when the pyruvate enters the inner compartment of a mitochondrion, where it becomes converted to carbon dioxide and an intermediate,

---

**aerobic** Involving or occurring in the presence of oxygen.
**aerobic respiration** Aerobic pathway that breaks down carbohydrates to produce ATP.
**anaerobic** Occurring in the absence of oxygen.
**glycolysis** Set of reactions in which glucose or another sugar is broken down to two pyruvate for a net yield of two ATP.
**photoautotroph** Photosynthetic autotroph.
**pyruvate** Three-carbon end product of glycolysis.

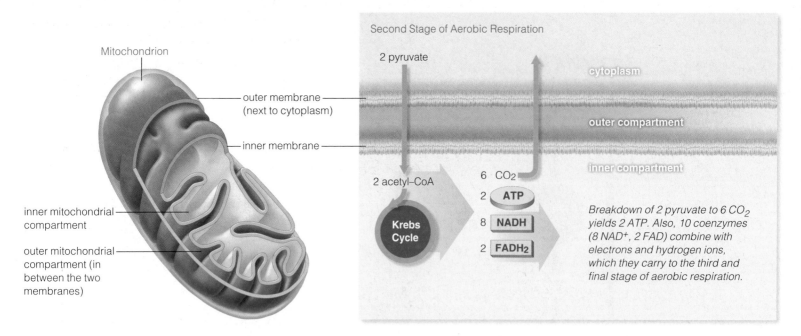

Second Stage of Aerobic Respiration

2 pyruvate

cytoplasm

outer membrane
(next to cytoplasm)

outer compartment

inner membrane

inner compartment

Mitochondrion

inner mitochondrial
compartment

outer mitochondrial
compartment (in
between the two
membranes)

2 acetyl–CoA

6  $CO_2$

2  ATP

Krebs
Cycle

8  NADH

2  FADH₂

*Breakdown of 2 pyruvate to 6 $CO_2$
yields 2 ATP. Also, 10 coenzymes
(8 NAD⁺, 2 FAD) combine with
electrons and hydrogen ions,
which they carry to the third and
final stage of aerobic respiration.*

**A**  An inner membrane divides a mitochondrion's interior into an inner compartment and an outer compartment. The second and third stages of aerobic respiration take place at the inner mitochondrial membrane.

**B**  The second stage starts after membrane proteins transport pyruvate from the cytoplasm to the inner compartment. Six carbon atoms enter these reactions (in two molecules of pyruvate), and six leave (in six $CO_2$). Two ATP form and ten coenzymes accept electrons and hydrogen ions.

**FIGURE 5.10 Animated!** The second stage of aerobic respiration: acetyl–CoA formation and the Krebs cycle.

acetyl–CoA (Figure 5.10). The **Krebs cycle** then breaks down the acetyl–CoA to carbon dioxide. Like the Calvin–Benson cycle, the Krebs cycle is often depicted as a wheel or disk, but it is not a physical object. It is a cyclic pathway, in which the product of the last reaction is also a starting material of the first reaction.

The overall reactions of the second stage of aerobic respiration convert two molecules of pyruvate to six molecules of carbon dioxide. Two ATP form. Also, 8 NAD⁺ and 2 FAD (flavin adenine dinucleotide, another coenzyme) combine with electrons and hydrogen ions, so 8 NADH and 2 FADH₂ form (Figure 5.10). At this point in aerobic respiration, one glucose molecule has been broken down completely; six carbon atoms have exited the cell, in six $CO_2$:

glucose  →(glycolysis)→  pyruvate (2)  →(2nd stage of aerobic respiration)→  carbon dioxide (6)

A total of four ATP have formed by the end of the first two stages of aerobic respiration, but almost all of the energy released from the breakdown of the glucose is now carried by twelve coenzymes (eight NAD⁺ and two FAD) that accepted electrons during the reactions. Energy carried by those electrons will drive the reactions of the third stage.

**The Big Energy Payoff: Aerobic Respiration Ends** The third and final stage of aerobic respiration, electron transfer phosphorylation, occurs in mitochondria (Figure 5.11). The reactions begin with NADH and FADH₂ that formed in the first two stages. These coenzymes now deliver their cargo of electrons and hydrogen ions to electron transfer chains in the inner mitochondrial membrane ❶.

Third Stage of Aerobic Respiration: Electron Transfer Phosphorylation

**FIGURE 5.11** The final stage of aerobic respiration: electron transfer phosphorylation.

❶ NADH and FADH$_2$ deliver electrons to electron transfer chains in the inner mitochondrial membrane.

❷ Electron flow through the chains causes hydrogen ions (H$^+$) to be pumped from the inner to the outer compartment.

❸ Oxygen (O$_2$) accepts electrons and hydrogen ions at the end of mitochondrial electron transfer chains, so water forms.

❹ The activity of the electron transfer chains causes a hydrogen ion gradient to form across the inner mitochondrial membrane.

❺ Hydrogen ions flow back to the inner compartment through ATP synthases. The flow drives the formation of ATP from ADP and phosphate (P$_i$).

**Figure It Out:** Which other pathway discussed in this chapter involves electron transfer phosphorylation?

*Answer: Light-dependent reactions of photosynthesis*

As the electrons pass through the electron transfer chains, they give up energy bit by bit. Some molecules of the chains use that energy to move hydrogen ions from the inner mitochondrial compartment to the outer one ❷.

At the end of the mitochondrial electron transfer chains, oxygen accepts electrons and combines with hydrogen ions, so water forms ❸. Aerobic respiration literally means "taking a breath of air," a name that refers to oxygen as the final electron acceptor in this pathway. Every breath you take provides your aerobically respiring cells with a fresh supply of oxygen.

As hydrogen ions are pumped from the inner to the outer compartment, a hydrogen ion concentration gradient forms across the inner mitochondrial membrane ❹. This gradient attracts hydrogen ions back toward the inner mitochondrial compartment. However, hydrogen ions cannot diffuse across a lipid bilayer without assistance. The ions can cross the inner mitochondrial membrane only by flowing through the interior of ATP synthases. The flow causes these transport proteins to attach a phosphate group to ADP, so ATP forms ❺. Thirty-two ATP typically form in the third stage of aerobic respiration. Add four ATP from the first and second stages, and the overall yield from the breakdown of one glucose molecule is thirty-six ATP:

$$C_6H_{12}O_6 \ + \ 6O_2 \ + \ 36\ ADP \longrightarrow 6CO_2 \ + \ 6H_2O \ + \ 36\ ATP$$
glucose     oxygen            carbon dioxide    water

> ## Aerobic respiration literally means "taking a breath of air."

## Take-Home Message
**How do cells typically access the chemical energy stored in carbohydrates?**

- Eukaryotic cells typically convert the chemical energy of carbohydrates to the chemical energy of ATP by the oxygen-requiring pathway of aerobic respiration.

- Aerobic respiration occurs in three stages: glycolysis; acetyl–CoA formation and the Krebs cycle; and electron transfer phosphorylation.

- Typically, thirty-six ATP form from the breakdown of one glucose molecule in aerobic respiration. Carbon dioxide and water also form.

**Krebs cycle** Cyclic pathway that, along with acetyl–CoA formation, breaks down two pyruvate to carbon dioxide for a net yield of two ATP and many reduced coenzymes.

# 5.7 Fermentation

**Fermentation** is a type of anaerobic pathway that harvests energy from carbohydrates. Bacteria and single-celled protists that inhabit sea sediments, animal guts, improperly canned food, sewage treatment ponds, deep mud, and other anaerobic habitats use fermentation. Some of these organisms, including the bacteria that cause botulism, do not tolerate aerobic conditions, and will die when exposed to oxygen. Others, such as single-celled fungi called yeasts, can switch between fermentation and aerobic respiration. Animal muscle cells use both pathways.

Aerobic respiration and fermentation begin with precisely the same set of reactions in the cytoplasm: glycolysis. Again, two pyruvate, two NADH, and two ATP form during the reactions of glycolysis. However, after that, fermentation and aerobic respiration pathways differ. The final steps of fermentation occur in the cytoplasm. In these reactions, pyruvate is converted to other molecules, but it is not fully broken down to carbon dioxide and water. Electrons do not flow through transfer chains, so no more ATP forms. However, electrons are removed from NADH, so $NAD^+$ is regenerated. Regenerating this coenzyme allows glycolysis—along with the small ATP yield it offers—to continue. Thus, the net ATP yield of fermentation consists of the two ATP that form in glycolysis.

**Alcoholic Fermentation** In **alcoholic fermentation**, the pyruvate from glycolysis is converted to ethyl alcohol, or ethanol. First, 3-carbon pyruvate is split into carbon dioxide and 2-carbon acetaldehyde. Then, electrons and hydrogen are transferred from NADH to the acetaldehyde, forming $NAD^+$ and ethanol (Figure 5.12). Bakers often use the alcoholic fermentation capabilities of one species of yeast, *Saccharomyces cerevisiae*, to make bread. These cells break down carbohydrates in bread dough, and release $CO_2$ by alcoholic fermentation. The dough expands (rises) as $CO_2$ forms bubbles in it. Some wild and cultivated strains of *Saccharomyces* are also used to produce wine. Crushed grapes are left in vats along with large populations of yeast cells, which convert the sugars in the juice to ethanol.

pyruvate    carbon dioxide    acetaldehyde    ethanol

**FIGURE 5.12 Animated!** Alcoholic fermentation. *Top*, a vintner examines a fermentation product of a *Saccharomyces* yeast. *Bottom*, the last stage of alcoholic fermentation produces ethanol and $NAD^+$.

**Lactate Fermentation** In **lactate fermentation**, the electrons and hydrogen ions carried by NADH are transferred directly to pyruvate. This reaction converts pyruvate to 3-carbon lactate (lactic acid), and also converts NADH to $NAD^+$:

pyruvate        lactate

Some lactate fermenters spoil food, but we use others to preserve it. For instance, *Lactobacillus acidophilus* digests lactose in milk. We use this bacteria to produce dairy products such as buttermilk, cheese, and yogurt. Yeasts ferment and preserve pickles, corned beef, sauerkraut, and kimchi.

**FIGURE 5.13** Lactate fermentation. *Right*, two types of fibers are visible in this cross-section through a human thigh muscle. Sprints (*above left*) and other intense bursts of activity are sustained by the light-colored fibers, which are fast-twitch fibers that make ATP by lactate fermentation. The dark-colored fibers, which are slow-twitch fibers that make ATP by aerobic respiration, contribute to endurance activities. Chickens (*above right*) spend most of their time walking. Their leg muscles consist mainly of slow-twitch fibers.

Animal skeletal muscles, which move bones, consist of cells fused as long fibers. The fibers differ in how they make ATP. Slow-twitch muscle fibers have many mitochondria and produce ATP by aerobic respiration. They dominate during prolonged activity, such as long runs. Slow-twitch fibers are red because they have an abundance of myoglobin, an oxygen-storing protein that is similar to hemoglobin.

Fast-twitch muscle fibers contain few mitochondria and no myoglobin, so they do not carry out a lot of aerobic respiration. Instead, they make most of their ATP by lactate fermentation. This pathway makes ATP quickly but not for long, so it is useful for quick, strenuous activities such as sprinting or weight lifting. It cannot support sustained activity. That is one reason chickens cannot fly very far: The flight muscles of a chicken are mostly fast-twitch fibers, which make up the "white" breast meat. Chickens fly only in short bursts. More often, a chicken walks or runs. Its leg muscles are mostly slow-twitch muscle, the "dark meat." Most human muscles consist of a mixture of fast-twitch and slow-twitch fibers (Figure 5.13), but the proportions vary among muscles and among individuals. Great sprinters tend to have more fast-twitch fibers. Great marathon runners tend to have more slow-twitch fibers. Section 20.4 offers a closer look at how skeletal muscles work.

## Take-Home Message  What is fermentation?

- ATP can form in fermentation pathways, which are anaerobic (do not require oxygen). Fermentation reactions regenerate the coenzyme NAD$^+$, without which glycolysis (and ATP production) would stop.

- The end product of lactate fermentation is lactate. The end product of alcoholic fermentation is ethanol. Both pathways have a net yield of two ATP per glucose molecule. The ATP forms during glycolysis.

**alcoholic fermentation** Anaerobic carbohydrate breakdown pathway that produces ATP and ethanol.

**fermentation** An anaerobic pathway by which cells harvest energy from carbohydrates.

**lactate fermentation** Anaerobic carbohydrate breakdown pathway that produces ATP and lactate.

# Alternative Energy Sources in the Body

**Excess dietary carbohydrate ends up as fat.**

**The Fate of Glucose at Mealtime** As you eat, glucose and other breakdown products of digestion are absorbed across the gut lining, and blood transports these small organic molecules throughout the body. The concentration of glucose in the bloodstream rises, and in response the pancreas (an organ) increases its rate of insulin secretion. Insulin is a hormone (a type of signaling molecule) that causes cells to take up glucose, so an increase in insulin production causes cells to take up glucose faster. Once inside a cell, the glucose is immediately converted to an intermediate of glycolysis.

Thus, when a cell takes in more than enough glucose, its ATP-forming machinery goes into high gear. Unless the ATP is used quickly, its concentration rises in the cytoplasm. The high concentration of ATP causes the intermediate to be diverted away from glycolysis and into a pathway that forms glycogen, a polysaccharide (Section 2.7). Liver and muscle cells especially favor the conversion of glucose to glycogen, and these cells maintain the body's largest stores of glycogen.

What happens if you eat too many carbohydrates? When the blood level of glucose gets too high, acetyl–CoA is diverted away from the Krebs cycle and into a pathway that makes fatty acids. That is why excess dietary carbohydrate ends up as fat.

Between meals, the blood level of glucose declines. The pancreas responds to low glucose levels in the blood by secreting glucagon, a hormone that causes liver cells to convert stored glycogen to glucose. The cells release glucose into the bloodstream, so the blood glucose level rises. Thus, hormones control whether the body's cells use glucose as an energy source immediately or save it for use at a later time.

Glycogen makes up about 1 percent of an average adult's total energy reserves, which is the energy equivalent of about two cups of cooked pasta. Unless you eat regularly, you will completely deplete your liver's glycogen stores in less than twelve hours.

**Energy From Fats** Of the total energy reserves in a typical adult who eats well, about 78 percent (about 10,000 kilocalories) is stored in body fat, and 21 percent in proteins. How does a human body access its fat reservoir? A fat molecule, recall, has a glycerol head and one, two, or three fatty acid tails (Section 2.8). The body stores most fats as triglycerides, which have three fatty acid tails. Triglycerides accumulate in fat cells of adipose tissue. This tissue serves as an energy reservoir, and it also insulates and pads the buttocks and other strategic areas of the body.

When blood glucose level falls, triglycerides are tapped to provide energy (Figure 5.14). Enzymes in fat cells cut the bonds between glycerol and the fatty acids, and both are released into the

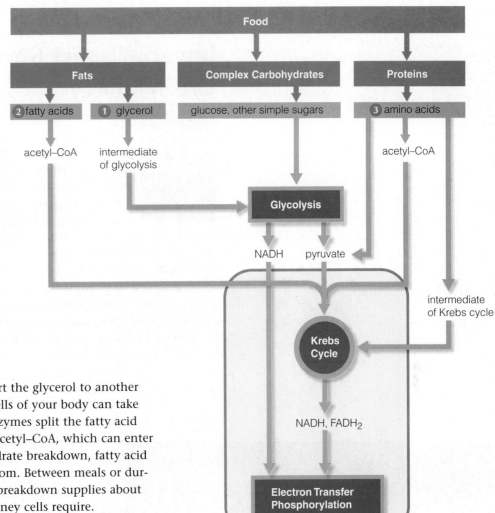

**FIGURE 5.14 Animated!**
Reaction sites where a variety of organic molecules enter aerobic respiration. Such molecules are energy sources for the body.

**1** Glycerol from fatty acid breakdown is converted to an intermediate of glycolysis.

**2** Fragments of fatty acids are converted to acetyl–CoA, which can enter the reactions of the Krebs cycle.

**3** Amino acids are converted to acetyl–CoA, pyruvate, or an intermediate of the Krebs cycle.

bloodstream. Enzymes in liver cells convert the glycerol to another intermediate of glycolysis **1**. Nearly all cells of your body can take up the free fatty acids. Inside the cells, enzymes split the fatty acid backbones and convert the fragments to acetyl–CoA, which can enter the Krebs cycle **2**. Compared to carbohydrate breakdown, fatty acid breakdown yields more ATP per carbon atom. Between meals or during steady, prolonged exercise, fatty acid breakdown supplies about half of the ATP that muscle, liver, and kidney cells require.

Diets that are extremely low in carbohydrates force the body to break down fats. The breakdown produces molecules called ketones, which most of your cells can use for energy instead of glucose. This metabolic state, which is normally associated with starvation, can raise LDL ("bad" cholesterol) and damage the kidneys and liver.

**Energy From Proteins** Some enzymes in your digestive system split dietary proteins into their amino acid subunits, which are then absorbed into the bloodstream. Cells use amino acids to build proteins or other molecules. Even so, when you eat more protein than your body needs, the amino acids become broken down further. The amino ($NH_3^+$) group is removed, and it becomes ammonia ($NH_3$), a waste product that the body eliminates in urine. Their carbon backbone is split, and acetyl–CoA, pyruvate, or an intermediate of the Krebs cycle forms, depending on the amino acid. Your cells can divert any of these organic molecules into the Krebs cycle **3**.

## Take-Home Message
**How are molecules other than glucose metabolized?**

■ In humans and other organisms, the entrance of organic compounds into an energy-releasing pathway depends on the kinds and proportions of carbohydrates, fats, and proteins in the diet.

# Impacts/Issues Revisited:
# Green Energy

Your body is about 9.5 percent carbon by weight, which means that you contain an enormous number of carbon atoms. Where did they all come from? You eat other organisms to get the carbon atoms your body uses for energy and for raw materials. Those atoms may have passed through other heterotrophs before you ate them, but at some point they were part of photoautotrophic organisms. Photoautotrophs strip carbon from carbon dioxide, then use the atoms to build organic compounds. Your carbon atoms—and those of most other organisms—were recently part of Earth's atmosphere, in molecules of carbon dioxide.

Photosynthesis removes carbon dioxide from the atmosphere, and locks its carbon atoms inside organic compounds. When photosynthesizers and other aerobic organisms break down the organic compounds for energy, carbon atoms are released in the form of $CO_2$, which then reenters the atmosphere.

Since photosynthesis evolved, these two processes have constituted a balanced cycle of the biosphere. You will learn more about the carbon cycle in Section 17.6. For now, know that the amount of carbon dioxide that photosynthesis removes from the atmosphere is roughly the same amount that organisms release back into it—at least it was, until humans came along.

As early as 8,000 years ago, humans began burning forests to clear land for agriculture. When trees and other plants burn, most of the carbon locked in their tissues is released into the atmosphere as carbon dioxide. Fires that occur naturally release carbon dioxide the same way.

Today, we are burning a lot more than our ancestors ever did. In addition to wood, we are burning fossil fuels—coal, petroleum, and natural gas—to satisfy our greater and greater demands for energy (Figure 5.15). Fossil fuels are the organic remains of ancient organisms. When we burn these fuels, the carbon that has been locked in them for hundreds of millions of years is released back into the atmosphere—mainly as carbon dioxide.

Our activities have put Earth's atmospheric cycle of carbon dioxide out of balance. We are adding far more $CO_2$ to the atmosphere than photosynthetic organisms are removing from it. Today, we release about 28 billion tons of carbon dioxide into the atmosphere each year, more than ten times the amount we released in the year 1900. Most of it comes from burning fossil fuels. How do we know? Researchers can determine how long ago the carbon atoms in a sample of $CO_2$ were part of a living organism by measuring the ratio of different carbon isotopes in it (you will read more about radioisotope dating techniques in Section 11.4). These results are correlated with fossil fuel extraction, refining, and trade statistics.

Researchers find pockets of our ancient atmosphere in Antarctica. Snow and ice have been accumulating in layers there, year after year, for the last 15 million years. Air and dust trapped in each layer reveal the composition of the atmosphere that prevailed when the layer formed. Thus, we now know that the

**FIGURE 5.15** Visible evidence of fossil fuel emissions in the atmosphere: the sky over New York City on a sunny day.

**FIGURE 5.16** Working toward a sustainable future. *Above*, biofuels researchers Ratna Sharma and Mari Chinn of North Carolina State University are trying to find an economically feasible way to manufacture biofuel from agricultural wastes and weeds such as switchgrass. *Right*, soils scientists Harry Pionke and Ron Schnabel examining a stand of switchgrass on a farm.

atmospheric $CO_2$ level had been relatively stable for about 10,000 years before the industrial revolution. Since 1850, the $CO_2$ level has been steadily rising. In 2008, it was higher than it had been in *24 million years*.

The increase in atmospheric carbon dioxide is having dramatic effects on climate. $CO_2$ contributes to global climate change. We are seeing a warming trend that mirrors the increase in $CO_2$ levels—Earth is now the warmest it has been for 12,000 years. The trend is affecting biological systems everywhere. Life cycles are changing: Birds are laying eggs earlier; plants are flowering earlier than usual; mammals are hibernating for shorter periods. Migration patterns and habitats are also changing. These changes may be too fast for many species, and the rate of extinctions is predicted to rise.

Under normal circumstances, extra carbon dioxide stimulates photosynthesis, which means extra carbon dioxide uptake. However, changes in temperature and moisture patterns as a result of global warming are offsetting this benefit because they are proving harmful to plants and other photosynthesizers.

Making biofuel production economically feasible is a high priority for today's energy researchers (Figure 5.16). Biofuels are a renewable source of energy: We can always make more of them simply by growing more biomass. Also, unlike fossil fuels, using plant matter for fuel recycles carbon that is already in the atmosphere, because plants remove carbon dioxide from the atmosphere as they grow. Other research efforts to minimize or reverse global climate change target photosynthesis. For example, scientists are trying to duplicate the function of photosystems in the laboratory. If successful, they will be able to harness the energy of light to split water into hydrogen, oxygen, and electrons—all of which can be used as clean, green sources of energy.

**How Would**
# YOU
☑ **Vote?**

Ethanol and other fuels manufactured from crops currently cost more than gasoline, but they are renewable energy sources and have fewer emissions. How much of a premium would you pay to drive a vehicle that runs on biofuels? See CengageNow for details, then vote online (cengagenow.com).

# Summary

## Section 5.1

Autotrophs make their own food using energy they get directly from the environment, and carbon from inorganic sources such as $CO_2$. By metabolic pathways of photosynthesis, plants and other autotrophs capture the energy of light and use it to build sugars from water and carbon dioxide. Heterotrophs get energy and carbon from molecules that other organisms have already assembled.

 **Section 5.2** Pigments such as chlorophyll *a* absorb visible light of particular wavelengths for photosynthesis. Light that is not absorbed is reflected as a pigment's characteristic color.

## Section 5.3

In chloroplasts, the light-dependent reactions of photosynthesis occur at a much-folded thylakoid membrane. The membrane forms a continuous compartment in the chloroplast's stroma, where the light-independent reactions occur.

$$6CO_2 + 6H_2O \xrightarrow{\text{light energy}} C_6H_{12}O_6 + 6O_2$$

carbon dioxide    water                      glucose    oxygen

CENGAGENOW™ Use the animation on CengageNow to view sites where photosynthesis takes place.

 **Section 5.4** In the light-dependent reactions, photosynthetic pigments in the thylakoid membrane absorb light energy and pass it to photosystems, which then release electrons. The photosystem replaces lost electrons by pulling them from water molecules, which then dissociate. The released oxygen atoms leave the cell as $O_2$. The electrons flow through electron transfer chains in the thylakoid membrane, and end up in NADPH. The activity of transfer chains cause a hydrogen ion gradient to form across the thylakoid membrane. The ions flow back across the membrane through ATP synthases. The flow causes these membrane transport proteins to produce ATP in the stroma.

CENGAGENOW™ Review the light-dependent reactions of photosynthesis with the animation on CengageNow.

## Section 5.5

 In the stroma of chloroplasts, the enzyme rubisco fixes carbon from $CO_2$ in the Calvin–Benson cycle. This cyclic pathway uses energy from ATP, carbon and oxygen from $CO_2$, and hydrogen and electrons from NADPH to make glucose and water. Alternative light-independent reactions minimize photorespiration in some types of plants.

CENGAGENOW™ See how glucose is produced in the light-independent reactions of photosynthesis with the animation on CengageNow.

## Section 5.6

Most modern organisms convert the chemical energy of carbohydrates to the chemical energy of ATP by oxygen-requiring aerobic respiration. In eukaryotes, this pathway finishes in mitochondria. Coenzymes pick up electrons in the first two stages, acetyl–CoA formation and the Krebs cycle. The energy of those electrons drives ATP synthesis in the third stage, electron transfer phosphorylation. Oxygen combines with the electrons and $H^+$ at the end of electron transfer chains, so water forms.

$$C_6H_{12}O_6 + 6O_2 + 36\ ADP \longrightarrow 6CO_2 + 6H_2O + 36\ ATP$$

glucose    oxygen                      carbon dioxide    water

CENGAGENOW™ Use the animation on CengageNow to see how each step in aerobic respiration contributes to a big energy harvest.

 **Section 5.7** Fermentation pathways finish in the cytoplasm. They do not use oxygen or electron transfer chains, so no ATP forms other than the small yield from glycolysis. The final steps regenerate $NAD^+$, which allows glycolysis to continue. The end product of lactate fermentation is lactate. The end product of alcoholic fermentation is ethyl alcohol, or ethanol.

CENGAGENOW™ Use the animation on CengageNow to compare alcoholic and lactate fermentation.

## Section 5.8

In humans and other organisms, the simple sugars from carbohydrate breakdown, the glycerol and fatty acids from fat breakdown, and the carbon backbones of amino acids from protein breakdown may enter aerobic respiration at various reaction steps.

CENGAGENOW™ Use the interaction on CengageNow to follow the breakdown of different organic molecules.

**Section 5.9** Human activities are disrupting the global cycling of carbon dioxide. We are adding more $CO_2$ to the atmosphere than photoautotrophs are removing from it, and the resulting imbalance fuels global warming.

# Self-Quiz    Answers in Appendix I

1. A cat eats a bird, which ate a caterpillar that chewed on a weed. Which organisms are autotrophs? Heterotrophs?

2. Photosynthetic autotrophs use _____ from the air as a carbon source and _____ as their energy source.

3. Light-dependent reactions in plants occur in the _____ .
   a. thylakoid membrane        c. stroma
   b. plasma membrane           d. cytoplasm

4. In the light-dependent reactions, _____ .
   a. carbon dioxide is fixed        c. $CO_2$ accepts electrons
   b. ATP forms                      d. sugars form

5. What accumulates inside the thylakoid compartment during the light-dependent reactions?
   a. glucose    b. RuBP    c. hydrogen ions    d. $CO_2$

6. Light-independent reactions proceed in the _____ .
   a. cytoplasm    b. plasma membrane    c. stroma

7. The Calvin–Benson cycle starts when _____ .
   a. light is available
   b. carbon dioxide is attached to RuBP
   c. electrons leave a photosystem

8. After photosynthesis evolved, its by-product, _____ , accumulated and changed the atmosphere.

# Digging Into Data

## Energy Efficiency of Biofuel Production From Corn, Soy, and Prairie Grasses

Most corn is grown intensively in vast swaths, which means farmers who grow it use fertilizers and pesticides, both of which are typically made from fossil fuels. Corn is an annual plant, and yearly harvests tend to cause runoff that depletes soil and pollutes rivers.

In 2006, David Tilman and his colleagues published the results of a 10-year study comparing the net energy output of various biofuels. The researchers grew a mixture of native perennial grasses without irrigation, fertilizer, pesticides, or herbicides, in sandy soil that was so depleted by intensive agriculture that it had been abandoned. They measured the usable energy in biofuels made from the grasses, from corn, and from soy. They also measured the energy it took to grow and produce each kind of biofuel (Figure 5.17).

1. About how much energy did ethanol produced from one hectare of corn yield? How much energy did it take to grow and produce that ethanol?

2. Which biofuel tested had the highest ratio of energy output to energy input?

3. Which of the three crops would require the least amount of land to produce a given amount of biofuel energy?

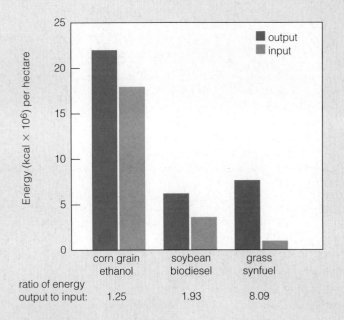

**FIGURE 5.17** Energy inputs and outputs of biofuels from corn and soy grown on fertile farmland, and grassland plants grown in infertile soil. One hectare is about 2.5 acres.

---

9. Is the following statement true or false? Unlike animals, which make many ATP by aerobic respiration, plants make all of their ATP by photosynthesis.

10. Which molecule does not form during glycolysis?
    a. NADH    b. pyruvate    c. $FADH_2$    d. ATP

11. Glycolysis starts and ends in the _____ .
    a. nucleus              c. plasma membrane
    b. mitochondrion        d. cytoplasm

12. In eukaryotes, aerobic respiration is completed in the _____ .
    a. nucleus              c. plasma membrane
    b. mitochondrion        d. cytoplasm

13. In eukaryotes, fermentation is completed in the _____ .
    a. nucleus              c. plasma membrane
    b. mitochondrion        d. cytoplasm

14. In the third stage of aerobic respiration, _____ is the final acceptor of electrons from glucose.
    a. water    b. hydrogen    c. oxygen    d. NADH

15. Match the event with its most suitable description.
    _____ glycolysis                a. ATP, NADH, $FADH_2$,
    _____ fermentation                 and $CO_2$ form
    _____ Krebs cycle               b. glucose to two pyruvates
    _____ electron transfer         c. $NAD^+$ regenerated, little ATP
          phosphorylation           d. $H^+$ flows through ATP
    _____ $CO_2$ fixation               synthases
                                    e. rubisco function

Additional questions are available on CENGAGENOW"

## Critical Thinking

1. About 200 years ago, Jan Baptista van Helmont wanted to know where growing plants get the materials necessary for increases in size. He planted a tree seedling weighing 5 pounds in a barrel filled with 200 pounds of soil and then watered the tree regularly. After five years, the tree weighed 169 pounds, 3 ounces, and the soil weighed 199 pounds, 14 ounces. Because the tree had gained so much weight and the soil had lost so little, he concluded that the tree had gained all of its additional weight by absorbing the water he had added to the barrel, but of course he was incorrect. What really happened?

2. At high altitudes, the oxygen levels are low. Climbers of very tall mountains risk altitude sickness, which is characterized by shortness of breath, weakness, dizziness, and confusion. The early symptoms of cyanide poisoning are the same as those for altitude sickness. Cyanide binds tightly to cytochrome c oxidase, a protein complex that is the last component of mitochondrial electron transfer chains. Cytochrome c oxidase with bound cyanide can no longer transfer electrons. Explain why cyanide poisoning starts with the same symptoms as altitude sickness.

3. As you learned, membranes impermeable to hydrogen ions are required for electron transfer phosphorylation. Membranes in mitochondria serve this purpose in eukaryotes. Prokaryotic cells do not have this organelle, but they do make ATP by electron transfer phosphorylation. How do you think they do it, given that they have no mitochondria?

Perfecting the methods for cloning animals brings us
ethically closer to the possibility of cloning humans.

## 6.1 Impacts/Issues: Here, Kitty, Kitty, Kitty, Kitty, Kitty

One of the most publicized demonstrations of the function of DNA occurred in 1997, when Scottish geneticist Ian Wilmut made the first genetic copy, or clone, of a fully grown animal. His team removed the nucleus (and the DNA it contained) from an unfertilized sheep egg. They replaced it with the nucleus of a cell taken from the udder of a different sheep. The hybrid egg became an embryo, and then a lamb. The lamb, whom the researchers named Dolly, was genetically identical to the sheep that had donated the udder cell.

At first, Dolly looked and acted like a normal sheep. But five years later, she was as fat and arthritic as a twelve-year-old sheep. The following year, Dolly contracted a lung disease that usually affects only old sheep, and she had to be euthanized. Dolly's telomeres hinted that she had developed health problems because she was a clone. Telomeres are short, repeated DNA sequences at the ends of chromosomes. They become shorter and shorter as an animal ages. When Dolly was only two years old, her telomeres were as short as those of a six-year-old sheep—the exact age of the adult animal that had been her genetic donor.

Since Dolly, many adult animals have been cloned, including mice, rats, rabbits, fish, pigs, cattle, goats, mules, deer, horses, cats, dogs, and a wolf. However, cloning mammals is still far from routine. It usually takes hundreds of attempts to produce one embryo, and most embryos that do form die before birth or shortly afterward. Many of the clones that survive have serious health problems.

What causes these problems? Even though all cells of an individual *inherit* the same DNA, an adult cell *uses* only a fraction of it compared to an embryonic cell. To make a clone from an adult cell, researchers must reprogram its DNA to function like the DNA of an egg. Even though we are getting better at doing that, we still have a lot to learn.

So why do we keep trying? The potential benefits are enormous. Already, cells of human–pig hybrid embryos are helping researchers unravel the molecular mechanisms of human genetic diseases. Cloned human cells may one day be induced to form replacement tissues or organs for people with incurable diseases. Endangered animals might be saved from extinction; extinct animals may be brought back. Livestock and pet animals are already being cloned commercially (Figure 6.1).

Perfecting the methods for cloning animals brings us closer to the possibility of cloning humans, both technically and ethically. For example, if cloning a lost cat for a grieving pet owner is acceptable, why would it not be acceptable to clone a lost child for a grieving parent? Different people have very different answers to such questions, so controversy over adult cloning continues to rage even as the techniques improve. Understanding the basis of heredity—what DNA is and how it works—will help inform your own opinions about the ethical issues surrounding cloning.

**FIGURE 6.1** Adult cloning. Compare the markings on Tahini, a Bengal cat (*top*) with those of her clones, Tabouli and Baba Ganoush (*bottom*). Eye color changes as a Bengal cat matures; both of the kittens later developed the same eye color as Tahini's.

**FIGURE 6.2 Animated!** Zooming in on chromosome structure. Tight packing allows a lot of DNA to fit into a very small nucleus.

❶ The DNA inside the nucleus of a eukaryotic cell is typically divided up into a number of chromosomes. *Left*, a human chromosome.

❷ At its most condensed, a duplicated chromosome is packed tightly into an X shape.

❸ A chromosome unravels as a single fiber, a hollow cylinder formed by coiled coils.

❹ The coiled coils consist of a long molecule of DNA (*blue*) and the proteins that are associated with it (*purple*).

❺ At regular intervals, the DNA molecule is wrapped twice around a core of histone proteins. In this "beads-on-a-string" structure, the "string" is the DNA, and each "bead" is called a nucleosome.

❻ The DNA molecule itself has two strands that are twisted into a double helix.

# 6.2 Chromosomes

All organisms pass DNA to offspring when they reproduce. Inside a cell, each DNA molecule is organized as a structure called a **chromosome** (Figure 6.2). Eukaryotic cells have a number of chromosomes ❶. During most of a cell's life, each of its chromosomes consists of one DNA molecule. As it prepares to divide, the cell duplicates its chromosomes, so that both of its offspring get a full set. After the chromosomes are duplicated, each consists of two DNA molecules, which are then called **sister chromatids**. Sister chromatids attach to each other at a constricted region called a **centromere**:

one chromosome (unduplicated)    one chromosome (duplicated)

If stretched out end to end, the 46 chromosomes in a human cell would be about 2 meters (6.5 feet) long. That is a lot of DNA to fit into a nucleus that is typically less than 10 micrometers in diameter! Interactions between a DNA molecule and the proteins that associate with it structurally organize a chromosome and help it pack tightly so it fits in a nucleus.

At its most condensed, a duplicated chromosome consists of two long, tangled filaments (the sister chromatids) bunched into a characteristic X shape ❷. A closer look reveals that each filament is actually a hollow tube formed by coils, like a phone cord ❸. The coils themselves consist of a twisted fiber of DNA and proteins ❹. The DNA molecule wraps twice at regular intervals around "spools" of proteins called **histones** ❺. In micrographs, the DNA–histone spools look like beads on a string. Each "bead" is called a **nucleosome**, the smallest unit of chromosomal organization in eukaryotes. As you will see in the next section, the DNA molecule consists of two strands twisted into a double helix ❻.

**centromere** Constricted region in a eukaryotic chromosome where sister chromatids are attached.

**chromosome** A structure that consists of DNA and associated proteins; carries part or all of a cell's genetic information.

**histone** Type of protein that structurally organizes eukaryotic chromosomes.

**nucleosome** A length of DNA wound around a spool of histone proteins.

**sister chromatid** One of two attached members of a duplicated eukaryotic chromosome.

| Table 6.1 | Examples of Chromosome Number | |
|---|---|---|
| **Species** | **Chromosome Number** | |
| Fruit fly | 8 | |
| Amoeba | 13 | |
| Garden pea | 14 | |
| Frog | 26 | |
| Cat | 38 | |
| Human | 46 | |
| Potato | 48 | |
| Pineapple | 50 | |
| Cow | 60 | |
| Dog | 78 | |
| Vizcacha rat | 102 | |
| Horsetail | 216 | |
| Adder's tongue fern | 1200 | |

## Chromosome Number

The genetic information of each eukaryotic species is distributed among some number of chromosomes, which differ in length and shape. The sum of all chromosomes in a cell of a given type is called the **chromosome number**. Each species has a characteristic chromosome number (Table 6.1). For example, the chromosome number of oak trees is 12, so the nucleus of a cell from an oak tree contains 12 chromosomes. The chromosome number of king crab cells is 208, so they have 208 chromosomes. That of human body cells is 46, so human body cells have 46 chromosomes.

Actually, human body cells have two of each type of chromosome, which means that their chromosome number is **diploid** ($2n$). The 23 pairs of chromosomes are like two sets of books numbered 1 to 23. There are two versions of each book: a pair. Except for a pairing of sex chromosomes (XY) in males, the two members of each pair have the same length and shape, and they hold information about the same traits. Think of them as two sets of books on how to build a house. Your father gave you one set. Your mother had her own ideas about wiring, plumbing, and so on. She gave you an alternate set that says slightly different things about many of those tasks.

## Types of Chromosomes

All except one pair of a diploid cell's chromosomes are **autosomes**, which are the same in both females and males. The two autosomes of a pair have the same length, shape, and centromere location. Members of a pair of **sex chromosomes** differ between females and males. The differences determine an individual's sex. The sex chromosomes of humans are called X and Y. Body cells of human females contain two X chromosomes (XX); those of human males contain one X and one Y chromosome (XY).

XX females and XY males are the rule among fruit flies, mammals, and many other animals, but there are other patterns. In butterflies, moths, birds, and certain fishes, males have two identical sex chromosomes, and females do not. Environmental factors (not sex chromosomes) determine sex in some species of invertebrates, turtles, and frogs. As an example, the temperature of the sand in which sea turtle eggs are buried determines the sex of the hatchlings.

In humans, a new individual inherits a combination of sex chromosomes that dictates whether it will become a male or a female. All eggs made by a human female have one X chromosome. One-half of the sperm cells made by a male carry an X chromosome; the other half carry a Y chromosome. If an X-bearing sperm fertilizes an X-bearing egg, the resulting individual will develop into a female. If the sperm carries a Y chromosome, the individual will develop into a male (Figure 6.3).

Karyotyping reveals an individual's diploid complement of chromosomes. With this technique, cells taken from an individual are treated to make their chromosomes condense, and stained so the chromosomes become visible under a microscope. The microscope reveals the chromosomes in every cell. A micro-

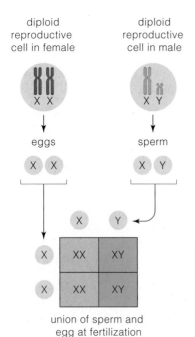

diploid reproductive cell in female

diploid reproductive cell in male

X X

X Y

eggs

sperm

X X

X Y

X Y

| | X | Y |
|---|---|---|
| X | XX | XY |
| X | XX | XY |

union of sperm and egg at fertilization

**FIGURE 6.3 Animated!** Pattern of sex determination in humans. The grid shows how sex chromosome combinations result in female (*pink*) or male (*blue*) offspring.

Figure It Out: About what proportion of human newborns would you expect to be male?

*Answer: About 50 percent*

**A** The chromosomes of one body cell are isolated, then stained to reveal differences in banding patterns.

**B** The image is reassembled so that the chromosomes are paired by size, centromere position, and other characteristics.

---

**FIGURE 6.4 Animated!** A karyotype is an image of a single cell's diploid set of chromosomes. This human karyotype shows 22 pairs of autosomes and a pair of X chromosomes.

**Figure It Out:** Was this cell taken from a female or a male?   *Answer: A female*

---

graph of a single cell is digitally rearranged so the images of the chromosomes are lined up by centromere location, and arranged according to size, shape, and length (Figure 6.4). The finished array constitutes the individual's **karyotype**, which is compared with a normal standard. A karyotype shows how many chromosomes are in the individual's cells. Comparison with a standard can also reveal any extra or missing chromosomes, and some structural abnormalities.

## Take-Home Message  **What are chromosomes?**

- A eukaryotic cell's DNA is divided among some characteristic number of chromosomes, which differ in length and shape.
- Members of a pair of sex chromosomes differ between males and females. Other chromosomes are autosomes—the same in males and females.
- Proteins that associate with DNA structurally organize chromosomes and allow them to pack tightly.

## 6.3  Fame and Glory

Each strand of DNA is a polymer of nucleotides that have been linked into a chain (Section 2.10). Even though a chain can be hundreds of millions of nucleotides long, only four kinds of nucleotides compose DNA. A DNA nucleotide has a five-carbon sugar, three phosphate groups, and one of four nitrogen-containing

**autosome** Any chromosome other than a sex chromosome.
**chromosome number** The sum of all chromosomes in a cell of a given type.
**diploid** Having two of each type of chromosome characteristic of the species (2*n*).
**karyotype** Image of an individual's complement of chromosomes arranged by size, length, shape, and centromere location.
**sex chromosome** Member of a pair of chromosomes that differs between males and females.

**adenine (A)**

deoxyadenosine triphosphate

**guanine (G)**

deoxyguanosine triphosphate

**thymine (T)**

deoxythymidine triphosphate

**cytosine (C)**

deoxycytidine triphosphate

**FIGURE 6.5** The four nucleotides in DNA. Each kind has three phosphate groups, a deoxyribose sugar (*orange*), and a nitrogen-containing base (*blue*) after which it is named.

**B**

**FIGURE 6.6** Key players in the discovery of the structure of DNA. Rosalind Franklin **A** and her x-ray diffraction image of DNA **B**. *Opposite*, Maurice Wilkins **C**; and **D** Watson (*left*) and Crick (*right*) with their model of DNA.

**A**

bases (Figure 6.5). Just how those four nucleotides—adenine (A), guanine (G), thymine (T), and cytosine (C)—are arranged in DNA was a puzzle that took over 50 years to solve. As molecules go, DNA is gigantic, and chromosomal DNA has a complex structural organization. Both factors made the molecule difficult to work with given the laboratory methods at the time.

In 1950, Erwin Chargaff, one of many researchers who had been trying to solve the structure of DNA, made two discoveries. First, the amounts of thymine and adenine in all DNA are the same, as are the amounts of cytosine and guanine. We call this discovery Chargaff's first rule:

$$A = T \text{ and } G = C$$

Chargaff's second discovery, or rule, is that the proportion of adenine and guanine differs among DNA of different species.

Meanwhile, American biologist James Watson and British biophysicist Francis Crick had been sharing their ideas about the structure of DNA. The helical pattern of secondary structure that occurs in many proteins (Section 2.9) had just been discovered, and Watson and Crick suspected that the DNA molecule was also a helix. They had spent many hours arguing about the size, shape, and bonding requirements of the four kinds of nucleotides that make up DNA. They had pestered chemists to help them identify bonds they might have overlooked. They had fiddled with cardboard cutouts, and made models from scraps of metal connected by suitably angled "bonds" of wire.

Rosalind Franklin (Figure 6.6**A**) had also been working on the structure of DNA. Like Crick, Franklin specialized in x-ray crystallography, a technique in which x-rays are directed through a purified and crystallized substance. Atoms in the substance's molecules scatter the x-rays in a pattern that can be captured as an image. Researchers use the pattern to calculate the size, shape, and spacing between any repeating elements of the molecules—all of which are details of molecular structure.

Franklin had already used x-ray crystallography to solve the complex and unorganized structure of coal. She had been told she would be the only one

**FIGURE 6.7 Animated!** Structure of DNA, as illustrated by a composite of three different models. The two sugar–phosphate backbones coil in a helix around internally positioned bases. **Figure It Out:** What do the yellow balls represent? *Answer: Phosphate groups*

in her department working on the structure of DNA, so she did not know that Maurice Wilkins was already doing the same thing just down the hall.

Wilkins and Franklin had been given identical samples of carefully prepared DNA. Franklin's meticulous work with her sample yielded the first clear x-ray diffraction image of DNA as it occurs inside cells (Figure 6.6**B**), and she gave a presentation on this work in 1952. DNA, she said, had two chains twisted into a double helix, with a backbone of phosphate groups on the outside, and bases arranged in an unknown way on the inside. She had calculated DNA's diameter, the distance between its chains and between its bases, the pitch (angle) of the helix, and the number of bases in each coil. Crick, with his crystallography background, would have recognized the significance of the work—if he had been there. Watson was in the audience but he was not a crystallographer, and he did not understand the implications of Franklin's image or her calculations.

Franklin started to write a research paper on her findings. Meanwhile, and perhaps without her knowledge, Wilkins (Figure 6.6**C**) reviewed her x-ray diffraction image with Watson, and Watson and Crick read a report containing her unpublished data. Franklin's data provided Watson and Crick with the last piece of the DNA puzzle. In 1953, they put together all of the clues that had been accumulating for the last fifty years and built the first accurate model of the DNA molecule (Figure 6.6**D**). On April 25, 1953, Rosalind Franklin's work appeared third in a series of articles about the structure of DNA in the journal *Nature*. Wilkins's research paper was the second article in the series. The work of Franklin and Wilkins supported with experimental evidence Watson and Crick's theoretical model, which was presented in the first article.

**The Double Helix** Watson and Crick proposed that DNA's structure consists of two chains (or strands) of nucleotides, running in opposite directions and coiled into a double helix (Figure 6.7). Bonds between the sugar of one nucleotide and the phosphate of the next form the backbone of each chain. Hydrogen bonds between the internally positioned bases hold the two strands together. Only two kinds of base pairings form: A to T, and G to C, which explains the first of Chargaff's rules.

# Variations in the base sequence of DNA are the foundation of life's diversity.

❶ The two strands of a DNA molecule are complementary: their nucleotides match up according to base-pairing rules (G to C, T to A).

❷ As replication starts, the two strands of DNA unwind at many sites along the length of the molecule.

❸ Each parent strand serves as a template for assembly of a new DNA strand from nucleotides, according to base-pairing rules.

❹ DNA ligase seals any gaps that remain between bases of the "new" DNA, so a continuous strand forms. The base sequence of each half-old, half-new DNA molecule is identical to that of the parent.

**FIGURE 6.8 Animated!** DNA replication. Each strand of a DNA double helix is copied; two double-stranded DNA molecules result.

Most scientists had assumed (incorrectly) that the bases had to be on the outside of the helix, because they would be more accessible to DNA-copying enzymes that way. You will see in the next section how DNA replication enzymes access the bases on the inside of DNA's double helix.

Dozens of scientists contributed to the discovery of DNA's structure, but only three received recognition from the general public for their work. Rosalind Franklin died at age 37, of ovarian cancer probably caused by extensive exposure to x-rays. Because the Nobel Prize is not given posthumously, she did not share in the 1962 honor that went to Watson, Crick, and Wilkins for the discovery of the structure of DNA.

**Patterns of Base Pairing** Just two kinds of base pairings give rise to the incredible diversity of traits we see among living things. How? Even though DNA is composed of only four bases, the *order* in which one base pair follows the next—the **DNA sequence**—varies tremendously among species (which explains Chargaff's second rule). For example, a small piece of DNA from a tulip, a human, or any other organism might be:

one base pair

Notice how the two strands of DNA match up. They are complementary, which means each base on one strand is suitably paired with a partner base on the other. This bonding pattern (A to T, G to C) is the same in all molecules of DNA. However, which base pair follows the next differs among species, and among individuals of the same species. The information encoded by that sequence is the basis of visible traits that define species and distinguish individuals. Thus DNA, the molecule of inheritance in every cell, is the basis of life's unity. Variations in its base sequence are the foundation of life's diversity.

## Take-Home Message  What is the structure of DNA?

- A DNA molecule consists of two nucleotide chains (strands) running in opposite directions and coiled into a double helix. Internally positioned nucleotide bases hydrogen-bond between the two strands. A pairs with T, and G with C.
- The sequence of bases along a DNA strand is genetic information.
- DNA sequences vary among species and among individuals. This variation is the basis of life's diversity.

# 6.4 DNA Replication and Repair

During most of its life, a cell contains only one set of chromosomes. However, when the cell reproduces, it must have two sets of chromosomes: one for each of its future offspring. By a process called **DNA replication**, a cell copies its chromosomes before it divides (Figure 6.8).

Before replication begins, each chromosome consists of one molecule of DNA—one double helix ❶. During DNA replication, an enzyme breaks the hydrogen bonds that hold the double helix together, so the two DNA strands unwind ❷. An enzyme called **DNA polymerase** assembles a complementary strand of DNA on each of the parent strands.

The sequence of a cell's DNA is its genetic information, as you will see in the next chapter. Descendant cells must get an exact copy of it, or inheritance will go awry. As a DNA polymerase moves along a strand of DNA, it uses the sequence of bases as a template, or guide, to assemble a new strand of DNA from free nucleotides (Figure 6.9A). The base sequence of the new strand is complementary to that of the template, because DNA polymerase follows base-pairing rules. The polymerase adds a T to the end of the new DNA strand when it reaches an A in the parent DNA sequence; it adds a G when it reaches a C; and so on ❸. Phosphate-group transfers (Section 4.3) from the nucleotides provide energy for their own attachment to the end of a growing strand of DNA. Another enzyme, **DNA ligase**, seals any gaps, so a new, continuous strand of DNA results.

As each new DNA strand lengthens, it winds up with its "parent" strand into a double helix (Figure 6.9B). So, after replication, two double-stranded molecules of DNA have formed. One strand of each molecule is parental (old), and the other is new (Figure 6.9C). Because each new strand of DNA is complementary in sequence to a parent strand, both double-stranded molecules that result from DNA replication are duplicates of the parent ❹.

**A**  **B**  **C**

**FIGURE 6.9** How a double-stranded molecule of DNA is replicated. **A** DNA polymerase uses a parental DNA strand as a template to assemble a new strand of DNA from nucleotides. **B** The two parental DNA strands (*blue*) stay intact. A new strand (*magenta*) is assembled on each of the parental (old) strands. **C** One strand of each DNA molecule that forms is new, and the other is parental.

**Checking for Mistakes** DNA is not always replicated with perfect accuracy. Sometimes the wrong base is added to a growing DNA strand. At other times, bases get lost, or extra ones get added. Either way, the new DNA strand will no longer match up perfectly with its parent strand.

Some errors occur after the DNA becomes damaged by exposure to radiation or toxic chemicals, because DNA polymerases do not copy damaged DNA very well. In most cases, **DNA repair mechanisms** fix damaged DNA by removing and replacing any damaged or mismatched bases before replication begins.

Most DNA replication errors occur simply because DNA polymerases add nucleotides to a growing strand of DNA very quickly—up to 1,000 bases per second. Mistakes are inevitable, and some DNA polymerases make many of them. Luckily, most DNA polymerases proofread their own work. They correct any mismatches by immediately reversing the synthesis reaction to remove a mismatched nucleotide, and then resuming synthesis. If an error remains uncorrected, other mechanisms usually stop the cell from dividing.

When proofreading and repair mechanisms fail, an error becomes a **mutation**—a permanent change in the DNA sequence. Mutations can alter DNA's genetic instructions, and the outcome may be harmful or not. Mutations are the original source of variations in traits—the raw material of evolution, as you will see in later chapters.

**DNA ligase** Enzyme that seals breaks or gaps in double-stranded DNA.

**DNA polymerase** DNA replication enzyme. Assembles a new strand of DNA based on the sequence of a DNA template.

**DNA repair mechanism** Any of several processes by which enzymes repair damaged DNA.

**DNA replication** Process by which a cell duplicates its DNA before it divides.

**DNA sequence** The order of nucleotide bases in a strand of DNA.

**mutation** Permanent change in DNA sequence.

## Take-Home Message How is DNA copied?

- A cell replicates its DNA before it divides. Each strand of the double helix serves as a template for synthesis of a new, complementary strand of DNA.

- DNA repair mechanisms and proofreading maintain the integrity of a cell's genetic information. Unrepaired errors may become mutations.

# 6.5 Cloning Adult Animals

The word "cloning" means making an identical copy of something. In biology, cloning can refer to a laboratory method by which researchers copy DNA fragments (a technique we discuss in Chapter 10). It can also refer to interventions in reproduction that result in an exact genetic copy of an organism.

Genetically identical organisms occur all the time in nature. They arise mainly by the process of asexual reproduction, which we discuss in Chapter 8. Embryo splitting, another natural process, results in identical twins. The first few divisions of a fertilized egg form a ball of cells that sometimes splits spontaneously. If both halves continue to develop independently, identical twins result. Artificial embryo splitting has been routine in research and animal husbandry for decades. With this technique, a ball of cells is grown from a fertilized egg in a laboratory. The ball is teased apart into two halves, each of which goes on to develop as a separate embryo. The embryos are implanted in surrogate mothers, who give birth to identical twins. Artificial twinning and any other technology that yields genetically identical individuals is called **reproductive cloning**.

Twins get their DNA from two parents, which typically differ in their DNA sequence. Thus, although identical twins produced by embryo splitting are identical to one another, they are not identical to either parent. When animal breeders want an exact copy of a specific individual, they may turn to a cloning method that starts with a single cell taken from an adult organism. Such procedures present more of a technical challenge than embryo splitting. Unlike a fertilized egg, a body cell from an adult will not automatically start dividing. It must first be tricked into rewinding its developmental clock.

All cells descended from a fertilized egg inherit the same DNA. Thus, the DNA in each living cell of an individual is like a master blueprint that contains enough information to build an entirely new individual. As different cells in a developing embryo start using different subsets of their DNA, they differentiate, or become different in form and function. In animals, differentiation is usually a one-way path. Once a cell specializes, all of its descendant cells will be special-

egg

donor
cell

**FIGURE 6.10 Animated!** Somatic cell nuclear transfer, using cattle cells. This series of micrographs was taken by scientists at Cyagra, a commercial company that specializes in cloning livestock.

➊ A cow egg is held in place by suction through a hollow glass tube called a micropipette. The DNA in the cell is identified by a *purple* stain.

➋ Another micropipette punctures the egg and sucks out the DNA. All that remains inside the egg's plasma membrane is cytoplasm.

➌ A new micropipette prepares to enter the egg at the puncture site. The pipette contains a cell grown from the skin of a donor animal.

➍ The micropipette enters the egg and delivers the skin cell to a region between the cytoplasm and the plasma membrane.

➎ After the pipette is withdrawn, the donor's skin cell is visible next to the cytoplasm of the egg. The transfer is complete.

➏ The egg is exposed to an electric current. This treatment causes the foreign cell to fuse with and empty its nucleus into the cytoplasm of the egg. The egg begins to divide, and an embryo forms. After a few days, the embryo may be transplanted into a surrogate mother.

ized the same way. By the time a liver cell, muscle cell, or other specialized cell forms, most of its DNA has been turned off, and is no longer used.

To clone an adult, scientists must first transform one of its differentiated cells into an undifferentiated cell by turning its unused DNA back on. In **somatic cell nuclear transfer** (SCNT), a researcher removes the nucleus from an unfertilized egg, then inserts into the egg a nucleus from an adult animal cell (Figure 6.10). A somatic cell is a body cell, as opposed to a reproductive cell (*soma* is a Greek word for body). If all goes well, the egg's cytoplasm reprograms the transplanted DNA to direct the development of an embryo, which is then implanted into a surrogate mother. The animal that is born to the surrogate is genetically identical with the donor of the nucleus (Figure 6.11). Dolly the sheep (pictured at *left*) and the other animals described in the chapter introduction were produced using SCNT.

Adult cloning is now a common practice among people who breed prized livestock. Among other benefits, many more offspring can be produced in a given time frame by cloning than by traditional breeding methods, and offspring can be produced after a donor animal is castrated or even dead.

The controversial issue with adult cloning is not necessarily about livestock. As the techniques become routine, cloning a human is no longer only within the realm of science fiction. Researchers are already using SCNT to produce human embryos for research, a practice called **therapeutic cloning**. The researchers harvest undifferentiated (stem) cells from the cloned human embryos. (We return to the topic of stem cells and their potential medical benefits in Chapter 19.) Reproductive cloning of humans is not the intent of such research, but somatic cell nuclear transfer would be the first step toward that end.

**FIGURE 6.11** Liz the cow (*right*) and her clone. The clone was produced by somatic cell nuclear transfer, as in Figure 6.10.

## Take-Home Message    What is cloning?

- Reproductive cloning technologies produce a clone: an exact genetic copy of an individual.
- Somatic cell nuclear transfer (SCNT) is a reproductive cloning method in which nuclear DNA of an adult donor is transferred to an egg with no nucleus. The hybrid cell develops into an embryo that is genetically identical to the donor.
- Therapeutic cloning uses SCNT to produce human embryos for research.

**How Would**
**YOU**
 **Vote ?**
Some view sickly or deformed clones as unfortunate but acceptable casualties of animal cloning research that also yields medical advances for human patients. Should animal cloning be banned? **See CengageNow for details, then vote online (cengagenow.com).**

# 6.6 Impacts/Issues Revisited:
# Here, Kitty, Kitty, Kitty, Kitty, Kitty

Human eggs are difficult to come by. They also come with a hefty set of ethical dilemmas. Thus, researchers have started to make hybrid embryos using adult human cells and pig eggs. Cells from the resulting embryos are being used to study, among other things, how fatal diseases progress. For example, embryos created using cells from people with genetic heart defects will allow researchers to study how the defect causes developing heart cells to malfunction. Such research may ultimately lead to treatments for people who suffer from fatal diseases.

**reproductive cloning**  Technology that produces genetically identical individuals.
**somatic cell nuclear transfer (SCNT)**  Method of reproductive cloning in which genetic material is transferred from an adult somatic cell into an unfertilized, enucleated egg.
**therapeutic cloning**  Using SCNT to produce human embryos for research.

# Summary

**Section 6.1** Making clones, or exact genetic copies, of adult animals is now a common practice in research and animal husbandry.

 **Section 6.2** A eukaryotic chromosome is a molecule of DNA together with associated proteins. The proteins organize the DNA so it can pack into a small nucleus. Diploid cells have two of each type of chromosome. Chromosome number is the sum of all chromosomes in cells of a given type. A human body cell has twenty-three pairs of chromosomes. Members of a pair of sex chromosomes differ among males and females. All others are autosomes. Autosomes of a pair have the same length, shape, and centromere location, and they carry the same genes. Karyotyping reveals an individual's chromosomes.

CENGAGENOW™ Explore chromosomes, sex determination in humans, and karyotyping with the animations on CengageNow.

 **Section 6.3** A DNA molecule consists of two strands of DNA coiled into a helix. Nucleotide monomers are joined to form each strand. A DNA nucleotide has a five-carbon sugar (deoxyribose), three phosphate groups, and one of four nitrogen-containing bases after which the nucleotide is named: adenine, thymine, guanine, or cytosine.

Bases of the two DNA strands in a double helix pair in a consistent way: adenine with thymine (A–T), and guanine with cytosine (G–C). The order of the bases (the DNA sequence) varies among species and among individuals. The DNA of each species has unique sequences that set it apart from the DNA of all other species.

CENGAGENOW™ Learn more about the structure of nucleotides and DNA with the animations on CengageNow.

**Section 6.4** A cell replicates its DNA before it divides. Each double-stranded molecule of DNA results in two double-stranded DNA molecules identical to the parent. One strand of each molecule is new, and the other is parental.

During the replication process, the double helix unwinds. DNA polymerase uses each strand as a template to assemble new, complementary strands of DNA from free nucleotides. DNA ligase seals any gaps to form a continuous strand.

DNA repair mechanisms fix damaged DNA. Proofreading by DNA polymerases corrects most base-pairing errors. Uncorrected errors may become mutations.

CENGAGENOW™ See how a DNA molecule is replicated with the animation on CengageNow.

 **Section 6.5** Reproductive cloning technologies produce genetically identical individuals (clones).

CENGAGENOW™ Observe procedures used to create clones of adult animals with the animation on CengageNow.

# Self-Quiz      Answers in Appendix I

1. The chromosome number _____ .
   a. refers to a particular chromosome pair in a cell
   b. is an identifiable feature of a species
   c. is like a set of books

2. What are the base-pairing rules for DNA?
   a. A–G, T–C            c. A–U, C–G
   b. A–C, T–G            d. A–T, G–C

3. One species' DNA differs from others in its _____ .
   a. sugars              c. base sequence
   b. phosphates          d. all of the above

4. When DNA replication begins, _____ .
   a. the two DNA strands unwind from each other
   b. the two DNA strands condense for base transfers
   c. two DNA molecules bond
   d. old strands move to find new strands

5. DNA replication requires _____ .
   a. template DNA            c. DNA polymerase
   b. free nucleotides        d. all of the above

6. Replication of a DNA molecule results in _____ .
   a. a single strand of DNA      c. two single strands of DNA
   b. a double-stranded DNA       d. two double strands of DNA

7. DNA polymerase adds nucleotides to _____ .
   a. double-stranded DNA      c. double-stranded RNA
   b. single-stranded DNA      d. single-stranded RNA

8. Show the complementary strand of DNA that forms on this template DNA fragment during replication: GGTTTCTTCAAGAGA

9. _____ is an example of reproductive cloning.
   a. Somatic cell nuclear transfer (SCNT)
   b. Multiple offspring from the same pregnancy
   c. Artificial embryo splitting
   d. a and c
   e. all of the above

10. Match the terms appropriately.
    _____ nucleotide          a. adds nucleotides to a
    _____ clone                  growing DNA strand
    _____ DNA ligase          b. copy of an organism
    _____ DNA polymerase      c. fills in gaps, seals breaks
                                 in a DNA strand
                              d. nitrogen-containing base,
                                 sugar, phosphate groups

Additional questions are available on CENGAGENOW™

# Critical Thinking

1. Mutations are permanent changes in a cell's DNA base sequence. They typically have negative consequences, but they are also the original source of genetic variation and the raw material of evolution. How can mutations accumulate, given that cells have repair systems that fix changes or breaks in DNA strands?

2. There may be millions of woolly mammoths frozen in the ice of Siberian glaciers. These huge elephant-like mammals have been extinct for about 10,000 years, but a few research groups are planning to resurrect one of them by cloning DNA isolated from frozen remains. What are some of the pros and cons, both technical and ethical, of cloning an extinct animal?

**A** Micrograph of three viruses injecting DNA into an *E. coli* cell.

Virus proteins labeled with 35S

DNA being injected into bacterium

35S remains outside cells

**B** In one experiment, bacteria were infected with virus particles labeled with a radioisotope of sulfur ($^{35}S$). The sulfur had labeled only viral proteins. The viruses were dislodged from the bacteria by whirling the mixture in a kitchen blender. Most of the radioactive sulfur was detected in the viruses, not in the bacterial cells. The viruses had not injected protein into the bacteria.

Virus DNA labeled with 32P

Labeled DNA being injected into bacterium

32P remains inside cells

**C** In another experiment, bacteria were infected with virus particles labeled with a radioisotope of phosphorus ($^{32}P$). The phosphorus had labeled only viral DNA. When the viruses were dislodged from the bacteria, the radioactive phosphorus was detected mainly inside the bacterial cells. The viruses had injected DNA into the cells—evidence that DNA is the genetic material of this virus.

**FIGURE 6.12 Animated!** The Hershey–Chase experiments. Alfred Hershey and Martha Chase tested whether the genetic material injected by bacteriophage into bacteria is DNA, protein, or both. The experiments were based on the knowledge that proteins contain more sulfur (S) than phosphorus (P), and DNA contains more phosphorus than sulfur.

# Digging Into Data

## The Hershey–Chase Experiments

By 1950, researchers had discovered bacteriophage, a type of virus that infects bacteria. These infectious particles carry hereditary information about how to make new viruses. After a virus infects a cell, the cell starts making new virus particles. Bacteriophages inject genetic material into bacteria, but was that material DNA, protein, or both? Alfred Hershey and Martha Chase decided to find out by exploiting long-known properties of protein (high sulfur content) and of DNA (high phosphorus content). They cultured bacteria in a medium containing an isotope of sulfur, $^{35}S$ (Section 2.2). In this medium, the protein (but not the DNA) of bacteriophage that infected the bacteria became labeled with $^{35}S$.

Hershey and Chase allowed the labeled viruses to infect bacteria. They knew from electron micrographs that phages attach to bacteria by their slender tails (Figure 6.12**A**). They reasoned it would be easy to break this precarious attachment, so they poured the mixture of virus and bacteria into a Waring blender and turned it on.

After blending, the researchers separated the bacteria from the virus-containing fluid, and measured the $^{35}S$ content of each separately. The fluid contained most of the $^{35}S$. Thus, the viruses had not injected protein into the bacteria (Figure 6.12**B**).

Hershey and Chase repeated the experiment using an isotope of phosphorus, $^{32}P$, which labeled the DNA (but not the proteins) of the bacteriophage. This time, they found that the bacteria contained most of the $^{32}P$. The viruses had injected DNA into the bacteria (Figure 6.12**C**).

The graph in Figure 6.12**D** is reproduced from Alfred Hershey and Martha Chase's 1952 publication. "Infected bacteria" refers to the percentage of bacteria that survived the blender.

**D**

From the Journal of General Physiology, 36(1), September 20, 1952: "Independent Functions of Viral Protein and Nucleic Acid in Growth of Bacteriophage."

1. Why did the amount of radioactivity in each set of samples change over time?

2. After 4 minutes in the blender, what percentage of $^{35}S$ was outside the bacteria? What percentage of $^{32}P$ was outside the bacteria?

4. How did the researchers know that the radioisotopes in the fluid came from outside the bacterial cells (extracellular) and not from bacteria that had broken apart?

5. The extracellular concentration of which isotope, $^{35}S$ or $^{32}P$, increased the most with blending? Why do these results imply that bacteriophage viruses inject DNA into bacteria?

Proteins are critical to all life processes,
so cells that cannot make them die very quickly.

## 7.1 Impacts/Issues: Ricin and Your Ribosomes

Ricin is a highly toxic, naturally occurring protein: A dose as small as a few grains of salt can kill an adult. Only botulinum and tetanus toxins are more deadly, and there is no antidote. Ricin effectively deters many animals from eating any part of the castor-oil plant (*Ricinus communis*), which grows wild in tropical regions worldwide and is widely cultivated for its seeds (Figure 7.1). Castor-oil seeds are the source of castor oil, an ingredient in plastics, cosmetics, paints, soaps, polishes, and many other items. After the oil is extracted from the seeds, the ricin is typically discarded along with the leftover seed pulp.

The lethal effects of ricin were known as long ago as 1888, but using ricin as a weapon is now banned by most countries under the Geneva Protocol. However, controlling its production is impossible, because it takes no special skills or equipment to manufacture the toxin from easily obtained raw materials. Thus, ricin appears periodically in the news.

For example, at the height of the Cold War, the Bulgarian writer Georgi Markov had defected to England and was working as a journalist for the BBC. As he made his way to a bus stop on a London street, an assassin used the tip of a modified umbrella to jam a small, ricin-laced ball into Markov's leg. Markov died in agony three days later.

More recently, police in 2003 acted on an intelligence tip and stormed a London apartment, where they found laboratory glassware and castor-oil beans. Traces of ricin were found in a United States Senate mailroom and State Department building, and also in an envelope addressed to the White House in 2004. In 2005, the FBI arrested a man who had castor-oil beans and an assault

FIGURE 7.1 Beautiful and deadly: seeds of the castor-oil plant, source of ribosome-busting ricin. Eating eight of these seeds can kill an adult.

rifle stashed in his Florida home. Jars of banana baby food laced with ground castor-oil beans also made the news in 2005. In 2006, police found pipe bombs and a baby food jar full of ricin in a Tennessee man's shed. In 2008, castor beans, firearms, and several vials of ricin were found in a Las Vegas motel room after its occupant was hospitalized for ricin exposure.

Ricin is toxic because it inactivates ribosomes, the organelles upon which amino acids are assembled into proteins in all cells (Sections 3.5 and 3.6). Proteins are critical to all life processes, so cells that cannot make them die very quickly. Someone who inhales ricin typically dies from low blood pressure and respiratory failure within a few days of exposure.

This chapter details how the information encoded by a gene becomes converted to the gene's product—an RNA or a protein. Even though it is extremely unlikely that your ribosomes will ever encounter ricin, protein synthesis is nevertheless worth appreciating for how it keeps you and all other organisms alive.

# 7.2 The Nature of Genetic Information

DNA is like a book, an encyclopedia that carries instructions for building a new individual. You already know the alphabet used to write the book: the four letters A, T, G, and C, for the four nucleotide bases adenine, thymine, guanine, and cytosine. A strand of DNA is a chain of those four kinds of nucleotides. The information it carries consists of which nucleotide follows the next along the strand—the DNA sequence (Section 6.3). Part of that information occurs in subsets called genes. A cell uses the sequence of a **gene** to build an RNA or protein product. Converting a gene's DNA sequence into its product starts with **transcription**: a process in which enzymes use the DNA sequence of a gene as a template to assemble a strand of RNA. Transcription makes an RNA copy of a gene. In other words, it *transcribes* the base sequence of a gene into a similar form: the base sequence of an RNA.

RNA is similar to a single strand of DNA in that both are chains of four kinds of nucleotides. However, the nucleotides that make up RNA differ slightly from those that make up DNA. The sugar in an RNA nucleotide is ribose, and that of a DNA nucleotide is a deoxyribose. Three of the bases (adenine, cytosine, and guanine) are the same in DNA and RNA nucleotides (Figure 7.2). The fourth base in RNA is uracil, not thymine.

Despite the seemingly small differences in structure, DNA and RNA have very different functions. DNA's important but only role is to store a cell's heritable information. By contrast, cells make several kinds of RNAs, each of which has a different function. Although all RNAs are encoded by DNA, **messenger RNA (mRNA)** is the only kind of RNA that carries a protein-building message. That message is encoded within the sequence of the mRNA itself by sets of three bases, "genetic words" that follow one another along the length of the mRNA. Like the words of a sentence, a series of genetic words can form a meaningful parcel of information—in this case, the sequence of amino acids of a protein. By the process of **translation**, the protein-building information in an mRNA is *translated* into a different language: a sequence of amino acids. The result is a polypeptide that twists and folds into a protein.

The processes of transcription and translation are part of **gene expression**, a multistep process by which information encoded in a gene becomes converted to an RNA or protein product. During gene expression, genetic information flows from DNA to RNA to protein:

$$\text{DNA} \xrightarrow{\text{transcription}} \textbf{mRNA} \xrightarrow{\text{translation}} \textbf{protein}$$

A cell's DNA sequence contains the information it needs to make the molecules of life. Each gene encodes an RNA, and RNAs interact to assemble proteins. Proteins (enzymes, in particular) assemble lipids and carbohydrates, replicate DNA, make RNA, and perform many other functions that keep the cell alive.

## Take-Home Message
### What is the information carried by DNA?

- The nucleotide base sequence of a gene encodes instructions for building an RNA or protein product.
- A cell transcribes the base sequence of a gene into RNA.
- Messenger RNA (mRNA) carries a protein-building message.

An RNA nucleotide: guanine (G), or guanosine triphosphate

**A** Guanine, one of the four nucleotides in RNA. The others (adenine, uracil, and cytosine) differ only in their component bases (*blue*). Three of the four bases in RNA nucleotides are identical to the bases in DNA nucleotides.

A DNA nucleotide: guanine (G), or deoxyguanosine triphosphate

**B** Compare the DNA nucleotide guanine. The only difference between the RNA and DNA versions of guanine (or adenine, or cytosine) is the hydrogen atom or hydroxyl group at one position on the sugar (shown in *green*).

**FIGURE 7.2** Comparison between **A** an RNA nucleotide and **B** a DNA nucleotide.

**gene** Part of a DNA base sequence; specifies an RNA or protein product.

**gene expression** Process by which the information in a gene becomes converted to an RNA or protein product.

**messenger RNA (mRNA)** Type of RNA that has a protein-building message.

**transcription** Process by which an RNA is assembled from nucleotides using the base sequence of a gene as a template.

**translation** Process by which a polypeptide chain is assembled from amino acids in the order specified by an mRNA.

RNA polymerase

gene region

promoter sequence in DNA

RNA

DNA winding up    DNA unwinding

**1** RNA polymerase binds to a promoter in the DNA. The binding positions the polymerase near a gene. In most cases, the base sequence of the gene occurs on only one of the two DNA strands. Only the DNA strand complementary to the gene sequence will be translated into RNA.

**2** The polymerase begins to move along the DNA and unwind it. As it does, it links RNA nucleotides into a strand of RNA in the order specified by the base sequence of the DNA. The DNA winds up again after the polymerase passes. The structure of the "opened" DNA at the transcription site is called a transcription bubble, after its appearance.

**FIGURE 7.3 Animated!** Transcription assembles a strand of RNA from nucleotides using a gene region in DNA as a template.

# 7.3 Transcription: DNA to RNA

Remember that DNA replication begins with one DNA double helix and ends with two DNA double helices (Section 6.4). The two double helices are identical to the parent molecule because the process of DNA replication follows base-pairing rules. A nucleotide can be added to a growing strand of DNA only if it base-pairs with the corresponding nucleotide of the parent strand: G pairs with C, and A pairs with T (Section 6.3):

DNA

A T G T A C T C A G T G T A C A
T A C A T G A G T C A C A T G T

DNA

The same base-pairing rules also govern RNA synthesis in transcription. An RNA strand is structurally so similar to a DNA strand that the two can base-pair if their base sequences are complementary. In such hybrid molecules, G pairs with C, and A pairs with U (uracil):

RNA

A U G U A C U C A G U G U A C A
T A C A T G A G T C A C A T G T

DNA

During transcription, a strand of DNA acts as a template upon which a strand of RNA is assembled from RNA nucleotides. A nucleotide can be added to a growing strand of RNA only if it is complementary to the corresponding nucleotide of the parent strand of DNA: G pairs with C, and A pairs with U. Thus, each new RNA is complementary in sequence to the DNA strand that served as its template. As in DNA replication, each nucleotide provides the energy for its own attachment to the end of a growing strand.

Transcription is similar to DNA replication in that one strand of a nucleic acid serves as a template for synthesis of another. However, in contrast with DNA replication, only part of one DNA strand (a gene) serves as the template, not the whole molecule. The enzyme **RNA polymerase**, not DNA polymerase, adds nucleotides to the end of a growing strand. Also, transcription results in a single strand of RNA, not two DNA double helices.

direction of transcription

**3** Zooming in on the gene region, we can see that RNA polymerase covalently bonds successive nucleotides into an RNA strand. The base sequence of the new RNA strand is complementary to the base sequence of its DNA template strand, so it is an RNA copy of the gene. **Figure It Out:** After the guanine, what is the next nucleotide that will be added to this growing strand of RNA?

*Answer: Another guanine (G)*

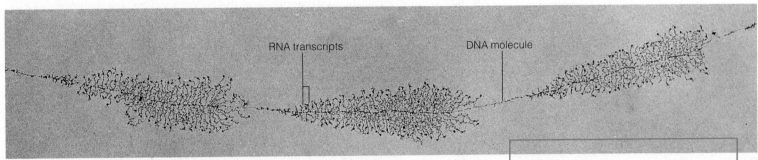

RNA transcripts          DNA molecule

**FIGURE 7.4** Many RNA polymerases typically transcribe the same gene at the same time. The composite structure that forms is called a "Christmas tree" after its shape. Here, three genes next to one another on a chromosome are being transcribed by many polymerases.

**Figure It Out:** Are the polymerases transcribing this DNA molecule moving from left to right or from right to left?

*Answer: Left to right (the transcripts get longer as the polymerases move along the DNA)*

**The Process of Transcription** Transcription occurs in the nucleus of eukaryotic cells. It begins with a chromosome, which is a double helix molecule of DNA. The process gets under way when an RNA polymerase and several regulatory proteins attach to a specific binding site in the DNA called a **promoter** (Figure 7.3). The binding positions the polymerase at a transcription start site close to a gene **1**. The polymerase starts moving along the DNA, over the gene **2**. As it moves, the polymerase unwinds the double helix just a bit so it can "read" the base sequence of the noncoding DNA strand. As it reads, the polymerase joins free RNA nucleotides into a chain, in the order dictated by that DNA sequence. As in DNA replication, each nucleotide provides the energy for its own attachment to the end of a growing strand.

When the polymerase reaches the end of the gene, the DNA and the new RNA strand are released. The new RNA strand is complementary in base sequence to the DNA strand from which it was transcribed **3**. It is an RNA copy of a gene. Typically, many polymerases transcribe a particular gene region at the same time, so many new RNA strands can be produced very quickly (Figure 7.4).

## Take-Home Message  How is RNA assembled?

■ In transcription, RNA polymerase uses the nucleotide base sequence of a gene region in a chromosome as a template to assemble a strand of RNA.

■ The new strand of RNA is a copy of the gene from which it was transcribed.

**promoter** In DNA, a sequence to which RNA polymerase binds.

**RNA polymerase** Enzyme that carries out transcription.

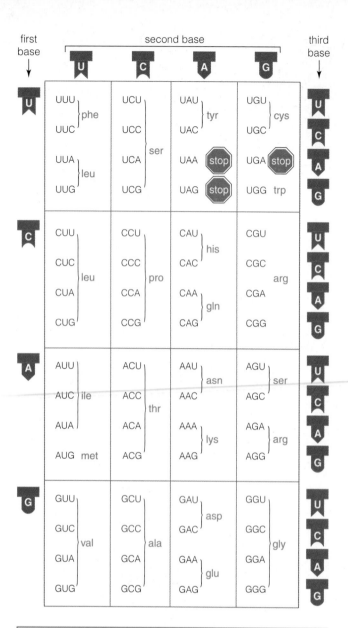

first base ↓
second base
third base ↓

**FIGURE 7.5 Animated!** The genetic code. The left column lists a codon's first base, the top row lists the second, and the right column lists the third. Amino acid names are abbreviated. The list below gives the complete names and the one-letter abbreviations. **Figure It Out:** Which codons specify lysine (lys)? *Answer: AAA and AAG*

| | |
|---|---|
| ala | alanine (A) |
| arg | arginine (R) |
| asn | asparagine (N) |
| asp | aspartic acid (D) |
| cys | cysteine (C) |
| glu | glutamic acid (E) |
| gln | glutamine (Q) |
| gly | glycine (G) |
| his | histidine (H) |
| ile | isoleucine (I) |

| | |
|---|---|
| leu | leucine (L) |
| lys | lysine (K) |
| met | methionine (M) |
| phe | phenylalanine (F) |
| pro | proline (P) |
| ser | serine (S) |
| thr | threonine (T) |
| trp | tryptophan (W) |
| tyr | tyrosine (Y) |
| val | valine (V) |

# 7.4 RNA Players in Translation

**mRNA and the Genetic Code** An mRNA is a disposable copy of a gene. Its job is to carry DNA's protein-building information to the other two types of RNA for translation. That protein-building information consists of a linear sequence of genetic "words" spelled with an alphabet of the four bases A, C, G, and U.

Each of the genetic "words" carried by an mRNA is three bases long, and each is a code—a **codon**—for a particular amino acid. There are four possible bases in each of the three positions of a codon, so there are a total of sixty-four (or $4^3$) mRNA codons. Collectively, the sixty-four codons constitute the **genetic code** (Figure 7.5). Which of the four nucleotides is in the first, second, and third position of a base triplet determines which amino acid the codon specifies. For instance, the codon AUG codes for the amino acid methionine (met), and UGG codes for tryptophan (trp).

One codon follows the next along the length of an mRNA, so the order of codons in an mRNA determines the order of amino acids in the polypeptide that will be translated from it. Thus, the base sequence of a gene is transcribed into the base sequence of an mRNA, which is in turn translated into an amino acid sequence:

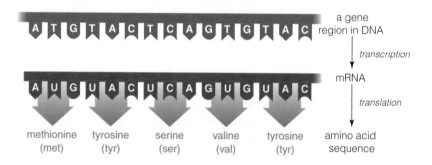

a gene region in DNA

transcription

mRNA

translation

methionine (met)  tyrosine (tyr)  serine (ser)  valine (val)  tyrosine (tyr)  amino acid sequence

There are only twenty kinds of amino acids found in proteins. Sixty-four codons are more than are needed to specify twenty amino acids, so some amino acids are specified by more than one codon. For instance, GAA and GAG both code for glutamic acid. Some codons signal the beginning and end of a protein-coding sequence. For example, the first AUG in an mRNA is the signal to start translation in most species. AUG also happens to be the codon for methionine, so methionine is always the first amino acid in new polypeptides of such organisms. UAA, UAG, and UGA do not specify an amino acid. They are signals that stop translation, so they are called stop codons. A stop codon marks the end of the protein-coding sequence in an mRNA.

The genetic code is highly conserved, which means that many organisms use the same code and probably always have. Prokaryotes and some protists have a few codons that vary, as do mitochondria and chloroplasts. The variation was a clue that led to a theory of how organelles evolved (we will return to this topic in Section 13.3).

**rRNA and tRNA—The Translators** Ribosomes and transfer RNAs (tRNA) interact to translate an mRNA into a polypeptide. A ribosome has one large and one small subunit, both of which consist

**A** large subunit of a ribosome   **B** small subunit of a ribosome

mRNA

tunnel

anticodon

trp

amino acid
attachment site

**FIGURE 7.6** A ribosome (*right*) consists of **A** a large subunit and **B** a small subunit. Structural protein components of the subunits are shown in *green*.

Notice the tunnel through the interior of the large subunit. rRNA components of the ribosome (*tan*) assemble a polypeptide chain, which threads through this tunnel as it forms. We show an mRNA (in *red*) attached to the small subunit.

an intact
ribosome

**FIGURE 7.7** tRNA. *Above*, models of the tRNA that carries the amino acid tryptophan. Each tRNA's anticodon is complementary to an mRNA codon. Each also carries the amino acid specified by that codon.

*Below*, during translation, tRNAs dock at an intact ribosome. Here, three tRNAs are docked at the small ribosomal subunit (the large subunit is not shown, for clarity). The anticodons of the tRNAs line up with complementary codons in an mRNA (shown in *red*).

of structural proteins and rRNA. **Ribosomal RNA (rRNA)** is the main component of the subunits. During translation, a large and a small subunit converge as an intact ribosome on an mRNA (Figure 7.6). **Transfer RNAs (tRNAs)** deliver amino acids to ribosomes in the order specified by the mRNA. Each tRNA has two attachment sites: One is an **anticodon**, a triplet of nucleotides that base-pairs with an mRNA codon (Figure 7.7). The other binds to an amino acid—the one specified by the codon. tRNAs with different anticodons carry different amino acids. You will see in the next section how those tRNAs deliver amino acids, one after the next, to a ribosome–mRNA complex during translation.

rRNA is one of the few examples of RNA with enzymatic activity: The rRNA of a ribosome, not the protein, forms a peptide bond between amino acids. As the amino acids are delivered, the ribosome joins them via peptide bonds into a new polypeptide chain (Section 2.9). Thus, the order of codons in an mRNA—DNA's protein-building message—becomes translated into a new protein.

## Take-Home Message  **What roles do mRNA, tRNA, and rRNA play during translation?**

- mRNA carries protein-building information. The bases in mRNA are "read" in sets of three during protein synthesis. Most of these base triplets (codons) code for amino acids. The genetic code consists of all sixty-four codons.

- Ribosomes, which consist of two subunits of rRNA and proteins, assemble amino acids into polypeptide chains.

- A tRNA has an anticodon complementary to an mRNA codon, and it has a binding site for the amino acid specified by that codon. tRNAs deliver amino acids to ribosomes.

**anticodon** Set of three nucleotides in a tRNA; base-pairs with mRNA codon.

**codon** In mRNA, a nucleotide base triplet that codes for an amino acid or stop signal during translation.

**genetic code** Set of sixty-four mRNA codons, each of which specifies an amino acid or stop signal in translation.

**ribosomal RNA (rRNA)** A type of RNA that becomes part of ribosomes.

**transfer RNA (tRNA)** Type of RNA that delivers amino acids to a ribosome during translation.

**FIGURE 7.8 Animated!**
Translation in eukaryotes.

**1** In eukaryotic cells, RNA is transcribed in the nucleus.

**2** Finished RNA moves into the cytoplasm through nuclear pores.

**3** Ribosomal subunits and tRNA converge on an mRNA.

**4** A polypeptide chain forms as the ribosome moves along the mRNA, linking amino acids together in the order dictated by the mRNA codons.

**5** Many ribosomes can translate an mRNA at the same time.

# 7.5 Translating the Code: RNA to Protein

Translation, the second part of protein synthesis, occurs in the cytoplasm of all cells (Figure 7.8). It has three stages: initiation, elongation, and termination. The initiation stage begins when a small ribosomal subunit binds to an mRNA. Next, the anticodon of a special tRNA called an initiator base-pairs with the first AUG codon of the mRNA. Then, a large ribosomal subunit joins the small subunit.

In the elongation stage, the ribosome assembles a polypeptide chain as it moves along the mRNA. The initiator tRNA carries the amino acid methionine, so the first amino acid of the new polypeptide chain is methionine. Another tRNA brings the second amino acid to the complex as its anticodons base-pair with the second codon in the mRNA. The ribosome joins the first two amino acids by way of a peptide bond (Section 2.9):

The first tRNA is released and the ribosome moves to the next codon. Another tRNA brings the third amino acid to the complex as its anticodons base-pair with the third codon of the mRNA. A peptide bond forms between the second and third amino acids:

The second tRNA is released and the ribosome moves to the next codon. Another tRNA brings the fourth amino acid to the complex as its anticodons base-pair with the fourth codon of the mRNA. A peptide bond forms between the third and fourth amino acids:

The new polypeptide chain grows as the ribosome causes peptide bonds to form between amino acids delivered by successive tRNAs.

Termination occurs when the ribosome reaches a stop codon in the mRNA. The mRNA and the polypeptide detach from the ribosome, and the ribosomal subunits separate from each other. Translation is now complete. The new polypeptide will join the pool of proteins in the cytoplasm, or it will enter rough ER of the endomembrane system (Section 3.6).

In cells that are making a lot of protein, many ribosomes may simultaneously translate the same mRNA, in which case they are called **polysomes**:

a polysome

Given that many polypeptides are translated from one mRNA, why would a cell also make many copies of an mRNA? Compared with DNA, RNA is not very stable. An mRNA may last only a few minutes before it is disassembled by enzymes in the cytoplasm. The fast turnover allows cells to adjust their protein synthesis quickly in response to changing needs.

**polysome** Cluster of ribosomes that are simultaneously translating an mRNA.

Transcription and translation both occur in the cytoplasm of prokaryotes, and these processes are closely linked in time and in space. Translation begins before transcription is done, so in these cells, a DNA transcription tree (Figure 7.4) may be decorated with polysome "balls."

Translation is an energy-intensive process. That energy is provided mainly in the form of phosphate-group transfers from the RNA nucleotide GTP (Figure 7.2**A**) to molecules involved in the process.

## Take-Home Message  How is mRNA translated into protein?

- Translation is an energy-requiring process that converts the protein-building information carried by an mRNA into a polypeptide.

- During initiation, an mRNA joins with an initiator tRNA and two ribosomal subunits.

- During elongation, amino acids are delivered to the complex by tRNAs in the order dictated by successive mRNA codons. As they arrive, the ribosome joins each to the end of the polypeptide chain.

- Termination occurs when the ribosome encounters a stop codon in the mRNA. The mRNA and the polypeptide are released, and the ribosome disassembles.

## 7.6 Mutated Genes and Their Products

Mutations are changes in the sequence of a cell's DNA. If a mutation changes the genetic instructions encoded in the DNA, an altered gene product may be the result. Remember, more than one codon can specify the same amino acid, so cells have a certain margin of safety. For example, a mutation that changes a UCU codon to UCC in an mRNA may not have further effects, because both codons specify serine. However, other mutations have drastic consequences.

The oxygen-binding properties of hemoglobin provide us with an example of how mutations can change the structure (and function) of a protein. A red blood cell carries oxygen molecules bound to hemoglobin molecules. As these cells circulate through the lungs, the hemoglobin proteins inside of them bind oxygen gas, then give it up in regions of the body with low oxygen levels. Then, the red blood cells return to the lungs and pick up more oxygen.

Hemoglobin can bind and release oxygen because of its structure. It consists of four polypeptides called globin chains, and each chain folds around a heme, a type of cofactor with an iron atom at its center. Oxygen binds to hemoglobin at those iron atoms. In adult humans, two alpha globin chains and two beta globin chains make up each hemoglobin molecule (Figure 7.9**A,B**). Defects in the chains can cause a condition called anemia, in which a person's blood is deficient in red blood cells or in hemoglobin. Either outcome limits the blood's ability to carry oxygen.

A **deletion** is a mutation in which one or more nucleotides are lost from DNA. The loss of a particular nucleotide from the beta globin gene causes beta thalassemia, a type of anemia. Like many other deletions, this one causes the reading frame of mRNA codons to shift. The shift garbles the genetic message, just as incorrectly grouping a series of letters garbles the meaning of a sentence:

The cat ate the rat.

T hec ata tet her at.

Th eca tat eth era t.

---

If a mutation changes the genetic instructions encoded in DNA, an altered gene product may be the result.

---

**base-pair substitution** Type of mutation in which a single base-pair changes.

**deletion** Mutation in which one or more base pairs are lost.

**insertion** Mutation in which one or more base pairs become inserted into DNA.

**A** Hemoglobin, an oxygen-transport protein in red blood cells. This protein consists of four globin chains: two alpha chains (*blue*) and two beta chains (*green*). Each globin chain folds up to form a pocket that cradles a type of cofactor called a heme (*red*). Oxygen binds to the iron atom at the center of each heme group.

FIGURE 7.9 **Animated!** Two common mutations of hemoglobin's beta globin chain.

**B** Part of the DNA, mRNA, and amino acid sequence of the beta chain of a normal hemoglobin molecule.

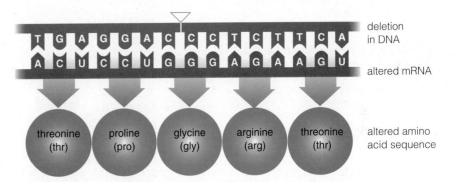

**C** A single base-pair deletion causes the reading frame for the rest of the mRNA to shift, so a completely different protein product forms. This mutation results in a defective globin chain. The outcome is thalassemia, a genetic disorder in which a person has an abnormally low amount of hemoglobin.

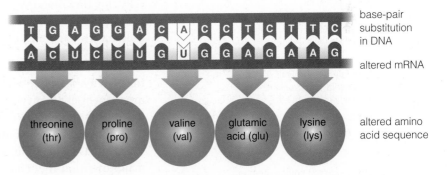

**D** A base-pair substitution in DNA replaces a thymine with an adenine. When the altered mRNA is translated, valine replaces glutamate as the sixth amino acid of the new polypeptide chain. Hemoglobin with this chain is called HbS, or sickle hemoglobin.

Expression of a beta globin gene with a thalassemia mutation results in a polypeptide that differs drastically from normal beta globin (Figure 7.9**C**). The result? Not enough hemoglobin molecules assemble, an outcome that is the source of the anemia.

Frameshifts may also be caused by **insertion** mutations, in which extra bases become inserted into DNA. Other mutations do not cause frameshifts. With a **base-pair substitution**, a nucleotide and its partner are replaced by a different base pair. A substitution may result in an amino acid change or a premature stop codon in a gene's protein product. Sickle-cell anemia, a type of anemia that is most common in people of African ancestry, arises because of a base-pair substitution. The substitution causes valine to be the sixth amino acid of the beta globin chain instead of glutamic acid (Figure 7.9**D**). Hemoglobin with this mutation in its beta chain is called sickle hemoglobin, or HbS.

Unlike glutamic acid, which carries a negative charge, valine carries no charge. As a result of that one substitution, a tiny patch of the beta globin chain changes from hydrophilic to hydrophobic, which in turn causes the hemoglobin's behavior to change slightly. HbS molecules stick together and form large, rodlike clumps under certain conditions. Red blood cells that contain the clumps become distorted into a crescent (sickle) shape. The sickled

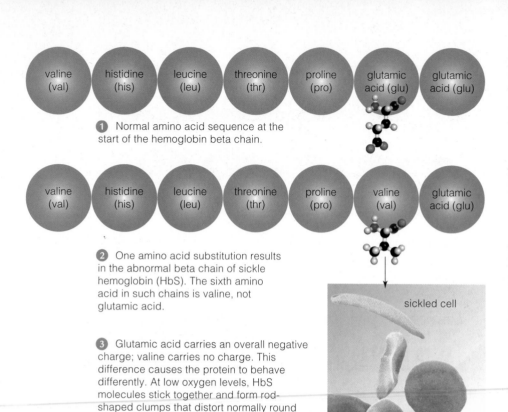

1  Normal amino acid sequence at the start of the hemoglobin beta chain.

2  One amino acid substitution results in the abnormal beta chain of sickle hemoglobin (HbS). The sixth amino acid in such chains is valine, not glutamic acid.

3  Glutamic acid carries an overall negative charge; valine carries no charge. This difference causes the protein to behave differently. At low oxygen levels, HbS molecules stick together and form rod-shaped clumps that distort normally round red blood cells into sickle shapes. (A sickle is a farm tool with a crescent-shaped blade.)

sickled cell

normal cell

**FIGURE 7.10 Animated!** How a single base-pair substitution causes sickle-cell anemia. *Below*, common symptoms of the disease.

4  Tionne "T-Boz" Watkins of the music group TLC is a celebrity spokesperson for the Sickle Cell Disease Association of America. She was diagnosed with sickle-cell anemia as a child.

*Clumping of cells in bloodstream*
↓
Circulatory problems, damage to brain, lungs, heart, skeletal muscles, gut, and kidneys
↓
Heart failure, paralysis, pneumonia, rheumatism, gut pain, kidney failure

*Spleen concentrates sickle cells*
↓
Enlargement of spleen; immune system function compromised

*Rapid destruction of sickle cells*
↓
Anemia, causing weakness, fatigue, impaired development, heart chamber dilation
↓
Impaired brain function, heart failure

cells clog tiny blood vessels, which in turn disrupts blood circulation throughout the body. Over time, repeated episodes of sickling can damage organs and even cause death (Figure 7.10).

**What Causes Mutations?** Insertion mutations are often caused by the activity of **transposable elements**, which are segments of DNA that can insert themselves anywhere in a chromosome. Certain kinds can move spontaneously from one place to another within the same chromosome, or to a different chromosome entirely. Transposable elements can be hundreds or thousands of base pairs long, so when one interrupts a gene sequence, it becomes a major insertion that changes the gene's product. These segments are common in the DNA of all species. For example, about 45 percent of human DNA consists of transposable elements or their remnants.

Many mutations occur spontaneously during DNA replication. That is not surprising, given the fast pace of replication (about twenty bases per second in humans, and one thousand bases per second in bacteria). DNA polymerases make mistakes at predictable rates, but most types fix errors as they occur (Section 6.4). Errors that remain uncorrected are mutations.

Harmful environmental agents also cause mutations. For example, some forms of energy such as x-rays can ionize atoms by knocking electrons right out of them. Such ionizing radiation can break chromosomes into pieces that may get lost during DNA replication (Figure 7.11A). Ionizing radiation also damages DNA indirectly when it penetrates living tissue, because it leaves a trail of destructive free radicals. Free radicals, remember, damage DNA (Section 5.6).

That is why doctors and dentists use the lowest possible doses of x-rays on their patients.

Nonionizing radiation boosts electrons to a higher energy level, but not enough to knock them out of an atom. DNA absorbs one kind, ultraviolet (UV) light. Exposure to UV light can cause two adjacent thymine bases to bond covalently to one another (Figure 7.11**B**). The resulting thymine dimer kinks the DNA. DNA polymerase may copy the kinked part incorrectly during replication, so a mutation becomes introduced into the DNA. Mutations that cause certain kinds of cancers begin with thymine dimers. Exposing unprotected skin to sunlight increases the risk of skin cancer because it causes thymine dimers to form in the DNA of skin cells.

Some natural or synthetic chemicals can also cause mutations. For instance, chemicals in cigarette smoke transfer small hydrocarbon groups to the bases in DNA. The altered bases mispair during replication, or stop replication entirely. Both events increase the chance of mutation.

**FIGURE 7.11** Two types of DNA damage that can lead to mutations. **A** Chromosomes from a human cell after exposure to gamma rays (a type of ionizing radiation). The broken pieces (*red* arrows) may get lost during DNA replication. **B** *Below*, a thymine dimer.

## Take-Home Message  **What is a mutation?**

- A mutation is a permanent change in the nucleotide base sequence of DNA. A base-pair substitution, insertion, or deletion may alter a gene product.

- Most mutations arise during DNA replication as a result of unrepaired DNA polymerase errors. Some mutations occur as a result of transposable elements, or after exposure to harmful radiation or chemicals.

thymine dimer

**B**

# 7.7 Eukaryotic Gene Controls

All of the cells in your body are descended from the same fertilized egg, so they all contain the same DNA—and the same genes. Some of the genes are transcribed by all cells; such genes affect structural features and metabolic pathways common to all cells. In other ways, however, nearly all of your body cells are specialized, or differentiated (Section 6.5). **Differentiation**, the process by which cells become specialized, occurs as different cell lineages begin to express different subsets of their genes. Which genes a cell uses determines the molecules it will produce, which in turn determines what kind of cell it will be. For example, most of your body cells express the genes that encode the enzymes of glycolysis, but only immature red blood cells use the genes that code for globin chains.

A cell rarely uses more than 10 percent of its genes at once. Which genes are expressed at any given time depends on many factors, such as conditions in the cytoplasm and extracellular fluid, and the type of cell. The factors affect controls governing all steps of gene expression, starting with transcription and ending with delivery of an RNA or protein product to its final destination. Such controls consist of processes that start, enhance, slow, or stop gene expression. For example, proteins called **transcription factors** affect whether and how fast certain genes are transcribed by binding directly to DNA. Some transcription factors prevent RNA polymerase from attaching to a promoter, which in turn prevents transcription of nearby genes. Others help RNA polymerase bind to a promoter, which speeds up transcription.

The remainder of this section introduces some specific examples and effects of gene controls in eukaryotes.

**differentiation** The process by which cells become specialized; occurs as different cell lineages begin to express different subsets of their genes.

**transcription factor** Protein that influences transcription by binding to DNA.

**transposable element** Small segment of DNA that can spontaneously move to a new location in a chromosome.

FIGURE 7.12 Eyes and *eyeless*. **A** A normal fruit fly has large, round eyes. **B** A fruit fly with a mutation in its *eyeless* gene develops with no eyes. **C** Eyes form wherever the *eyeless* gene is expressed in fly embryos—here, on a wing.

Humans, mice, squids, and other animals have a gene called *PAX6*, which is so similar to *eyeless* that it also triggers eye development when expressed in fly embryos. In humans, a *PAX6* mutation results in missing irises, a condition called aniridia **D**. Compare a normal iris **E**.

## Homeotic Genes

**Homeotic genes** control the formation of specific body parts. All homeotic genes encode transcription factors with a homeodomain, a region of about sixty amino acids that can bind to a promoter or some other DNA sequence. Homeotic genes are one type of **master gene**, because their products affect expression of many other genes. The expression of a master gene causes other genes to be expressed, with the outcome being the completion of an intricate task such as the formation of an eye.

The function of many homeotic genes has been discovered by manipulating their expression, one at a time. With a **gene knockout**, researchers inactivate a gene by introducing a mutation or deleting it entirely. Then they observe how an organism that carries the knockout differs from normal individuals. The differences are clues to the function of the missing gene product.

Homeotic genes are expressed in animals during embryonic development. The process begins long before body parts develop, as various master genes are expressed in local areas of the early embryo. The master gene products form in concentration gradients that span the entire embryo. Depending on where they are located within the gradients, embryonic cells begin to transcribe different homeotic genes. Products of these homeotic genes form in specific areas of the embryo. The different products cause cells to differentiate into tissues that form specific structures such as wings or a head.

Researchers often name homeotic genes based on what happens in their absence. For instance, fruit flies with a mutated *eyeless* gene develop with no eyes (Figure 7.12**A,B**). *Dunce* is required for learning and memory. *Wingless*, *wrinkled*, and *minibrain* are self-explanatory. *Tinman* is necessary for development of a heart. Flies with a mutated *groucho* gene have too many bristles above their eyes. One gene was named *toll*, after what a German researcher exclaimed upon seeing the disastrous effects of its mutation (*toll* means "cool!" in German).

Homeotic genes control development by the same mechanisms in all eukaryotes, and many are interchangeable among different species. Thus, we can infer that they evolved in the most ancient eukaryotic cells. Homeodomains often differ among species only in conservative substitutions—one amino acid has replaced another with similar chemical properties. Consider the *eyeless* gene. Eyes form in embryonic fruit flies wherever this gene is expressed: typically in the head, but also in wings, legs, or other parts (Figure 7.12**C**). Humans, squids, mice, fish, and many other animals have a gene called *PAX6*, which is similar to *eyeless*. In humans, *PAX6* mutations cause eye disorders such as aniridia, in which a person's irises are underdeveloped or missing (Figure 7.12**D,E**). *PAX6* works across different species. For example, if the *PAX6* gene from a human or mouse is inserted into an *eyeless* mutant fly, it has the same effect as the *eyeless* gene: An eye forms wherever it is expressed. Such studies are evidence of a shared ancestor among these evolutionarily distant animals.

## Sex Chromosome Genes

In humans and other mammals, a female's cells each contain two X chromosomes, one inherited from her mother, the other one from her father. One X chromosome is always tightly condensed (Figure 7.13). We call the condensed X chromosomes "Barr bodies," after Murray Barr, who discovered them. RNA polymerase cannot access most of the genes on the condensed chromosome. According to the theory of **dosage compensation**, the inactivation equalizes expression of X chromosome genes between the sexes. The body cells of male mammals (XY) have one set of X chromosome genes. The body cells of female mammals (XX) have two sets, but only one is expressed. Normal development of female embryos depends on this control.

The human X chromosome carries 1,336 genes. Some of those genes are associated with sexual traits, such as the distribution of body fat and hair. However, most of the genes on the X chromosome govern nonsexual traits such as blood clotting and color perception. Such genes are expressed in both males and females. Males, remember, also inherit one X chromosome.

The human Y chromosome carries only 307 genes, but one of them is the *SRY* gene—the master gene for male sex determination. Its expression in XY embryos triggers the formation of testes, which are male gonads (Figure 7.14). Some of the cells in these primary male reproductive organs make testosterone, a sex hormone that controls the emergence of male secondary sexual traits such as facial hair, increased musculature, and a deep voice. We know that *SRY* is the master gene that controls emergence of male sexual traits because mutations in this gene cause XY individuals to develop external genitalia that appear female. An XX embryo has no Y chromosome, no *SRY* gene, and much less testosterone, so primary female reproductive organs (ovaries) form instead of testes. Ovaries make estrogens and other sex hormones that will govern the development of female secondary sexual traits, such as enlarged, functional breasts, and fat deposits around the hips and thighs.

Structures that will give rise to external genitalia appear at seven weeks

*SRY* expressed          no *SRY* present

penis

vaginal opening

birth approaching

**FIGURE 7.14** Development of reproductive organs in human embryos. An early human embryo appears neither male nor female. Gene expression determines what reproductive organs form.

In an XY embryo, the *SRY* gene product triggers the formation of testes, male gonads that secrete testosterone. This hormone initiates development of other male traits. In an XX embryo, ovaries form in the absence of the Y chromosome and its *SRY* gene.

normal cells in organized clusters

irregular clusters of cancer cells

**FIGURE 7.15** Breast cancer: an outcome of failed gene expression controls. *Right*, this micrograph shows irregular clusters of cancer cells that infiltrated milk ducts in breast tissue. *Above*, Robin Shoulla. Diagnostic tests revealed abnormal cells such as these in her body when she was seventeen years old.

**cancer** Disease that occurs when a malignant neoplasm physically and metabolically disrupts body tissues.
**tumor** Abnormally growing and dividing mass of cells.

**Cancer: Gene Expression Out of Control** Every second, millions of cells in your skin, bone marrow, gut lining, liver, and elsewhere are dividing and replacing their worn-out, dead, and dying predecessors. They do not divide at random. Many gene expression controls regulate cell growth and division. When those controls fail, cancer is the outcome.

**Cancer** is a multistep process in which abnormally growing and dividing cells disrupt body tissues. Gene expression controls that usually keep cells from getting overcrowded in tissues are lost, so cancer cell populations may reach extremely high densities. Unless chemotherapy, surgery, or another procedure eradicates them, cancer cells can put an individual on a painful road to death. Each year, cancers cause 15 to 20 percent of all human deaths in developed countries alone.

Cancer typically begins with a mutation in a gene whose product is part of the controls over cell growth and division. The mutation may be inherited, or it may be a new one, as when DNA becomes damaged by environmental agents (Section 7.6). If the mutation alters the gene's protein product so that it no longer works properly, one level of control over the cell's growth and division has been lost. Such genes typically have at least two backups: other genes whose products regulate the same process. If the backup genes also mutate, the cell begins to divide over and over, and its descendants form an abnormal mass called a **tumor**. Tumor cells sometimes lose the membrane recognition proteins that keep them in their home tissue, in which case they break free and establish themselves in other parts of the body—a process of cancer called metastasis.

Mutations in some genes predispose individuals to develop certain kinds of cancer. Tumor suppressor genes are named because tumors are more likely to occur when these genes mutate. Two examples are *BRCA1* and *BRCA2*. A mutated version of one or both of these genes is often found in breast and ovarian cancer cells. If a *BRCA* gene mutates in one of three especially dangerous ways, a woman has an 80 percent chance of developing breast cancer before the age of seventy.

*BRCA* proteins promote transcription of genes that encode DNA repair enzymes (Section 6.4). Any mutations that alter this function also alter a cell's capacity to repair damaged DNA. Other mutations are likely to accumulate, and that sets the stage for cancer.

*BRCA* proteins also bind to receptors for the hormones estrogen and progesterone, which are abundant in breast and ovarian tissues. Binding regulates the transcription of growth factor genes. Among other things, growth factors stimulate cells to divide during normal, cyclic renewals of breast and ovarian tissues. When a mutation results in a *BRCA* protein that cannot bind to hormone receptors, the growth factors are overproduced. Cell division goes out of control, and tissue growth becomes disorganized. In other words, cancer develops.

Because mutations in genes such as *BRCA* can be inherited, cancer is not only a disease of the elderly. Robin Shoulla was only seventeen when she was diagnosed with metastatic breast cancer (Figure 7.15). At an age when most young women are thinking about school, parties, and potential careers, she was dealing with radical mastectomy: the removal of a breast, all lymph nodes under the arm, and skeletal muscles in the chest wall under the breast. She was pleading with her oncologist not to use her jugular vein for chemotherapy and wondering if she would survive to see the next year. Robin's ordeal was one of more than 200,000 new cases of breast cancer in the United States each year. About 5,700 of those cases occur in women and men under thirty-four years of age.

Robin Shoulla survived. Although radical mastectomy is rarely performed today (a modified procedure is less disfiguring), it is the only option when cancer cells invade muscles under the breast. It was Robin's only option. Now, seventeen years later, she has what she calls a normal life—career, husband, children. Her goal as a cancer survivor: "To grow very old with gray hair and spreading hips, smiling."

## Take-Home Message  What is gene expression control?

- Cells of multicelled organisms differentiate when they start expressing a unique subset of their genes, an outcome of controls that govern gene expression.
- All steps between transcription and delivery of gene product are regulated.
- Controlling gene expression is critical for proper development and functioning of a eukaryotic body. Mutations that disrupt the normal system of controls can cause developmental problems, or cancer in an adult.

How Would YOU Vote?

Some women who are genetically at high risk of developing breast cancer opt for preventive surgical removal of their breasts before cancer develops. Statistically, many of those women never would have developed cancer. Should surgery be restricted to cancer treatment? See CengageNow for details, then vote online (cengagenow.com).

# 7.8

## Impacts/Issues Revisited: Ricin and Your Ribosomes

One of ricin's two polypeptide chains is an enzyme that removes a specific adenine base from one of the rRNA chains in the large ribosomal subunit. Once that happens, the ribosome stops working. Protein synthesis grinds to a halt as the ricin inactivates the cell's ribosomes, and the cell quickly dies. A modified form of ricin is currently being tested as a treatment for some kinds of cancer. The ricin is attached to an antibody that can find cancer cells in a person's body. Researchers hope that the attached ricin will kill the cancer cells without harming normal cells.

# Summary

**Section 7.1** The ability to make proteins is critical to all life processes.

**Section 7.2** The genetic information in DNA consists of its base sequence. Genes are subunits of that sequence. A cell uses the information in a gene to make an RNA or protein product. The process of gene expression involves transcription (DNA to RNA), and translation (mRNA, or messenger RNA, to protein). Translation requires the participation of tRNA (transfer RNA) and rRNA (ribosomal RNA).

$$\text{DNA} \xrightarrow{\text{transcription}} \textbf{mRNA} \xrightarrow{\text{translation}} \textbf{protein}$$

**Section 7.3** In transcription, RNA polymerase binds to a promoter in the DNA near a gene. It assembles a strand of RNA by linking RNA nucleotides in the order dictated by the base sequence of the gene. Thus, the new RNA is a copy of the gene from which it was transcribed.

CENGAGENOW™ Explore transcription with the animation on CengageNow.

**Section 7.4** mRNA carries DNA's protein-building information. The information consists of a series of codons, sets of three nucleotides. Sixty-four codons, most of which specify amino acids, constitute the genetic code. Each tRNA has an anticodon that can base-pair with a codon, and it binds to the kind of amino acid specified by the codon. rRNA and proteins make up the two subunits of ribosomes.

methionine (met)  tyrosine (tyr)  serine (ser)  valine (val)  tyrosine (tyr)

CENGAGENOW™ Learn about the genetic code with the interaction on CengageNow.

**Section 7.5** Genetic information carried by an mRNA directs the synthesis of a polypeptide during translation. First, an mRNA, an initiator tRNA, and two ribosomal subunits converge. The intact ribosome then joins successive amino acids, which are delivered by tRNAs in the order specified by the codons in the mRNA. Translation ends when the polymerase encounters a stop codon.

met  val  leu

CENGAGENOW™ See the translation of an mRNA with the animation on CengageNow.

**Section 7.6** Insertions, deletions, and base-pair substitutions are mutations that arise by replication error, transposable element activity, or exposure to environmental hazards. A mutation that changes a gene's product may have harmful effects. Sickle-cell anemia, which is caused by a base-pair substitution in the hemoglobin beta chain gene, is one example.

CENGAGENOW™ Investigate the effects of mutation with the animation on CengageNow.

**Section 7.7** Controls over gene expression are the basis of differentiation, the process by which cells in a multicelled body become specialized. Such controls operate at every step between gene and gene product, and are a critical part of the embryonic development and normal functioning of a multicelled body.

# Self-Quiz   Answers in Appendix I

1. A chromosome contains many genes that are transcribed into different _____ .
   - a. proteins
   - b. polypeptides
   - c. RNAs
   - d. a and b

2. A binding site for RNA polymerase is called a _____ .
   - a. homeotic gene
   - b. promoter
   - c. transcription factor
   - d. b and c

3. Energy that drives transcription is provided mainly by _____ .
   - a. ATP
   - b. RNA nucleotides
   - c. GTP
   - d. all are correct

4. An RNA molecule is typically _____ ; a DNA molecule is typically _____ .
   - a. single-stranded; double-stranded
   - b. double-stranded; single-stranded
   - c. both are single-stranded
   - d. both are double-stranded

5. RNAs form by _____ ; proteins form by _____ .
   - a. replication; translation
   - b. translation; transcription
   - c. transcription; translation
   - d. replication; transcription

6. Up to how many amino acids can be encoded by a gene that consists of 45 nucleotides?

7. Most codons specify a(n) _____ .
   - a. protein
   - b. polypeptide
   - c. amino acid
   - d. mRNA

8. Anticodons pair with _____ .
   - a. mRNA codons
   - b. DNA codons
   - c. RNA anticodons
   - d. amino acids

9. Energy that drives translation is provided mainly by _____ .
   - a. ATP
   - b. RNA nucleotides
   - c. GTP
   - d. all are correct

10. Where does transcription take place in a eukaryotic cell?
    - a. nucleus
    - b. ribosome
    - c. cytoplasm
    - d. b and c are correct

11. Where does translation take place in a eukaryotic cell?
    - a. nucleus
    - b. ribosome
    - c. cytoplasm
    - d. b and c are correct

# Digging Into Data

## *BRCA* Mutations in Women Diagnosed With Breast Cancer

Investigating a correlation between specific cancer-causing mutations and the risk of mortality in humans is challenging, in part because each cancer patient is given the best treatment available at the time. There are no "untreated control" cancer patients, and ideas about which treatments are best change quickly as new drugs become available and new discoveries are made.

Figure 7.16 shows results from a 2007 study by Pal Moller and his colleagues. The researchers looked for *BRCA* mutations in 442 women who had been diagnosed with breast cancer, and followed their treatments and progress over several years.

All of the women in the study had at least two affected close relatives, so their risk of developing breast cancer due to an inherited factor (such as a *BRCA* mutation) was estimated to be greater than that of the general population.

1. According to this study, what is a woman's risk of dying of cancer if two of her close relatives have breast cancer?

2. What is her risk of dying of cancer if she carries a mutated *BRCA1* gene?

3. According to these results, is a *BRCA1* or *BRCA2* mutation more dangerous in breast cancer cases?

4. What other data would you have to see in order to make a conclusion about the effectiveness of preventive mastectomy or oophorectomy?

| *BRCA* Mutations in Women Diagnosed With Breast Cancer | | | | |
|---|---|---|---|---|
| | *BRCA1* | *BRCA2* | No *BRCA* Mutation | Total |
| Total number of patients | 89 | 35 | 318 | 442 |
| Avg. age at diagnosis | 43.9 | 46.2 | 50.4 | |
| Preventive mastectomy | 6 | 3 | 14 | 23 |
| Preventive oophorectomy | 38 | 7 | 22 | 67 |
| Number of deaths | 16 | 1 | 21 | 38 |
| Percent died | 18.0 | 2.8 | 6.9 | 8.6 |

**FIGURE 7.16** Results from a 2007 study investigating *BRCA* mutations in women diagnosed with breast cancer. All women in the study had a family history of the disease.

Some of the women underwent preventive mastectomy (removal of the noncancerous breast) during their course of treatment. Others had preventive oophorectomy (surgical removal of the ovaries) to prevent the possibility of getting ovarian cancer.

*Top,* model of the unmutated *BRCA1* protein.

---

12. Use Figure 7.5 to translate this nucleotide base sequence into an amino acid sequence, starting at the first base:

    GGUUUCUUGAAGAGA

13. Translate the sequence of bases in the previous question, starting at the second base.

14. Homeotic gene products _____ .
    a. map out the overall body plan in embryos
    b. control the formation of specific body parts

15. Which of the following includes all of the others?
    a. homeotic genes
    b. master genes
    c. *SRY* gene
    d. *PAX 6*

16. A cell with a Barr body is _____ .
    a. prokaryotic
    b. a sex cell
    c. from a female mammal
    d. infected by Barr virus

17. Match each term with the most suitable description.
    _____ genetic message
    _____ sequence
    _____ polysome
    _____ *eyeless*
    _____ genetic code
    _____ differentiation
    _____ transposable element

    a. cells become specialized
    b. gets around
    c. read as base triplets
    d. linear order of bases
    e. occurs only in groups
    f. set of 64 codons
    g. homeotic

Additional questions are available on CENGAGENOW™

## Critical Thinking

1. An anticodon has the sequence GCG. What amino acid does this tRNA carry? What would be the effect of a mutation that changed the C of the anticodon to a G?

2. Each position of a codon can be occupied by one of four (4) nucleotides. What is the minimum number of nucleotides per codon necessary to specify all 20 of the amino acids that are found in proteins?

3. Unlike most rodents, guinea pigs are well developed at the time of birth. Suppose a breeder decides to separate baby guinea pigs from their mothers three weeks after they were born. He wants to raise the males and the females in different cages. However, he has trouble identifying the sex of young guinea pigs. Suggest how a quick look through a microscope can help him identify the females.

4. Cigarette smoke contains at least fifty-five different chemicals identified as carcinogenic (cancer-causing) by the International Agency for Research on Cancer (IARC). When these carcinogens enter the bloodstream, enzymes convert them to a series of chemical intermediates that are easier to excrete. Some of the intermediates bind irreversibly to DNA. Propose a hypothesis about why such binding causes cancer.

# 8 How Cells Reproduce

# Immortal cell lines allow researchers to study human diseases without experimenting on people.

## 8.1 Impacts/Issues: Henrietta's Immortal Cells

Each human starts out as a fertilized egg. By the time of birth, the human body consists of about a trillion cells, all descended from that single cell. Even in an adult, billions of cells divide every day as new cells replace worn-out ones. However, human cells tend to divide a few times and die within weeks when grown in the laboratory.

Researchers started trying to coax human cells to become immortal—to keep dividing outside of the body—in the mid-1800s. Why? Many human diseases occur only in human cells. Immortal cell lineages, or cell lines, would allow researchers to study human diseases (and potential cures for them) without experimenting on people.

At Johns Hopkins University, George and Margaret Gey were among the researchers trying to culture human cells. They had been working on the problem for almost thirty years when, in 1951, their assistant Mary Kubicek prepared a sample of human cancer cells. Mary named the cells *HeLa*, after the first and last names of the patient from whom the cells had been taken.

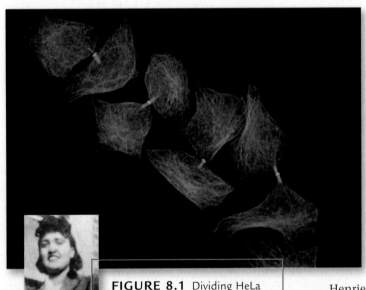

The HeLa cells began to divide, again and again. The cells were astonishingly vigorous. They quickly coated the inside of their test tube and consumed the nutrient broth in which they were bathed. Four days later, there were so many cells that the researchers had to transfer them to more tubes. The cell populations increased at a phenomenal rate. The cells were dividing every twenty-four hours and coating the inside of the tubes within days.

Sadly, cancer cells in the patient were dividing just as fast. Just six months after she had been diagnosed with cervical cancer, malignant cells had invaded tissues throughout her body. Two months after that, Henrietta Lacks, a young African American woman from Baltimore, was dead.

Although Henrietta passed away, her cells lived on in the Geys' laboratory (Figure 8.1). The Geys were able to grow poliovirus in HeLa cells, a practice that enabled them to find out which strains of the virus cause polio. That work was a critical step in the development of polio vaccines, which have since saved millions of lives.

**FIGURE 8.1** Dividing HeLa cells (*above*), a cellular legacy of Henrietta Lacks (*left*), who was a young casualty of cancer.

Henrietta Lacks's cells, frozen away in tiny tubes and packed in Styrofoam boxes, continue to be shipped among laboratories all over the world. Researchers use those cells to investigate cancer, viral growth, protein synthesis, and the effects of radiation. They helped several researchers win Nobel Prizes for research in medicine and chemistry. Some HeLa cells even traveled into space for experiments on the *Discoverer XVII* satellite.

Henrietta Lacks was thirty-one, a wife and mother of five, when runaway cell divisions killed her. Her legacy continues to help people, through her cells that are still dividing, again and again, more than fifty years after she died. Understanding why cancer cells are immortal—and why we are not—begins with understanding the structures and mechanisms that cells use to divide.

| Table 8.1 | Comparison of Division Mechanisms | | |
|---|---|---|---|
| | | Mechanism | |
| Function | Mitosis | Meiosis | Prokaryotic Fission |
| Increases in body size during growth | X | | |
| Replacement of dead or worn-out cells | X | | |
| Repair of damaged tissues | X | | |
| Asexual reproduction | X | | X |
| Sexual reproduction | | X | |

**FIGURE 8.2** A multicelled animal develops by repeated divisions of a fertilized egg. This photo shows early frog embryos, each a product of three divisions of one fertilized egg. **Figure It Out:** Each of these embryos consists of how many cells? *Answer: Eight*

# 8.2 Multiplication by Division

A cell reproduces by dividing in two. Each of its cellular offspring must inherit a complete set of chromosomes, or it will not grow or function properly. Each descendant cell must also inherit some of the parent's cytoplasm, which contains all the enzymes, organelles, and other metabolic machinery necessary for life. A descendant cell that inherits a blob of cytoplasm is getting startup metabolic machinery that will keep it running until it can make its own.

In general, a eukaryotic cell cannot simply split in two, because only one of its descendant cells would get the nucleus (and the DNA). Thus, a cell's cytoplasm splits only after its DNA has been packaged into more than one nucleus by way of mitosis or meiosis. These two processes have much in common, but their outcomes differ (Table 8.1).

**Mitosis** is a nuclear division mechanism that maintains the chromosome number. Mitosis and cytoplasmic division are the basis of increases in body size during development (Figure 8.2), and ongoing replacements of damaged or dead cells. Many species of plants, animals, fungi, and protists also make copies of themselves, or reproduce asexually, by mitosis and cytoplasmic division. Prokaryotes (bacteria and archaeans) also reproduce asexually, but they do it by prokaryotic fission, a mechanism that we consider in Section 13.4.

**Meiosis**, a nuclear division mechanism that halves the chromosome number, is the basis of sexual reproduction. In humans and all other mammals, meiosis in reproductive cells results in sperm and eggs. Spores, which protect and disperse new generations, form by meiosis during the life cycle of fungi, plants, and many kinds of protists.

## Take-Home Message  What is cell division and why does it happen?

- When a cell divides, each descendant cell receives a set of chromosomes and some cytoplasm. In eukaryotic cells, the nucleus divides first, then cytoplasm.

- Mitosis is a nuclear division mechanism that maintains the chromosome number. It is the basis of body size increases, cell replacements, and tissue repair in multicelled eukaryotes; and asexual reproduction in single-celled and some multicelled eukaryotes.

- In eukaryotes, a nuclear division mechanism called meiosis precedes the formation of gametes or spores. It is the basis of sexual reproduction.

**meiosis** Nuclear division process that halves the chromosome number. Basis of sexual reproduction.

**mitosis** Nuclear division mechanism that maintains the chromosome number. Basis of body growth, tissue repair and replacement in multicelled eukaryotes; also asexual reproduction in some plants, animals, fungi, and protists.

# 8.3 The Life of a Cell

Just as we describe the series of events in an animal's life as a life cycle, we can describe the events that occur from the time a cell forms until the time it divides as a **cell cycle** (Figure 8.3). There are three phases to the cell cycle: mitosis and cytoplasmic division (topics of the following sections), and interphase. During **interphase**, a cell increases its mass, roughly doubles the number of its cytoplasmic components, and replicates its DNA. Interphase is typically the longest phase, and it consists of three stages:

    ❶ G1, the first interval (or gap) of cell growth before DNA replication

    ❷ S, the time of synthesis (DNA replication)

    ❸ G2, the second interval (or gap) when the cell prepares to divide

Gap intervals were named because outwardly they seem to be periods of inactivity. Actually, most cells going about their metabolic business are in G1. Cells preparing to divide enter S, when they copy their DNA. During G2, they make the proteins that will drive mitosis. Once S begins, DNA replication usually proceeds at a predictable rate and ends before the cell divides.

Different types of cells proceed through the cell cycle at different rates. For example, the stem cells in your red bone marrow divide every 12 hours. Their descendants become red blood cells that replace 2 to 3 million worn-out ones in your blood each second. Cells in the tips of a bean plant root divide every 19 hours. The cells in a fruit fly embryo divide every 10 minutes.

Gene expression controls (Section 7.7) affect the rate of the cell division. Some of the controls function as built-in brakes on the cell cycle. Apply the brakes that work in G1, and the cycle stalls in G1. Lift the brakes, and the cycle runs again. Sometimes the brakes are not lifted. For example, the nerve cells of adult humans are stuck in G1 of interphase. Because the cell cycle of these cells cannot proceed, they do not divide. Thus, damaged nerve cells cannot be replaced by new ones.

If such controls over the cell cycle stop working, the body may be endangered. As you will see shortly, cancer begins this way. Crucial controls are lost, and the cell cycle spins out of control.

**FIGURE 8.3 Animated!** The eukaryotic cell cycle. The length of the intervals differs among cells. G1, S, and G2 are part of interphase.

❶ G1 is the interval of growth before DNA replication. The cell's chromosomes are unduplicated during this stage.

❷ S is the time of synthesis. The name refers to DNA synthesis, because the cell copies its DNA during this stage.

❸ G2 is the interval after DNA replication and before mitosis. The cell prepares to divide during this phase.

❹ Mitosis begins as interphase ends.

❺ The nucleus divides during mitosis.

❻ At the end of mitosis, the cytoplasm typically divides, and the cycle begins anew in interphase for each descendant cell.

mitosis ends,
interphase begins

interphase ends,
mitosis begins

**A** An unduplicated pair of chromosomes in a cell in G1.

**B** By G2, each chromosome has been duplicated.

**C** Mitosis and cytoplasmic division package one copy of each chromosome into each of two new cells.

**FIGURE 8.4** How mitosis maintains the chromosome number.

**Chromosomes During the Cell Cycle** Remember from Section 6.2 that human body cells have 46 chromosomes—two of each type. Except for a pairing of sex chromosomes (XY) in males, the chromosomes of each pair are **homologous**, which means they have the same length, shape, and collection of genes (*hom–* means alike). Typically, each member of a chromosome pair was inherited from one of two parents.

With mitosis followed by cytoplasmic division, a diploid parent cell produces two diploid descendant cells. Both offspring have the same number and kind of chromosomes as the parent. Thus, mitosis maintains the chromosome number. However, it is not just that each new cell gets twelve or forty-eight or two hundred and eight chromosomes. If only the total mattered, then one of the cell's offspring might get, say, two pairs of chromosome 22 and no pairs whatsoever of chromosome 9. A cell cannot function properly without a full complement of DNA, which means it needs to have one copy of each chromosome.

When a cell is in G1, each of its chromosomes consists of one double-stranded DNA molecule (Figure 8.4**A**). A cell replicates its DNA in S. By G2, each chromosome consists of *two* double-stranded DNA molecules (Figure 8.4**B**). The two molecules stay attached to one another at the centromere until mitosis is almost over. Until they separate, the two DNA molecules are called sister chromatids. By the time a cell enters mitosis (Figure 8.3 ❹), its chromosomes have already been duplicated. As you will see in the next section, mitosis parcels one copy of each chromosome (one sister chromatid) into each of two new nuclei ❺. When the cytoplasm divides, the two nuclei are packaged into separate cells (Figure 8.4**C**). Each new cell has a full complement of unduplicated chromosomes, and each starts the cell cycle over again in G1 of interphase ❻.

## Take-Home Message  What is a cell cycle?

- A cell cycle is a sequence of stages (interphase, mitosis, and cytoplasmic division) through which a cell passes during its lifetime.

- During interphase, a new cell increases its mass, doubles the number of its cytoplasmic components, and duplicates its chromosomes. The cycle ends after the cell undergoes mitosis and then divides its cytoplasm.

**cell cycle** A series of events from the time a cell forms until its cytoplasm divides.

**homologous** Refers to the two members of a pair of chromosomes with the same length, shape, and genes.

**interphase** In a eukaryotic cell cycle, the interval between mitotic divisions when a cell grows, roughly doubles the number of its cytoplasmic components, and replicates its DNA.

**FIGURE 8.5 Animated!** Mitosis. Micrographs here and opposite show plant cells (onion root, *left*), and animal cells (whitefish embryo, *right*). *This page*, interphase cells are shown for comparison, but interphase is not part of mitosis.

*Opposite page*, the stages of mitosis. The drawings show a diploid (2n) animal cell. For clarity, only two pairs of chromosomes are illustrated, but nearly all eukaryotic cells have more than two. The two chromosomes of the pair inherited from one parent are *pink*; the two chromosomes from the other parent are *blue*.

Onion root cell (Interphase)

Whitefish embryo cell (Interphase)

# 8.4 Mitosis

A cell's chromosomes are loosened during interphase to allow for transcription and DNA replication. In preparation for nuclear division, they begin to condense tightly (Figure 8.5 ❶). Transcription and DNA replication stop as the chromosomes pack into their more easily transported compact form.

We can tell that a cell is in **prophase**, the first stage of mitosis, when its chromosomes have condensed so much that they are visible under a light microscope ❷. "Mitosis" is from the Greek word for thread, *mitos*, after the threadlike appearance of chromosomes during nuclear division.

Most animal cells have a centrosome, a region near the nucleus that organizes microtubules while they are forming. The centrosome usually includes two barrel-shaped centrioles, and it is duplicated just before prophase begins. During prophase, one of the two centrosomes (along with its pair of centrioles) moves to the opposite side of the cell, and microtubules that will form a spindle begin to grow from both centrosomes. A **spindle** is a dynamic network of microtubules that attaches to and moves chromosomes during nuclear division. Motor proteins (Section 3.6) traveling along the microtubules help the spindle grow in the appropriate directions.

As prophase ends, the nuclear envelope breaks up and spindle microtubules penetrate the nuclear region ❸. Some microtubules from each spindle pole stop growing after they overlap in the middle of the cell. Others continue to grow until they reach a chromosome and attach to it. At that point, one chromatid of each chromosome is attached to microtubules extending from one spindle pole, and its sister chromatid is attached to microtubules extending from the other spindle pole. The opposing sets of microtubules begin a tug-of-war by adding and losing tubulin subunits. As the microtubules grow and shrink, they push and pull the chromosomes. When all the microtubules are the same length, the chromosomes are aligned midway between the spindle poles ❹. The alignment marks **metaphase** (from *meta*, the ancient Greek word for between).

During **anaphase**, microtubules of the spindle separate the sister chromatids of each duplicated chromosome, and move them toward opposite spindle poles ❺. Each DNA molecule has now become a separate chromosome. Anaphase ends as the chromosomes are heading toward opposite spindle poles.

**Telophase** begins when the two clusters of chromosomes reach the spindle poles ❻. Each cluster consists of the parental complement of chromosomes—two of each, if the parent cell was diploid. A new nucleus forms around each

**anaphase** Stage of mitosis in which sister chromatids separate and move to opposite spindle poles.

**metaphase** Stage of mitosis during which the cell's chromosomes align midway between poles of the spindle.

**prophase** Stage of mitosis in which chromosomes condense and become attached to a newly forming spindle.

**spindle** Dynamically assembled and disassembled array of microtubules that moves chromosomes during nuclear division.

**telophase** Stage of mitosis during which chromosomes arrive at the spindle poles and decondense, and new nuclei form.

centrosome

### ① Early Prophase
Mitosis begins. In the nucleus, the DNA begins to appear grainy as it organizes and condenses. The centrosome is duplicated.

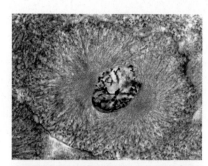

### ② Prophase
The chromosomes become visible as distinct structures as they condense further. Microtubules assemble and move one of the two centrosomes to the opposite side of the nucleus, and the nuclear envelope breaks up.

### ③ Transition to Metaphase
The nuclear envelope is gone, and the chromosomes are at their most condensed. Spindle microtubules assemble and attach sister chromatids to opposite spindle poles.

pole    pole

microtubule of spindle

### ④ Metaphase
All of the chromosomes are aligned midway between the spindle poles. Microtubules attach each chromatid to one of the spindle poles, and its sister to the opposite pole.

### ⑤ Anaphase
Motor proteins moving along spindle microtubules drag the chromatids toward the spindle poles, and the sister chromatids separate. Each sister chromatid is now a separate chromosome.

### ⑥ Telophase
The chromosomes reach the spindle poles and decondense. A nuclear envelope forms around each cluster. Mitosis is over.

cluster as the chromosomes loosen up again. Thus, two nuclei form. The parent cell in our example was diploid, so each new nucleus is diploid too. Once two nuclei have formed, telophase is over, and so is mitosis.

## Take-Home Message
### What happens during mitosis?

- Each chromosome in a cell's nucleus was duplicated before mitosis begins, so each consists of two DNA molecules (sister chromatids).

- In prophase, the chromosomes condense and a spindle forms. The nuclear envelope breaks up. Spindle microtubules attach to the chromosomes.

- At metaphase, the chromosomes (still duplicated) are aligned midway between the spindle poles.

- In anaphase, microtubules separate the sister chromatids of each chromosome, and pull them toward opposite spindle poles. Each DNA molecule is now a separate chromosome.

- In telophase, two clusters of chromosomes reach the spindle poles. A new nuclear envelope forms around each cluster.

- Two new nuclei form at the end of mitosis. Each one has the same chromosome number as the parent cell's nucleus.

## 8.5 Cytoplasmic Division Mechanisms

A cell's cytoplasm usually divides after mitosis, so two cells form, each with their own nucleus. The process of cytoplasmic division differs among eukaryotes.

Typical animal cells divide simply by pinching in two. How? The cell cortex, which is the mesh of cytoskeletal elements just under the plasma membrane, includes a band of actin and myosin filaments that wraps around the cell's mid-section. The band of filaments is called a **contractile ring** because it contracts when its component proteins are energized by ATP. When the ring contracts, it shrinks, and it drags the plasma membrane inward as it does. The sinking plasma membrane is visible on the outside of the cell as an indentation between the former spindle poles (Figure 8.6**A,B**). The indentation is called a **cleavage furrow**. The furrow advances around the cell, deepening as it does, until the cytoplasm (and the cell) is pinched in two (Figure 8.6**C,D**). Two new cells form this way. Each has a nucleus and some of the parent cell's cytoplasm, and each is enclosed in its own plasma membrane.

**FIGURE 8.6 Animated!** Cytoplasmic division of an animal cell.

**A** After mitosis is completed, the spindle begins to disassemble.

**B** At the midpoint of the former spindle, a ring of actin and myosin filaments attached to the plasma membrane contracts.

**C** This contractile ring pulls the cell surface inward as it shrinks.

**D** The ring contracts until it pinches the cell in two.

**A** The plane of division was established before mitosis began. Vesicles cluster here when mitosis ends.

**B** As the vesicles fuse with each other, they form a cell plate along the plane of division.

cell plate forming

**C** The cell plate expands outward along the plane of division. When it reaches the plasma membrane, it attaches to the membrane and partitions the cytoplasm.

**D** The cell plate matures as two new cell walls that join with the parent cell wall, so each descendant cell becomes enclosed by its own cell wall.

**FIGURE 8.7 Animated!** Cytoplasmic division of a plant cell.

Dividing plant cells face a particular challenge because they have cell walls that are stiffened with cellulose (Section 2.7). The mechanism that pinches an animal cell in two would not be strong enough to pinch a plant cell wall. Accordingly, plant cells have an extra step in their cytoplasmic division process, which begins before mitosis is finished. By the end of anaphase in a plant cell, a set of short microtubules has formed on either side of the division plane. These microtubules now guide vesicles from Golgi bodies and the cell surface to the division plane (Figure 8.7**A**). There, the vesicles and their wall-building contents start to fuse into a disk-shaped **cell plate** (Figure 8.7**B**). The plate grows outward until its edges reach the plasma membrane (Figure 8.7**C**). It attaches to the membrane, and so partitions the cytoplasm. In time, the cell plate will develop into a primary cell wall that merges with the parent cell's wall. Thus, by the end of division, each of the descendant cells will be enclosed by its own plasma membrane and its own cell wall (Figure 8.7**D**).

## Take-Home Message How do cells divide?

- After mitosis, the cytoplasm of the parent cell typically is partitioned into two descendant cells, each with its own nucleus. The process of cytoplasmic division differs between plants and animals.

- In animal cells, a contractile ring pinches the cytoplasm in two. In plant cells, a cell plate that forms midway between the spindle poles partitions the cytoplasm when it reaches and connects to the parent cell wall.

## 8.6 Sexual Reproduction and Meiosis

**Introducing Alleles** An individual's genes collectively contain the information necessary to make a new individual. With **asexual reproduction**, one parent produces offspring, so all of its offspring inherit the same number and kinds of genes. Mutations aside, then, all offspring of asexual reproduction are genetically identical copies of the parent, or **clones**.

**asexual reproduction** Reproductive mode by which offspring arise from one parent and inherit that parent's genes only.

**cell plate** After nuclear division in a plant cell, a disk-shaped structure that forms a cross-wall between the two new nuclei.

**cleavage furrow** In a dividing animal cell, the indentation where cytoplasmic division will occur.

**clone** A genetically identical copy of an organism.

**contractile ring** A thin band of actin and myosin filaments that wraps around the midsection of an animal cell. During cytoplasmic division, the band contracts and pinches the cytoplasm in two.

## FIGURE 8.8

A chromosome pair. The two appear identical in this micrograph, but any gene might differ in DNA sequence from its partner on the other chromosome.

Inheritance is far more complicated with **sexual reproduction**, a process in which two parents contribute genes to offspring. So why sex? Variation in forms and combinations of heritable traits is typical of sexually reproducing populations. Some forms of traits help an organism survive under conditions that prevail in its environment. If those conditions change, some of the diverse offspring of sexual reproducers may have forms of traits or combinations of them that help these individuals to survive the change. All offspring of asexual reproducers are adapted the same way to the environment—and equally vulnerable to changes in it. Sexual reproduction mixes up the genetic information of two individuals that have different forms of heritable traits. It brings together adaptive traits, and separates adaptive traits from maladaptive ones, in far fewer generations than does mutation alone.

The body cells of multicelled organisms that reproduce sexually contain pairs of chromosomes. Typically, one chromosome of each pair is maternal and the other is paternal (Figure 8.8). Except for the pair of nonidentical sex chromosomes, the two chromosomes of every pair carry the same set of genes. If the information in every gene pair were identical, then sexual reproduction would produce clones, just like asexual reproduction. Just imagine: The entire human population might consist of clones, in which case everybody would look alike.

But the two genes of a pair are often not identical. Why not? Mutations that inevitably accumulate in DNA change its sequence. Thus, the genes of a pair might encode slightly different forms of the gene's product.

Different forms of the same gene are called **alleles**. Alleles influence differences in thousands of traits. For example, the mutated genes that cause sickle-cell anemia and thalassemia (Section 7.6) are two of over 700 known alleles of the human beta globin gene. Alleles are one reason that the individuals of a sexually reproducing species do not all look exactly the same. The offspring of sexual reproducers inherit new combinations of alleles, which is the basis of new combinations of traits.

**Meiosis Halves the Chromosome Number** Sexual reproduction involves the fusion of reproductive cells from two parents. The process begins with meiosis, a nuclear division process that halves the chromosome number. Meiosis occurs in immature reproductive cells (germ cells) of multicelled eukaryotes that reproduce sexually. In animals, meiosis in germ cells results in mature reproductive cells called **gametes**. A sperm cell is an example of a male gamete. An egg is a female gamete. Gametes usually form inside special reproductive structures or organs (Figure 8.9).

Gametes have a single set of chromosomes, so they are **haploid** ($n$): Their chromosome number is half of the diploid ($2n$) number. Human body cells are diploid, with 23 pairs of homologous chromosomes. Meiosis of a human germ cell ($2n$) normally produces gametes with 23 chromosomes: one of each pair ($n$). The diploid chromosome number is restored at **fertilization**, when two haploid gametes (one egg and one sperm, for example) fuse to form a **zygote**, which is the first cell of a new individual.

The process of meiosis is similar to mitosis in certain respects. A cell duplicates its DNA before the division process starts. The two DNA molecules and associated proteins stay attached at the centromere. For as long as they remain attached, they are sister chromatids. As in mitosis, the microtubules of a spindle move the chromosomes to opposite poles of the cell. However, meiosis sorts the chromosomes into new nuclei twice. Two consecutive nuclear divisions form

Reproductive organs of a human male

testis (where sperm originate)

Reproductive organs of a human female

ovary (where eggs develop)

## FIGURE 8.9 Animated!

Meiosis of germ cells in reproductive organs gives rise to gametes.

four haploid nuclei. There is typically no interphase between the two divisions, which are called meiosis I and II:

In meoisis I, every duplicated chromosome aligns with its partner. After they are sorted and arranged this way, each homologous chromosome is pulled away from its partner:

each chromosome in the cell pairs with its homologous partner  then the partners separate

After the homologous chromosomes are pulled apart, each ends up in one of two new nuclei. At this stage, the chromosomes are still duplicated (sister chromatids are still attached to one another). During meiosis II, the sister chromatids of each chromosome are pulled apart, so each becomes an individual, unduplicated chromosome:

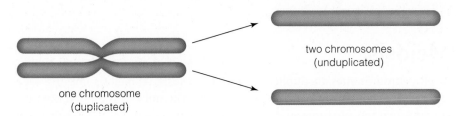

two chromosomes
(unduplicated)

one chromosome
(duplicated)

Meiosis distributes the duplicated chromosomes of a diploid nucleus ($2n$) into four new nuclei. Each new nucleus is haploid ($n$), with one unduplicated version of each chromosome.

Sexual reproduction mixes up the genetic information of two individuals that have different forms of heritable traits.

## Take-Home Message How does sexual reproduction introduce variation in heritable traits?

- The cells of sexually reproducing organisms have pairs of homologous chromosomes, with pairs of genes. Paired genes may vary in sequence as alleles.

- Alleles are the basis of traits. Sexual reproduction mixes up alleles from two parents. It results in new combinations of alleles—thus new combinations of traits—in offspring.

- Meiosis occurs in immature reproductive cells of sexually reproducing eukaryotes. It halves the diploid ($2n$) chromosome number, to the haploid number ($n$), for forthcoming gametes.

- When two gametes fuse at fertilization, the chromosome number is restored. The new individual has two sets of chromosomes, one from each parent.

**alleles** Forms of a gene that encode slightly different versions of the gene's product.

**fertilization** Fusion of a sperm nucleus and an egg nucleus, the result being a single-celled zygote.

**gamete** Mature, haploid reproductive cell.

**haploid** Having one of each type of chromosome characteristic of the species.

**sexual reproduction** Reproductive mode by which offspring arise from two parents and inherit genes from both.

**zygote** Cell formed by fusion of gametes; first cell of a new individual.

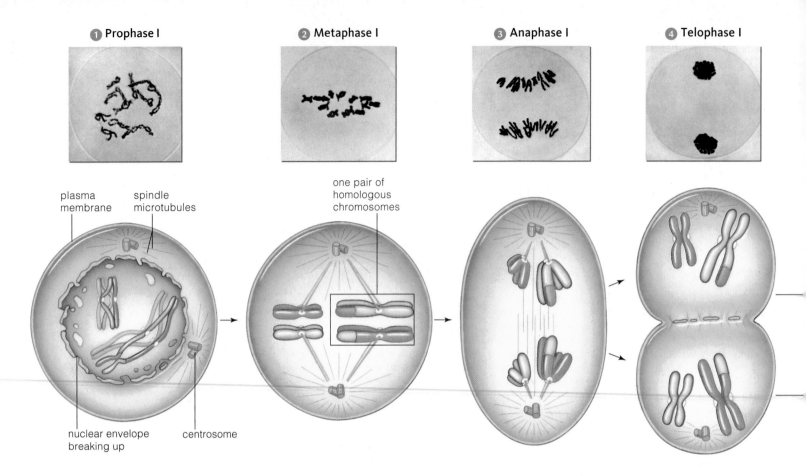

**①Prophase I**  **②Metaphase I**  **③Anaphase I**  **④Telophase I**

plasma membrane   spindle microtubules

one pair of homologous chromosomes

nuclear envelope breaking up   centrosome

**FIGURE 8.10 Animated!** Meiosis. Two pairs of chromosomes are illustrated in a diploid (2*n*) animal cell. Homologous chromosomes are indicated in *blue* and *pink*. Micrographs show meiosis in a lily plant cell (*Lilium regale*).

① Prophase I. The (duplicated) chromosomes condense, and spindle microtubules attach to them as the nuclear envelope breaks up.

② Metaphase I. The (duplicated) chromosomes are aligned midway between spindle poles.

③ Anaphase I. Homologous chromosomes separate.

④ Telophase I. Two clusters of chromosomes reach the spindle poles. A new nuclear envelope encloses each cluster, so two haploid (*n*) nuclei form.

⑤ Prophase II. The (still duplicated) chromosomes condense, and spindle microtubules attach to each sister chromatid as the nuclear envelope breaks up.

⑥ Metaphase II. The chromosomes are aligned midway between the spindle poles.

⑦ Anaphase II. Sister chromatids separate and become individual chromosomes (unduplicated).

⑧ Telophase II. A cluster of (unduplicated) chromosomes reaches each spindle pole. A new nuclear envelope encloses each cluster, so four haploid (*n*) nuclei form.

# 8.7 Meiosis

A cell's chromosomes are duplicated prior to meiosis. As meiosis I begins, each chromosome consists of two sister chromatids. The nucleus is diploid (2*n*): It contains two sets of chromosomes, one from each parent. During the first stage of meiosis, prophase I, the chromosomes condense, and homologous chromosomes align tightly and swap segments (Figure 8.10). The centrosome (with its two centrioles) is duplicated, and one centriole pair moves to the opposite side of the cell as the nuclear envelope breaks up. Spindle microtubules begin to extend from the centrosomes ①. By the end of prophase I, spindle microtubules connect the chromosomes to the spindle poles. Each chromosome is now attached to one spindle pole, and the homologous chromosome of the pair is attached to the other. The microtubules grow and shrink, pushing and pulling the chromosomes as they do. At metaphase I, all of the microtubules are the same length, and the chromosomes are aligned midway between the poles of the spindle ②.

In anaphase I, the spindle microtubules separate homologous chromosomes and pull them toward opposite spindle poles ③. During telophase I, the chromosomes reach the spindle poles ④. New nuclear envelopes form around the two clusters of chromosomes as the DNA loosens up. Each of the two haploid (*n*) nuclei that form contains one set of (duplicated) chromosomes. The cytoplasm may divide at this point to form two haploid cells, but the DNA is not replicated before meiosis II begins.

During prophase II, the chromosomes condense as a new spindle forms. One centriole moves to the opposite side of each new nucleus, and the nuclear envelopes break up. By the end of prophase II, microtubules connect the chro-

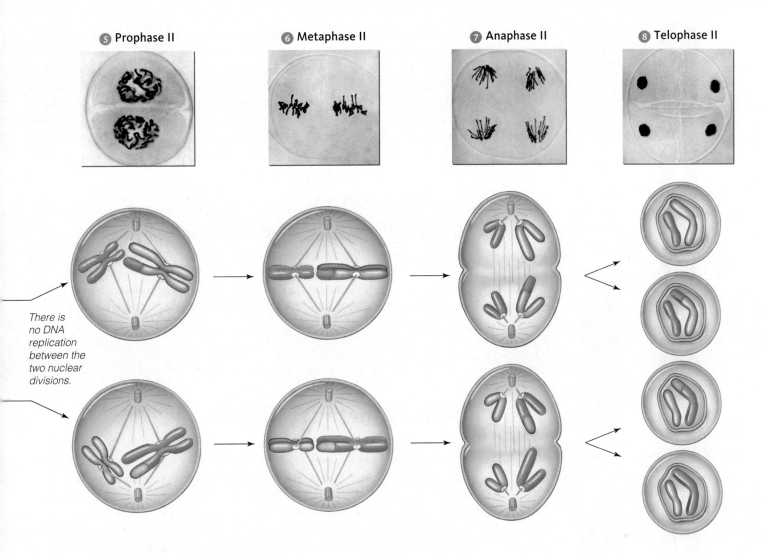

**5 Prophase II**　　**6 Metaphase II**　　**7 Anaphase II**　　**8 Telophase II**

*There is no DNA replication between the two nuclear divisions.*

mosomes to the spindle poles. Each chromatid is now attached to one spindle pole, and its sister is attached to the other **5**. The microtubules grow and shrink, pushing and pulling the chromosomes as they do. At metaphase II, all of the microtubules are the same length, and the chromosomes are aligned midway between the spindle poles **6**.

In anaphase II, the spindle microtubules pull the sister chromatids apart **7**. Each chromosome now consists of one molecule of DNA. During telophase II, the chromosomes (unduplicated) reach the spindle poles **8**. New nuclear envelopes form around the four clusters of chromosomes as the DNA loosens up. Each of the four haploid (*n*) nuclei that form contains one set of (unduplicated) chromosomes. The cytoplasm may divide to form four haploid cells.

**Crossing Over** Early in prophase I of meiosis, all chromosomes in a germ cell condense. When they do, each is drawn close to its homologue. The chromatids of one homologous chromosome become tightly aligned with the chromatids of the other along their length:

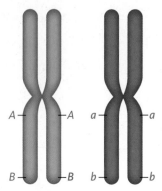

**A** Here, we focus on only two genes. One gene has alleles *A* and *a*; the other has alleles *B* and *b*.

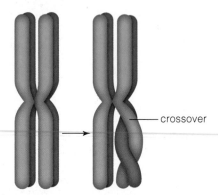

crossover

**B** Close contact between the homologous chromosomes promotes crossing over between nonsister chromatids, so paternal and maternal chromatids exchange segments.

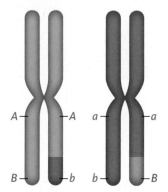

**C** Crossing over mixes up paternal and maternal alleles on homologous chromosomes.

**FIGURE 8.11 Animated!** Crossing over. *Blue* signifies a paternal chromosome, and *pink*, its maternal homologue. For clarity, we show only one pair of homologous chromosomes and one crossover, but more than one crossover may occur in each chromosome pair.

This tight, parallel orientation favors **crossing over**, a process by which a chromosome and its homologous partner exchange corresponding pieces of DNA (Figure 8.11). Crossing over is a normal and frequent process in meiosis, but the rate of crossing over varies among species and among chromosomes. In humans, between 46 and 95 crossovers occur per meiosis, so each chromosome crosses over at least once. Each crossover event is an opportunity for homologous chromosomes to exchange alleles. Thus, crossing over introduces novel combinations of alleles in both members of a pair of homologous chromosomes, which results in novel combinations of traits among offspring.

## Take-Home Message **What happens during meiosis?**

- During meiosis, the nucleus of a diploid (*2n*) cell divides twice. Four haploid (*n*) nuclei form, each with a full set of chromosomes—one of each type.

- Crossing over is recombination between nonsister chromatids of homologous chromosomes during prophase I. It makes new combinations of parental alleles.

## 8.8 From Gametes to Offspring

All gametes are typically haploid, but they differ in their details. For example, human male gametes—**sperm**—have one flagellum. Opossum sperm have two, and roundworm sperm have none. A flowering plant's male gamete is simply a sperm nucleus. We leave most of the details of sexual reproduction for later chapters, but you will need to know a few concepts before you get there.

In plants, two kinds of multicelled bodies form. **Sporophytes** are typically diploid, and spores form by meiosis in their specialized parts (Figure 8.12**A**). Spores consist of one or a few haploid cells. These cells undergo mitosis and give rise to a **gametophyte**, a multicelled haploid body inside which one or more gametes form. As an example, sequoia trees are sporophytes. Male and female gametophytes develop inside different types of cones that form on each tree. In flowering plants, gametophytes form in flowers.

The gametes of animals arise by mitosis of diploid germ cells (Figure 8.12**B**). In male animals, a germ cell develops into a primary spermatocyte. This large cell divides by meiosis, producing four haploid cells that develop into spermatids. Each spermatid matures as a sperm.

In female animals, a germ cell becomes a primary oocyte, which is an immature egg. This cell undergoes meiosis and division, as occurs with a primary spermatocyte. However, the cytoplasm of a primary oocyte divides unequally, so the cells that result differ in size and function. Two haploid cells form when the primary oocyte divides after meiosis I. One of the cells is called a first polar body. The other cell, the secondary oocyte, is much larger because it gets nearly all of the parent cell's cytoplasm. This cell undergoes meiosis II and cytoplasmic division. One of the two cells that forms is a second polar body. The other cell gets most of the cytoplasm and matures into a female gamete, which is called an ovum (plural, ova), or **egg**.

Polar bodies are not nutrient-rich or plump with cytoplasm, and generally do not function as gametes. In time they degenerate. Their formation simply ensures that the egg will have a haploid chromosome number, and also will get enough metabolic machinery to support early divisions of the new individual.

**Fertilization** At fertilization, the fusion of two gametes produces a zygote. Fertilization restores the parental chromosome number. If meiosis did not precede fertilization, the chromosome number would double with every generation. If the chromosome number changes, so does the individual's set of genetic instructions. This set is like a fine-tuned blueprint that must be followed exactly, page by page, in order to build a body that functions normally. Changes in the blueprint can have lethal consequences, particularly in animals.

Fertilization also contributes to the variation that we see among offspring of sexual reproducers. Think about it in terms of human reproduction. Cells that give rise to human gametes have twenty-three pairs of homologous chromosomes. Each time a human germ cell undergoes meiosis, the four gametes that form end up with one of 8,388,608 (or $2^{23}$) possible combinations of homologous chromosomes. On top of that, any number of genes may occur as different alleles on the maternal and paternal chromosomes, and crossing over makes mosaics of that genetic information. Then, out of all the male and female gametes that form, which two actually get together at fertilization is a matter of chance. Are you getting an idea of why such fascinating combinations of traits show up among the generations of your own family tree?

**A** Life cycle of plants

**B** Life cycle of animals

**FIGURE 8.12** Comparing the life cycles of animals and plants. **A** Generalized life cycle for most plants. A sequoia tree is a sporophyte. **B** Generalized life cycle for animals. The zygote is the first cell to form when the nuclei of two gametes, such as a sperm and an egg, fuse at fertilization.

## Take-Home Message
**Where does meiosis fit into the life cycle of plants and animals?**

- Meiosis and cytoplasmic division precede the development of haploid gametes in animals and spores in plants.
- The union of two haploid gametes at fertilization results in a diploid zygote.

# 8.9 When Control Is Lost

**Checkpoint Genes and Tumors** What happens when something goes wrong during mitosis or meiosis? Suppose sister chromatids do not separate as they should during mitosis. As a result, one descendant cell ends up with too many chromosomes and the other with too few. Or suppose DNA gets damaged by free radicals, chemicals, or environmental assaults such as ultraviolet radiation. Such problems are frequent and inevitable, so the cell cycle has built-in checkpoints that allow problems to be corrected before the cycle advances.

**crossing over** Process in which homologous chromosomes exchange corresponding segments during meiosis.
**egg** Mature female gamete, or ovum.
**gametophyte** A haploid, multicelled body in which gametes form during the life cycle of plants.
**sperm** Mature male gamete.
**sporophyte** Diploid, spore-producing body of a plant.

FIGURE 8.13 Checkpoint genes put the brakes on cancer. Exposure to ionizing radiation damaged the DNA inside this breast cell nucleus. *Red* dots pinpoint the location of BRCA1 protein, which has clustered around breaks in the cell's chromosomes. The combined action of BRCA1 and other checkpoint gene products blocks mitosis until the breaks are fixed.

Certain proteins, the products of "checkpoint" genes, can monitor whether a cell's DNA has been copied completely, whether it is damaged, and even whether enough nutrients to support cell growth are available. These proteins interact to advance, delay, or stop the cell cycle. Some checkpoint gene products activate a cascade of signaling events that ultimately causes the cell to die (you will read more about this cellular self-destruct mechanism in Section 26.2).

Sometimes a mutation modifies a checkpoint gene so that its protein product no longer works properly. The result may be that the cell skips interphase, and division occurs over and over with no resting period. Or, damaged DNA may be replicated, a process that frequently introduces new mutations (Section 7.6). In still other cases, a mutation alters the signals that make an abnormal cell commit suicide. When checkpoint mechanisms fail, a cell loses control over its cell cycle, and its descendants form a tumor.

Checkpoint genes whose products inhibit mitosis are called tumor suppressors, because tumors form when they are missing. The *BRCA* genes that you read about in Section 7.7 are examples. BRCA proteins regulate, among other things, the expression of enzymes that repair broken DNA (Figure 8.13). That is why mutations in these genes are often found in many types of cancer cells. Viruses such as HPV (human papillomavirus) cause a cell to make proteins that interfere with some checkpoint gene products. Infection with HPV causes noncancerous skin growths called warts, and some kinds are associated with cervical cancers.

**Cancer** Moles and other tumors are neoplasms: abnormal masses of cells that lost control over how they grow and divide (Figure 8.14). Ordinary skin moles are among the noncancerous, or benign, neoplasms. They grow very slowly, and their cells retain the surface recognition proteins that keep them in their home tissue ❶. Unless a benign neoplasm grows too large or becomes irritating, it poses no threat to the body.

A malignant neoplasm is one that is dangerous to health. Cancer occurs when the abnormally dividing cells of a malignant neoplasm disrupt body tissues, physically and metabolically (Figure 8.15). These typically disfigured cells can break loose from home tissues ❷, slip into and out of blood vessels and lymph vessels ❸, and invade other tissues where they do not belong ❹.

Cancer cells typically display the following three characteristics:

- First, cancer cells grow and divide abnormally.

- Second, cancer cells often have an altered plasma membrane and cytoplasm. The membrane may be leaky and have altered or missing proteins. The cytoskeleton may be shrunken, disorganized, or both. The balance of metabolism is often shifted, as in an amplified reliance on ATP formation by fermentation rather than by aerobic respiration.

FIGURE 8.14 **Animated!** Metastasis.

❶ Benign cancer cells grow slowly and stay in their home tissue.

❷ Malignant cancer cells can break away from their home tissue.

❸ The metastasizing cells become attached to the wall of a blood vessel or lymph vessel. They release digestive enzymes that create an opening in the wall, then enter the vessel.

❹ The cells creep or tumble along inside blood vessels, then leave the bloodstream the same way they got in. They start new tumors in new tissues.

❶ benign tumor

❷ malignant tumor

**FIGURE 8.15** Skin cancer: one outcome of cell cycle checkpoint failure. **A** A basal cell carcinoma is the most common type. This slow-growing, raised lump is typically uncolored, reddish-brown, or black.

**B** The second most common form of skin cancer is a squamous cell carcinoma. This pink growth, firm to the touch, grows under the surface of skin.

**C** Malignant melanoma spreads fastest. Cells form dark, encrusted lumps that may itch or bleed easily.

- Third, cancer cells often have a weakened capacity for adhesion. Because their recognition proteins are altered or lost, they do not stick together the way normal cells do, and may break away form their home tissue to establish colonies elsewhere in the body. Metastasis is the name for this process of abnormal cell migration and tissue invasion.

Researchers already know about many mutations that contribute to cancer. They are working to identify drugs that target and destroy cancer cells or stop them from dividing. For example, HeLa cells were used in early tests of taxol, a drug that keeps microtubules from disassembling. If spindle fibers cannot disassemble, mitosis stops. Frequent divisions of cancer cells make them more vulnerable to this poison than normal cells. Such research may yield drugs that can put the brakes on cancer.

## Take-Home Message **How does cancer start?**

- Built-in checkpoints are gene expression controls that advance, delay, or block the cell cycle in response to internal and external conditions.

- The failure of cell cycle checkpoints results in the uncontrolled cell divisions that characterize cancer.

# 8.10 Impacts/Issues Revisited: Henrietta's Immortal Cells

These days, physicians and researchers are required to obtain a signed consent form before they take tissue samples from a patient, but not in the 1950s. It was common at that time for doctors to experiment on patients without their knowledge or consent. Thus, the young resident who was treating Henrietta Lacks's cancerous cervix probably never thought twice about asking permission before he took a sample of it. That sample was the one that the Geys used to establish the HeLa cell line. No one in Henrietta's family knew about the cells until 25 years after she died, and they have not received any compensation to date. It is now illegal to sell one's own organs or tissues, but no one is under a legal obligation to share profits reaped from research on a patient's tissues—or cell lines derived from them—with the donor.

**How Would**

**YOU**  **Vote?**

No one asked Henrietta Lacks's permission to use her cells. Her family did not find out about them until twenty-five years after she died. HeLa cells are still being sold worldwide. Should the family of Henrietta Lacks share in the profits? See CengageNow for details, then vote online (cengagenow.com).

# Summary

**Sections 8.1 and 8.2** A cell reproduces by dividing in two. Each descendant cell receives a full set of chromosomes and some cytoplasm. Nuclear division mechanisms partition chromosomes of a parent cell into new nuclei. The cytoplasm divides by a separate mechanism. Mitosis and cytoplasmic division are the basis of growth, cell replacements, and tissue repair in multicelled species, and asexual reproduction in many species (Figure 8.16). Meiosis, the basis of sexual reproduction in eukaryotes, precedes the formation of gametes or sexual spores.

**Section 8.3** A cell cycle starts when a new cell forms, and ends when the cell reproduces. Most of a cell's activities, including DNA replication, occur in interphase. Mitosis maintains the chromosome number.

CENGAGENOW™ Investigate the stages of the cell cycle with the interaction on CengageNow.

**Section 8.4** During mitosis, duplicated homologous chromosomes line up at the spindle equator, then sister chromatids move apart to opposite spindle poles. Nuclear envelopes form around the two clusters of chromosomes, forming two new nuclei with the parental chromosome number.

CENGAGENOW™ See mitosis proceed with the animation on CengageNow.

**Section 8.5** Mechanisms of cytoplasmic division differ. In animal cells, a contractile ring pinches the cytoplasm in two. In plant cells, a cross-wall forms.

CENGAGENOW™ Compare the cytoplasmic division of plant and animal cells with the animation on CengageNow.

**Section 8.6** Offspring of asexual reproduction are clones. Offspring of sexual reproduction vary in shared traits. In sexual reproduc-

tion, meiosis in germ cells forms haploid gametes that fuse at fertilization. Offspring of most sexual reproducers inherit pairs of chromosomes, one of each pair from the mother and the other from the father. Except for a pair of nonidentical sex chromosomes, the members of a chromosome pair have the same length, shape, and set of genes. Paired genes on homologous chromosomes often vary slightly in DNA sequence, in which case they are called alleles.

**Section 8.7** Meiosis shuffles parental combinations of alleles. In meiosis, two nuclear divisions halve the parental chromosome number. In the first nuclear division, duplicated homologous chromosomes line up and cross over, then move apart, toward opposite spindle poles. Two new nuclear envelopes form around the two clusters of still-duplicated chromosomes. The second nuclear division separates sister chromatids. Four haploid nuclei typically form. Each has one complete set of unduplicated chromosomes.

CENGAGENOW™ Explore what happens in the stages of meiosis with the animation on CengageNow.

**Section 8.8** Haploid gametes form by meiosis during the life cycles of plants and animals. Familiar plants are diploid sporophytes that make haploid spores. Germ cells in the reproductive organs of animals give rise to sperm or eggs. The fusion of two haploid gamete nuclei during fertilization restores the parental chromosome number in the zygote, the first cell of the new individual.

CENGAGENOW™ See how eggs and sperm form with the animation on CengageNow.

**Section 8.9** Checkpoint gene products are gene expression controls that regulate the cell cycle. Disruption of checkpoint gene products, such as by mutations or

| meiosis | | | | | | | | |
|---|---|---|---|---|---|---|---|---|
| Prophase I | Metaphase I | Anaphase I | Telophase I | Prophase II | Metaphase II | Anaphase II | Telophase II |

| mitosis | | | |
|---|---|---|---|
| Prophase | Metaphase | Anaphase | Telophase |

**FIGURE 8.16** Comparison of mitosis and meiosis. We begin both processes with a diploid cell that has two pairs of chromosomes. The chromosomes are duplicated before nuclear division begins. Mitosis maintains the chromosome number. Meiosis halves it, to the haploid number.

# Digging Into Data

### HeLa Cells Are a Genetic Mess

HeLa cells (*left*) continue to be an extremely useful tool in cancer research. One early finding was that HeLa cells vary in chromosome number. The panel of chromosomes in Figure 8.17, originally published in 1989 by Nicholas Popescu and Joseph DiPaolo, shows all of the chromosomes in a single metaphase HeLa cell.

1. What is the chromosome number of this HeLa cell?

2. How many extra chromosomes does this cell have, compared to a normal human body cell?

3. Can you tell that this cell came from a female? How?

**FIGURE 8.17** Chromosomes in a HeLa cell.

---

viruses, causes tumors that may end up as cancer. Cancer cells may metastasize—break loose and colonize distant tissues.

CENGAGENOW™ See how cancers spread through the body with the animation on CengageNow.

## Self-Quiz    Answers in Appendix I

1. How many chromatids does a duplicated chromosome have?

2. Mitosis and cytoplasmic division function in _____ .
   a. asexual reproduction of single-celled eukaryotes
   b. growth and tissue repair in multicelled species
   c. gamete formation in prokaryotes
   d. both a and b

3. _____ maintains the chromosome number; _____ halves it.
   a. mitosis; meiosis           b. meiosis; mitosis

4. Generally, a pair of homologous chromosomes _____ .
   a. carry the same genes       c. are the same length, shape
   b. interact at meiosis        d. all of the above

5. A cell with two of each type of chromosome has a(n) _____ chromosome number.
   a. diploid    b. haploid    c. tetraploid    d. abnormal

6. Interphase is the part of the cell cycle when _____ .
   a. a cell ceases to function
   b. a cell forms its spindle apparatus
   c. a cell grows and duplicates its DNA
   d. mitosis proceeds

7. After mitosis, the chromosome number of the two new cells is _____ the parent cell's.
   a. the same as            c. rearranged compared to
   b. one-half of            d. doubled compared to

8. Only _____ is not a stage of mitosis.
   a. prophase    b. interphase    c. metaphase    d. anaphase

9. Meiosis and cytoplasmic division function in _____ .
   a. asexual reproduction of single-celled eukaryotes
   b. growth and tissue repair
   c. sexual reproduction
   d. both a and b

10. The cell shown at *right* is in anaphase II. I know this because _____ .

11. Sexual reproduction always requires _____ .
    a. mitosis              c. spore formation
    b. fertilization        d. a and b

12. What is the name for alternative forms of the same gene?

13. Match each term with the best description.
    ____ prophase          a. homologous chromosomes
    ____ telophase            aligned at the spindle equator
    ____ metaphase I       b. maybe none between meiosis I, II
    ____ metaphase II      c. unduplicated chromosomes aligned
    ____ interphase           at the spindle equator
    ____ anaphase II       d. chromosomes start to condense
    ____ prophase I        e. new nuclei form
    ____ anaphase I        f. homologous chromosomes move apart
                           g. sister chromatids move apart
                           h. homologues swap segments

Additional questions are available on CENGAGENOW™

## Critical Thinking

1. The anticancer drug taxol was first isolated from Pacific yews (*Taxus brevifolia*), which are slow-growing trees. Bark from about six yew trees provided enough taxol to treat one patient, but removing the bark killed the trees. Fortunately, taxol is now produced using plant cells that grow in big vats rather than in trees. What challenges do you think had to be overcome to get plant cells to grow and divide in laboratories?

2. Suppose you have a way to measure the amount of DNA in one cell during the cell cycle. You first measure the amount at the G1 phase. At what points in the rest of the cycle will you see a change in the amount of DNA per cell?

3. Why do you think that sexual reproduction tends to give rise to greater genetic diversity among offspring in fewer generations than asexual reproduction does?

4. Which nuclear division, meiosis I or meiosis II, is most like mitosis? Why?

# 9 Patterns of Inheritance

> Most CF patients live no longer than thirty years, at which time their tormented lungs usually fail.

# 9.1 Impacts/Issues: Menacing Mucus

In 1988, researchers discovered a gene that, when mutated, causes cystic fibrosis (CF). Cystic fibrosis is the most common fatal genetic disorder in the United States. The gene in question, *CFTR*, encodes a protein that moves chloride ions out of epithelial cells. Sheets of these cells line the passageways and ducts of the lungs, liver, pancreas, intestines, reproductive system, and skin. When the CFTR protein pumps chloride ions out of these cells, water follows the ions by osmosis. This two-step process maintains a thin film of water on the surface of the epithelial sheets. Mucus slides easily over the wet sheets of cells.

The most common CF mutation is a deletion of one codon that specifies the 508th amino acid of the CFTR protein, a phenylalanine. The deletion disrupts membrane trafficking of CFTR so that newly assembled polypeptides are stranded in the endoplasmic reticulum. The protein itself can function properly, but it never reaches the cell surface to do its job.

One outcome is that the transport of chloride ions out of epithelial cells is disrupted. If not enough chloride ions leave the cells, not enough water leaves them either, so the surfaces of epithelial cell sheets are not as wet as they should be. Mucus that normally slips and slides through the body's tubes sticks to them instead. Thick, sticky globs of mucus accumulate and clog the passageways of the lungs, making breathing difficult.

The CFTR protein also functions as a receptor that alerts the body to the presence of bacteria. Bacteria bind to CFTR. The binding triggers endocytosis, which speeds the immune system's defensive responses. Without the CFTR protein on the surface of epithelial cell linings, disease-causing bacteria that enter the ducts and passageways of the body can persist there. Thus, chronic bacterial infections of the intestine and lungs are hallmarks of cystic fibrosis.

Daily routines of posture changes and thumps on the chest and back help clear the lungs of some of the thick mucus, and antibiotics help control infections, but there is no cure. Even with a lung transplant, most CF patients live no longer than thirty years, at which time their tormented lungs usually fail (Figure 9.1).

More than 10 million people carry the CF mutation in one of their two copies of the *CFTR* gene, but most of them do not realize it. Cystic fibrosis only occurs when a person inherits two mutated genes, one from each parent. This unlucky event occurs in about 1 of 3,300 births. Why is it that people with one copy of a mutated CFTR gene are healthy, but people with two copies are ill with cystic fibrosis? Why is the mutation that causes CF so common if its effects are so devastating? You will begin to find the answers to such questions in this chapter, in which we introduce principles of inheritance—how new individuals are put together in the image of their parents.

Cody, 23

Jeff, 21

Lindsay, 22

Ben, 23

Savannah, 19

Brandon, 18

**FIGURE 9.1** A few of the many victims of cystic fibrosis. At least one young person dies every day in the United States from complications of this disease.

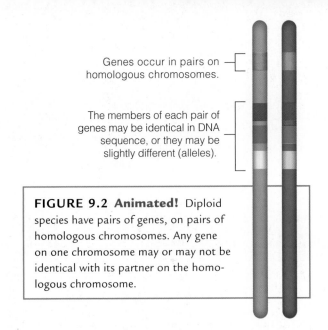

Genes occur in pairs on homologous chromosomes.

The members of each pair of genes may be identical in DNA sequence, or they may be slightly different (alleles).

**FIGURE 9.2 Animated!** Diploid species have pairs of genes, on pairs of homologous chromosomes. Any gene on one chromosome may or may not be identical with its partner on the homologous chromosome.

**FIGURE 9.3 Animated!**
Breeding garden pea plants.

❶ In this example, pollen from a plant that breeds true for purple flowers is brushed onto the flower of a plant that breeds true for white flowers.

❷ Seeds develop inside pods of the cross-fertilized plant. The seeds grow into new plants.

❸ Every plant that arises from this cross has purple flowers. Predictable patterns such as this offer evidence of how inheritance works.

# 9.2 Tracking Traits

**Alleles and Phenotype** By the mid-1800s, most people had an idea that parents contribute hereditary material to their offspring. At the time, no one knew about genes, meiosis, or chromosomes. Some thought that hereditary material must be fluid, with fluids from both parents blending at fertilization like milk into coffee. However, the idea of "blending inheritance" failed to explain the obvious. For example, if parental fluids blended, then children of the same parents would all have the same eye color, which would be a blended shade of their parents' eye colors. But children of the same parents often differ

in eye color. Meanwhile, an Austrian monk named Gregor Mendel (*left*) had been collecting evidence of how inheritance really works. He was carefully documenting how traits are passed from generation to generation of garden pea plants. This plant is self-fertilizing, which means that its flowers make both male and female gametes. Pea plants can be easily cross-fertilized by transferring pollen from the flower of one plant to the flower of another.

Mendel knew that some pea plants "breed true" for traits such as white flowers. Breeding true means that offspring have the same form of the trait as the parent(s), generation after generation. For example, all offspring of pea plants that breed true for white flowers also have white flowers.

Flower color is an example of a pea plant's **phenotype**, its set of observable traits. Mendel did not know that phenotype is governed by pairs of genes on pairs of homologous chromosomes (Figure 9.2). He also did not know that variation in traits occurs because genes of a pair often vary slightly in sequence, as alleles (Section 8.6). A pea plant breeds true for a trait such as white flowers because it has identical alleles that govern that trait. An individual with identical alleles is said to be **homozygous** for the gene (*homo*– means the same; *zygotos* is a Greek word that means linked).

Mendel crossed pea plants that bred true for different forms of a trait, and discovered that the phenotypes of the resulting **hybrid** plants occur in predictable patterns (Figure 9.3). The patterns he saw were clues about the plants'

**homozygous** Having identical alleles of a gene.
**hybrid** The offspring of a cross between two individuals that breed true for different forms of a trait.
**phenotype** An individual's observable traits.

**FIGURE 9.4** Gene segregation. Homologous chromosomes separate during meiosis, so the pairs of genes they carry separate too. Each of the resulting gametes carries only one of the two members of each gene pair.

For clarity, we show nuclei of reproductive cells that carry only one chromosome.

**1** All gametes produced by a parent homozygous for a dominant allele carry the dominant allele.

**2** All gametes produced by a parent homozygous for a recessive allele carry the recessive allele.

**3** If these two parents are crossed, the union of any of their gametes at fertilization produces a zygote with both alleles. Thus, all of the offspring of this cross will be heterozygous.

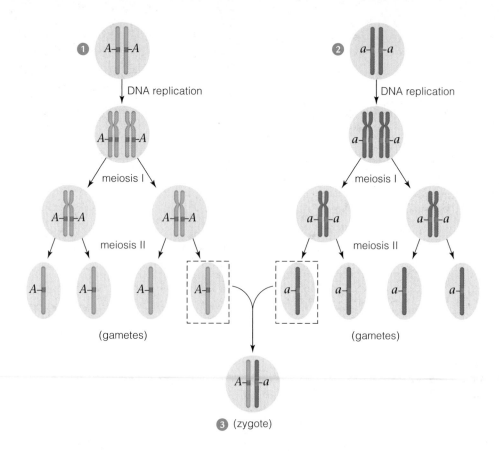

**genotype**, which refers to the particular alleles that an individual carries. The patterns occur because the effect of some alleles masks the effect of others. We say that an allele is **dominant** if its effect masks that of a **recessive** allele paired with it. Uppercase italic letters (*A*) usually refer to dominant alleles and lowercase italic letters (*a*) refer to their recessive partners.

Consider a gene that specifies flower color in pea plants. For this gene, the allele that specifies purple is dominant over the allele that specifies white. Let's designate the purple color allele *A*, and the white color allele *a*. So, a pea plant with two *A* alleles (*AA*) has purple flowers, and one with two *a* alleles (*aa*) has white flowers. Mendel crossed plants that bred true for purple flowers (*AA*) with plants that bred true for white flowers (*aa*). All of the offspring of this cross had purple flowers. Why? Homologous chromosomes separate during meiosis, so each gamete that forms carries only one of the two alleles (Figure 9.4 **1**, **2**). If plants homozygous for different alleles are crossed (*AA* × *aa*), only one outcome is possible: All of the offspring will have one of each allele (*Aa*) **3**. All of them carry the dominant allele *A*, so all of them will have purple flowers. Individuals that have nonidentical alleles are **heterozygous** for the gene (*hetero–*, mixed).

**Mendelian Inheritance Patterns** Dominance relationships among alleles can sometimes be determined by breeding heterozygous individuals together. The pattern in which traits show up among offspring of such crosses may indicate whether one allele is dominant over the other. For example, a **monohybrid cross** is used to check for a dominance relationship between alleles of one gene. In a monohybrid cross, individuals that are identically heterozygous at one gene are bred together (*Aa* × *Aa*), and the traits that show up among the offspring are observed. Mendel made hundreds of monohybrid crosses, and recorded the traits of thousands of their offspring.

female gametes

male gametes

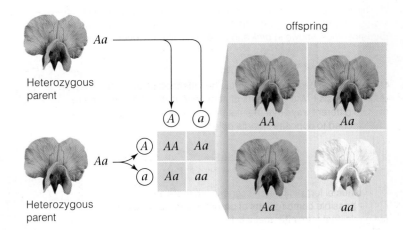

**A** Making a Punnett square. The possible parental gametes are listed on the top and left sides of the grid (in circles). Each square is filled in with the combination of alleles that would result if the gametes in the corresponding row and column met up.

**FIGURE 9.5 Animated!** Example of a monohybrid cross.

**Figure It Out:** How many genotypes are possible among the offspring of this cross?

*Answer: Three: AA, Aa, and aa*

**B** A Punnett square shows that the ratio of dominant-to-recessive phenotypes among offspring of a monohybrid cross is about 3:1 (3 purple to 1 white).

He discovered that about three of every four of those offspring had one trait (such as purple flowers), and about one of every four had the other trait (white flowers). The phenotypic ratio of 3:1 indicates that the traits Mendel studied were specified by alleles with a clear dominant–recessive relationship. To understand why, we have to revisit probability—the chance that a particular outcome will occur (Section 1.7). That chance depends on the total number of possible outcomes. Grids called **Punnett squares** allow us to determine the probability of genetic outcomes of a cross. Figure 9.5**A** shows how to construct a Punnett square, using a monohybrid cross between our purple-flowered heterozygotes as an example (*Aa* × *Aa*). With respect to the flower color gene, only two types of gametes (*A* and *a*) can form in each *Aa* plant. So, in a monohybrid cross between two *Aa* plants, those two types of gametes can meet up in four possible ways at fertilization:

| Possible Event | Outcome |
|---|---|
| Sperm *A* meets egg *A* | offspring is *AA* |
| Sperm *A* meets egg *a* | offspring is *Aa* |
| Sperm *a* meets egg *A* | offspring is *Aa* |
| Sperm *a* meets egg *a* | offspring is *aa* |

In our example, three out of those four possible outcomes include at least one copy of the dominant allele *A*. Each time fertilization occurs, there are 3 chances in 4 that the resulting offspring will inherit an *A* allele, and have purple flowers. There is 1 chance in 4 that it will inherit two recessive *a* alleles, and have white flowers. Thus, the probability that a particular offspring of this cross will have purple or white flowers is 3 purple to 1 white, which we represent as a ratio of 3:1 (Figure 9.5**B**).

If the probability of one individual inheriting a particular genotype is difficult to imagine, think about probability in terms of the phenotypes of many offspring of our monohybrid cross. In this example, there will be roughly three purple-flowered plants for every white-flowered one. A phenotypic ratio of 3:1 is typical of the offspring of a monohybrid cross with dominant and recessive alleles, which is the pattern that Mendel saw.

A monohybrid cross tracks alleles of one gene pair. What about alleles of two gene pairs? How two gene pairs get sorted into gametes depends partly on whether the two genes are on the same chromosome. Remember, chromosomes line up and then separate during meiosis (Section 8.7). Homologous chromo-

**dominant** Refers to an allele that masks the effect of a recessive allele paired with it.

**genotype** The particular alleles carried by an individual.

**heterozygous** Having two different alleles of a gene.

**monohybrid cross** Experiment in which individuals with different alleles of a gene are crossed.

**Punnett square** Diagram used to predict the outcome of a cross.

**recessive** Refers to an allele with an effect that is masked by a dominant allele on the homologous chromosome.

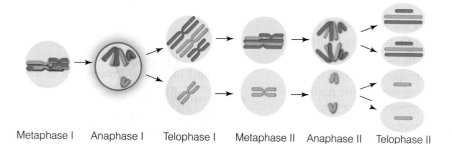

Metaphase I    Anaphase I    Telophase I    Metaphase II    Anaphase II    Telophase II

**A**

---

**FIGURE 9.20** Nondisjunction during meiosis. **A** *Above*, of the two pairs of homologous chromosomes shown in this example, one fails to separate during anaphase I of meiosis. *Below*, one outcome of nondisjunction, Down syndrome **B**, occurs when an individual has three copies of chromosome 21 **C**.

---

1  2  3  4  5

6  7  8  9  10  11  12

13  14  15  16  17  18

19  20  21  22  X  Y

**C**

---

Chromosome number changes often arise through **nondisjunction**, in which one or more pairs of chromosomes do not separate properly during mitosis or meiosis (Figure 9.20**A**). Nondisjunction affects the chromosome number at fertilization. For example, suppose that a normal gamete fuses with an $n+1$ gamete (one that has an extra chromosome). The new individual will be trisomic ($2n+1$), having three of one type of chromosome and two of every other type. As another example, if an $n-1$ gamete fuses with a normal $n$ gamete, the new individual will be $2n-1$, or monosomic.

Trisomy and monosomy are types of **aneuploidy**, a condition in which cells have too many or too few copies of a chromosome. Autosomal aneuploidy is usually fatal in humans, and it causes many miscarriages. However, about seventy percent of flowering plant species, and some insects, fishes, and other animals are **polyploid**, which means that their cells have three or more of each type of chromosome.

### Autosomal Change and Down Syndrome

A few trisomic humans are born alive, but only those that have trisomy 21 will reach adulthood. A newborn with three chromosomes 21 will develop Down syndrome. This autosomal disorder is the most common type of aneuploidy in humans; it occurs once in 800 to 1,000 births and affects more than 350,000 people in the United States alone. Figure 9.20**C** shows a karyotype for a trisomic 21 male. The affected individuals have upward-slanting eyes, a fold of skin that starts at the inner corner of each eye, a deep crease across the sole of each palm and foot, one (instead of two) horizontal furrows on their fifth fingers, slightly flattened facial features, and other symptoms (Figure 9.20**B**).

Not all of the outward symptoms develop in every individual. That said, trisomic 21 individuals tend to have moderate to severe mental impairment and heart problems. Their skeleton grows and develops abnormally, so older children have short body parts, loose joints, and misaligned bones of the fingers, toes, and hips. The muscles and reflexes are weak, and motor skills such as speech develop slowly. With medical care, trisomy 21 individuals live about fifty-five years. Early training can help affected individuals learn to care for themselves and to take part in normal activities.

The incidence of nondisjunction generally rises with the increasing age of the mother. Nondisjunction may occur in the father, although far less frequently. Trisomy 21 is one of the hundreds of conditions that can be detected easily through prenatal diagnosis (Section 9.8).

### Change in the Sex Chromosome Number

Nondisjunction also causes alterations in the number of X and Y chromosomes, with a frequency of about 1 in 400 live births. Most often, such alterations lead to difficulties in learning and impaired motor skills such as a speech delay, but problems may be so subtle that the underlying cause is never diagnosed.

### Female Sex Chromosome Abnormalities

Individuals with Turner syndrome have an X chromosome and no corresponding X or Y chromosome (XO). About 1 in 2,500 to 10,000 newborn girls are XO (Figure 9.21). At least 98 percent of XO embryos will spontaneously abort early in pregnancy, so there are fewer cases compared with other sex chromosome abnormalities. XO individuals are not as disadvantaged as other aneuploids. They grow up well proportioned but short (with an average height of four feet, eight inches). Most do not have functional ovaries, so they do not make enough sex hormones to become sexually mature. The development of secondary sexual traits such as breasts is also affected.

A female may inherit three, four, or five X chromosomes. The resulting XXX syndrome occurs in about 1 of 1,000 births. Only one X chromosome is typically active in female cells (Section 7.7), so having extra X chromosomes usually does not result in physical or medical problems.

**Male Sex Chromosome Abnormalities** About 1 out of every 500 males has an extra X chromosome (XXY). Most cases are an outcome of nondisjunction during meiosis. The resulting disorder, Klinefelter syndrome, develops at puberty. XXY males tend to be overweight, tall, and within a normal range of intelligence. They make more estrogen and less testosterone than normal males, and this hormone imbalance has feminizing effects. Affected men tend to have small testes and prostate glands, low sperm counts, sparse facial and body hair, high-pitched voices, and enlarged breasts. Testosterone injections during puberty can reverse these traits.

About 1 in 500 to 1,000 males has an extra Y chromosome (XYY). Adults tend to be taller than average and have mild mental impairment, but most are otherwise normal. XYY men were once thought to be predisposed to a life of crime. This misguided view was based on sampling error (too few cases in narrowly chosen groups such as prison inmates) and bias (the researchers who gathered the karyotypes also took the personal histories of the participants).

**FIGURE 9.21** A 6-year-old with Turner's syndrome. Affected girls tend to be shorter than average, but daily hormone injections can help them reach normal height.

## Take-Home Message **What are the effects of chromosome number changes?**

- Nondisjunction can change the number of autosomes or sex chromosomes in gametes. Such changes usually cause genetic disorders in offspring.
- Sex chromosome abnormalities are usually associated with learning difficulties, speech delays, and motor skill impairment.

# 9.8 Some Prospects in Human Genetics

With the first news of pregnancy, parents-to-be typically wonder if their baby will be healthy. Quite naturally, they want their baby to be free of genetic disorders, and most babies are. Many prospective parents have difficulty coming to terms with the possibility that a child of theirs might develop a severe genetic disorder, but sometimes that happens. What are their options?

**Genetic Counseling** Genetic counseling starts with diagnosis of parental genotypes, pedigrees, and genetic testing for known disorders. Using information gained from these tests, genetic counselors can predict a couple's probability of having a child with a genetic disorder.

Parents-to-be commonly ask genetic counselors to compare the risks associated with diagnostic procedures against the likelihood that their future child will be affected by a severe genetic disorder. At the time of counseling, they also should consider the small overall risk (3 percent) that complications during the

**aneuploidy** A chromosome abnormality in which there are too many or too few copies of a particular chromosome.
**nondisjunction** Failure of sister chromatids or homologous chromosomes to separate during meiosis or mitosis.
**polyploid** Having three or more of each type of chromosome characteristic of the species.

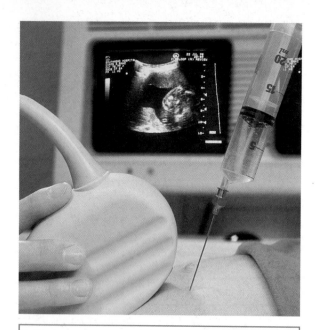

**FIGURE 9.22 Animated!** Amniocentesis. A pregnant woman's doctor draws a sample of amniotic fluid into a syringe. The path of the needle is monitored by an ultrasound device. Amniotic fluid contains fetal cells and wastes that can be analyzed for genetic disorders.

birth process can affect any child. They should talk about their age, because the risk of having a child with a genetic disorder increases with the age of the parents.

As a case in point, suppose a first child or a close relative has a severe disorder. A genetic counselor will evaluate the pedigrees of the parents, and the results of any genetic tests. Using this information, counselors can predict risks for disorders in future children. The same risk will apply to each pregnancy.

**Prenatal Diagnosis** Doctors commonly use methods of prenatal diagnosis to determine the sex of embryos or fetuses and to screen for more than 100 known genetic problems. Prenatal means before birth. Embryo is a term that applies until eight weeks after fertilization, after which fetus is appropriate.

Suppose a forty-five-year-old woman becomes pregnant and worries about Down syndrome. Between fifteen and twenty weeks after conception, she might opt for amniocentesis (Figure 9.22). In this diagnostic procedure, a physician uses a syringe to withdraw a small sample of fluid from the amniotic cavity. The "cavity" is a fluid-filled sac, enclosed by a membrane—the amnion—that in turn encloses the fetus. The fetus normally sheds some cells into the fluid. Cells suspended in the fluid sample can be analyzed for many genetic disorders, including Down syndrome, cystic fibrosis, and sickle-cell anemia.

Chorionic villi sampling (CVS) is a diagnostic procedure similar to amniocentesis. A physician withdraws a few cells from the chorion, which is a membrane that surrounds the amnion and helps form the placenta. The placenta is an organ that keeps the blood of mother and embryo separate, while allowing substances to be exchanged between them. Unlike amniocentesis, CVS can be performed as early as eight weeks into pregnancy.

It is now possible to see a live, developing fetus with a procedure called fetoscopy. In fetoscopy, a fiber-optic device called an endoscope is used to directly visualize and photograph the fetus, umbilical cord, and placenta in high resolution (Figure 9.23). Characteristic physical effects of certain genetic abnormalities or disorders can be diagnosed by fetoscopy.

All three prenatal diagnosis procedures are associated with risks to the fetus. Risks include punctures, infections, and loss of too much amniotic fluid (if the amnion does not reseal itself quickly). Amniocentesis increases the risk of miscarriage by 1 to 2 percent. CVS occasionally disrupts the placenta's development and thus causes underdeveloped or missing fingers and toes in 0.3 percent of newborns. Fetoscopy raises the miscarriage risk by 2 to 10 percent.

**Preimplantation Diagnosis** Preimplantation diagnosis is a procedure associated with *in vitro* fertilization. Sperm and eggs from prospective parents are mixed so that an egg becomes fertilized. Then, mitotic cell divisions turn the fertilized egg into a ball of eight cells within forty-eight hours.

All of the cells in the tiny, free-floating ball (*left*) have the same genes, but they are not yet committed to being specialized. Doctors can remove one of these undifferentiated cells and analyze its genes. If it has no detectable genetic defects, the ball may be inserted into the mother's uterus. The withdrawn cell will not be missed, and the ball can develop into an embryo. Many of the resulting "test-tube babies" are born in good health. Some couples who are at risk of passing on alleles associated with cystic fibrosis, muscular dystrophy, or another genetic disorder have opted for this procedure.

**Phenotypic Treatments** Surgery, prescription drugs, hormone replacement therapy, and often dietary controls can minimize and in some cases eliminate the symptoms of many genetic disorders. For instance, strict dietary

Our ability to tinker with genetics may have surpassed
our ability to understand the impact of the tinkering.

## 10.1 Impacts/Issues: Golden Rice or Frankenfood?

Vitamin A is necessary for good vision, growth, and immune system function. A small child can get enough of it just by eating a carrot every few days. Nonetheless, around 140 million children under the age of six become seriously ill from vitamin A deficiency every year. Vitamin A–deficient children do not grow as they should, and they succumb easily to infection. As many as 500,000 of them become blind, and of those half die within a year of losing their sight. These are some harsh statistics for such an easily prevented deficiency.

It is no coincidence that populations with the highest incidence of vitamin A deficiency also are the poorest. Most people in impoverished populations tend to eat few animal products, vegetables, or fruits—all foods that are rich sources of vitamin A. Correcting and preventing vitamin A deficiency can be as simple as supplementing the diet with these foods, but changes in dietary habits are often limited by cultural traditions and poverty. Political and economic issues have hampered long-term vitamin supplementation programs.

Geneticists Ingo Potrykus and Peter Beyer wanted to help impoverished people by improving the nutritional value of rice. Why rice? Rice is the dietary staple for 3 billion people in developing countries around the world. Economies, traditions, and cuisines are based on growing and eating rice. So, growing and eating rice that happens to contain enough vitamin A to prevent deficiency would be compatible with traditional methods of agriculture and dietary preferences.

The body can easily convert beta-carotene, an orange photosynthetic pigment, into vitamin A. However, getting rice grains to make beta-carotene is beyond the scope of conventional plant breeding methods. For example, corn seeds (the kernels) make and store beta-carotene, but even the best gardener cannot cross-breed rice plants with corn plants.

Potrykus and Beyer genetically modified rice plants to make beta-carotene in their seeds—in the grains of Golden Rice (Figure 10.1). Like many other **genetically modified organisms** (GMOs), Golden Rice is **transgenic**, which means it carries genes from a different species. GMOs are made in laboratories, not on farms, but they are an extension of breeding practices used for many thousands of years to coax new plants and new breeds of animals from wild species.

No one wants children to suffer or die. However, many people are opposed to any GMO. Some worry that our ability to tinker with genetics has surpassed our ability to understand the impact of the tinkering. Should we be more cautious? Two people created a way to keep millions of children from dying. How much of a risk should we as a society take to help those children?

At this time, geneticists hold molecular keys to the kingdom of inheritance. As you will see, what they are unlocking is already having an impact on life in the biosphere.

**FIGURE 10.1** Golden Rice: miracle of modern science or Frankenfood? Rice plants with artificially inserted genes make and store the orange pigment beta-carotene in their seeds, or rice grains.

1. A restriction enzyme recognizes a specific base sequence in DNA (*green* boxes) from two sources.

2. The enzyme cuts DNA from both sources into fragments that have sticky ends.

3. The DNA fragments from the two sources are mixed together. The matching sticky ends base-pair with each other.

4. DNA ligase joins the fragments of DNA where they overlap. Molecules of recombinant DNA are the result.

**FIGURE 10.2** Making recombinant DNA.

# 10.2

# Finding Needles in Haystacks

**Cut and Paste** In the 1950s, excitement over the discovery of DNA's structure gave way to frustration: No one could determine the order of nucleotides in a molecule of DNA. Identifying a single base among thousands or millions of others turned out to be a huge technical challenge.

A seemingly unrelated discovery offered a solution. Some types of bacteria resist infection by viruses that inject their DNA into bacterial cells. Werner Arber, Hamilton Smith, and their coworkers discovered that special enzymes inside these bacteria chop up any injected viral DNA before it has a chance to integrate into the bacterial chromosome. The enzymes restrict viral growth; hence their name, restriction enzymes. A **restriction enzyme** can cut DNA wherever a specific nucleotide sequence occurs, regardless of the source of the DNA. For example, the enzyme *Eco*RI (named after the organism from which it was isolated, *E. coli*) cuts DNA only at the sequence GAATTC.

The discovery allowed researchers to cut huge molecules of chromosomal DNA into manageable fragments. It also allowed them to combine DNA fragments from different organisms to make **recombinant DNA** (Figure 10.2). Making recombinant DNA typically involves cutting DNA from multiple sources with the same restriction enzyme 1. Many restriction enzymes leave single-stranded tails ("sticky ends") on DNA fragments 2. When the DNA fragments from different sources are mixed together, their matching sticky ends base-pair together 3. DNA ligase is used to join the fragments as hybrid molecules 4.

Making recombinant DNA is the first step in **DNA cloning**, a set of laboratory methods that uses living cells to make many copies of specific DNA fragments. For example, researchers often insert DNA fragments into **plasmids**, small circles of bacterial DNA independent of the chromosome. Before a bacterium divides, it copies any plasmids it carries along with its chromosome, so both descendant cells get one of each. If a plasmid carries a fragment of foreign DNA, that fragment gets copied and distributed to descendant cells along with the plasmid. Thus, plasmids can be used as **cloning vectors**, which are molecules that carry foreign DNA into host cells (Figure 10.3). A host cell that takes up a cloning vector can be grown in the laboratory to yield a huge population of genetically identical cells called **clones**. Each clone contains a copy of the vector and the fragment of foreign DNA it carries. Researchers can harvest the DNA fragment from the clones in large quantities.

Cloning isolates a small fragment of DNA away from a larger molecule. The development of this laboratory technique was a critical step that allowed researchers to unravel the genetic information that DNA carries (Section 7.2).

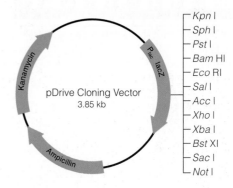

**FIGURE 10.3** A commercial plasmid cloning vector. Restriction enzyme recognition sequences are indicated on the *right* by the name of the enzyme that cuts them. Researchers insert foreign DNA into the vector at these sites.

Bacterial genes (*green*) help researchers identify host cells that take up a vector with inserted DNA.

**clone** A genetically identical copy of DNA, a cell, or an organism.

**cloning vector** A DNA molecule that can accept foreign DNA, be transferred to a host cell, and get replicated in it.

**DNA cloning** Set of procedures that uses living cells to make many identical copies of a DNA fragment.

**genetically modified organism (GMO)** An organism whose genome has been deliberately modified.

**plasmid** A small, circular DNA molecule in bacteria, replicated independently of the chromosome.

**recombinant DNA** A DNA molecule that contains genetic material from more than one organism.

**restriction enzyme** Type of enzyme that cuts specific base sequences in DNA.

**transgenic** Refers to an organism that has been genetically modified to carry a gene from a different species.

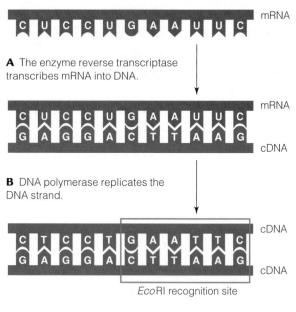

**A** The enzyme reverse transcriptase transcribes mRNA into DNA.

**B** DNA polymerase replicates the DNA strand.

*Eco*RI recognition site

**C** The result is a double-stranded molecule of DNA that can be cut and pasted into a cloning vector.

**FIGURE 10.4** Making cDNA. mRNA must be transcribed into cDNA for cloning.

**Thirty PCR cycles may amplify the number of template DNA molecules a billionfold.**

**cDNA Cloning** Researchers who study eukaryotic genes and their expression work with messenger RNA. mRNA cannot be cloned directly, because restriction enzymes and DNA ligase cut and paste only double-stranded DNA. However, mRNA can be used as a template to make double-stranded DNA in a test tube. **Reverse transcriptase**, a replication enzyme from certain types of viruses, assembles a strand of complementary DNA, or **cDNA**, on an mRNA template (Figure 10.4**A**,**B**). DNA polymerase added to the mixture strips the RNA from the hybrid molecule as it copies the cDNA into a second strand of DNA. The outcome is a double-stranded DNA copy of the original mRNA (Figure 10.4**C**). Like any other DNA, double-stranded cDNA may be cut with restriction enzymes and pasted into a cloning vector using DNA ligase.

**Libraries** The entire set of genetic material—the **genome**—of most organisms consists of thousands of genes. To study or manipulate a single gene, researchers must first separate it from all of the others. Researchers can isolate a gene by cutting an organism's DNA into pieces, and then cloning all the pieces. The result is a genomic library, a set of clones that collectively contain all of the DNA in an organism's genome.

In genomic or cDNA libraries, a cell that contains a particular DNA fragment of interest may be mixed up with thousands or millions of others that do not. All the cells look the same, so researchers get tricky to find that one clone among all of the others—the needle in the haystack. Using a probe is one trick. A **probe** is a fragment of DNA labeled with a tracer (Section 2.2). Researchers design probes to match a targeted DNA sequence. For example, they might synthesize a short chain of nucleotides based on a known DNA sequence, then attach a radioactive phosphate group to it.

The nucleotide sequence of a probe is complementary to that of the targeted gene, so the probe can base-pair with the gene. Base pairing between DNA (or DNA and RNA) from more than one source is called **nucleic acid hybridization**. A probe mixed with DNA from a library base-pairs with (hybridizes to) the targeted gene. Researchers pinpoint a clone that hosts the gene by detecting the label on the probe. The clone is then cultured, and the DNA fragment of interest is extracted in bulk from the cultured cells.

**PCR** The polymerase chain reaction (**PCR**) is a technique used to mass-produce copies of a particular DNA fragment without having to clone it. The reaction can transform a needle in a haystack—that one-in-a-million DNA fragment—into a huge stack of needles with a little hay in it (Figure 10.5). The starting material for PCR is any sample of DNA with at least one molecule of a target sequence. It might be DNA from a mixture of 10 million different clones, a sperm, a hair left at a crime scene, or a mummy. Essentially any sample that has DNA in it can be used for PCR.

First, the starting material is mixed with DNA polymerase, nucleotides, and primers ❶. **Primers** are short single strands of DNA that base-pair with a certain sequence—here, on either end of the DNA to be amplified (or mass-produced). Researchers expose the reaction mixture to repeated cycles of high and low temperature. High temperature disrupts the hydrogen bonds that hold the two strands of a DNA double helix together (Section 6.3). During a high-temperature cycle, every molecule of double-stranded DNA unwinds and becomes single-stranded ❷. During a low-temperature cycle, the single DNA strands hybridize with complementary partner strands, and double-stranded DNA forms again.

Most DNA polymerases denature at the high temperatures required to separate DNA strands. The kind that is used in PCR reactions, *Taq* polymerase, is from *Thermus aquaticus*. This bacterial species lives in hot springs and hydrothermal vents, so its DNA polymerase is necessarily heat-tolerant.

*Taq* polymerase recognizes hybridized primers as places to start DNA synthesis. During a low-temperature cycle, it starts synthesizing DNA where primers have hybridized with template ❸. Synthesis proceeds along the template strand until the temperature rises and the DNA separates into single strands ❹. The newly synthesized DNA is a copy of the target.

When the mixture cools, the primers rehybridize, and DNA synthesis begins again. The number of copies of the target DNA can double with each cycle of heating and cooling ❺. Thirty PCR cycles may amplify the number of template DNA molecules a billionfold.

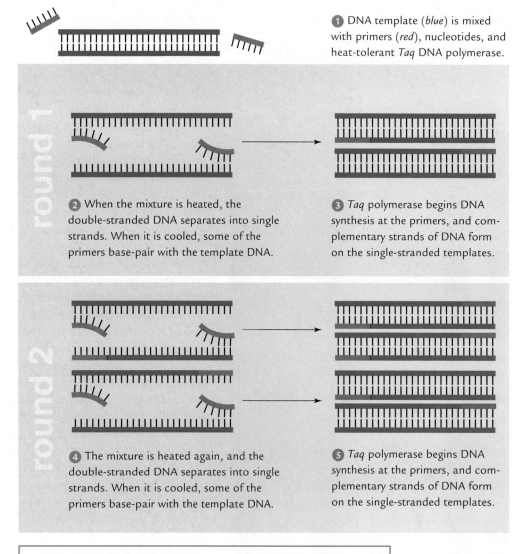

❶ DNA template (*blue*) is mixed with primers (*red*), nucleotides, and heat-tolerant *Taq* DNA polymerase.

**round 1**

❷ When the mixture is heated, the double-stranded DNA separates into single strands. When it is cooled, some of the primers base-pair with the template DNA.

❸ *Taq* polymerase begins DNA synthesis at the primers, and complementary strands of DNA form on the single-stranded templates.

**round 2**

❹ The mixture is heated again, and the double-stranded DNA separates into single strands. When it is cooled, some of the primers base-pair with the template DNA.

❺ *Taq* polymerase begins DNA synthesis at the primers, and complementary strands of DNA form on the single-stranded templates.

**FIGURE 10.5 Animated!** Two rounds of PCR. Each cycle of this reaction can double the number of target DNA molecules. Thirty cycles can amplify a template DNA a billionfold.

## Take-Home Message    What techniques allow researchers to study DNA?

- DNA cloning uses living cells to mass-produce DNA fragments. Restriction enzymes cut DNA into pieces that are inserted into cloning vectors. The resulting recombinant DNA molecules are introduced into host cells, which copy the DNA as they divide.

- Researchers make DNA libraries or use PCR to isolate one gene from the many other genes in a genome.

- Probes are used to identify one clone that hosts a DNA fragment of interest among many other clones in a DNA library.

- PCR, the polymerase chain reaction, quickly mass-produces copies of a particular DNA fragment.

**cDNA** DNA synthesized from an RNA template by the enzyme reverse transcriptase.

**genome** An organism's complete set of genetic material.

**nucleic acid hybridization** Base-pairing between DNA or RNA from different sources.

**PCR** Polymerase chain reaction. Method that rapidly generates many copies of a specific DNA fragment.

**primer** Short, single strand of DNA designed to hybridize with a DNA fragment.

**probe** Short fragment of DNA labeled with a tracer; designed to hybridize with a nucleotide sequence of interest.

**reverse transcriptase** A viral enzyme that uses mRNA as a template to make a strand of cDNA.

## 10.3 Studying DNA

**DNA Fingerprinting** Each human has a unique set of fingerprints. Like members of other sexually reproducing species, each also has a **DNA fingerprint**, a unique array of DNA sequences. More than 99 percent of the DNA in all humans is the same, but the other fraction of 1 percent is unique to an individual. Some of the unique sequences are sprinkled throughout the genome as short tandem repeats, which are many copies of the same 2- to 10-base-pair sequences, positioned one after the next along the length of a chromosome.

For example, one person's DNA might contain fifteen repeats of the bases TTTTC in a certain location. Another person's DNA might have TTTTC repeated two times in the same location. One person might have ten repeats of CGG; another might have fifty. These repetitive sequences slip spontaneously into DNA during replication, and their numbers grow or shrink over generations.

DNA fingerprinting reveals differences in the number of tandem repeats among individuals. With this technique, PCR is used to copy a region of a chromosome known to have tandem repeats of 4 or 5 nucleotides. The size of the copied DNA fragment differs among most individuals, because the number of tandem repeats in that region also differs. Thus, the genetic differences between individuals can be detected by **electrophoresis**, a technique in which an electric field pulls DNA fragments through a semisolid gel. DNA fragments of different sizes move through the gel at different rates. The shorter the fragment, the faster it moves, because shorter fragments slip through the tangled molecules of the gel faster than longer fragments do. All fragments of the same length move through the gel at the same speed. Thus, DNA fragments gather into discrete bands according to length as they migrate through the gel (Figure 10.6).

Several regions of chromosomal DNA are amplified by PCR and subjected to electrophoresis. The banding patterns on the resulting gel constitute an individual's DNA fingerprint, which, for all practical purposes, is unique. Unless two people are identical twins, the chances that they have identical tandem repeats in even three regions of DNA is 1 in 1,000,000,000,000,000,000—or one in a quintillion—which is far more than the number of people alive on Earth.

A standard set of thirteen short tandem repeat regions is typically tested to make a DNA fingerprint usable as evidence in a U.S. court. DNA fingerprints are now routinely used to resolve paternity disputes and criminal cases. A few drops of blood, semen, or cells from a hair follicle at a crime scene or on a suspect's clothing yield enough DNA to amplify with PCR for a DNA fingerprint. The technique is used not only to convict the guilty, but also to exonerate the innocent: As of this writing, DNA fingerprinting evidence has helped release more than 160 innocent people from prison.

DNA fingerprinting has many applications. For example, it was used to identify the remains of many individuals who died in the World Trade Center on September 11, 2001. It confirmed that human bones exhumed from a shallow pit in Siberia belonged to five individuals of the Russian imperial family, all shot to death in secrecy in 1918. Researchers also use DNA fingerprinting to study population dispersal in humans and other animals. Because only a tiny amount of DNA is necessary, such studies are not limited to living populations. Short tandem repeats on the Y chromosome are also used to determine genetic relationships among male relatives and descendants, and to trace an individual's ethnic heritage.

---

Evidence from Crime Scene

Size Reference | Control DNA | Size Reference | Victim | Suspect 1 | Suspect 2 | Female Cells | Semen | Size Reference | Boyfriend | Control DNA | Control DNA | Size Reference

**FIGURE 10.6** DNA fingerprinting in an actual investigation of sexual assault. A short tandem repeat region was amplified from evidence at the crime scene: the perpetrator's semen and the victim's cells. The two samples were compared with the same tandem repeat region amplified from DNA of the victim, her boyfriend, and two suspects (1 and 2).

Note the three samples of control DNA (to confirm that the PCR was working correctly), and the four size reference samples.

The photo shows an x-ray film image of an electrophoresis gel from a forensics laboratory. The bands represent DNA fragments labeled with a radioactive tracer. **Figure It Out:** Which of the two suspects was found to be guilty?

*Answer: Suspect 1*

**FIGURE 10.7** Sequencing, a method of determining the sequence of a fragment of DNA. On this computer screen, the four bases (adenine, thymine, guanine, and cytosine) are color-coded green, red, yellow, and blue, respectively. The order of colors represents the sequence of the DNA fragment.

## The Human Genome Project

Around 1986, people were arguing about sequencing the human genome. **Sequencing** is a method of determining the order of nucleotide bases in an isolated DNA fragment (Figure 10.7). Many insisted that deciphering the sequence of the human genome would have enormous payoffs for medicine and research. Others said the project would divert funds from work that was more urgent—and that also had a better chance of success. At that time, sequencing 3 billion bases was a daunting task: It would take at least 6 million sequencing reactions, all done by hand. Given the techniques available, the work would have taken more than fifty years to complete.

But techniques kept getting better, so more bases could be sequenced in less time. Automated (robotic) DNA sequencing and PCR had just been invented. Both of these techniques were still cumbersome and expensive, but many researchers sensed their potential. Waiting for faster technologies seemed the most efficient way to sequence 3 billion bases, but how fast did they need to be before the project could begin?

Private companies started to sequence the human genome in 1987. Walter Gilbert, one of the early inventors of DNA sequencing, started a company that intended to sequence and patent the human genome. This development provoked widespread outrage, but it also spurred commitments in the public sector. In 1988, the National Institutes of Health (NIH) effectively annexed the project by hiring James Watson (of DNA structure fame) to head the official Human Genome Project, and providing $200 million per year to fund it. A consortium formed between the NIH and international institutions that were sequencing different parts of the genome. Watson set aside 3 percent of the funding for studies of ethical and social issues arising from the research. He later resigned over a patent disagreement, and geneticist Francis Collins took his place.

Amid ongoing squabbles over patent issues, Celera Genomics formed in 1998. With biologist Craig Venter at its helm, the company intended to commercialize genetic information. Celera started to sequence the genome using new, faster techniques, because the first to have the complete sequence had a legal basis for patenting it. The competition motivated the public consortium to move its efforts into high gear.

Then, in 2000, U.S. President Bill Clinton and British Prime Minister Tony Blair jointly declared that the sequence of the human genome could not be patented. Celera kept on sequencing anyway. Celera and the public consortium separately published about 90 percent of the sequence in 2001. By 2003, fifty years after the discovery of the structure of DNA, the sequence of the human genome was officially completed. At this writing, about 99 percent of its coding regions have been identified. Researchers have not discovered what all of the

**DNA fingerprint** An individual's unique array of short tandem repeats.

**electrophoresis** Technique that separates DNA fragments by size.

**sequencing** Method of determining the order of nucleotides in DNA.

| Table 10.1 | A Few Sequenced Genomes | | |
|---|---|---|---|
| Organism | Complete | Size (×10⁶ bases) | Protein-Coding Genes |
| Yeast | 1997 | 12 | 6,532 |
| Roundworm | 1999 | 101 | 20,176 |
| Arabidopsis | 2000 | 120 | 18,641 |
| Fruit fly | 2000 | 120 | 14,141 |
| Human | 2001 | 2,858 | 20,067 |
| Mouse | 2002 | 2,562 | 22,010 |
| Rat | 2004 | 2,705 | 19,684 |
| Zebrafish | 2005 | 1,533 | 18,957 |
| Chimpanzee | 2005 | 2,836 | 23,186 |
| Dog | 2005 | 2,385 | 15,914 |
| Chicken | 2007 | 1,013 | 12,351 |
| Horse | 2007 | 2,429 | 15,567 |
| Cow | 2007 | 2,623 | 16,954 |
| Macaque | 2007 | 2,778 | 18,379 |
| Duckbill platypus | 2008 | 1,840 | 11,201 |

genes encode, only where they are in the genome. What do we do with this vast amount of data? The next step is to find out what the sequence means.

**Genomics** Investigations into the genomes of humans and other species have converged into the new research field of **genomics**. Structural genomics focuses on determining the three-dimensional structure of the proteins encoded by a genome. Comparative genomics compares genomes of different species; similarities and differences reflect evolutionary relationships.

The human genome sequence is a massive collection of seemingly cryptic data. One way we are able to decipher it is by comparing it to genomes of other organisms (Table 10.1), the premise being that all organisms are descended from shared ancestors, so all genomes are related to some extent. We see evidence of such genetic relationships just by comparing the sequence data. For example, the human and mouse sequences are about 78 percent identical; the human and banana sequences are about 50 percent identical.

Intriguing as these percentages might be, gene-by-gene comparisons offer more practical benefits. We have learned about the function of many human genes by studying their counterpart genes in other species. For example, researchers studying a human gene might disable expression of the same gene in mice. The effects of the gene's absence on mice are clues to its function in humans. These types of knockout experiments are revealing the function of many human genes. For example, researchers comparing the human and mouse genomes discovered a human version of the mouse gene *APOA5*. This gene encodes a protein that, as part of HDL lipoproteins, helps transport dietary fats in the blood. Mice with an *APOA5* knockout have four times the normal level of triglycerides in their blood. The researchers then looked for—and found—a correlation between *APOA5* mutations and high triglyceride levels in humans. High triglycerides are a risk factor for coronary artery disease.

## Take-Home Message  **What are some of the ways researchers study DNA, and how do we use what they discover?**

- Electrophoresis is used to separate different sized fragments of DNA.
- A DNA fingerprint is an individual's unique array of short tandem repeats. DNA fingerprinting is used in forensics, as court evidence, and in other applications.
- Analysis of the human genome sequence is yielding new information about human genes and how they work. The information has practical applications in medicine, research, and other fields.

# 10.4 Genetic Engineering

Traditional cross-breeding methods can alter genomes, but only if individuals with the desired traits will interbreed. **Genetic engineering**, a laboratory process by which deliberate changes are introduced into an individual's genome, takes gene-swapping to an entirely new level. A gene may be transferred to the

**genetic engineering** Process by which deliberate changes are introduced into an individual's genome.
**genomics** The study of genomes.

genome of another species (or even another genus) to produce a transgenic organism. Or, a gene may be altered and reinserted into an individual of the same species. Both methods result in genetically modified organisms (GMOs).

## Genetically Modified Microorganisms

The most common GMOs are bacteria and yeast. These cells have the metabolic machinery to make complex organic molecules, and they are easily modified. For example, the *E. coli* on the *left* have been modified to produce a fluorescent protein from jellyfish. The cells are genetically identical, so the visible variation in fluorescence among them reveals differences in gene expression. Such differences may help us discover why some bacteria of a population become dangerously resistant to antibiotics, and others do not.

Bacteria and yeast have been modified to produce medically important proteins. Diabetics were among the first beneficiaries of such organisms. Insulin for their injections was once extracted from animals, but it provoked an allergic reaction in some people. Human insulin, which does not provoke allergic reactions, has been produced by transgenic *E. coli* since 1982. Slight modifications of the gene have also yielded fast-acting and slow-release human insulin.

Engineered microorganisms also produce proteins used in food manufacturing. For example, cheese is traditionally made with an extract of calf stomachs, which contain the enzyme chymotrypsin. Most cheese manufacturers now use chymotrypsin made by genetically modified bacteria. Other examples are GMO-made enzymes that improve the taste and clarity of beer and fruit juice, slow bread staling, or modify fats.

**Designer Plants** *Agrobacterium tumefaciens* is a species of bacteria that infects many plants, including peas, beans, potatoes, and other important crops. It carries a plasmid with genes that cause tumors to form on infected plants; hence the name Ti plasmid (for *Tumor-inducing*). Researchers use the Ti plasmid as a vector to transfer foreign or modified genes into plants. They remove the tumor-inducing genes from the plasmid, then insert desired genes. Whole plants can be grown from plant cells that take up the modified plasmid (Figure 10.8).

Modified *A. tumefaciens* bacteria are used to deliver genes into some food crop plants, including soybeans, squash, and potatoes. Researchers also transfer genes into plants by way of electric or chemical shocks, or by blasting them with DNA-coated pellets.

As crop production expands to keep pace with human population growth, it places unavoidable pressure on ecosystems everywhere. Irrigation leaves mineral and salt residues in soils. Tilled soil erodes, taking topsoil with it. Runoff clogs rivers, and fertilizer in it causes algae to grow so fast that fish suffocate. Pesticides can harm humans, other animals, and beneficial insects.

Pressured to produce more food at lower cost and with less damage to the environment, many farmers have begun to rely on genetically modified crop plants. Some of these modified plants carry genes that impart resistance to devastating plant diseases. Others offer improved yields, such as a strain of transgenic wheat that has double the yield of unmodified wheat. GMO crops such as *Bt* corn and soy help farmers use smaller amounts of toxic pesticides. Organic farmers often spray their crops with spores of *Bt* (*Bacillus thuringiensis*), a bacterial species that makes a protein toxic only to insect larvae. Researchers transferred the gene encoding the *Bt* protein into plants. The engineered plants produce the *Bt* protein, but otherwise they are identical to unmodified plants.

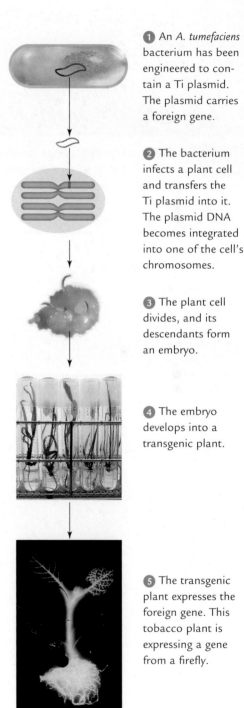

① An *A. tumefaciens* bacterium has been engineered to contain a Ti plasmid. The plasmid carries a foreign gene.

② The bacterium infects a plant cell and transfers the Ti plasmid into it. The plasmid DNA becomes integrated into one of the cell's chromosomes.

③ The plant cell divides, and its descendants form an embryo.

④ The embryo develops into a transgenic plant.

⑤ The transgenic plant expresses the foreign gene. This tobacco plant is expressing a gene from a firefly.

**FIGURE 10.8 Animated!** Using the Ti plasmid to make a transgenic plant.

**FIGURE 10.9** Genetically modified crops can help farmers use less pesticide. *Left*, the *Bt* gene conferred insect resistance to the genetically modified plants that produced this corn. *Right*, corn produced by unmodified plants is more vulnerable to insect pests.

Insect larvae die shortly after eating their first (and only) GMO meal. Farmers can use much less pesticide on crops that make their own (Figure 10.9).

Transgenic crop plants are also being developed for regions that are affected by severe droughts, such as Africa. Genes that confer drought tolerance and insect resistance are being transferred into crop plants such as corn, beans, sugarcane, cassava, cowpeas, banana, and wheat. Such crops may help people that rely on agriculture for food and income in drought-stricken, impoverished regions of the world.

The USDA Animal and Plant Health Inspection Service (APHIS) regulates the introduction of GMOs into the environment. At this writing, the agency has deregulated seventy-four genetically modified crop plants, which means the plants are approved for unregulated use in the United States.

The most widely planted GMO crops include corn, sorghum, cotton, soy, canola, and alfalfa engineered for resistance to glyphosate. Rather than tilling the soil to control weeds, farmers can spray their fields with this herbicide, which kills the weeds but not the engineered crops. However, weeds are becoming resistant to glyphosate, so spraying it no longer kills the weeds in glyphosate-resistant crop fields. The engineered gene is also appearing in wild plants and in nonengineered crops, which means that transgenes can (and do) escape into the environment. The genes are probably being transferred from transgenic plants to nontransgenic ones via pollen carried by wind or insects.

Controversy raised by such GMO use invites you to read the research and form your own opinions. The alternative is to be swayed by media hype (the term "Frankenfood," for instance), or by reports from possibly biased sources (such as herbicide manufacturers).

**Biotech Barnyards** Traditional cross-breeding has produced animals so unusual that transgenic animals may seem a bit mundane in comparison (Figure 10.10**A**). Cross-breeding is also a form of genetic manipulation, but many transgenic animals would probably never occur in nature (Figure 10.10**B,C**).

The first genetically modified animals were mice. Today, such mice are commonplace, and they are invaluable in research. We have discovered the function of many human genes by inactivating their counterparts in mice. *APOA5* (discussed in the previous section) is an example. Genetically modified mice are also used as models of many human diseases. For example, researchers inactivated the molecules involved in the control of glucose metabolism, one by one, in

**xenotransplantation** Transplant of an organ from one species into another.

mice. Studying the effects of the knockouts has resulted in much of our current understanding of how diabetes works in humans. Genetically modified animals such as these mice are allowing researchers to study human diseases (and their potential cures) without experimenting on humans.

Genetically modified animals also make proteins that have medical and industrial applications. Various transgenic goats produce proteins used to treat cystic fibrosis, heart attacks, blood clotting disorders, and even nerve gas exposure. Milk from goats transgenic for lysozyme, an antibacterial protein in human milk, may protect infants and children in developing countries from acute diarrheal disease. Goats transgenic for a spider silk gene produce the protein in their milk. Once researchers figure out how to spin it like spiders do, the silk may be used to manufacture fashionable fabrics, bulletproof vests, sports equipment, and biodegradable medical supplies. Rabbits make human interleukin-2, a protein that triggers divisions of immune cells. Genetic engineering has also given us dairy goats with heart-healthy milk, low-fat pigs, pigs with environmentally friendly low-phosphate manure, extra-large sheep, and cows that are resistant to mad cow disease.

Many people view transgenic animal research as unconscionable. Many others see it as simply an extension of thousands of years of acceptable animal husbandry practices: The techniques have changed, but not the intent. We humans still have a vested interest in improving our livestock.

**Knockout Cells and Organ Factories** Millions of people suffer with organs or tissues that are damaged beyond repair. In any given year, more than 80,000 of them are on waiting lists for an organ transplant in the United States alone. Human donors are in such short supply that illegal organ trafficking is now a common problem.

Pigs are a potential source of organs for transplantation, because pig and human organs are about the same in both size and function. However, the human immune system battles anything it recognizes as nonself. It rejects a pig organ at once, because it recognizes a particular protein on the plasma membrane of pig cells. Within a few hours, blood coagulates inside the organ's vessels and dooms the transplant. Drugs can suppress the immune response, but they also render organ recipients particularly vulnerable to infection.

Researchers have produced genetically modified pigs that lack the offending protein on their cells. The human immune system may not reject tissues or organs transplanted from these pigs. Transferring an organ from one species into another is called **xenotransplantation**. Critics of xenotransplantation are concerned that, among other things, pig-to-human transplants would invite pig viruses to cross the species barrier and infect humans, perhaps catastrophically. Their concerns are not unfounded. Evidence suggests that some of the worst pandemics arose when animal viruses adapted to new hosts: humans.

## Take-Home Message   **What is genetic engineering?**

- Genetic engineering is the directed alteration of an individual's genome, and it results in a genetically modified organism (GMO).

- A transgenic organism carries a gene from a different species. Transgenic organisms, including bacteria and yeast, are used in research, medicine, and industry.

- Plants with modified or foreign genes are now common farm crops.

- Animals that would be impossible to produce by traditional breeding methods are being created by genetic engineering.

**FIGURE 10.10** Modified livestock.

**A** Featherless chicken developed by traditional cross-breeding methods. Such chickens survive in deserts where cooling systems are not an option.

**B** A goat transgenic for a human protein that inhibits blood clotting. **C** *Left*, a pig transgenic for a jellyfish protein that fluoresces yellow. Its nontransgenic littermate is on the *right*.

# Genetically Modified Humans

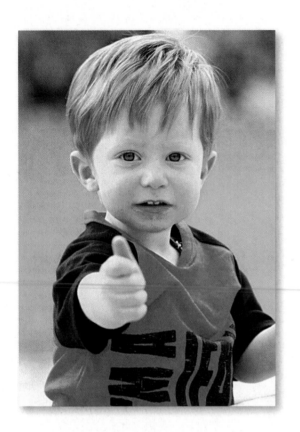

**Getting Better** We know of more than 15,000 serious genetic disorders. Collectively, they cause 20 to 30 percent of infant deaths each year, and account for half of all mentally impaired patients and a fourth of all hospital admissions. They also contribute to many age-related disorders, including cancer, Parkinson's disease, and diabetes. Drugs and other treatments can minimize the symptoms of some genetic disorders, but gene therapy is the only cure. **Gene therapy** is the transfer of recombinant DNA into an individual's body cells, with the intent to correct a genetic defect or treat a disease. The transfer, which occurs by way of viral vectors or lipid clusters, inserts an unmutated gene into an individual's chromosomes.

Human gene therapy is a compelling reason to embrace genetic engineering research. It is now being tested as a treatment for cystic fibrosis, hemophilia A, several types of cancer, and inherited diseases of the eye, the ear, and the immune system. The results are encouraging. For example, little Rhys Evans (*left*) was born with a severe immune disorder, SCID-X1. SCID-X1 stems from mutations in the *IL2RG* gene, which encodes a receptor for an immune signaling molecule. Children affected by this disorder can survive only in germ-free isolation tents, because they cannot fight infections. In 1998, a viral vector was used to insert unmutated copies of *IL2RG* into cells taken from the bone marrow of eleven boys with SCID-X1. Each child's modified cells were infused back into his bone marrow. Months later, ten of the boys left their isolation tents for good. Their immune systems had been repaired by the gene therapy. Since then, gene therapy has freed many other SCID-X1 patients from life in an isolation tent. Rhys is one of them.

**Getting Worse** Manipulating a gene within the context of a living individual is unpredictable even when we know its sequence and where it is within the genome. No one, for example, can predict where a virus-injected gene will insert into chromosomes. Its insertion might disrupt other genes. If it interrupts a gene that is part of the controls over cell division, then cancer might be the outcome. Three boys from the 1998 SCID-X1 clinical trial have since developed a type of bone marrow cancer called leukemia, and one of them died. The researchers had wrongly predicted that cancer related to the gene therapy would be rare. Research now implicates the very gene targeted for repair, especially when combined with the viral vector that delivered it.

Other unanticipated problems sometimes occur with gene therapy. Jesse Gelsinger had a rare genetic deficiency of a liver enzyme that helps the body rid itself of ammonia, a toxic by-product of protein breakdown. Jesse's health was fairly stable while he was on a low-protein diet, but he had to take a lot of medication. In 1999, Jesse volunteered to be in a clinical trial of a gene therapy. He had a severe allergic reaction to the viral vector, and four days after receiving the treatment, his organs shut down and he died. He was 18. Our understanding of how the human genome works clearly lags behind our ability to modify it.

**Getting Perfect** The idea of selecting the most desirable human traits, **eugenics**, is an old one. It has been used as a justification for some of the most horrific episodes in human history, including the genocide of 6 million Jews during World War II. Thus, it continues to be a hotly debated social issue. For example, using gene therapy to cure human genetic disorders seems like a socially acceptable goal to most people. However, imagine taking this idea a bit

**eugenics** Idea of deliberately improving the genetic qualities of the human race.
**gene therapy** The transfer of a normal or modified gene into an individual with the goal of treating a genetic defect or disorder.

further. Would it also be acceptable to engineer the genome of an individual who is within a normal range of phenotype in order to modify a particular trait? Researchers have already produced mice that have improved memory, enhanced learning ability, bigger muscles, and longer lives. Why not people?

Given the pace of genetic research, the eugenics debate is no longer about how we would engineer desirable traits, but how we would choose the traits that are desirable. Realistically, cures for many severe but rare genetic disorders will not be found, because the financial return will not even cover the cost of the research. Eugenics, however, might just turn a profit. How much would potential parents pay to be sure that their child will be tall or blue-eyed? Would it be okay to engineer "superhumans" with breathtaking strength or intelligence? How about a treatment that can help you lose that extra weight, and keep it off permanently? The gray area between interesting and abhorrent can be very different depending on who is asked. In a survey conducted in the United States, more than 40 percent of those interviewed said it would be fine to use gene therapy to make smarter and cuter babies. In one poll of British parents, 18 percent would be willing to use it to keep a child from being aggressive, and 10 percent would use it to keep a child from growing up to be homosexual.

**Getting There**  Some people are adamant that we must never alter the DNA of anything. The concern is that gene therapy puts us on a slippery slope that may result in irreversible damage to ourselves and to the biosphere. We as a society may not have the wisdom to know how to stop once we set foot on that slope. One is reminded of our peculiar human tendency to leap before we look. And yet, something about the human experience allows us to dream of such things as wings of our own making, a capacity that carried us into space. In this brave new world, the questions before you are these: What do we stand to lose if serious risks are not taken? And, do we have the right to impose the consequences of taking such risks on those who would choose not to take them?

## *Take-Home Message*  Do we genetically modify people?

- Genes can be transferred into a person's cells to correct a genetic defect or treat a disease. However, the outcome of altering a person's genome remains unpredictable given our current understanding of how the genome works.

# 10.6

# Impacts/Issues Revisited:
# Golden Rice or Frankenfood?

Beta-carotene is an orange photosynthetic pigment (Section 5.2) that is remodeled by cells of the small intestine into vitamin A. Potrykus and Beyer transferred two genes in the beta-carotene synthesis pathway into rice plants—one gene from corn and one from bacteria. Both genes are under the control of a promoter that works only in seeds. The transgenic rice plants make beta-carotene in their seeds—in the grains of Golden Rice. One cup of Golden Rice has enough beta-carotene to satisfy a child's daily recommended amount of vitamin A. The rice was ready in 2005, but is still not available for human consumption. The biosafety experiments required by regulatory agencies are far too expensive for a humanitarian agency in the public sector. Most of the transgenic organisms used for food today were carried through the deregulation process by private companies.

**How Would**

# YOU

☑ **Vote?**

Packaged food in the United States must have a nutrition label, but there is no requirement that genetically modified foods be labeled as such. Should food producers and distributors be required to identify products made from GMO plants or livestock? **See CengageNow for details, then vote online (CengageNow.com).**

# Summary

**Section 10.1** Genes from one species may be inserted into an individual of a different species to make a transgenic organism, or a gene may be modified and reinserted into an individual of the same species. The result of either process is a genetically modified organism (GMO).

**Section 10.2** Recombinant DNA consists of the fused DNA of different organisms. In DNA cloning, restriction enzymes cut DNA into pieces, then DNA ligase splices the pieces into plasmids or other cloning vectors. The resulting hybrid molecules are inserted into host cells such as bacteria. When a host cell divides, it forms huge populations of genetically identical descendant cells, or clones. Each clone has a copy of the foreign DNA.

RNA cannot be cloned directly. Reverse transcriptase, a viral enzyme, is used to copy single-stranded RNA into cDNA for cloning.

A library is a collection of cells that host different fragments of DNA, often representing an organism's entire genome. Researchers can use probes to identify cells that host a specific fragment of DNA. Base pairing between nucleic acids from different sources is called nucleic acid hybridization.

The polymerase chain reaction (PCR) uses primers and a heat-resistant DNA polymerase to rapidly increase the number of molecules of a DNA fragment.

CENGAGENOW™ Learn how researchers isolate and copy genes, and survey their tools with the interaction and animation on CengageNow.

**Section 10.3** Short tandem repeats are multiple copies of a short DNA sequence that follow one another along a chromosome. The number and distribution of short tandem repeats, unique in each

individual, is revealed by electrophoresis as a DNA fingerprint.

The genomes of several organisms have been sequenced. Genomics, or the study of genomes, is providing insights into the function of the human genome.

CENGAGENOW™ Observe the process of DNA fingerprinting with the animations on CengageNow.

**Section 10.4** Recombinant DNA technology and genome analysis are the basis of genetic engineering, which is directed modification of an organism's genetic makeup with the intent to modify its phenotype.

Genetically modified bacteria and yeast produce medically valuable proteins. Transgenic crop plants are helping farmers produce food more efficiently. Genetically modified animals produce human proteins, and may one day provide a source of organs and tissues for transplantation into humans.

CENGAGENOW™ See how the Ti plasmid is used to genetically modify plants with the animation on CengageNow.

**Section 10.5** With gene therapy, a gene is transferred into body cells to correct a genetic defect or treat a disease. As with any new technology, the potential benefits of genetically modifying humans must be weighed against the potential risks, including social implications.

## Self-Quiz    Answers in Appendix I

1. _____ cut(s) DNA molecules at specific sites.
   a. DNA polymerase        c. Restriction enzymes
   b. DNA probes            d. Reverse transcriptase

2. A _____ is a small circle of bacterial DNA that contains only a few genes and is separate from the bacterial chromosome.
   a. plasmid               c. nucleus
   b. chromosome            d. double helix

3. By reverse transcription, _____ is assembled on a(n) _____ template.
   a. mRNA; DNA             c. DNA; ribosome
   b. cDNA; mRNA            d. protein; mRNA

4. For each species, all _____ in the complete set of chromosomes is the _____ .
   a. genomes; phenotype    c. mRNA; start of cDNA
   b. DNA; genome           d. cDNA; start of mRNA

5. A set of cells that host various DNA fragments collectively representing an organism's entire set of genetic information is a _____ .
   a. genome                c. genomic library
   b. clone                 d. GMO

6. PCR can be used to _____ .
   a. increase the number of specific DNA fragments
   b. check DNA fingerprints
   c. modify a human genome
   d. a and b are correct

7. Fragments of DNA can be separated by electrophoresis according to _____ .
   a. sequence    b. length    c. species

8. Sequencing determines the order of bases in _____ .
   a. DNA                   c. electrophoresis
   b. PCR                   d. RNA

9. Which of the following can be used to carry foreign DNA into host cells? Choose all correct answers.
   a. RNA                   e. lipid clusters
   b. viruses               f. blasts of pellets
   c. PCR                   g. xenotransplantation
   d. plasmids              h. sequencing

10. A transgenic organism _____ .
    a. carries a gene from another species
    b. has been genetically modified
    c. both a and b

11. _____ can be used to correct a genetic defect.
    a. Xenotransplantation   d. Cloning vectors
    b. Gene therapy          e. a and b
    c. Cloning               f. all of the above

# Digging Into Data

## Enhanced Spatial Learning Ability in Mice with Autism Mutation

Autism is a neurobiological disorder with a range of symptoms that include impaired social interactions, stereotyped patterns of behavior such as hand-flapping or rocking, and, occasionally, greatly enhanced intellectual abilities.

Autism may have a genetic basis. Some autistic people have a mutation in neuroligin 3, a type of cell adhesion protein (Section 3.4) that connects brain cells to one another. One mutation changes amino acid 451 from arginine to cysteine.

Mouse and human neuroligin 3 are very similar. In 2007, Katsuhiko Tabuchi and his colleagues genetically modified mice to carry the same arginine-to-cysteine substitution in their neuroligin 3. The mutation caused an increase in transmission of some types of signals between brain cells. Mice with the mutation had impaired social behavior, and, unexpectedly, enhanced spatial learning ability. Figure 10.11 shows the results from some of their tests.

1. In the first test, how many days did unmodified mice need to learn to find the location of a hidden platform within 10 seconds?

2. Did the modified or the unmodified mice learn the location of the platform faster in the first test?

3. Which mice learned faster the second time around?

4. Which mice showed the greatest improvement in memory between the first and the second test?

**FIGURE 10.11** Enhanced spatial learning ability in mice with a mutation in neuroligin 3 (R451C), compared with unmodified (wild-type) mice. **A** The mice were tested in a water maze, in which a platform is submerged a few millimeters below the surface of a deep pool of warm water. The platform is not visible to swimming mice.

Mice do not particularly enjoy swimming, so they locate a hidden platform as fast as they can. When tested again, they can remember its location by checking visual cues around the edge of the pool. **B** How quickly they remember the platform's location is a measure of spatial learning ability. The platform was moved and the experiment was repeated for the second test.

12. Match the terms with the best description.

_____ DNA fingerprint
_____ Ti plasmid
_____ nucleic acid hybridization
_____ eugenics
_____ restriction enzyme
_____ transgenic
_____ GMO

a. having a foreign gene
b. cuts DNA at a specific sequence
c. a person's unique collection of short tandem repeats
d. base pairing of DNA or DNA and RNA from different sources
e. selecting "desirable" traits
f. genetically modified
g. used in some gene transfers

Additional questions are available on CENGAGENOW™

# Critical Thinking

1. The *FOXP2* gene encodes a transcription factor associated with vocal learning in mice, bats, birds, and humans. Mutations in *FOXP2* result in altered vocalizations in mice, and severe language disorders in humans. The chimpanzee, gorilla, and rhesus *FOXP2* proteins are identical; the human version differs in two of 715 amino acids. The change of two amino acids may have contributed to the development of language in humans. Would it be okay to transfer the human *FOXP2* gene into a nonhuman primate?

Spoken language is a complex, epistatic trait (Section 9.3). Thus, biologists do not anticipate that the transfer of the *FOXP2* gene alone would confer speaking ability upon a nonhuman recipient.

What do you think might happen if this prediction is incorrect, and an animal transgenic for *FOXP2* learned how to speak?

2. Animal viruses can mutate so that they infect humans, occasionally with disastrous results. In 1918, an influenza pandemic that apparently originated with a strain of avian flu killed 50 million people worldwide. Researchers isolated samples of that virus, which was called influenza A(H1N1) strain, from bodies of infected people preserved in Alaskan permafrost since 1918. From the samples, the researchers reconstructed the DNA sequence of the viral genome, then reconstructed the virus. Being 39,000 times more infectious than modern influenza strains, the reconstructed A(H1N1) virus proved to be 100 percent lethal in mice.

The researchers reconstructed the virus because understanding how the A(H1N1) strain works may help us defend ourselves against similar influenza strains. For example, they are using the reconstructed virus to discover which of its mutations made it so infectious and deadly in humans. Their work is urgent. A dangerous new strain of avian influenza in Asia shares some mutations with the A(H1N1) strain. Even now, researchers are working to test the effectiveness of antiviral drugs and vaccines on the reconstructed virus, and to develop new ones.

Critics of the A(H1N1) reconstruction are concerned. If the virus escapes its high-security containment facilities (even though it has not done so yet), it might cause another pandemic. Worse, terrorists could use the published DNA sequence and methods to make the virus for horrific purposes. Do you think this research makes our society more or less safe?

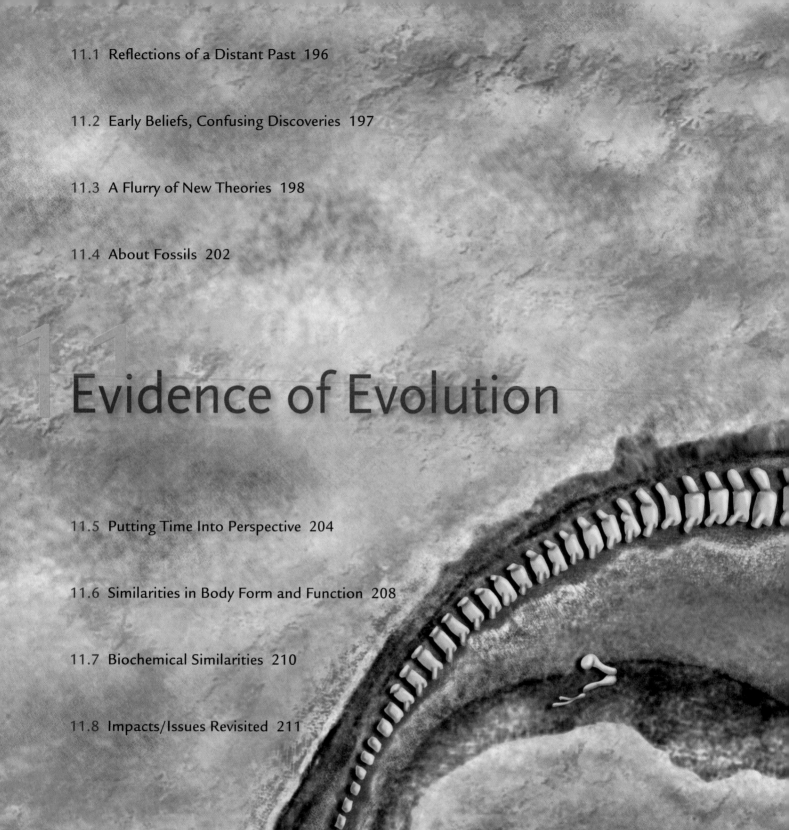

# 11 Evidence of Evolution

> Natural phenomena in the past can be explained by the same physical, chemical, and biological processes that operate today.

## 11.1

## Impacts/Issues: Reflections of a Distant Past

How do you think about time? Is your understanding limited to your own generation? Perhaps you can conceive of a few hundred years of human events, but how about a few million? Envisioning the distant past requires an intellectual leap from the familiar to the unknown.

One way to make that leap involves, surprisingly, asteroids. Asteroids are small planets hurtling through space. They range in size from 1 to 1,500 kilometers (roughly 0.5 to 1,000 miles) wide. Millions of them orbit around the sun between Mars and Jupiter—cold, stony leftovers from the formation of our solar system. Asteroids are difficult to see even with the best telescopes, because they do not emit light. Many cross Earth's orbit, but most of those pass us by before we know about them. Some have passed too close for comfort.

The mile-wide Barringer Crater in Arizona is difficult to miss (Figure 11.1). A 300,000-ton asteroid made this impressive pockmark in the desert sandstone when it slammed into Earth 50,000 years ago. The impact was 150 times more powerful than the bomb that leveled Hiroshima.

No human could have witnessed the impact, so how can we know anything about what happened? We often find physical evidence of events that occurred before we were around to see them. Geologists were able to infer the most probable cause of the Barringer Crater by analyzing tons of meteorites, melted sand, and other rocky clues at the site.

Similar evidence points to even larger asteroid impacts in the more distant past. For example, a **mass extinction**, or permanent loss of major groups of organisms, occurred 65.5 million years ago. It is marked by an unusual, worldwide layer of rock called the K–T boundary layer. There are plenty of dinosaur fossils below the K–T boundary layer. Above it, in rock layers that were deposited more recently, there are no dinosaur fossils anywhere. An impact crater off the coast of what is now the Yucatán Peninsula dates to about 65.5 million years ago. Coincidence? Many scientists say no. They have inferred from the evidence that the impact of an asteroid about 20 km (12 miles) wide caused a global catastrophe that wiped out the dinosaurs.

You are about to make an intellectual leap through time, to places that were not even known about a few centuries ago. We invite you to launch yourself from this premise: Natural phenomena that occurred in the past can be explained by the same physical, chemical, and biological processes that operate today. That premise is the foundation for scientific research into the history of life. The research represents a shift from experience to inference—from the known to what can only be surmised—and it gives us astonishing glimpses into the distant past.

**FIGURE 11.1** From evidence to inference. What made the Barringer Crater? Rocky evidence points to a 300,000-ton asteroid that collided with Earth 50,000 years ago.

# 11.2 Early Beliefs, Confusing Discoveries

The seeds of biological inquiry were taking hold in the Western world more than 2,000 years ago. Aristotle, the Greek philosopher, was making connections between observations in an attempt to explain the order of the natural world. Like few others of his time, Aristotle viewed nature as a continuum of organization, from lifeless matter through complex plants and animals. Aristotle was one of the first **naturalists**, people who observe life from a scientific perspective.

By the fourteenth century, Aristotle's earlier ideas about nature had been transformed into a rigid view of life, in which a "great chain of being" extended from the lowest form (snakes), to humans, to spiritual beings. Each link in the chain was a species, and each was said to have been forged at the same time in a perfect state. A species would never change after it had been created, because any variation from its ideal form and function would constitute imperfection. Once every species had been discovered, the meaning of life would be revealed.

European naturalists that embarked on globe-spanning survey expeditions brought back tens of thousands of plants and animals from Asia, Africa, North and South America, and the Pacific Islands. Each newly discovered species was carefully catalogued as another link in the chain of being.

By the late 1800s, Alfred Wallace and a few other naturalists were seeing patterns in where species live and how they might be related, and had started to think about the natural forces that shape life. These naturalists were pioneers in **biogeography**, the study of patterns in the geographic distribution of species. Some of the patterns raised questions that could not be answered within the framework of prevailing belief systems. For example, globe-trotting explorers had discovered plants or animals living in extremely isolated places. The isolated species looked suspiciously similar to species living across vast expanses of open ocean, or on the other side of impassable mountain ranges. Could different species be related? If so, how could the related species end up geographically isolated from one another?

The birds in Figure 11.2, for example, share very similar features, although each lives on a different continent. All three flightless birds sprint about on long, muscular legs in flat, open grasslands about the same distance from the equator. All raise their long necks to watch for predators. Wallace thought that the unique set of similarities might mean that the three types of birds are descendants of an ancient common ancestor (and he was correct), but he had no idea how they could have ended up on different continents.

**FIGURE 11.2** Similar species that are native to distant geographic realms.

*Above*, **A** South American rhea, **B** Australian emu, and **C** African ostrich. All three types of ratite birds live in similar habitats. These related birds are unlike most other birds in several traits, including their long, muscular legs and their inability to fly.

*Below*, similar-looking, unrelated plants: a spiny cactus native to the hot deserts of the American Southwest **D**, and a spiny spurge native to southwestern Africa **E**.

**biogeography** Study of patterns in the geographic distribution of species and communities.
**mass extinction** Simultaneous loss of many lineages from Earth.
**naturalist** Person who observes life from a scientific perspective.

FIGURE 11.3 Vestigial body parts. **A** Pythons and boa constrictors have tiny leg bones, but snakes do not walk. **B** We humans use our legs, but not our coccyx (tail) bones.

Naturalists of the time also had trouble classifying organisms that are very similar in some features, but different in others. For example, the plants in Figure 11.2**D,E** are native to different continents. Both live in hot deserts where water is seasonally scarce. Both have rows of sharp spines that deter herbivores, and both store water in their thick, fleshy stems. However, their reproductive parts are very different, so these plants cannot be as closely related as their outward appearance might suggest.

**Comparative morphology**, the study of body plans and structures among groups of organisms, added to the confusion when naturalists discovered body parts with no apparent function. According to prevailing beliefs, each species had been created in a perfect state. If that were so, then why were there useless parts such as leg bones in snakes (which do not walk), or the vestiges of a tail in humans (Figure 11.3)?

Fossils were puzzling too. Geologists mapping rock formations exposed by erosion or quarrying had discovered identical sequences of rock layers in different parts of the world. Deep layers held fossils of simple marine life. Layers above them held similar but more intricate fossils. In higher layers, fossils that were similar but even more intricate looked like modern species. The photos on the *right* show one such series, ten fossilized foraminiferan shells from ten stacked layers of sedimentary rock. What did these fossil sequences mean? Fossils of gigantic animals that had no living representatives were also being unearthed. If the animals had been perfect at the time of creation, why were they now extinct?

Taken as a whole, findings from biogeography, comparative morphology, and geology did not fit with prevailing beliefs of the nineteenth century. If species had not been created in a perfect state (and fossil sequences and "useless" body parts implied they had not), then perhaps species had changed over time.

## Take-Home Message How have observations of the natural world changed our thinking?

- Increasingly extensive observations of nature in the nineteenth century did not fit with prevailing belief systems.
- The cumulative findings from biogeography, comparative morphology, and geology led to new ways of thinking about the natural world.

# 11.3 A Flurry of New Theories

**Squeezing New Evidence Into Old Beliefs** In the nineteenth century, naturalists were faced with increasing evidence that life on Earth, and even Earth itself, had changed over time. Around 1800, Georges Cuvier, an expert in zoology and paleontology, was trying to make sense of the new information. He had observed abrupt changes in the fossil record, and knew that many fossil species seemed to have no living counterparts. Given this evidence,

**catastrophism** Now-abandoned hypothesis that catastrophic geologic forces unlike those of the present day shaped Earth's surface.

**comparative morphology** Scientific study of body plans and structures among groups of organisms.

**evolution** Change in a line of descent.

**theory of uniformity** Idea that gradual, repetitive processes occurring over long time spans shaped Earth's surface.

he proposed a startling idea: Many species that had once existed were now extinct. Cuvier also knew about evidence that Earth's surface had changed. For example, he had seen fossilized seashells on mountainsides far from modern seas. Like most others of his time, he assumed Earth's age to be in the thousands, not millions, of years. He reasoned that geologic forces unlike those known today would have been necessary to raise sea floors to mountaintops in this short time span. Catastrophic geological events would have caused extinctions, after which surviving species repopulated the planet. Cuvier's idea came to be known as **catastrophism**. We now know it is incorrect; geologic processes have not changed over time.

Another scholar, Jean-Baptiste Lamarck, was thinking about processes that drive **evolution**, or change in a line of descent. Lamarck thought that a species gradually improved over generations because of an inherent drive toward perfection, up the chain of being. This drive directed an unknown "fluida" into body parts needing change. By Lamarck's hypothesis, environmental pressures and internal needs cause changes in an individual's body, and offspring inherit the changes. Try using Lamarck's hypothesis to explain why the giraffe's neck is very long. We might predict that some short-necked ancestor of the modern giraffe stretched its neck to browse on leaves beyond the reach of other animals. The stretches may have even made its neck a bit longer. By Lamarck's hypothesis, that animal's offspring would inherit a longer neck, and after many generations strained to reach ever loftier leaves, the modern giraffe would have been the result. Lamarck was correct in thinking that environmental factors affect a species' traits, but incorrect about how inheritance works.

## Voyage of the Beagle

In 1831, the twenty-two-year-old Charles Darwin was wondering what to do with his life. Ever since he was eight, he had wanted to hunt, fish, collect shells, or watch insects and birds—anything but sit in school. After attempting to study medicine in college, he earned a degree in theology from Cambridge. All through school, however, Darwin spent most of his time with faculty members who embraced natural history. Botanist John Henslow arranged for Darwin to become a naturalist aboard the *Beagle*, a ship about to embark on a survey expedition to South America.

The *Beagle* set sail for South America in December, 1831 (Figure 11.4). The young man who had hated school and had no formal training in science quickly became an enthusiastic naturalist. During the *Beagle*'s five-year voyage, Darwin found many unusual fossils. He saw diverse species living in environments that ranged from the sandy shores of remote islands to the plains high in the Andes. Along the way, he read the first volume of a new and popular book, Charles Lyell's *Principles of Geology*. Lyell was a proponent of what became known as the **theory of uniformity**, the idea that gradual, repetitive change had shaped Earth. For many years, geologists had been chipping away at the sandstones, limestones, and other types of rocks that form from accumulated sediments in lakebeds, river bottoms, and ocean floors. These rocks held evidence that gradual processes of geologic change operating in the present were the same ones that operated in the distant past.

The theory of uniformity held that strange catastrophes were not necessary to explain Earth's surface. Over great spans of time, gradual, everyday geologic processes such as erosion could have sculpted Earth's current landscape. The theory challenged the prevailing belief that Earth was 6,000 years old. According to traditional scholars, people had recorded everything that happened in those 6,000 years—and in all that time, no one had mentioned seeing a species evolve. However, by Lyell's calculations, it must have taken millions of years to sculpt Earth's surface. Darwin's exposure to Lyell's ideas gave him insights into the

**FIGURE 11.4  A** Charles Darwin. **B** Voyage of the *Beagle*, during which Darwin discovered many puzzling fossils and species. In the Andes, for example, he found fossils of marine organisms in rock layers 3.6 kilometers (2.2 miles) above sea level.

**FIGURE 11.5** Ancient relatives? **A** A modern armadillo, about a foot long. **B** Fossil of a glyptodon, an automobile-sized mammal that lived between about 2 million and 15,000 years ago.

Glyptodons and armadillos are widely separated in time, but they share a restricted distribution and unusual traits, including a shell and helmet of keratin-covered bony plates—a material similar to crocodile and lizard skin. (The fossil in **B** is missing its helmet.) Their unique shared traits were a clue that helped Darwin develop a theory of evolution by natural selection.

**adaptation** (**adaptive trait**) A heritable trait that enhances an individual's fitness.

**fitness** The degree of adaptation to an environment, as measured by an individual's relative genetic contribution to future generations.

**natural selection** A process of evolution in which individuals of a population who vary in the details of heritable traits survive and reproduce with differing success.

geological history of the regions he would encounter on his journey. Was million of years enough time for species evolve? Darwin thought that it was.

**Natural Selection** Darwin sent to England the thousands of specimens he had collected on his voyage. Among them were fossil glyptodons from Argentina. These armored mammals are extinct, but they have many traits in common with modern armadillos (Figure 11.5). For example, armadillos live only in places where glyptodons once lived. Like glyptodons, armadillos have helmets and protective shells that consist of unusual bony plates. Could the odd shared traits mean that glyptodons were ancient relatives of armadillos? If so, perhaps traits of their common ancestor had changed in the line of descent that led to armadillos. But why would such changes occur?

Back in England, Darwin pondered his notes and fossils. He also read an essay by one of his contemporaries, economist Thomas Malthus. Malthus had correlated increases in human population size with famine, disease, and war. He proposed that humans run out of food, living space, and other resources because they tend to reproduce beyond the capacity of their environment to sustain them. When that happens, the individuals of a population must either compete with one another for the limited resources, or develop technology to increase their productivity. Darwin realized that Malthus's ideas had wider application: All populations, not just human ones, have the capacity to produce more individuals than their environment can support.

Darwin also thought about species he had observed during his voyage. He knew that individuals of a species were not always identical. They had many traits in common, but they might vary in size, color, or other traits. It dawned on Darwin that having a particular version of a variable trait might give an individual an advantage over competing members of its species. The trait might enhance the individual's ability to survive and reproduce in its particular environment. Darwin realized that in any population, some individuals have traits that make them better suited to their environment than others. In other words, individuals of a natural population vary in **fitness**. We define fitness as the degree of adaptation to a specific environment, and measure it as relative genetic contribution to future generations. A trait that enhances an individual's fitness is called an evolutionary **adaptation**, or **adaptive trait**.

Over many generations, individuals with the most adaptive traits tend to survive longer and reproduce more than their less fit rivals. Darwin understood that this process, which he called **natural selection**, could be a driving force of evolution. If an individual has a form of a trait that makes it better suited to an environment, then it is better able to survive. If an individual is better able to

FIGURE 11.6 Alfred Wallace, codiscoverer of natural selection.

survive, then it has a better chance of living long enough to produce offspring. If individuals that bear an adaptive, heritable trait produce more offspring than those that do not, then the frequency of that trait will tend to increase in the population over successive generations. Table 11.1 summarizes this reasoning.

**Great Minds Think Alike** Darwin wrote out his ideas about natural selection, but let ten years pass without publishing them. In the meantime, Alfred Wallace, who had been studying wildlife in the Amazon basin and the Malay Archipelago, wrote an essay and sent it to Darwin for advice. Wallace's essay had outlined Darwin's theory! Wallace had written earlier letters to Lyell and Darwin about patterns in the geographic distribution of species; he too had connected the dots. Wallace is now called the father of biogeography (Figure 11.6).

In 1858, just weeks after Darwin received Wallace's essay, their similar theories were presented jointly at a scientific meeting. Wallace was still in the field and knew nothing about the meeting, which Darwin did not attend. The next year, Darwin published *On the Origin of Species*, which laid out detailed evidence in support of his theory. Many scholars readily accepted the idea of descent with modification, or evolution. However, there was a fierce debate over the idea that evolution occurs by natural selection. Decades would pass before experimental evidence from the field of genetics led to its widespread acceptance in the scientific community.

As you will see in the remainder of this chapter, Darwin's theory is supported by and helps explain the fossil record as well as similarities in the form, function, and biochemistry of living things.

| Table 11.1 | Principles of Natural Selection |
|---|---|

**Observations about populations**

- Natural populations have an inherent reproductive capacity to increase in size over time.

- As a population expands, resources that are used by its individuals (such as food and living space) eventually become limited.

- When resources are limited, the individuals of a population compete for them.

**Observations about genetics**

- Individuals of a species share certain traits.

- Individuals of a natural population vary in the details of those shared traits.

- Shared traits have a heritable basis, in genes. Alleles (slightly different forms of a gene) arise by mutation.

**Inferences**

- A certain form of a shared trait may make its bearer better able to survive.

- The individuals of a population that are better able to survive tend to leave more offspring.

- Thus, an allele associated with an adaptive trait tends to become more common in a population over time.

## *Take-Home Message* How did new evidence change the way people in the nineteenth century thought about the history of life?

- In the 1800s, fossils and other evidence led some naturalists to propose that Earth and the species on it had changed over time. The naturalists also began to reconsider the age of Earth.

- These ideas set the stage for Darwin's theory of evolution by natural selection. Natural selection is the differential survival and reproduction among individuals of a population that vary in the details of shared, inherited traits.

- Traits favored by natural selection are said to be adaptive. An adaptive trait increases the chances that an individual bearing it will survive and reproduce.

**A** A 30-million-year-old fossil of *Elomeryx*. This small terrestrial mammal was a member of the same artiodactyl group that gave rise to hippopotamuses, pigs, deer, sheep, cows, and whales.

**B** *Rodhocetus*, an ancient whale, lived about 47 million years ago. Its distinctive ankle bones point to a close evolutionary connection to artiodactyls. Inset: compare a *Rodhocetus* ankle bone (*left*) with that of a modern artiodactyl, a pronghorn antelope (*right*).

**C** *Dorudon atrox*, an ancient whale that lived about 37 million years ago. Its artiodactyl-like ankle bones (*left*) were much too small to have supported the weight of its huge body on land, so this mammal had to be fully aquatic.

**FIGURE 11.7** New links in the ancient lineage of whales. With their artiodactyl-like ankle bones, *Rodhocetus* and *Dorudon* were probably offshoots of the ancient artiodactyl-to-modern-whale lineage as it transitioned back to life in water. Modern cetaceans do not have even a remnant of an ankle bone.

# 11.4 About Fossils

Even before Darwin's time, **fossils** were recognized as stone-hard evidence of earlier forms of life. Most fossils are mineralized bones, teeth, shells, seeds, spores, or other hard body parts. Trace fossils such as footprints and other impressions, nests, burrows, trails, eggshells, or feces (*left*) are evidence of an organism's activities.

The process of fossilization begins when an organism or its traces become covered by sediments or volcanic ash. Water seeps into the remains, and metal ions and other inorganic compounds dissolved in the water gradually replace the minerals in the bones and other hard tissues. Sediments that accumulate on top of the remains exert increasing pressure on them. After a very long time, the pressure and mineralization process transform the remains into rock.

Most fossils are found in layers of sedimentary rock such as mudstone, sandstone, and shale. These rocks form as rivers wash silt, sand, volcanic ash, and other particles from land to sea. The particles settle on sea floors in horizontal layers that vary in thickness and in composition. After hundreds of millions of years, the layers of sediments became compacted into layers of rock.

We study layers of sedimentary rock in order to understand the historical context of fossils we find in them. Usually, the deeper layers in a stack were the first to form, and those closest to the surface formed most recently. Thus, the deeper the layer of sedimentary rock, the older the fossils it contains. A layer's composition and thickness relative to other layers is also a clue about local or global events that were occurring as it formed. For instance, layers of sedimentary rock deposited during ice ages are thinner than other layers. Why? Tremendous volumes of water froze and became locked in glaciers during the ice ages. Rivers dried up, and sedimentation slowed. When the glaciers melted, sedimentation resumed and the layers became thicker.

**The Fossil Record** We have fossils for more than 250,000 known species. Considering the current range of biodiversity, there must have been many millions more, but we will never know all of them. Why not?

The odds are against finding evidence of an extinct species, because fossils are relatively rare. Most of the time, an organism's remains are quickly obliterated by scavengers or decay. Organic materials decompose in the presence of oxygen, so remains endure only if they are encased in an air-excluding material such as sap, tar, ice, or mud. Remains that do become fossilized are often deformed, crushed, or scattered by erosion and other geologic assaults. For us to find a fossil of an extinct species, at least one specimen had to be buried before it decomposed or something ate it. The burial site had to escape destructive geologic events, and it had to end up where we might be able to find it.

However, despite these challenges, the fossil record is substantial enough to help us reconstruct patterns in the history of life. We have been able to find fossil evidence of the evolutionary history of many species, as illustrated by the following example.

Evolutionary biologists had thought for a long time that the ancestors of whales probably walked on land. The skull and lower jaw of cetaceans—which include whales, dolphins, and porpoises—have distinctive features that are also characteristic of ancient carnivorous land animals. DNA sequence comparisons suggested that those animals were probably artiodactyls, hooved mammals with two or four toes on each foot. Modern representatives of the line of descent—the **lineage**—include hippopotamuses, camels, pigs, deer, sheep, and cows.

We have fossil skeletons representing gradual changes in thirty genera between the ancient artiodactyls and modern whales. However, until recently the skeletons of these transitional forms were incomplete, so the story of the transition remained speculative. Then, in 2000, archaeologists found two of the missing pieces of the puzzle in Pakistan when they collected complete fossil skeletons of two ancient whales. Intact, sheeplike ankle bones and ancient whalelike skull bones present in the same skeletons provide clear evidence of the transition from terrestrial to aquatic life (Figure 11.7).

**Radiometric Dating** A radioisotope is a form of an element with an unstable nucleus (Section 2.2). Atoms of a radioisotope become atoms of other elements as their nucleus disintegrates. Such decay is not influenced by temperature, pressure, chemical bonding state, or moisture; it is influenced only by time. Like the ticking of a perfect clock, each type of radioisotope decays at a constant rate into predictable products called daughter elements. For example, radioactive uranium 238 decays into thorium 234, which decays into something else, and so on until it becomes lead 206. The time it takes for half of a radioisotope's atoms to decay into a product is called **half-life** (Figure 11.8A). The half-life of uranium 238 to lead 206 decay is 4.5 billion years.

The predictability of radioactive decay can be used to find the age of a volcanic rock—the date it cooled. Rock deep inside Earth is hot and molten, so atoms swirl and mix in it. Rock that reaches the surface cools and hardens. As the rock cools, minerals crystallize in

zircon

it. Each kind of mineral has a characteristic structure and composition. For example, the mineral zircon consists primarily of ordered arrays of zircon silicate molecules ($ZrSiO_4$). Some of the molecules in a zircon crystal have uranium atoms substituted for zirconium atoms, but never lead atoms. Thus, new zircon crystals that form as molten rock cools contain no lead. However, uranium decays into lead at a predictable rate. Thus, over time, uranium atoms disappear from a zircon crystal, and lead atoms accumulate in it. The ratio of uranium atoms to lead atoms in a zircon crystal can be measured precisely. That ratio can be used to calculate how long ago the crystal formed (its age).

We have just described **radiometric dating**, a method that can reveal the age of a material by measuring its content of a radioisotope and daughter elements. The oldest known terrestrial rock, a tiny zircon crystal from Australia, is 4.404 billion years old.

Recent fossils that still contain carbon can be dated by measuring their carbon 14 content (Figure 11.8B–D). Most of the $^{14}C$ in a fossil will have decayed after about 60,000 years. The age of fossils older than that can be estimated only by dating volcanic rocks in lava flows above and below the fossil-containing rock.

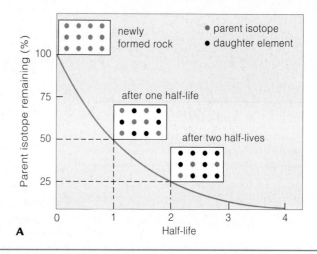

A

**FIGURE 11.8 Animated!** Radiometric dating. **A** Half-life, the time it takes for half of the atoms in a sample of radioisotope to decay. **B–D** Using radiometric dating to find the age of a fossil. Carbon 14 ($^{14}C$) is a radioisotope of carbon. It forms in the atmosphere and combines with oxygen to become $CO_2$, which enters food chains by way of photosynthesis.

Figure It Out: How much of any radioisotope remains after two of its half-lives have passed?

*Answer: 25 percent*

**B** Long ago, trace amounts of $^{14}C$ and a lot more $^{12}C$ were incorporated into the tissues of a nautilus. The carbon atoms were part of organic molecules in the nautilus's food. As long as it was alive, the nautilus gained carbon atoms from its food. Thus, the proportion of $^{14}C$ to $^{12}C$ in its tissues stayed the same.

**C** When the nautilus died, it stopped eating, so its body stopped gaining carbon. The $^{14}C$ in its body continued to decay, so the amount of $^{14}C$ decreased relative to the amount of $^{12}C$. Half of the $^{14}C$ decayed in 5,370 years, half of what was left decayed after another 5,370 years, and so on.

**D** Fossil hunters discover the fossil. They measure its $^{14}C$ to $^{12}C$ ratio and use it to calculate the number of half-life reductions since the organism died. For example, if the $^{14}C$ to $^{12}C$ ratio is one-eighth of the ratio in living organisms, then this nautilus died about 16,000 years ago.

# Take-Home Message  What are fossils?

- Fossils are evidence of organisms that lived in the remote past, a stone-hard historical record of life.

- Researchers use the predictability of radioisotope decay to estimate the age of rocks and fossils.

**fossil** Physical evidence of an organism that lived in the ancient past.

**half-life** Characteristic time it takes for half of a quantity of a radioisotope to decay.

**lineage** Line of descent.

**radiometric dating** Method of estimating the age of a rock or fossil by measuring the content and proportions of a radioisotope and its daughter elements.

# Putting Time Into Perspective

FIGURE 11.9 Animated! The geologic time scale correlated with some of the sedimentary rock layers of the Grand Canyon.

Radiometric dating and fossils allow us to recognize similar sequences of sedimentary rock layers around the world. Transitions between some of the layers mark boundaries of great intervals of time in the **geologic time scale**, or chronology of Earth's history (Figure 11.9). Each layer holds clues to life on Earth during the period of time that it formed. For example, the Grand Canyon's

| Eon | Era | Period | Epoch | mya | Major Geologic and Biologic Events |
|---|---|---|---|---|---|
| PHANEROZOIC | CENOZOIC | QUATERNARY | Recent | 0.01 | Modern humans evolve. Major extinction event is now under way. |
| | | | Pleistocene | 1.8 | |
| | | TERTIARY | Pliocene | 5.3 | Tropics, subtropics extend poleward. Climate cools; dry woodlands and grasslands emerge. Adaptive radiations of mammals, insects, birds. |
| | | | Miocene | 23.0 | |
| | | | Oligocene | 33.9 | |
| | | | Eocene | 55.8 | |
| | | | Paleocene | 65.5 ◄ | **Major extinction event**, perhaps precipitated by asteroid impact. Mass extinction of all dinosaurs and many marine organisms. |
| | MESOZOIC | CRETACEOUS | Late | | |
| | | | | 99.6 | |
| | | | Early | | Climate very warm. Dinosaurs continue to dominate. Important modern insect groups appear (bees, butterflies, termites, ants, and herbivorous insects including aphids and grasshoppers). Flowering plants originate and become dominant land plants. |
| | | | | 145.5 | |
| | | JURASSIC | | | Age of dinosaurs. Lush vegetation; abundant gymnosperms and ferns. Birds appear. Pangea breaks up. |
| | | | | 199.6 ◄ | **Major extinction event** |
| | | TRIASSIC | | | Recovery from the major extinction at end of Permian. Many new groups appear, including turtles, dinosaurs, pterosaurs, and mammals. |
| | | | | 251 ◄ | **Major extinction event** |
| | PALEOZOIC | PERMIAN | | | Supercontinent Pangea and world ocean form. Adaptive radiation of conifers. Cycads and ginkgos appear. Relatively dry climate leads to drought-adapted gymnosperms and insects such as beetles and flies. |
| | | | | 299 | |
| | | CARBONIFEROUS | | | High atmospheric oxygen level fosters giant arthropods. Spore-releasing plants dominate. Age of great lycophyte trees; vast coal forests form. Ears evolve in amphibians; penises evolve in early reptiles (vaginas evolve later, in mammals only). |
| | | | | 359 ◄ | **Major extinction event** |
| | | DEVONIAN | | | Land tetrapods appear. Explosion of plant diversity leads to tree forms, forests, and many new plant groups including lycophytes, ferns with complex leaves, and seed plants. |
| | | | | 416 | |
| | | SILURIAN | | | Radiations of marine invertebrates. First appearances of land fungi, vascular plants, bony fish, and perhaps terrestrial animals (millipedes, spiders). |
| | | | | 443 ◄ | **Major extinction event** |
| | | ORDOVICIAN | | | Major period for first appearances. The first land plants, fish, and reef-forming corals appear. Gondwana moves toward the South Pole and becomes frigid. |
| | | | | 488 | |
| | | CAMBRIAN | | | Earth thaws. Explosion of animal diversity. Most major groups of animals appear (in the oceans). Trilobites and shelled organisms evolve. |
| | | | | 542 | |
| PROTEROZOIC | | | | | Oxygen accumulates in atmosphere. Origin of aerobic metabolism. Origin of eukaryotic cells, then protists, fungi, plants, animals. Evidence that Earth mostly freezes over in a series of global ice ages between 750 and 600 mya. |
| | | | | 2,500 | |
| ARCHAEAN AND EARLIER | | | | | 3,800–2,500 mya. Origin of prokaryotes.<br><br>4,600–3,800 mya. Origin of Earth's crust, first atmosphere, first seas. Chemical, molecular evolution leads to origin of life (from protocells to anaerobic prokaryotes). |

A  Transitions in sedimentary rock layers mark great time spans in Earth's history (not to the same scale). mya: millions of years ago.

Dates from International Commission on Stratigraphy data, 2007.

B  We can reconstruct some of the events in the history of life by studying rocky clues in the layers. Here, the *red* triangles mark times of great mass extinctions. "First appearance" refers to appearance in the fossil record, not necessarily the first appearance on Earth; we often discover fossils that are significantly older than previously discovered specimens.

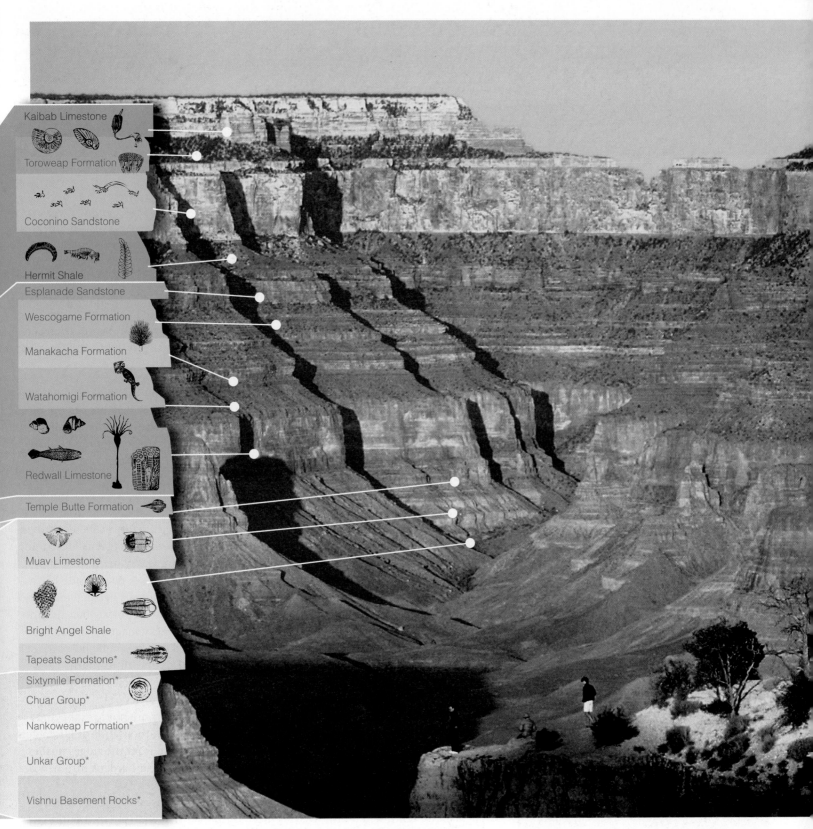

Kaibab Limestone

Toroweap Formation

Coconino Sandstone

Hermit Shale

Esplanade Sandstone

Wescogame Formation

Manakacha Formation

Watahomigi Formation

Redwall Limestone

Temple Butte Formation

Muav Limestone

Bright Angel Shale

Tapeats Sandstone*

Sixtymile Formation*

Chuar Group*

Nankoweap Formation*

Unkar Group*

Vishnu Basement Rocks*

**C** Sedimentary rock layers exposed by erosion in the Grand Canyon. Each layer has a characteristic composition and set of fossils (some are shown) that reflect events during its deposition. For example, Coconino Sandstone, which stretches from California to Montana, consists mainly of greatly weathered sand. Ripple marks and reptile tracks are the only fossils in it. Many think it is the remains of a vast sand desert, like the Sahara is today. *Layers not visible in this view.

**geologic time scale** Chronology of Earth history.

trench      hot spot ④      ridge      trench      rift

**FIGURE 11.10** Plate tectonics. Huge pieces of Earth's outer layer of rock slowly drift apart and collide. As the plates move, they raft continents around the globe.

① At oceanic ridges, huge plumes of molten rock welling up from Earth's interior drive the movement of tectonic plates. New crust spreads outward as it forms on the surface, forcing adjacent tectonic plates away from the ridge and into trenches elsewhere.

② At trenches, the advancing edge of one plate plows under an adjacent plate and buckles it.

③ Faults are ruptures in Earth's crust where plates meet. Plates move apart at rifts. The aerial photo *below* shows about 4.2 kilometers (2.6 miles) of the San Andreas Fault, which extends 1,300 km (800 miles) through California. This fault is a boundary between two tectonic plates slipping by one another.

④ Plumes of molten rock rupture a tectonic plate at what are called "hot spots." The Hawaiian Islands have been forming this way.

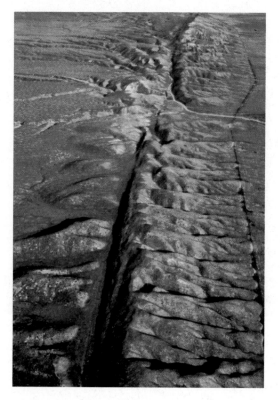

uppermost layer, Kaibab limestone, is its youngest. The layer consists mainly of limestone, a sandy sedimentary rock that forms at the bottom of shallow oceans. It also contains fossils of marine organisms. If the Kaibab limestone layer was originally deposited at the bottom of an ocean, a lot more rock must have formed on top of it in the last 250 million years. What happened to that rock? Part of the answer can be found in a neighboring park, Utah's Bryce Canyon, where about 12,000 feet (3,650 meters) of sedimentary rock layers occur on top of Kaibab limestone. These younger layers no longer exist in the Grand Canyon because they have eroded away.

**Drifting Continents, Changing Seas** Wind, water, and other natural forces continuously sculpt the surface of Earth, but they are only part of a bigger picture of geologic change. Earth itself also changes dramatically. For instance, the Atlantic coasts of South America and Africa seem to "fit" like jigsaw puzzle pieces. By one model, all continents were once part of a bigger supercontinent—**Pangea**—that had split into fragments and drifted apart. The idea explained why the same types of fossils occur in sedimentary rock on both sides of the vast Atlantic Ocean.

At first, most scientists did not accept this model, which was called continental drift. Continents drifting about Earth seemed to be an outrageous idea, and no one knew what would drive such movement. However, evidence that supported the model kept turning up. For instance, molten rock deep inside Earth wells up and solidifies on the surface. Some iron-rich minerals become magnetic as they solidify, and their magnetic poles align with Earth's poles when they do. If continents never moved, then all of these ancient rocky magnets would be aligned north-to-south, like compass needles. Indeed, the magnetic poles of rock formations on different continents are aligned—but not north-to-south. They point in many different directions. Either Earth's magnetic poles veer dramatically from their north–south axis, or the continents wander.

Then, deep-sea explorers discovered that ocean floors are not as static and featureless as had been assumed. Immense ridges stretch thousands of kilometers across the sea floor (Figure 11.10). Molten rock spewing from the ridges pushes old sea floor outward in both directions ①, then cools and hardens into new sea floor. Elsewhere, older sea floor plunges into deep trenches ②.

Such discoveries swayed the skeptics. Finally, there was a plausible mechanism for continental drift. By this mechanism, Earth's relatively thin outer layer of rock is cracked into immense plates, like a gigantic cracked eggshell. The plates grow from undersea ridges and continental rifts ③, and they sink into trenches. As the plates move, they act like colossal conveyer belts, rafting continents on top of them to new locations. The movement is no more than about

**A** 420 mya   **B** 237 mya   **C** 152 mya   **D** 65.5 mya   **E** 14 mya

FIGURE 11.11 **Animated!** A series of reconstructions of the drifting continents. **A** The supercontinent Gondwana (*yellow*) had begun to break up by the Silurian. **B** The supercontinent Pangea formed during the Triassic, then **C** began to break up in the Jurassic. **D** K–T boundary. **E** The continents reached their modern configuration in the Miocene.

10 centimeters (4 inches) a year—about half as fast as your toenails grow—but that is enough to carry a continent all the way around the world after 40 million years or so. Evidence of the movement is all around us, in various geological features of our landscapes ④.

Researchers soon applied the theory of continental movement, which is now called **plate tectonics**, to some long-standing puzzles. For example, fossils of a type of fern (*Glossopteris*) and of an early reptile (*Lystrosaurus*) had been found in an unusual, 260 million-year-old geologic formation that occurs in Africa, India, South America, and Australia. The formation consists of a sequence of rock layers so complex that the identical sequence is quite unlikely to have formed in more than one place. However, the formation also predates Pangea, which started to form 237 million years ago.

The fern's seeds were too heavy to float or to be wind-blown over an ocean, and the reptile was not built to be able to swim between continents. Researchers suspected that both organisms evolved on a supercontinent that had broken up by the time Pangea formed. The older supercontinent, **Gondwana**, included most of the land masses now in the Southern Hemisphere as well as India and Arabia (Figure 11.11). Based on this hypothesis, the researchers predicted that *Glossopteris* and *Lystrosaurus* fossils and the same geologic formation would also occur in Antarctica, which was mostly unexplored at the time. Later expeditions found the formations and the fossils. The discovery supported the prediction—and the plate tectonics theory.

We now know that many modern species, including the ratite birds pictured in Figure 11.2**A–C**, live only in places that were once part of Gondwana. After it formed, Gondwana drifted south, across the South Pole, then north until it merged with other continents to form Pangea.

At least five times since Earth's outer layer of rock solidified 4.55 billion years ago, a single supercontinent with one ocean lapping at its coastline formed and then split up again. The resulting changes in Earth's surface, atmosphere, and waters have had a profound impact on the course of life's evolution. A continent's climate changes—often dramatically so—with its position on Earth. Colliding continents physically separate organisms living in oceans, and bring together those that had been living apart on land. Continents that break up separate organisms living on land, and bring together aquatic ones. Such changes are a major driving force of evolution, as you will see in the next chapter. Lineages that cannot adapt die out, and new evolutionary opportunities open up for the survivors.

## Take-Home Message   What events have influenced life's history on Earth?

■ Slow movements of Earth's crust have changed the land, atmosphere, and oceans, and so have influenced the course of life's evolution.

**Gondwana** Supercontinent that formed more than 500 million years ago.

**Pangea** Supercontinent that formed about 237 million years ago and broke up about 152 million years ago.

**plate tectonics** Theory that Earth's outer layer of rock is cracked into plates, the slow movement of which rafts continents to new locations over geologic time.

## 11.6 Similarities in Body Form and Function

How do we know about evolution that occurred in the ancient past? Like asteroid impacts, evolution also leaves evidence that it occurred. Fossils are one example, but organisms that are alive today provide others. To a biologist, remember, evolution means change in a line of descent. Clues about the history of a lineage may be revealed by comparative morphology, because similarities in the structure of body parts are often evidence of a common ancestor. Similar body parts that reflect shared ancestry are called **homologous structures** (*hom*– means the same). Such structures may be used for different purposes in different groups, but the same genes direct their development.

**Morphological Divergence** A body part that appears very different in different lineages may be quite similar in some underlying aspect of form. For example, even though vertebrate forelimbs are not the same in size, shape, or function from one group to the next, they clearly are alike in the structure and positioning of bony elements. They also are alike in the patterns of nerves, blood vessels, and muscles that develop inside of them. In addition, comparisons of the early embryos of different vertebrates reveal strong resemblances in patterns of bone development. Such similarities are evidence of shared ancestry.

Populations that are not interbreeding tend to diverge genetically, and in time they diverge morphologically. Change from the body form of a common ancestor is an evolutionary pattern called **morphological divergence**. We have evidence from fossilized limb bones that all modern land vertebrates share an ancestor, a "stem reptile" that crouched low to the ground on four legs. Descendants of this ancestor diversified into many new habitats on land, and gave rise to the groups we call reptiles, birds, and mammals. A few lineages that had become adapted to walking on land even returned to life in the seas.

The stem reptile's five-toed limbs were evolutionary clay. Over millions of years, they became molded into limbs with very different functions across many lineages (Figure 11.12). In extinct reptiles called pterosaurs, most birds, and bats, they have been modified for flight. In penguins and porpoises, the limbs are now flippers useful for swimming. In humans, five-toed limbs became modified into the arms and hands, in which the thumb evolved in opposition to the fingers. An opposable thumb was the basis of more precise motions and a firmer grip. Among elephants, the limbs are now strong and pillarlike, capable of supporting a great deal of weight. Limbs degenerated to nubs in pythons and boa constrictors, and to nothing at all in other snakes.

**FIGURE 11.12** Morphological divergence among vertebrate forelimbs, starting with the bones of a stem reptile. The number and position of many skeletal elements were preserved when these diverse forms evolved; notice the bones of the forearms. Certain bones were lost over time in some of the lineages (compare the digits numbered 1 through 5). The drawings are not to the same scale.

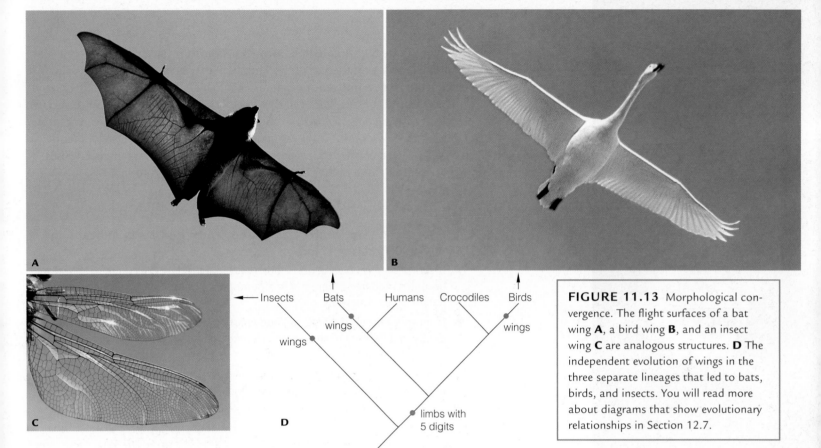

A

B

C

D

Insects   Bats   Humans   Crocodiles   Birds

wings

wings

wings

wings

limbs with
5 digits

FIGURE 11.13 Morphological convergence. The flight surfaces of a bat wing **A**, a bird wing **B**, and an insect wing **C** are analogous structures. **D** The independent evolution of wings in the three separate lineages that led to bats, birds, and insects. You will read more about diagrams that show evolutionary relationships in Section 12.7.

## Morphological Convergence

Similar body parts are not always homologous. Similar structures may evolve independently in separate lineages as adaptations to the same environmental pressures, in which case they are called analogous structures. **Analogous structures** look alike in different lineages but did not evolve in a shared ancestor; they evolved independently after the lineages diverged. Evolution of similar body parts in different lineages is known as **morphological convergence**.

We can sometimes identify analogous structures by studying their underlying form. For example, bird, bat, and insect wings all perform the same function: flight. However, several clues tell us that the flight surfaces of these wings are not homologous. The wing surfaces are adapted to the same physical constraints that govern flight, but the adaptations are different. In the case of birds and bats, the limbs themselves are homologous, but the adaptations that make those limbs useful for flight differ. The surface of a bat wing is a thin, membranous extension of the animal's skin. By contrast, the surface of a bird wing is a sweep of feathers, which are specialized structures derived from skin. Insect wings differ even more. An insect wing forms as a saclike extension of the body wall. Except at forked veins, the sac flattens and fuses into a thin membrane. The veins are reinforced with chitin, which structurally support the wing. The unique adaptations for flight are evidence that wing surfaces of birds, bats, and insects are analogous structures—they evolved after the ancestors of these modern groups diverged (Figure 11.13).

## Comparative Embryology

The development of an embryo into the body of a plant or animal is orchestrated by layer after layer of master gene expression (Section 7.7). The failure of any single master gene to participate in this symphony of expression can result in a drastically altered body plan, typically with devastating consequences.

**analogous structures** Similar structures that evolved separately in different lineages.
**homologous structures** Similar body parts that reflect shared ancestry among lineages.
**morphological convergence** Evolutionary pattern in which similar body parts evolve separately in different lineages.
**morphological divergence** Evolutionary pattern in which a body part of an ancestor changes in its descendants.

Because a mutation in a master gene typically unravels development, these genes tend to be highly conserved, which means they have changed very little or not at all over evolutionary time. Thus, a master gene with a similar sequence and function across different lineages is evidence that those lineages are related.

For example, master genes called homeotic genes guide formation of specific body parts during development. A mutation in one homeotic gene can disrupt details of the body's form, so these genes (and the patterns of development they govern) are often conserved in related lineages. When the same master genes direct development, embryos develop in similar ways (Figure 11.14).

## Take-Home Message  Do similarities in body form and parts indicate an evolutionary relationship?

- In morphological divergence, a body part inherited from a common ancestor becomes modified differently in different lines of descent. Such parts are called homologous structures.

- In morphological convergence, body parts that appear alike evolved independently in different lineages, not in a common ancestor. Such parts are called analogous structures.

- Similarities in patterns of embryonic development are the result of master genes that have been conserved over evolutionary time.

## 11.7 Biochemical Similarities

Each lineage has a unique set of traits that is a mixture of ancestral and novel characteristics, including biochemical features such as the nucleotide sequence of its DNA. Inevitable mutations change that sequence over time. The process of mutation is random, so the changes can occur anywhere in a chromosome.

We can use our knowledge of mutations to investigate how species are related. Most mutations are neutral, which means they have no effect on fitness and are not affected by natural selection. Think about what happens when one species splits into two. After the split occurs, each species begins to accumulate different neutral mutations independently. Mutations occur at a predictable rate, so the number of accumulated differences between species indicates how long ago they shared an ancestor. The more recent the divergence, the less time there has been for unique mutations to accumulate. That is why the DNA sequences of closely related species are more similar than those of distantly related ones.

Comparing the DNA of different species is now very fast and accurate, thanks to DNA sequencing and fingerprinting (Section 10.3). Comparative genomics studies have shown us (for example) that about 30 percent of the 6,609 yeast genes have homologous genes in the human genome. So do 50 percent of the 30,971 fruit fly genes and 40 percent of the 19,023 roundworm genes.

**FIGURE 11.14** Comparative embryology. All vertebrates go through an embryonic stage in which they have four limb buds and a tail. From *top* to *bottom*: human, mouse, bat, chicken, and alligator embryos.

```
        honeycreeper ...CRDVQFGWLIRNLHANGASFFFICIYLHIGRGIYYGSYLNK--ETWNIGVILLLTLMATAFVGYVLPWGQMSFWG...
   Gough Island finch ...CRDVQFGWLIRNIHANGASFFFICIYLHIGRGLYYGSYLYK--ETWNVGVILLLTLMATAFVGYVLPWGQMSFWG...
         song sparrow ...CRDVQFGWLIRNLHANGASFFFICIYLHIGRGIYYGSYLNK--ETWNVGIILLLALMATAFVGYVLPWGQMSFWG...
           deer mouse ...CRDVNYGWLIRYMHANGASMFFICLFLHVGRGMYYGSYTFT--ETWNIGIVLLFAVMATAFMGYVLPWGQMSFWG...
    Asiatic black bear ...CRDVHYGWIIRYMHANGASMFFICLFMHVGRGLYYGSYLLS--ETWNIGIILLFTVMATAFMGYVLPWGQMSFWG...
        bogue (a fish) ...CRDVNYGWLIRNLHANGASFFFICIYLHIGRGLYYGSYLYK--ETWNIGVVLLLLVMGTAFVGYVLPWGQMSFWG...
               human ...TRDVNYGWIIRYLHANGASMFFICLFLHIGRGLYYGSFLYS--ETWNIGIILLATMATAFMGYVLPWGQMSFWG...
   thale cress (a plant) ...MRDVEGGWLLRYMHANGASMFLIVVYLHIFRGLYHASYSSPREFVWCLGVVIFLLMIVTAFIGYVLPWGQMSFWG...
          baboon louse ...ETDVMNGWMVRSIHANGASWFFIMLYSHIFRGLWVSSFTQP--LVWLSGVIILFLSMATAFLGYVLPWGQMSFWG...
         baker's yeast ...MRDVHNGYILRYLHANGASFFFMVMFMHMAKGLYYGSYRSPRVTLWNVGVIIFTLTIATAFLGYCCVYGQMSHWG...
```

Amino acid sequence comparisons are also used to determine relationships among species. Two species with many identical proteins are likely to be close relatives. Two species with few similar proteins probably have not shared an ancestor for a long time because many mutations have accumulated in the DNA of their separate lineages.

Some essential genes have evolved very little; they are highly conserved across diverse species. One such gene encodes cytochrome *b* (Figure 11.15). This protein is an important component of electron transfer chains in mitochondria. In humans, its primary structure consists of 378 amino acids.

In amino acid sequence comparisons, similarities among species are a legacy of shared ancestry. The amino acids that differ also provide clues about evolution. For example, when one amino acid replaces another of similar charge, size, and polarity, the function of the resulting protein may be unchanged. However, when one amino acid is replaced by another with very different properties, the change in the protein can be dramatic. Such nonconservative substitutions often affect phenotype, and most mutations that affect phenotype are selected against. Thus, we are more likely to see nonconservative substitutions in lineages that diverged long ago. Nonconservative substitutions, deletions, and insertions are often at the root of differences in phenotype among divergent lineages.

**FIGURE 11.15** Alignment of part of the amino acid sequence of mitochondrial cytochrome *b*. This protein is a crucial component of mitochondrial electron transfer chains.

One-letter abbreviations for the amino acids are spelled out in Figure 7.5 (Section 7.4). Amino acids that differ from the honeycreeper sequence are shown in *red*. Gaps are indicated by dashes.

**Figure It Out:** Of the amino acid sequences shown here, which most closely matches the honeycreeper sequence?    Answer: *The Gough Island finch sequence*

## Take-Home Message
### How does biochemistry reflect evolutionary history?

■ DNA and amino acid sequence differences are greatest among lineages that diverged long ago, and less among lineages that diverged more recently.

## 11.8

## Impacts/Issues Revisited:
## Reflections of a Distant Past

The K–T boundary layer (*left*) consists of an unusual clay that formed 65 million years ago, worldwide (the red pocketknife is shown for scale). The clay is rich in iridium, an element rare on Earth's surface but common in asteroids. After finding the iridium, researchers looked for evidence of an asteroid big enough to cover the entire Earth with its debris. They found a crater that is about 65 million years old, buried under sediments off the coast of Mexico's Yucatán Peninsula. It is so big—273.6 kilometers (170 miles) across and 1 kilometer (3,000 feet) deep—that no one had realized it was a crater. This crater is evidence of an asteroid impact 40 million times more powerful than the one that made the Barringer Crater, certainly big enough to have influenced life on Earth in a big way.

**How Would**

☑ **Vote?**

Many theories and hypotheses about events in the ancient past are necessarily based on traces left by those events, not on data collected by direct observations. Is indirect evidence ever enough to prove a theory about a past event? See CengageNow for details, then vote online (cengagenow.com).

# Summary

**Section 11.1** Events of the ancient past can be explained by the same physical, chemical, and biological processes that operate in today's world.

**Section 11.2** By the 19th century, naturalists on globe-spanning survey expeditions were bringing back increasingly detailed observations of nature. Studies of biogeography and comparative morphology led to new ways of thinking about the natural world.

**Section 11.3** Prevailing belief systems may influence interpretation of the underlying cause of a natural event. Nineteenth-century naturalists tried to explain the accumulating evidence of evolution. Charles Darwin and Alfred Wallace came up with a theory of how species evolve:

A population tends to grow until it begins to exhaust environmental resources—food, shelter from predators, and so on. As that happens, competition for those resources intensifies among individuals of the population.

Individuals with forms of traits that make them more competitive tend to produce more offspring.

Adaptive traits (adaptations) that impart greater fitness to an individual become more common in a population over generations, compared with less competitive forms.

Differential survival and reproduction of individuals of a population that vary in the details of shared traits is called natural selection. It is one of the processes that drives evolution.

**Section 11.4** Many fossils are found in stacked layers of sedimentary rock. Younger fossils usually occur in more recently deposited layers, on top of older fossils in older layers. Fossils are relatively scarce, so the fossil record will always be incomplete. Even so, it helps us to reconstruct the history of life. The characteristic half-life of a radioisotope allows us to determine the age of rocks and fossils using a technique called radiometric dating.

CENGAGENOW™ Learn more about fossil formation and half-life with the animation and interaction on CengageNow.

**Section 11.5** Transitions in the fossil record became boundaries for great intervals of the geologic time scale. The scale correlates geologic and evolutionary events. Earth's tectonic plates raft land masses to new positions over geologic time. The movements have had profound impacts on evolution.

CENGAGENOW™ Investigate the geologic time scale and learn more about the drifting continents with the interaction and animation on CengageNow.

**Section 11.6** Homologous structures are evidence of a common ancestor. Analogous structures are body parts that look alike in different lineages but did not evolve in a common ancestor. Similarities in patterns of embryonic development often reflect shared ancestry.

**Section 11.7** We can discover and clarify evolutionary relationships through comparisons of nucleic acid and protein sequences. Neu-

tral mutations tend to accumulate in DNA at a predictable rate, so lineages that diverged recently have more nucleotide or amino acid sequences in common than ones that diverged long ago.

CENGAGENOW™ Use the interaction on CengageNow to learn more about amino acid sequence comparisons.

## Self-Quiz    Answers in Appendix I

1. Which of the following is not part of natural selection?
   a. environmental resources    c. neutral mutations
   b. differences in traits    d. competition among individuals

2. The number of species on an island depends on the size of the island and its distance from a mainland. This statement would most likely be made by _____ .
   a. an explorer    c. a geologist
   b. a biogeographer    d. a philosopher

3. The bones of a bird's wing are similar to the bones in a bat's wing. This observation is an example of _____ .
   a. uniformity    c. comparative morphology
   b. evolution    d. a lineage

4. Evolution is _____ .
   a. natural selection    c driven by natural selection
   b. change in a line of descent  d. b and c are correct

5. If the half-life of a radioisotope is 20,000 years, then a sample in which three-quarters of that radioisotope has decayed is _____ years old.
   a. 15,000    c. 30,000
   b. 26,667    d. 40,000

6. _____ has/have influenced the fossil record.
   a. Sedimentation and compaction
   b. Tectonic plate movements
   c. Prevailing belief systems
   d. a and b

7. Evidence suggests that life originated in the _____ .
   a. Archaean    c. Phanerozoic
   b. Proterozoic    d. Cambrian

8. The Cretaceous ended _____ million years ago.

9. Forces of geologic change include _____ (select all that are correct).
   a. erosion    e. tectonic plate movements
   b. fossilization    f. wind
   c. volcanoes    g. asteroid impacts
   d. evolution    h. hot spots

10. Through _____ , a body part of an ancestor is modified differently in different lines of descent.
   a. analogous structures    c. morphological convergence
   b. homologous structures    d. morphological divergence

11. Homologous structures among major groups of organisms may differ in _____ .
   a. size    c. function
   b. shape    d. all of the above

12. Some mutations are neutral because they do not affect _____ .
   a. amino acid sequence
   c. the chances of survival
   b. nucleotide sequence
   d. body form

13. By altering steps in the program by which embryos develop, a mutation in a _____ may lead to major differences in body form between related lineages.
   a. coprolite
   c. homologous structure
   b. homeotic gene
   d. all of the above

14. Match the terms with the most suitable description.
   _____ fitness
   _____ fossils
   _____ natural selection
   _____ half-life
   _____ catastrophism
   _____ uniformity
   _____ analogous structures
   _____ sedimentary rock
   _____ homologous structures

   a. measured by reproductive success
   b. geologic change occurs continuously
   c. geologic change occurs in sudden major events
   d. good for finding fossils
   e. survival of the fittest
   f. characteristic of a radioisotope
   g. insect wing and bird wing
   h. human arm and bird wing
   i. evidence of life in distant past

Additional questions are available on **CENGAGENOW™**

# Critical Thinking

1. Radiometric dating does not measure the age of an individual atom. It is a measure of the age of a quantity of atoms—a statistic. As with any statistical measure, its values may deviate around an average (sampling error, Section 1.7). Imagine that one sample of rock is dated ten different ways. Nine of the tests yield an age close to 225,000 years. One test yields an age of 3.2 million years. Do the nine consistent results imply that the one that deviates is incorrect, or does the one odd result invalidate the nine that are consistent?

11:21:10 a.m. mammals, dinosaurs
11:37:18 a.m. flowering plants
11:59:59 a.m. first humans
10:40:57 a.m. early fishes
12:00:00 a.m. Earth's crust solidifies
phanerozoic
2:05:13 a.m. prokaryotes
5:28:41 a.m. eukaryotes

2. If you think of geologic time spans as minutes, life's history might be plotted on a clock such as the one shown on the right. According to this clock, the most recent epoch started in the last 0.1 second before noon. Where does that put you?

# Digging Into Data

## Abundance of Iridium in the K–T Boundary Layer

In the late 1970s, geologist Walter Alvarez was investigating the composition of the 1-centimeter-thick layer of clay that marks the Cretaceous–Tertiary (K–T) boundary all over the world. He asked his father, Nobel Prize–winning physicist Luis Alvarez, to help him analyze the elemental composition of the layer. The photo shows Luis and Walter Alvarez with a section of the K–T boundary layer.

The Alvarezes and their colleagues tested the layer in Italy and in Denmark. The researchers discovered that the K–T boundary layer had a much higher iridium content than the surrounding rock layers. Some of their results are shown in the table in Figure 11.16.

Iridium belongs to a group of elements (Appendix VI) that are much more abundant in asteroids and other solar system materials than they are in Earth's crust. The Alvarez group concluded that the K–T boundary layer must have originated with extraterrestrial material. They calculated that an asteroid 14 kilometers (8.7 miles) in diameter would contain enough iridium to account for the iridium in the K–T boundary layer.

1. What was the iridium content of the K–T boundary layer?

2. How much higher was the iridium content of the boundary layer than the sample taken 0.7 meters above the layer?

| Sample Depth | Average Abundance of Iridium (ppb) |
|---|---|
| + 2.7 m | < 0.3 |
| + 1.2 m | < 0.3 |
| + 0.7 m | 0.36 |
| boundary layer | 41.6 |
| – 0.5 m | 0.25 |
| – 5.4 m | 0.30 |

**FIGURE 11.16** Abundance of iridium in and near the K–T boundary layer in Stevns Klint, Denmark. Many rock samples taken from above, below, and at the boundary layer were tested for iridium content. Depths are given as meters above or below the boundary layer.

The iridium content of an average Earth rock is 0.4 parts per billion (ppb) of iridium. An average meteorite contains about 550 parts per billion of iridium.

# 12 Processes of Evolution

12.1

## Impacts/Issues:  Rise of the Super Rats

Slipping in and out of the pages of human history are rats—*Rattus*—the most notorious of mammalian pests. Rats thrive in urban centers, where garbage is plentiful and natural predators are not (Figure 12.1). The average city in the United States sustains about one rat for every ten people. Part of their success stems from an ability to reproduce very quickly. Rat populations can expand within weeks to match the amount of garbage available for them to eat. Unfortunately for us, rats carry pathogens and parasites that cause bubonic plague, typhus, and other infectious diseases. They chew their way through walls and wires, and eat or foul 20 to 30 percent of our total food production. Rats cost us about $19 billion per year.

For years, people have been fighting back with poisons, including arsenic and cyanide. Baits laced with warfarin, an organic compound that interferes with blood clotting, were popular in the 1950s. Rats that ate the poisoned baits died within days after bleeding internally or losing blood through cuts or scrapes. Warfarin was very effective, and compared to other rat poisons, it had much less impact on harmless species. It quickly became the rodenticide of choice. In 1958, however, a Scottish researcher reported that warfarin was not working against some rats. Similar reports from other European countries followed. About twenty years later, about 10 percent of rats caught in urban areas of the United States were resistant to warfarin. What happened?

To find out, researchers compared warfarin-resistant rats with still-vulnerable rats. They traced the difference to a gene on one of the rat chromosomes. Certain mutations in the gene were common among warfarin-resistant rat populations but rare among vulnerable ones. Warfarin inhibits the gene's product, an enzyme that recycles vitamin K after it has been used to activate blood clotting factors. The mutations made the enzyme insensitive to warfarin.

"What happened" was evolution by natural selection. As warfarin exerted pressure on rat populations, the populations changed. The previously rare mutations became adaptive. Rats that had an unmutated gene died after eating warfarin. The lucky ones that had one of the mutations survived and passed it to their offspring. The rat populations recovered quickly, and a higher proportion of rats in the next generation carried the mutations. With each onslaught of warfarin, the frequency of the mutation in rat populations increased.

Selection pressures can and often do change. When warfarin resistance increased in rat populations, people stopped using warfarin. The frequency of the mutation in rat populations declined, probably because rats with the mutation are not as healthy as normal rats. Now, savvy exterminators in urban areas know that the best way to control a rat infestation is to exert another kind of selection pressure: Remove their source of food, which is usually garbage. Then the rats will eat each other.

**FIGURE 12.1** Rats thrive wherever people do. Dousing buildings and soil with poisons does not usually exterminate rat populations, which recover quickly. The practice selects for rats that are resistant to the poisons.

# Making Waves in the Gene Pool

Remember from Section 1.2 that a population is a group of individuals of the same species in some specified area. The individuals of a species—and a population—share certain features. For example, giraffes normally have very long necks, brown spots on white coats, and so on. These are examples of morphological traits (*morpho*– means form). Individuals of a species also share physiological traits, such as metabolic activities. They also respond the same way to certain stimuli, as when hungry giraffes feed on tree leaves. These are behavioral traits. Genotype gives rise to phenotype, so individuals of a population have the same traits because they have the same genes. Together, the genes of a population comprise a pool of genetic resources called a **gene pool**.

Almost every shared trait varies a bit among individuals of a population (Figure 12.2). Alleles of shared genes are the main source of this variation. Many traits have two or more distinct forms, or morphs. A trait with only two forms is dimorphic (*di*– means two). Purple and white flower color in the pea plants that Gregor Mendel studied is an example of a dimorphic trait (Section 9.2). Dimorphic flower color occurs in this case because the interaction of two alleles with a clear dominance relationship gives rise to the trait. Traits with more than two distinct forms are polymorphic (*poly*–, many). Human blood type, which is determined by the codominant *ABO* alleles, is one example (Section 9.3). Traits that vary continuously among the individuals of a population often arise by interactions among alleles of several genes, and may be influenced by environmental factors (Section 9.4).

In earlier chapters, you learned about the processes that introduce variation in traits among individuals of a species. Table 12.1 summarizes the key events involved. Mutation is the source of new alleles. Other events shuffle the alleles into different combinations, but what a shuffle that is! There are $10^{116,446,000}$ possible combinations of human alleles. Not even $10^{10}$ people are living today. Unless you have an identical twin, it is unlikely that another person with your precise genetic makeup has ever lived, or ever will.

**Mutation Revisited** Being the original source of new alleles, mutations are worth another look—this time within the context of their impact on populations. We cannot predict when or in which individual a particular gene will mutate. We can, however, predict the average mutation rate of a species, which is the probability that a mutation will occur in a given interval. In humans, that rate is about 175 mutations per person per generation.

Many mutations give rise to structural, functional, or behavioral alterations that reduce an individual's chances of surviving and reproducing. Even one

| Table 12.1 | Sources of Variation in Traits Among Individuals of a Species | |
|---|---|
| **Genetic Event** | **Effect** |
| Mutation | Source of new alleles |
| Crossing over at meiosis I | Introduces new combinations of alleles into chromosomes |
| Independent assortment at meiosis I | Mixes maternal and paternal chromosomes |
| Fertilization | Combines alleles from two parents |
| Changes in chromosome number or structure | Transposition, duplication, or loss of chromosomes |

**gene pool** All of the genes in a population.

> No pattern of evolution is purposeful. Evolution simply fills the nooks and crannies of opportunity.

biochemical change may be devastating. For instance, the skin, bones, tendons, lungs, blood vessels, and other vertebrate organs incorporate the protein collagen. If the collagen gene mutates in a way that changes the protein's function, the entire body may be affected. A mutation that drastically changes phenotype is called a **lethal mutation** because it results in death.

A **neutral mutation** changes the base sequence in DNA, but the alteration has no effect on survival or reproduction. It neither helps nor hurts the individual. For instance, if you carry a mutation that keeps your earlobes attached to your head instead of swinging freely, attached earlobes should not in itself stop you from surviving and reproducing as well as anybody else. So, natural selection does not affect the frequency of this particular mutation in a population.

Occasionally, a change in the environment favors a mutation that had previously been neutral or even somewhat harmful. The warfarin resistance gene in rats is an example. Even if a beneficial mutation bestows only a slight advantage, natural selection can increase its frequency in a population over time because it operates on traits with a genetic basis. Natural selection, remember, is the differential survival and reproduction among individuals of a population that vary in the details of their shared traits (Section 11.3).

Mutations have been altering genomes for billions of years, and they are still at it. Cumulatively, they have given rise to Earth's staggering biodiversity. Think about it. The reason you do not look like an avocado or an earthworm or even your next-door neighbor began with mutations that occurred in different lines of descent.

### Allele Frequencies

**Allele frequency** refers to an allele's abundance among individuals of a population. Change in allele frequency is the same thing as change in a line of descent—evolution. Evolution within a population or species is called **microevolution**.

A theoretical reference point, **genetic equilibrium**, occurs when the allele frequencies of a population do not change (in other words, the population is not evolving). Genetic equilibrium can only occur if every one of the following five conditions are met: (1) mutations never occur; (2) the population is infinitely large; (3) the population is isolated from all other populations of the species (no gene flow); (4) mating is random; and (5) all individuals survive and produce the same number of offspring. As you can imagine, all five conditions are never met in nature, so natural populations are never in equilibrium. Microevolution is always occurring in natural populations, because the processes that drive it are always in play. The remaining sections of this chapter explore those processes—mutation, natural selection, genetic drift, and gene flow—and their effects. Remember, even though we can recognize patterns of evolution, none of them are purposeful. Evolution simply fills the nooks and crannies of opportunity.

**allele frequency** Abundance of a particular allele among members of a population.

**directional selection** Mode of natural selection in which phenotypes at one end of a range of variation are favored.

**genetic equilibrium** Theoretical state in which a population is not evolving.

**lethal mutation** Mutation that drastically alters phenotype; causes death.

**microevolution** Change in allele frequencies in a population or species.

**neutral mutation** A mutation that has no effect on survival or reproduction.

## Take-Home Message  What mechanisms drive evolution?

- We partly characterize a natural population by shared morphological, physiological, and behavioral traits. Most of those traits have a heritable basis.
- Different alleles are the basis of differences in the details of a population's shared traits.
- Alleles of all individuals in a population comprise the population's gene pool.
- Natural populations are always evolving, which means that allele frequencies in their gene pool are always changing over generations.
- Microevolution is evolutionary change in a population or species.

# 12.3 Natural Selection Revisited

With natural selection (Section 11.3), differential survival and reproduction alters allele frequencies of a population over many generations. We observe different patterns of natural selection depending on the selection pressures and organisms involved. For example, individuals with a trait at one extreme of a range of variation may be selected against, and those at the other extreme favored. In other cases, midrange forms are favored, and the extremes are selected against. Or, forms at the extremes of the range of variation are favored, and intermediate forms are selected against.

## Directional Selection
With **directional selection**, allele frequencies shift in a consistent direction, so forms at one end of a range of phenotypic variation become more common over time (Figure 12.3). The following examples show how field observations provide evidence of directional selection.

Peppered moths feed and mate at night, and rest motionless on trees during the day. Their behavior and coloration camouflage them from day-flying, moth-eating birds. Light-colored moths were the most common form in preindustrial England. A dominant allele that resulted in the dark color was rare. The air was clean, and light-gray lichens grew on the trunks and branches of most trees. Light moths were camouflaged when they rested on the lichens (Figure 12.4**A**), but dark moths were not (Figure 12.4**B**).

By the 1850s, the dark moths were appearing more frequently. Why? The industrial revolution had begun, and smoke from coal-burning factories was beginning to change the environment. Air pollution was killing the lichens. Researchers hypothesized that dark moths were now better camouflaged from predators on the soot-darkened trees than light moths (Figure 12.4**C**,**D**).

In the 1950s, H. B. Kettlewell bred both moth forms in captivity and marked hundreds so that they could be easily identified after being released in the wild. He released them near highly industrialized areas around Birmingham and near an unpolluted part of Dorset. His team recaptured more of the dark moths in the polluted area and more light

**FIGURE 12.4** Directional selection of two forms of a trait in different settings. **A** Light peppered moths on a nonsooty tree trunk are hidden from predators. **B** Dark ones stand out. In places where soot darkens tree trunks, the dark color **C** is more adaptive than **D** the light color.

Time 1

Number of individuals in population

Range of values for the trait

Time 2

Time 3

**FIGURE 12.3 Animated!** Directional selection. The bell curves indicate continuous variation in a butterfly wing-color trait. *Red* arrows indicate which forms are being selected against; *green*, forms that are being favored.

**FIGURE 12.5** Directional selection in populations of rock pocket mice.

**1** Mice with dark fur are more common in areas with dark basalt rock.

**2** Mice with light fur are more common in areas with light-colored granite.

**3** Mice with coat colors that do not match their surroundings are more easily seen by predators, so they are preferentially eliminated from the populations.

ones near Dorset. They also observed predatory birds eating more light moths in Birmingham, and more dark moths in Dorset.

Pollution controls went into effect in 1952. Tree trunks became free of soot, and lichens made a comeback. Moth phenotypes shifted in the reverse direction: Wherever pollution decreased, the frequency of dark moths decreased as well. Many other researchers since Kettlewell have confirmed the rise and fall of the dark-colored form of the peppered moth.

Directional selection also affects the color of rock pocket mice in Arizona's Sonoran Desert. Rock pocket mice are small mammals that spend the day sleeping in underground burrows, emerging at night to forage for seeds (Figure 12.5). The Sonoran Desert is dominated by outcroppings of light brown granite. There are also patches of dark basalt rock, the remains of ancient lava flows. Most of the mice in populations that inhabit the dark rock have dark gray coats **1**. Most of the mice in populations that inhabit the light brown granite have light brown coats **2**. Why the difference? Individuals that match the rock color in each habitat are camouflaged from their natural predators. Night-flying owls more easily see mice that do not match the rocks **3**, and they preferentially eliminate easily seen mice from each population. Predation by owls causes a directional shift in the frequency of alleles that affect coat color.

Researchers analyzed genes of mice from granite and basalt populations to find out which genes predation is affecting. They found that allele frequencies differed at a gene that influences deposition of the dark pigment melanin. Compared to granite-dwelling populations, populations living on basalt have a much higher frequency of four mutations that cause increased melanin deposition.

**stabilizing selection** Mode of natural selection in which intermediate phenotypes are favored over extremes.

Our attempts to control the environment can result in directional selection, as is the case with the warfarin-resistant rats. The use of antibiotics is another example. When your grandparents were still young, scarlet fever, tuberculosis, and pneumonia caused one-fourth of the annual deaths in the United States alone. Since the 1940s, we have been relying on antibiotics such as penicillin to fight these and other dangerous bacterial diseases. We also use them in other, less dire circumstances. Antibiotics are used preventively, both in humans and in livestock. They are part of the daily rations of millions of cattle, pigs, chickens, fish, and other animals that are raised on factory farms.

Bacteria evolve at an accelerated rate compared with humans, in part because they reproduce very quickly. For example, the common intestinal bacteria *E. coli* can divide every 17 minutes. Each new generation is an opportunity for mutation, so the gene pool of a bacterial population varies greatly. Thus, it is very likely that some cells will have alleles that allow them to survive an antibiotic treatment. Then, natural selection takes over. A typical two-week course of antibiotics can potentially exert selection pressure on over a thousand generations of bacteria, and antibiotic-resistant strains may be the outcome.

Antibiotic-resistant bacteria have plagued hospitals for many years, and now they are becoming similarly common in schools. Even as researchers scramble to find new antibiotics, this trend is bad news for the millions of people each year who contract cholera, tuberculosis, or another dangerous bacterial disease.

**FIGURE 12.7** Stabilizing selection in sociable weavers (*top*). Graph shows the number of birds (out of 977) that survived a breeding season.

Figure It Out: What is the optimal weight of a sociable weaver bird? *Answer: About 29 grams*

**Stabilizing Selection** With **stabilizing selection**, an intermediate form of a trait is favored, and extreme forms are not. This mode of selection tends to preserve the midrange phenotypes in a population (Figure 12.6). For example, the body weight of sociable weaver birds is subject to stabilizing selection. Weaver birds build large communal nests in the African savanna. Between 1993 and 2000, Rita Covas and her colleagues captured, tagged, weighed, and released birds living in communal nests before the breeding season began. The researchers then recaptured and weighed the surviving birds after the breeding season was over.

Covas's field studies indicated that body weight in sociable weavers is a trade-off between the risks of starvation and predation (Figure 12.7). Foraging is not easy in the sparse habitat of an African savanna, and leaner birds do not store enough fat to avoid starvation. A meager food supply selects against birds with low body weight. Fatter birds may be more attractive to predators, and not as agile when escaping. Predators select against birds of high body weight. Thus, birds of intermediate weight have the selective advantage, and make up the bulk of sociable weaver populations.

Time 1

Time 2

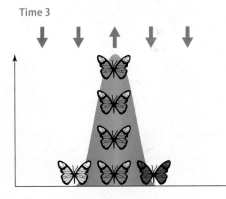

Time 3

**FIGURE 12.6 Animated!** Stabilizing selection eliminates extreme forms of a trait, and maintains the predominance of an intermediate phenotype in a population. *Red* arrows indicate which forms are being selected against; *green*, forms that are being favored. Compare the data set from a field experiment shown in Figure 12.7.

Time 1

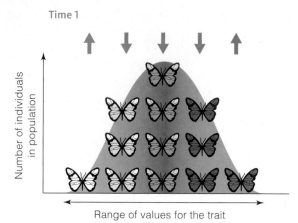

Number of individuals in population

Range of values for the trait

Time 2

Time 3

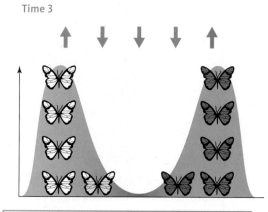

**FIGURE 12.8 Animated!** Disruptive selection eliminates midrange forms of a trait, and maintains extreme forms.

**Disruptive Selection** With **disruptive selection**, forms of a trait at both ends of a range of variation are favored, and intermediate forms are selected against (Figure 12.8). Consider the black-bellied seedcracker native to Cameroon, Africa. These finches are dimorphic for bill size. They tend to have either a large bill or a small one—but no sizes between (Figure 12.9). It is as if every human adult were four feet or six feet tall, with no one of intermediate height. Large-billed and small-billed birds live side by side, and mate with one another without regard to bill size.

Factors that affect seedcracker feeding performance maintain the dimorphism in bill size. The finches feed mainly on the seeds of two types of sedge, which is a grasslike plant. One sedge produces hard seeds; the other, soft seeds. Small-billed birds are better at opening the soft seeds, and large-billed birds are better at cracking the hard ones. During Cameroon's wet seasons, all seeds are abundant, and all seedcrackers feed on both types of seeds. During the region's dry seasons, sedge seeds are scarce, and each bird focuses on eating the seeds that it opens most efficiently. Small-billed birds feed mainly on soft seeds, and large-billed birds feed mainly on hard seeds. Birds with intermediate-sized bills cannot open either type of seed as efficiently as the other birds, so they are less likely to survive the dry seasons.

lower bill 12 mm wide

lower bill 15 mm wide

**FIGURE 12.9**
Disruptive selection in African seedcrackers. Birds with bills that are about 12 *or* 15 millimeters wide are favored. The difference is a result of competition for scarce food during dry seasons.

# Take-Home Message
**How does natural selection drive evolution?**

- With directional selection, allele frequencies underlying a range of variation shift in a consistent direction in response to selection pressure.
- With stabilizing selection, an intermediate phenotype is favored, and extreme forms are eliminated.
- With disruptive selection, an intermediate form of a trait is selected against, and extreme phenotypes are favored.

# 12.4 Factors That Affect Variation in Traits

Selection pressures that operate on natural populations are typically not as clear-cut as the examples in the previous section might suggest. Non-ecological pressures, including random genetic change, are part of natural selection. Complex interactions among genes and the environment also play a role.

**Nonrandom Mating** Not all natural selection occurs as a result of interactions between a species and its environment. Competition within a species also drives evolution. Consider how the individuals of many sexually reproducing species have a distinct male or female phenotype—a sexual dimorphism. Individuals of one sex (often males) tend to be more colorful, larger, and more aggressive than individuals of the other sex. These traits seem puzzling because they take energy and time away from an individual's survival activities. Some are probably maladaptive because they attract predators. Why do they persist?

The answer is **sexual selection**, in which the genetic winners outreproduce others of a population because they are better at securing mates. In sexual selection, the most adaptive forms of a trait are those that help individuals defeat same-sex rivals for mates, or are the ones most attractive to the opposite sex.

By choosing among mates, a male or female acts as a selective agent on its own species. For example, the females of some species will shop for a mate among males that vary slightly in appearance and courtship behavior. Females choose males that display species-specific cues that often include flashy body parts or behaviors (Figure 12.10**A**). Such traits can be a physical hindrance and they may attract predators. However, a flashy male's survival despite his obvious handicap implies health and vigor, two traits that are likely to improve a female's chances of bearing healthy, vigorous offspring. The selected males pass the alleles for their attractive traits to the next generation of males. Females pass alleles that influence mate preference to the next generation of females.

Gerald Wilkinson and his colleagues demonstrated female preference for an exaggerated male trait in the stalk-eyed fly. The eyes of this Malaysian species form on long, horizontal eyestalks that provide no obvious adaptive advantage to their bearers, other than perhaps provoking sexual interest in other flies (Figure 12.10**B**). The researchers predicted that if eyestalk length is a sexually selected trait, then males with longer eyestalks would be more attractive to female flies than males with shorter eyestalks. They bred males with extra-long eyestalks, and found those males were indeed preferred by the female flies. Such experiments show how exaggerated traits can arise by sexual selection in nature.

The females of some species cluster in defendable groups when they are sexually receptive. When they do, males are likely to compete for access to clusters. Competition for ready-made harems favors combative males (Figure 12.10**C**).

**FIGURE 12.10** Sexual selection in action.

**A** This male bird of paradise (*Paradisaea raggi ana*) is engaged in a flashy courtship display. He caught the eye (and, perhaps, the sexual interest) of the smaller, less colorful female. The males of this species of bird compete fiercely for females, which are selective. (Why do you suppose the females are not as flashy as the males?)

**B** Ooh, what sexy eyestalks! Stalk-eyed flies cluster on aerial roots to mate, and females cluster preferentially around males with the longest eyestalks. This photo, taken in Kuala Lumpur, Malaysia, shows a male with very long eyestalks (*top*) that has captured the interest of the three females below him.

**C** Male elephant seals fight for sexual access to a cluster of females.

**disruptive selection** Mode of natural selection that favors two forms in a range of variation; intermediate forms are selected against.

**sexual selection** Mode of natural selection in which some individuals outreproduce others of a population because they are better at securing mates.

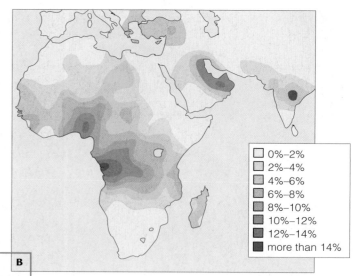

| | |
|---|---|
| ☐ | 0%–2% |
| ☐ | 2%–4% |
| ☐ | 4%–6% |
| ☐ | 6%–8% |
| ☐ | 8%–10% |
| ☐ | 10%–12% |
| ☐ | 12%–14% |
| ■ | more than 14% |

**FIGURE 12.11** Malaria and sickle-cell anemia. **A** Distribution of malaria cases (*orange*) reported in Africa, Asia, and the Middle East in the 1920s, before the start of programs to control mosquitoes, which transmit *Plasmodium*. **B** Distribution (by percentage) of people that carry the sickle-cell allele. Notice the correlation between the maps. **C** Physician searching for mosquito larvae in Southeast Asia.

**Balanced Polymorphism** Any mode of natural selection may maintain two or more alleles of a gene in a population. This state, which is called **balanced polymorphism**, occurs when environmental conditions favor heterozygotes (individuals with nonidentical alleles of a gene). For example, certain environments select for balanced polymorphism of the human *Hb* gene. This gene encodes the beta globin chain of hemoglobin, the oxygen-transporting protein in blood. $Hb^A$ is the normal allele, and the $Hb^S$ allele carries a mutation that causes homozygotes to develop sickle-cell anemia (Section 7.6). Individuals homozygous for the $Hb^S$ allele often die in their teens or early twenties.

Despite being so harmful, the $Hb^S$ allele persists at very high frequency among the human populations in tropical and subtropical regions of Asia and Africa. Why? Populations with the highest frequency of the $Hb^S$ allele also have the highest incidence of malaria (Figure 12.11). Mosquitoes transmit the parasitic agent of malaria, *Plasmodium*, to human hosts. The protozoan multiplies in the liver and then in red blood cells. The cells rupture and release new parasites during severe, recurring bouts of illness.

It turns out that $Hb^A/Hb^S$ heterozygotes are more likely to survive malaria than people who make only normal hemoglobin. Several mechanisms are possible. For example, infected cells of heterozygotes take on a sickle shape. The abnormal shape brings infected cells to the attention of the immune system, which destroys them—along with the parasites they harbor. Infected cells of $Hb^A/Hb^A$ homozygotes do not sickle, and the parasite may remain hidden from the immune system.

The persistence of the $Hb^S$ allele may be a matter of relative evils. Malaria and sickle-cell anemia are both potentially deadly. In areas where malaria is common, $Hb^A/Hb^S$ heterozygotes are more likely to survive and reproduce than $Hb^A/Hb^A$ homozygotes. Heterozygotes are not completely healthy, but they do make enough normal hemoglobin to survive. Malaria or not, they are more likely to live long enough to reproduce than $Hb^S/Hb^S$ homozygotes. The result is that nearly one-third of individuals that live in the most malaria-ridden regions of the world are $Hb^A/Hb^S$ heterozygotes.

**balanced polymorphism** Maintenance of two or more alleles for a trait in some populations, as a result of natural selection against homozygotes.

**bottleneck** Reduction in population size so severe that it reduces genetic diversity.

**fixed** Refers to an allele for which all members of a population are homozygous.

**founder effect** Change in allele frequencies that occurs after a small number of individuals establish a population.

**genetic drift** Change in allele frequencies in a population due to chance alone.

**Genetic Drift** **Genetic drift** is a random change in allele frequencies over time, brought about by chance alone. We explain genetic drift in terms of probability—the chance that some event will occur (Section 1.7). The probability of an event occurring is expressed as a percentage. For instance, if 10 million people enter a drawing, each has the same probability of winning: 1 in 10 million, or a very improbable 0.00001 percent.

Remember, sample size is important in probability. For example, every time you flip a coin, there is a 50 percent chance it will land heads up. With 10 flips, the proportion of times heads actually land up may be very far from 50 percent. With 1,000 flips, that proportion is more likely to be near 50 percent. We can apply the same rule to populations. Because population sizes are not infinite, there will be random changes in allele frequencies. These random changes have a minor impact on large populations. However, such changes can lead to dramatic shifts in the allele frequencies of small populations.

Imagine two populations. Population I has 10 individuals, and population II has 100. Say an allele *b* occurs in both populations at a 10 percent frequency. Only one person carries the allele in population I. If that person does not reproduce, allele *b* will be lost from population I. However, ten people in population II carry the allele. All ten would have to die without reproducing for the allele to be lost from population II. Thus, the chance that population I will lose allele *b* is greater than that for population II. Steven Rich and his colleagues demonstrated this effect in populations of flour beetles (Figure 12.12).

Random change in allele frequencies can lead to the loss of genetic diversity and to the homozygous condition. These outcomes of genetic drift are possible in all populations, but they are more likely to occur in small ones. When all individuals of a population are homozygous for one allele, we say that the allele has become **fixed**. Once an allele is fixed, its frequency will not change again unless mutation or gene flow introduces new alleles.

## Bottlenecks and the Founder Effect

Genetic drift can be dramatic when a few individuals rebuild a population or start a new one, such as occurs after a bottleneck. A **bottleneck** is a drastic reduction in population size brought about by severe pressure. If a contagious disease, habitat loss, or overhunting nearly wipes out a population, the allele frequencies in the survivors will have been altered at random. For example, northern elephant seals (shown in Figure 12.10**C**) were once on the brink of extinction, with only twenty known survivors in the world in the 1890s. Hunting restrictions implemented since then have allowed the population to recover to about 170,000 individuals. Every seal is homozygous for all of the genes analyzed to date.

In one type of bottleneck, a small group of individuals founds a new population. The group is not representative of the original population in terms of allele frequencies, so the new population is not representative of it either. This outcome is called the **founder effect**. If a founding group is very small, the new population's genetic diversity may be quite reduced. For instance, imagine a patch of pink and yellow lily flowers on a mainland. By chance, a seabird lands on a yellow lily, and a few seeds stick to its feathers. The bird flies to a remote island and drops the seeds. Most of the seeds have the allele for yellow flowers. The seeds sprout, and a small, isolated population of lily plants establishes itself;

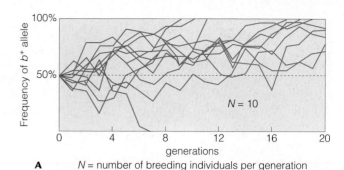

**A** N = number of breeding individuals per generation

**B** N = number of breeding individuals per generation

**FIGURE 12.12 Animated!** Genetic drift in flour beetles (*Tribolium castaneum*, shown *below* on a flake of cereal). Randomly selected beetles heterozygous for alleles $b^+$ and *b* were maintained in populations of **A** 10 or **B** 100 individuals for 20 generations.

Graph lines in **B** are smoother than in **A**, indicating that drift was greatest in the sets of 10 beetles and least in the sets of 100. Allele $b^+$ was lost in one population (one graph line ends at 0). Notice that the average frequency of allele $b^+$ rose at the same rate in both groups, an indication that natural selection was at work too: Allele $b^+$ was weakly favored.

**Figure It Out:** In how many populations did allele $b^+$ become fixed?

*Answer: Six*

10 mm

**FIGURE 12.13** An Amish child with Ellis–van Creveld syndrome. The syndrome is characterized by dwarfism, polydactyly, and heart defects, among other symptoms. The recessive allele that causes it is unusually common in the Old Order Amish of Lancaster County, an outcome of the founder effect and moderate inbreeding.

most of the plants have yellow flowers. In the absence of gene flow or natural selection for flower color, genetic drift may fix the allele for yellow flowers.

Genetic drift particularly affects allele frequency in inbred populations. **Inbreeding** is nonrandom breeding or mating between close relatives, which share a large number of alleles. Inbreeding lowers the genetic diversity of a population. Loss of diversity tends to be a bad thing, because more people become homozygous for recessive alleles with harmful effects. This is one reason that most societies discourage or forbid incest, which is mating between parents and children or between siblings. However, more distant relatives such as cousins do often mate in some societies.

The Old Order Amish in Lancaster County, Pennsylvania, offer an example. Amish people marry only within their community. Intermarriage with other groups is not permitted, and no "outsiders" are allowed to join the community. As a result, Amish populations are moderately inbred, and many of their individuals are homozygous for harmful alleles. The Lancaster population has an unusually high frequency of a recessive allele associated with Ellis–van Creveld syndrome (Figure 12.13). The particular allele that affects the Lancaster population has been traced to one man and his wife, who were among a group of 400 Amish who immigrated to the United States in the mid-1700s. As a result of the founder effect and inbreeding since then, about 1 of 8 people in the population is now heterozygous for the allele, and 1 in 200 is homozygous.

**Gene Flow** Individuals tend to mate or breed most frequently with other members of their own population. However, most populations of a species are not completely isolated from one another, and there may be intermating among adjacent populations. Also, individuals sometimes leave one population and join another. **Gene flow**, the movement of alleles among populations, occurs in both cases. Gene flow tends to keep allele frequencies stable, so it counters the effects of mutation, natural selection, and genetic drift. It is most pronounced among populations of animals, which tend to be more mobile, but it also occurs in plant populations.

Many opponents of genetic engineering are concerned about gene flow from transgenic organisms into wild populations. The flow is already occurring: The *bt* gene and herbicide-resistance genes (Section 10.4) have been found in weeds and unmodified crop plants adjacent to test fields of transgenic plants. The long-term effects of this gene flow are currently unknown.

**gene flow** The movement of alleles into and out of a population, as by individuals that immigrate or emigrate.
**inbreeding** Nonrandom mating among close relatives.
**reproductive isolation** Absence of gene flow between populations; part of speciation.
**speciation** Process by which new species arise from existing species.

## *Take-Home Message* **What mechanisms maintain or reduce phenotypic variation in natural populations?**

- With sexual selection, some version of a trait gives an individual an advantage over others in securing mates. Sexual dimorphism is one outcome of sexual selection.

- Environmental pressures may maintain diversity by favoring balanced polymorphism (persistence of two or more alleles at high frequency in a population).

- Genetic drift is a random change in allele frequencies over generations. The magnitude of its effect is greatest in small populations, such as one that endures a bottleneck.

- Gene flow is the physical movement of alleles into and out of a population. It tends to counter the evolutionary effects of mutation, natural selection, and genetic drift on a population.

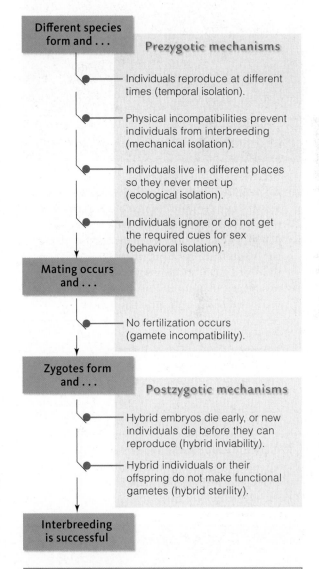

FIGURE 12.14 Four butterflies, two species: Which are which? Two forms of the species *Heliconius melpomene* are on the *top* row; two of *H. erato* are on the *bottom* row. These two species never cross-breed. Their alternate but similar patterns of coloration evolved as a shared warning signal to local predators that the butterflies taste terrible.

# 12.5 Speciation

Mutation, natural selection, and genetic drift operate on all natural populations, and they do so independently in populations that are not interbreeding. When gene flow does not keep populations alike, genetic changes accumulate in each one independently. Sooner or later, the genetic divergences lead to new species. The evolutionary process by which new species arise is called **speciation**.

There are tremendous differences between species such as petunias and whales, beetles and emus, and so on. Such organisms look very different, so it is easy to tell them apart. Their separate lineages probably diverged so long ago that many changes accumulated in them. Species that share a more recent ancestor may be much more difficult to tell apart (Figure 12.14).

Evolutionary biologist Ernst Mayr defined a species as one or more groups of individuals that potentially can interbreed, produce fertile offspring, and do not interbreed with other groups. This "biological species concept" is useful but it is not universally applicable. For example, not all populations of a species actually continue to interbreed. In many cases, we may never know whether populations separated by a great distance could interbreed successfully even if they did get together. Also, populations often continue to interbreed even as they diverge into separate species. Thus, it is useful to remember that a "species" is a convenient but artificial construct of the human mind.

Every species is an outcome of its own unique history and interactions with the environment, so speciation is not a predictable process. The details differ with every speciation event, but we can identify some recurring patterns. For example, speciation is often triggered by a physical barrier that arises and cuts off gene flow between populations. However speciation happens, reproductive isolation is always part of the process.

**Reproductive Isolation** **Reproductive isolation** refers to the end of gene flow between populations. It is part of the process by which sexually reproducing species attain and maintain their separate identities. By preventing successful interbreeding, mechanisms of reproductive isolation reinforce differences between diverging populations. Several prezygotic mechanisms are barriers to pollination or mating, and postzygotic mechanisms result in weak or infertile hybrids (Figure 12.15).

Some populations cannot interbreed because the timing of their reproduction differs. Periodical cicadas (*left*) are examples. Cicadas feed on roots as they mature underground, then emerge to reproduce every 17 years. There are three species of cicada. Each has a sibling species with nearly identical form and behavior, except that the siblings emerge on a 13-year cycle instead of a 17-year cycle. Sibling species have the potential to interbreed, but they can only get together every 221 years!

In other cases, the size or shape of an individual's reproductive parts prevent it from mating with members of another population. For example, black sage

---

**Different species form and . . .**

**Prezygotic mechanisms**

- Individuals reproduce at different times (temporal isolation).
- Physical incompatibilities prevent individuals from interbreeding (mechanical isolation).
- Individuals live in different places so they never meet up (ecological isolation).
- Individuals ignore or do not get the required cues for sex (behavioral isolation).

**Mating occurs and . . .**

- No fertilization occurs (gamete incompatibility).

**Zygotes form and . . .**

**Postzygotic mechanisms**

- Hybrid embryos die early, or new individuals die before they can reproduce (hybrid inviability).
- Hybrid individuals or their offspring do not make functional gametes (hybrid sterility).

**Interbreeding is successful**

FIGURE 12.15 **Animated!** How reproductive isolating mechanisms prevent interbreeding. The mechanisms include barriers to meeting, mating, or pollination; barriers to fertilization; and reduced fitness or fertility of hybrid offspring.

anther

**FIGURE 12.16** Mechanical isolation in sage.
**A** The pollen-bearing anthers of white sage flowers are at the tips of filaments that project high above the petals. **B** Honeybees that land on white sage flowers are too small to touch the anthers, so only larger insects such as bumblebees **C** can pollinate this species. **D** Black sage flowers are too small to support bumblebees. This species is pollinated mainly by smaller bees, including honeybees.

**FIGURE 12.17 Animated!** Behavioral isolation. Species-specific courtship displays precede sex among many birds, including these albatrosses.

(*Salvia mellifera*) and white sage (*S. apiana*) grow in the same areas, but hybrids rarely form because the flowers of the two species have become specialized for different pollinators. The pollen-bearing parts (anthers) of white sage flowers are at the tips of long filaments that extend far above two large petals (Figure 12.16**A**). The anthers are too far above the petals to reach the back of a small bee, so honeybees and other small bees cannot pollinate white sage (Figure 12.16**B**). Thus, this species is pollinated mainly by bumblebees and other bees that are big enough to brush the anthers (Figure 12.16**C**). Large bees have difficulty finding footing on the tiny flowers of black sage, so this species is pollinated mainly by smaller bees (Figure 12.16**D**).

Populations adapted to different microenvironments in the same region may be ecologically isolated. For example, two species of manzanita (a plant) native to the Sierra Nevada mountain range rarely hybridize. One species that is better adapted for conserving water inhabits dry, rocky hillsides high in the foothills. The other lives on lower slopes where water stress is not as intense. The physical separation makes cross-pollination unlikely.

In animals, behavioral differences can stop gene flow between related species. For instance, males and females of some bird species engage in courtship displays before sex (Figure 12.17). A female recognizes the vocalizations and movements of a male of her species as an overture to sex, but females of different species do not.

Even if gametes of different species do meet up, they often have molecular incompatibilities that prevent them from fusing. Gamete incompatibility may be the primary speciation route of animals that fertilize their eggs by releasing free-swimming sperm in water.

As populations begin to diverge, so do their genes. Even chromosomes of species that diverged recently may have major differences. Thus, a hybrid zygote may have extra or missing genes, or genes with incompatible products. In either case, its development probably will not proceed correctly and the resulting embryo will die prematurely. Hybrid offspring that survive may have reduced fitness, such as occurs with ligers and tigons (offspring of lions and tigers), which have more health problems and a shorter life expectancy than individuals of either parent species.

Some interspecies crosses produce robust but sterile offspring. For example, the offspring of a female horse (64 chromosomes) mated with a male donkey (62 chromosomes) is a mule. The mule's 63 chromosomes cannot pair up evenly during meiosis, so this animal makes few viable gametes. If hybrids are fertile, their offspring usually have lower fitness with each successive generation. A mismatch between nuclear and mitochondrial DNA may be the cause (mitochondrial DNA is inherited from the mother only).

## Allopatric Speciation

Genetic changes that lead to a new species usually begin with physical separation between populations, so **allopatric speciation** may be the most common way that new species form (*allo*– means different; *patria*, fatherland). By this speciation mode, a physical barrier separates two population and ends gene flow between them. Then, reproductive isolating mechanisms arise, so even if the populations meet up again their individuals could not interbreed.

Whether a geographic barrier can block gene flow depends on an organism's means of travel or the way its gametes disperse. Populations of most species are separated by distance, and gene flow between them is usually intermittent. The Great Wall of China is an example of a barrier that arose abruptly. As it was being built, the wall cut off gene flow among nearby populations of wind-pollinated plants. DNA sequences show that trees, shrubs, and herbs on either side of the wall are now diverging genetically.

Geographic isolation can occur slowly, such as when plate tectonics (Section 11.5) caused the Isthmus of Panama to form. This land bridge between continents cut off the flow of water—and gene flow among populations of aquatic organisms—as it separated one large ocean into what are now the Pacific and the Atlantic oceans (Figure 12.18).

## Sympatric Speciation

In **sympatric speciation**, populations inhabiting the same geographic region speciate in the absence of a physical barrier between them (*sym*– means together). Sympatric speciation can occur in an instant with a change in chromosome number. Nondisjunction during meiosis can change the chromosome number at fertilization (Section 9.7). Or, the chromosome number doubles when body cells duplicate their chromosomes but fail to divide during mitosis. In plants, the resulting polyploid cells can proliferate to form shoots and flowers. If the flowers self-fertilize, a new species may be the result.

Sometimes a new species arises by chromosome multiplication in one parent. In other cases, a species originates after related species hybridize, and then the chromosome number multiplies in the offspring. Common bread wheat is an example (Figure 12.19).

**FIGURE 12.18** Allopatric speciation in snapping shrimp (*right*). As the Isthmus of Panama (*below*) formed about 3.5 million years ago, it cut off gene flow among populations of these aquatic shrimp. Individuals from opposite sides of the isthmus are so similar that they might interbreed, but they are now behaviorally isolated: Instead of mating when they are brought together, they snap their claws at one another aggressively.

Pacific Ocean

Caribbean Sea

Gulf of Panama

| Triticum monococcum (einkorn) | Unknown species of Triticum | spontaneous chromosome doubling | T. turgidum (emmer) | T. tauschii (goatgrass) | T. aestivum (common bread wheat) |
|---|---|---|---|---|---|
| 14AA × | 14BB → 14AB | | 28AABB × | 14DD → | 42AABBDD |

**FIGURE 12.19 Animated!** Sympatric speciation in wheat. ❶ Einkorn has a diploid chromosome number of 14 (two sets of 7, shown here as 14 AA). Wild einkorn probably hybridized with another wild species having the same chromosome number (14 BB) about 11,000 years ago. The resulting hybrid was diploid (14 AB).

❷ About 8,000 years ago, the chromosome number of an AB hybrid plant spontaneously doubled. The resulting species, emmer, is tetraploid: it has two sets of 14 chromosomes (28 AABB). ❸ Emmer probably hybridized with a wild goatgrass having a diploid chromosome number of 14 (two sets of 7 DD). The resulting common bread wheat has six sets of 7 chromosomes (42 AABBDD).

**allopatric speciation** Speciation pattern in which a physical barrier that separates members of a population ends gene flow between them.

**sympatric speciation** Pattern in which speciation occurs in the absence of a physical barrier.

# 16 Population Ecology

# Ecology is the study of interactions among organisms, and between organisms and their environment.

## Impacts/Issues: A Honkin' Mess

Visit a grassy park or a golf course in many parts of the United States and you may need to watch where you step. Wide expanses of grass with a nearby body of water are extremely inviting to Canada geese, or *Branta canadensis* (Figure 16.1). These plant-eating birds produce an abundance of slimy, green feces that can soil shoes, stain clothes, and discourage picnics. Goose feces also wash into ponds and waterways. The added nutrients encourage bacteria and algae to grow, clouding the water and making swimming unappealing and possibly dangerous. Goose feces can contain microbes that sicken humans.

Canada geese are becoming increasingly common. For example, Michigan had about 9,000 in 1970, and has 300,000 today. Controlling their number is challenging, because several different Canada goose populations spend time in the United States. A **population** is a group of organisms of the same species who live in a specific location. Members of a population breed with one another more often than they breed with members of other populations. In the past, nearly all Canada geese seen in the United States were migratory. They nested in northern Canada, flew to the United States to spend the winter, then returned to Canada. The common name of the species reflects this tie to Canada.

Most Canada geese still migrate, but some populations are permanent residents of the United States. Canada geese breed where they were raised, and the nonmigratory birds are generally descendants of geese deliberately introduced to a park or hunting preserve. During the winter, migratory birds often mingle with nonmigratory ones. For example, a bird that breeds in Canada and flies to Virginia for the winter finds itself alongside geese that have never left Virginia.

Life is harder for migratory geese than for nonmigratory ones. Flying hundreds of miles to and from a northern breeding area takes lots of energy and is dangerous. A bird that does not migrate can devote more energy to producing young than a migratory one can. If the nonmigrant lives in a suburban or urban area, it also benefits from an unnatural abundance of food (grass) and an equally unnatural lack of predators. Not surprisingly, the biggest increases in Canada geese have been among nonmigratory birds living where humans are plentiful.

Migratory birds are protected under federal law and by international treaties. However, in 2006, increasing complaints about Canada geese led the U.S. Fish and Wildlife Service to exempt this species from some protections. The agency encouraged wildlife managers to look for ways to reduce nonmigratory Canada goose populations, without unduly harming migratory birds. To do so, these biologists need to know about the traits that characterize different goose populations, as well as how these populations interact with one another, with other species, and with their physical environment.

These sorts of questions are the focus of the science of **ecology**, the study of interactions among organisms, and between organisms and their physical environment. Ecology is not the same as environmentalism, which is advocacy for protection of the environment. However, environmentalists often cite the results of ecological studies when drawing attention to environmental concerns.

**FIGURE 16.1** Canada geese in a California park during the summer.

# Characteristics of Populations

When studying a population, ecologists collect information about the genes, reproductive traits, and behavior of its component individuals. They also look at **demographics**—vital statistics that describe the population, such as its size, density, and distribution.

## Overview of the Demographics

**Population size** refers to the number of individuals in a population. **Population density** is the number of individuals in some specified area or volume of a habitat, such as the number of frogs per acre of rain forest or the number of amoebas per liter of pond water. Density tells you how many individuals are in an area but not how they are dispersed through it.

**Population distribution** describes how individuals are spread through their habitat. It may be clumped, nearly uniform, or random (Figure 16.2**A**). In nature, individuals of most species tend to clump together for one or more reasons. First, each species is adapted to a limited set of ecological conditions that usually occur in patches. For example, geese tend to cluster in an area that has plenty of food and a body of water. Plants survive only where soil, water, and sunlight are adequate. Second, the offspring of many species do not disperse far from their parents. As the saying goes, the nut does not fall far from the tree. Many larvae and immature forms of animals are not very mobile. For example, sponges are usually clumped because larvae settle close to their parents. Asexual reproduction also results in clumping. Third, many animals spend their lives in social groups that offer protection and other advantages. For example, chimpanzees live in cooperative groups of about fifty individuals (Figure 16.2**B**).

When individuals are more evenly spaced than we would expect them to be by chance, they show a nearly uniform dispersal pattern. This pattern often arises as a result of territoriality or stiff competition for some essential resource. Some mature desert shrubs are uniformly distributed (Figure 16.2**C**). Their roots compete for resources, discouraging close growth.

We observe a random pattern of population dispersion only when habitat conditions are nearly uniform, resource availability is fairly constant, and members of a population neither attract nor avoid one another. This combination of factors is fairly unusual. Wolf spiders, which are solitary hunters on forest floors, are one example.

**demographics**  Statistics that describe a population.
**ecology**  The study of interactions among organisms, and between organisms and their environment.
**population**  A group of organisms of the same species who live in a specific location and breed with one another more often than they breed with members of other populations.
**population density**  The number of organisms of a particular population in a given area.
**population distribution**  The way in which members of a population are spread out in their environment.
**population size**  Number of individuals in a population.

clumped

nearly uniform

**A**   random

**FIGURE 16.2** Population distribution. **A** Three types of distribution patterns. **B** Chimpanzees, which live in social groups, have a clumped distribution. Among the advantages of social living is the ability to learn from others. These chimps are using sticks to "fish" for termites in their nest, a behavior learned by imitation. **C** Competition for resources among creosote bushes, a type of desert shrub, results in a nearly uniform distribution among mature plants.

**FIGURE 16.7** Two individuals marked for population studies. **A** Florida Key deer with a neck ring and **B** a Costa Rican owl butterfly with numbers written on its wing.

# Life History Patterns

So far, we have looked at populations as if all of their members are identical during any given interval. However, the individuals of a population are at many different stages in a life cycle. Individuals at each stage may interact in a different way with other organisms and with the environment. Those at different stages may also make use of different resources, as when caterpillars eat leaves and butterflies sip nectar. They may also be more or less vulnerable to predation or other threats. Species, and even populations within a species, vary in their **life history pattern**—a set of heritable traits such as rate of development, age at first reproduction, number of breeding events, and life span. In this section, we look at how such life history traits vary and the evolutionary basis for this variation.

## Survivorship Patterns

Each species has a characteristic life span, but only a few individuals survive to the maximum age possible. Death is more likely at some ages than others. To gather information about the age-specific risk of death, researchers focus on a **cohort**, a group of individuals that are all born at about the same time. Members of the cohort are tracked from birth until the last one dies. Marking the members of a cohort allows a researcher to keep track of them (Figure 16.7).

A **survivorship curve** is a plot showing how many members of a cohort remain alive over time. Three types of survivorship curves are common.

A type I curve indicates survivorship is high until late in life. Populations of large animals that bear one or, at most, a few offspring at a time and give these young extended parental care show this pattern (Figure 16.8**A**). For example, a female elephant has one calf at a time and cares for it for several years. Type I curves are typical of human populations with access to good health care.

A type II curve indicates that death rates do not vary much with age (Figure 16.8**B**). In lizards, small mammals, and big birds, old individuals are about as likely to die of disease or predation as young ones.

A type III curve indicates that the death rate for a population peaks early in life. It is typical of species that produce many small offspring and provide little or no parental care. Figure 16.8**C** shows how the curve plummets for sea urchins, which release great numbers of eggs. Sea urchin larvae are soft and tiny, so fish, snails, and sea slugs devour most of them before protective hard parts can develop. A type III curve is common for marine invertebrates, insects, fishes, fungi, and for annual plants such as dandelions.

## Reproductive Strategies

Natural selection influences the timing of reproduction and how much parental investment goes into each offspring. For any species, the evolutionarily favored reproductive strategy is the one that maximizes lifetime reproductive success.

Some species such as bamboo and Pacific salmon reproduce once, then die. Others such as oak trees, mice, and humans reproduce repeatedly. A one-shot strategy is evolutionarily favored when an individual is unlikely to have a second chance to reproduce. For Pacific salmon, reproduction requires a life-threatening journey from the sea to a stream. For bamboo, environmental conditions that favor reproduction occur only sporadically.

Some species produce lots of tiny young and do not care for them. Other species produce fewer, larger offspring. Population density influences whether an individual will do better by maximizing the quantity or the quality of its offspring. At a low population density, there will be little competition for resources, so individuals who turn resources into offspring fast are at a selective

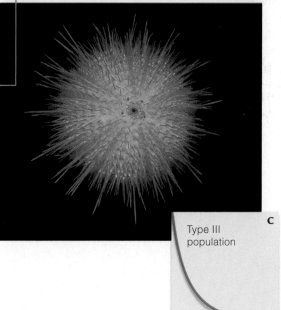

**FIGURE 16.8** Three generalized types of survivorship curves and examples of species with each type.

**A** Elephants have type I survivorship, with low mortality until advanced age.

**B** Snowy egrets have a type II curve, with a fairly constant death rate throughout the life cycle.

**C** Sea urchins have a type III curve, with high early mortality. Larval sea urchins are tiny, soft-bodied, and highly vulnerable to predation. Adults, like this one, are well protected by a hard endoskeleton and spines. Some species of sea urchin can live for more than 100 years.

advantage. Such individuals maximize their reproductive success by reproducing while still young, producing many small offspring, and investing very little in each offspring. Selection that favors parents who produce many offspring as quickly as possible, is called **r-selection**. Species that frequently colonize new habitats or live in unpredictable habitats often are subject to r-selection. As a result, they tend to have small body size and a short generation time.

When population density nears the carrying capacity, individuals who can outcompete others for resources have the selective advantage. In species in which populations are often at or near carrying capacity, selection favors parents who maximize the competitive quality of a few offspring, rather than the number of offspring. Such selection is called **K-selection**. Species living in stable environments often are subject to K-selection. As a result, they tend to have a big body and long generation time.

Among plants, life history traits of dandelions and other opportunistic weeds reflect r-selection, whereas redwood trees have K-selected traits. Among mammals, mice have r-selected traits, and elephants K-selected ones.

## Evolving Life History Traits
Often, different populations within a species live in slightly different environments and have history traits that reflect these differences. For example, in one long-term study, biologists David Reznick and John Endler documented the evolutionary effects of predation on the life history traits of one species of small fish, the guppy, *Poecilia reticulata*. Their study began with fieldwork in the mountains of Trinidad, an island in the

**cohort** Group of individuals born during the same interval.

**life history pattern** Set of traits related to growth, survival, and reproduction such as life span, age-specific mortality, age at first reproduction, and number of breeding events.

**K-selection** Selection favoring individuals that compete well in crowded conditions; selection for offspring quality.

**r-selection** Selection favoring individuals that produce many offspring fast; selection for offspring quantity.

**survivorship curve** Graph showing the decline in numbers of a cohort over time.

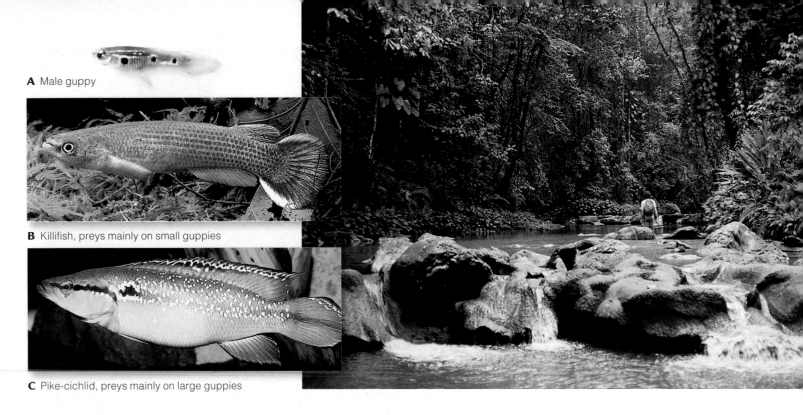

**A** Male guppy

**B** Killifish, preys mainly on small guppies

**C** Pike-cichlid, preys mainly on large guppies

**FIGURE 16.9** Experimental evidence that predation affects life history traits in guppies. **A–C** Guppies and their predators from Trinidad. *Upper right*, biologist David Reznick working in a Trinidad stream.

**D** Bar graphs comparing guppy populations raised in the presence of different predators.

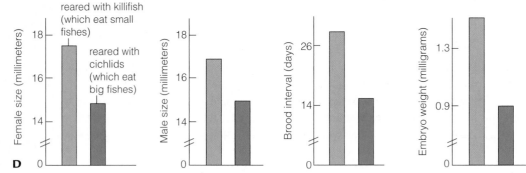

southern Caribbean Sea. Here, guppies live in shallow freshwater streams (Figure 16.9). Waterfalls in the streams act as barriers; they keep guppies from moving from one part of the stream to another, isolating them genetically. Waterfalls also keep predators from moving from one part of a stream to another. As a result, different guppy populations are preyed upon by different predators.

The two kinds of guppy predators in this habitat, killifishes and pike-cichlids, differ in their body size and feeding habits. A killifish is a relatively small fish. It preys on the small, immature guppies but ignores big adults. Pike-cichlids are large fish. They tend to pursue big, mature guppies, and ignore small ones. Many of the streams have one of these predators, but not the other.

Reznick and Endler discovered that the guppies living with pike-cichlids grow faster and have a smaller body size at maturity than guppies in streams containing killifish. Also, guppies in streams with pike-cichlids reproduce earlier, have more offspring at a time, and breed more often (Figure 16.9**D**).

To determine whether these life history differences have a genetic basis, guppies from the two habitats were reared for several generations in aquariums. The results support the hypothesis that the differences are inherited. Descendants of guppies from streams where there were pike-cichlids showed different life history traits than descendants of guppies from streams with killifishes, even when both groups were raised under identical conditions.

Based on their field and laboratory observations, Reznick and Endler hypothesized that predation pressure shapes guppy life history patterns. They set up a field experiment by introducing some guppies to a site upstream from one waterfall. Before the experiment, this waterfall had been an effective barrier to dispersal, preventing guppies and all predators except killifish from moving upstream. The guppies that were introduced to the experimental site were from a population that had evolved with pike-cichlids downstream from the waterfall. That part of the stream was designated the control site.

Eleven years later, researchers revisited the stream. They found that the guppy population at the upstream experimental site had evolved. Exposure to a novel predator had caused shifts in growth rate, age at first reproduction, and other life history traits. Guppies at the control site showed no such changes.

The evolution of life history traits in response to predation pressure is not merely interesting to researchers. It has great economic importance. Just as guppies evolved in response to predators, the North Atlantic codfish (*Gadus morhua*) evolved in response to human fishing. North Atlantic codfish can be quite large (Figure 16.10). From the mid-1980s to early 1990s, the number of fisherman pursuing codfish rose. Fishermen kept the largest fish, and threw smaller ones back. This human behavior put codfish that became sexually mature when they were young and small at an advantage, and such fish became increasingly common. As codfish numbers declined, fishermen kept smaller and smaller fish.

In 1992, Canada banned cod fishing in some areas. That ban, and later restrictions, came too late to stop the Atlantic cod population from plummeting as a result of overfishing. The population still has not recovered from this decline. Looking back, a rapid decline in age at first reproduction was a sign that the cod population was under great pressure. Had biologists recognized this change in a life history trait as a warning sign, they might have been able to save this fishery and protect the livelihood of thousands of workers. Monitoring the life history data for other economically important fishes may help prevent overfishing of other species in the future.

**FIGURE 16.10** A fisherman with a large Atlantic codfish. A human preference for big codfish selected for fish that matured while still young and small.

## Take-Home Message  What factors shape life history patterns?

- Life history traits such as the age at which an organism first reproduces and the number of times it reproduces are subject to natural selection.

- When resources are plentiful and population size is low, individuals who produce lots of offspring have an advantage. When resources are scarce, the ability of offspring to compete becomes more important. In this case, producing fewer, higher quality offspring is favored.

- Predators influence the life history traits of their prey.

# 16.5 Human Populations

**Population Size and Growth Rate**  More than 6.7 billion people now share the planet, and that number continues to grow by more than 200,000 every day. That adds up to more than 80 million additional people every year. Unless birth rates decline to match the still declining death rates, these annual

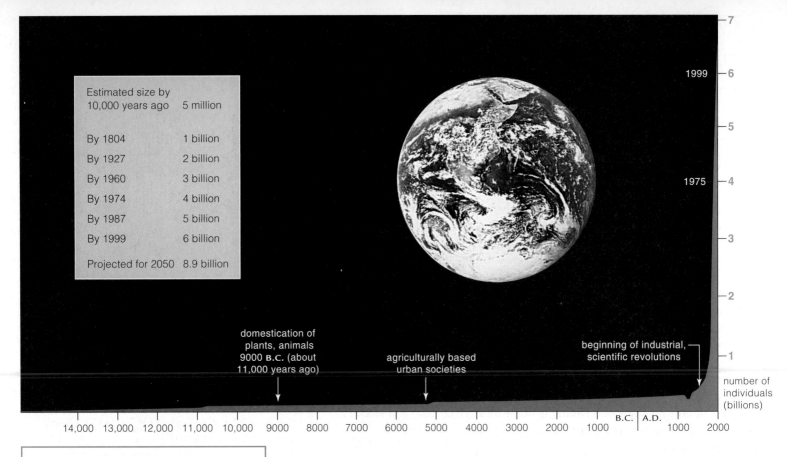

| Estimated size by 10,000 years ago | 5 million |
| --- | --- |
| By 1804 | 1 billion |
| By 1927 | 2 billion |
| By 1960 | 3 billion |
| By 1974 | 4 billion |
| By 1987 | 5 billion |
| By 1999 | 6 billion |
| Projected for 2050 | 8.9 billion |

domestication of
plants, animals
9000 B.C. (about
11,000 years ago)

agriculturally based
urban societies

beginning of industrial,
scientific revolutions

number of
individuals
(billions)

14,000 13,000 12,000 11,000 10,000 9000 8000 7000 6000 5000 4000 3000 2000 1000 B.C. A.D. 1000 2000

**FIGURE 16.11** Growth curve (*red*) for the world human population. The *orange* box lists how long it took for the human population to increase from 5 million to 6 billion.

additions will drive a larger absolute increase in the human population far into the foreseeable future

How did we get into this predicament? For most of its history, the human population grew very slowly. The growth rate began to increase about 10,000 years ago, and during the past two centuries, it soared (Figure 16.11). Three trends promoted the large increases. First, humans were able to migrate into new habitats and expand into new climate zones. Second, humans developed new technologies that increased the carrying capacity of existing habitats. Third, humans sidestepped some limiting factors that restrain growth of other species.

Early humans evolved in the dry woodlands of Africa, then moved into the savannas. We assume they subsisted mainly on plant foods, but they probably also scavenged bits of meat. Bands of hunter–gatherers moved out of Africa about 2 million years ago. By 44,000 years ago, their descendants were established in much of the world (Section 15.7).

Few species can expand into such a broad range of habitats, but the early humans had large brains that allowed them to develop the necessary skills. They learned how to start fires, build shelters, make clothing, manufacture tools, and cooperate in hunts. With the advent of language, knowledge of such skills did not die with the individual. Compared to most species, humans have a greater capacity to disperse fast over long distances and to become established in physically challenging new environments.

Beginning about 11,000 years ago, bands of hunter–gatherers were shifting to agriculture. Instead of counting on the migratory game herds, they were settling in fertile valleys and other regions that favored seasonal harvesting of fruits and grains. They developed a more dependable food supply. A pivotal factor was the domestication of wild grasses, including species ancestral to modern wheat and rice. Now people harvested, stored, and planted seeds all in one place. They domesticated animals as sources of food and to pull plows. They dug irrigation ditches and diverted water to croplands.

**age structure** Of a population, distribution of individuals among various age groups.
**total fertility rate** Average number of children born to a woman in a particular population.

Agricultural productivity became a basis for increases in population growth rates. Towns and cities formed. Later, food supplies increased yet again. Farmers started to use chemical fertilizers, herbicides, and pesticides to protect their crops. Transportation and food distribution improved. Even at its simplest, the management of food supplies through agricultural practices increased the carrying capacity for the human population.

Until about 300 years ago, malnutrition and infectious diseases kept the death rate high enough to more or less balance the birth rate. Infectious diseases are density-dependent factors. Plagues swept through crowded cities. In the mid-1300s, one-third of Europe's population was lost to a pandemic known as the Black Death. Waterborne diseases such as cholera that are associated with poor sanitation ran rampant. Then plumbing improved and vaccines and medications began to cut the death toll from disease. Births increasingly outpaced deaths, and exponential growth accelerated.

The industrial revolution took off in the middle of the eighteenth century. People had discovered how to harness the energy of fossil fuels, starting with coal. Within decades, cities of western Europe and North America became industrialized. World War I sparked the development of more technologies. After the war, factories that had produced wartime goods turned to mass production of cars, tractors, and other affordable goods. Advances in agricultural practices meant that fewer farmers were required to support a larger population.

In sum, by controlling disease agents and tapping into fossil fuels—a concentrated source of energy—the human population sidestepped many factors that had previously limited its rate of increase.

Where have our colonization of many habitats and ongoing advances in technology and infrastructure gotten us? It took more than 100,000 years for the human population size to reach 1 billion. It took just 123 years to reach 2 billion, 33 more to reach 3 billion, 14 more to reach 4 billion, and then 13 more to get to 5 billion. It took only 12 more years to arrive at 6 billion!

**Fertility Rates and Future Growth** Most governments now recognize that population growth, resource depletion, pollution, and quality of life are interconnected. Many offer family planning programs. The United Nations Population Division estimates that globally, more than 60 percent of married women use family planning methods.

The **total fertility rate** is the average number of children born to the women of a population during their reproductive years. In 1950, the worldwide total fertility rate averaged 6.5. By 2003, it had declined to 2.8 but was still above the replacement level, which is the number of children a couple must bear to replace themselves. At present, this replacement level is 2.1 for developed countries and as high as 2.5 in some developing countries. (It is higher in developing countries because more female children die before reaching reproductive age.)

World population is expected to reach 8.9 billion by 2050, and possibly to decline as the century ends. At present, China (with 1.3 billion people) and India (with 1.1 billion) dwarf other countries; together, they hold 38 percent of the world population. Next in line is the United States, with 305 million.

Compare the **age structure**, or distribution of individuals among age groups, for these three countries (Figure 16.12). Notice especially the size of the age groups that will be reproducing during the next fifteen years. The broader the base of an age structure diagram, the greater the proportion of young people, and the greater the expected growth. Government polices that favor couples who have only one child have helped China to narrow its pre-reproductive base.

Even if every couple now alive decides to bear no more than two children, world population growth will not slow for many years, because 1.9 billion people

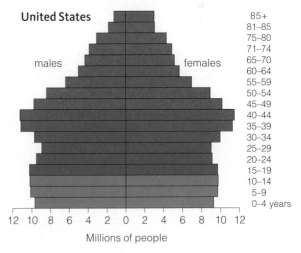

**FIGURE 16.12 Animated!** Age structure diagrams for the world's three most populous countries. The width of each bar represents the number of individuals in a 5-year age group. *Green* bars represent people in their pre-reproductive years. The *left* side of each chart indicates males; the *right* side, females.

Figure It Out: Which country has the largest number of people in the 45 to 49 age group? *Answer: China*

| Stage 1 Preindustrial | Stage 2 Transitional | Stage 3 Industrial | Stage 4 Postindustrial |

**FIGURE 16.13 Animated!** Demographic transition model for changes in population growth rates and sizes, correlated with long-term changes in the economy.

**Figure It Out:** In which stage are death rates highest?　　*Answer: The preindustrial stage*

are about to enter the reproductive age bracket. More than one-third of the world population is in the broad pre-reproductive base.

While some countries face overpopulation, others have a declining birth rate and an increasing average age. In some developed countries, the decreasing total fertility rate and increasing life expectancy have resulted in a high proportion of older adults. In Japan, people over 65 currently make up about 20 percent of the population. In the United States, the proportion of people over 65 is projected to reach this level by 2030. In 2050, there could be as many as 31 million Americans over age 85.

**Economics and Population Growth** We can correlate changes in population growth with changes that often unfold in four stages of economic development. These four stages are at the heart of the **demographic transition model** (Figure 16.13). By this model, living conditions are harshest during the preindustrial stage, before technological and medical advances become widespread. Birth and death rates are both high, so the growth rate is low ❶.

Next, in the transitional stage, industrialization begins. Food production and health care improve. The death rate drops fast, but the birth rate declines more slowly ❷. As a result, the population growth rate increases rapidly.

During the industrial stage, when industrialization is in full swing, the birth rate declines. People move from the country to cities, where birth control is available and couples tend to want smaller families. The birth rate moves closer to the death rate, and the population grows less rapidly ❸.

In the postindustrial stage, a population's growth rate becomes negative. The birth rate falls below the death rate, and population size slowly decreases ❹.

The United States, Canada, Australia, the bulk of western Europe, Japan, and much of the former Soviet Union have reached the industrial stage. Developing countries such as Mexico are now in the transitional stage, with people continuing to migrate from agricultural regions to cities.

The demographic transition model is based on analysis of what happened when western Europe and North America industrialized. Whether it can accurately predict changes in modern developing countries remains to be seen. Less developed countries now receive aid from highly developed countries, but must also compete against these countries in a global market. There are also regional differences in how the transition to an industrial stage is proceeding. In Asia, rising affluence is increasing life expectancy and reducing the birth rate, as

**demographic transition model** Model describing the changes in human birth and death rates that occur as a region becomes industrialized.

predicted. However, in sub-Saharan Africa, the AIDS epidemic is keeping some countries from moving out of the lowest stage of economic development.

Moreover, a global shift toward industrialized life-styles is straining Earth's finite resources. The average person in an industrialized nation uses far more nonrenewable resources than a person in a less developed country. For example, the United States accounts for about 4.6 percent of the world's population, yet it uses about 25 percent of the world's minerals and energy supply. Billions of people living in India, China, and other less developed nations would like to own the same kinds of consumer goods that people in developed countries enjoy. Earth does not have the resources to make that possible. The World Resources Institute estimates that for everyone now alive to have an average American life-style would require the resources of four Earths. Finding ways to meet the wants and needs of expanding populations with limited resources will be a challenge.

> For everyone now alive to live like an average American would require the resources of four Earths.

## Take-Home Message  **What factors affect human population growth?**

- Through expansion into new regions, invention of agriculture, and technological innovation, the human population has temporarily skirted environmental resistance to growth. Its size has been skyrocketing since the industrial revolution.

- Birth rates typically fall as nations become more industrialized, but per capita consumption of resources increases.

# 16.6

# Impacts/Issues Revisited:
# A Honkin' Mess

Like Canadian geese, white-tailed deer (*right*) are benefiting from human alteration of their habitat. States are struggling to control rising deer numbers. For example, Ohio had about 17,000 deer in 1977. It now has more than 700,000. The deer destroy landscaping and cause accidents when they try to cross roads. An overabundance of deer is also contributing to a rise in Lyme disease. The bacteria that cause this disease are transferred by ticks that feed on both humans and deer. More deer means more disease-carrying ticks are around and can bite humans.

Rising deer numbers adversely affect other native species. In West Virginia,

**How Would**
# YOU
☑ **Vote ?**

Encouraging hunting is the least expensive way to reduce the numbers of a wild species that has become a threat or nuisance because of its increased numbers. Do you favor hunting as a way to control the size of these populations? See CengageNow for details, then vote online (cengagenow.com).

deer are overbrowsing plants that grow on the forest floor. They eat the young seedlings that would otherwise replenish the forest. The deer are also decimating the wild ginseng population. Ginseng gathered from Appalachian forests is an important export crop. Biologist James McGraw argues that controlling deer is essential to saving West Virginia's forests, and will require either reintroducing big predators or increasing deer hunting.

# Summary

**Section 16.1** A population is a group of individuals that live in a given area and tend to mate with one another. By our actions, we humans have encouraged the growth of certain wild populations. The study of populations is one aspect of the field of biology known as ecology.

**Section 16.2** Populations vary in their demographics, or characteristics such as density and distribution. Most often populations have a clumped distribution because of limited dispersal, a need for resources that are clumped, and/or the benefits of living in a social group.

CENGAGENOW™ Learn how scientists can measure population size with the animation on CengageNow.

**Section 16.3** The growth rate for a population during a specified interval is determined by rates of birth, death, immigration, and emigration. In cases of exponential growth, the population increases by a fixed percentage of the whole with each successive interval. This trend plots out as a J-shaped curve. As long as a population's per capita birth rate is above its per capita death rate, its growth rate will be exponential.

Any essential resource that is in short supply becomes a limiting factor for population growth. The logistic growth model describes how population growth is affected by density-dependent factors, such as disease or competition for resources. The population slowly increases in size, goes through a rapid growth phase, then levels off in size once carrying capacity is reached. Carrying capacity is

the maximum number of individuals that can be sustained indefinitely by the resources available in their environment. Population size can also be reduced as a result of density-independent factors such as adverse weather. These factors can affect any population regardless of its size.

CENGAGENOW™ Learn about exponential and logistic population growth with the animation on CengageNow.

**Section 16.4** The time to maturity, number of reproductive events, number of offspring per event, and life span are aspects of a life history pattern. Such patterns are often studied in a cohort, a group of individuals that were born in the same time interval.

Three types of survivorship curves are common: a high death rate late in life, a constant rate at all ages, or a high rate early in life. Life histories have a genetic basis and are subject to natural selection. Depending on the environments, individuals may maximize their reproductive success by reproducing once, or many times. At low population density, individuals who make many offspring fast have an advantage. At a higher population density, individuals who invest more in fewer, higher quality offspring are at an advantage.

Predation can also alter life history patterns. Predators (including humans) act as selective agents on prey populations.

**Section 16.5** The human population has surpassed 6.7 billion. Expansion into new habitats and agriculture allowed early increases. Later, medical and technological innovations raised the carrying capacity and removed many limiting factors.

A population's total fertility rate is the average number of children born to women during their reproductive years. The global total fertility rate is declining and most countries have family planning programs of some sort. Even so, the pre-reproductive base of the world population is so large that population size will continue to increase for many years.

The demographic transition model predicts how human population growth rates will change with industrialization. Generally, the death rate and birth rate both fall with rising industrialization, but conditions in countries can vary in ways that affect this trend.

Developed nations have a much higher per capita consumption of resources than developing nations. Earth does not have enough resources to support the current population in the style of the developed nations.

CENGAGENOW™ Compare the age structures of populations in different countries and learn about the demographic transition model with the interaction on CengageNow.

**Section 16.6** Increases in wildlife populations can have negative impacts on other species and on human health.

# Self-Quiz    Answers in Appendix I

1. Most commonly, individuals of a population show a _____ distribution through their habitat.
   a. clumped                     c. nearly uniform
   b. random                      d. none of the above

2. The rate at which population size grows or declines depends on the rate of _____ .
   a. births        c. immigration      e. a and b
   b. deaths        d. emigration       f. all of the above

3. For a given species, the maximum rate of population increase under ideal conditions is the _____ .
   a. biotic potential              c. environmental resistance
   b. carrying capacity             d. density control

4. Resource competition, disease, and predation are _____ controls on population growth rates.
   a. density-independent           c. age-specific
   b. population-sustaining         d. density-dependent

5. An increase in the population of a prey species in an environment would most likely _____ the carrying capacity for that species' predators.
   a. increase                      c. not affect
   b. decrease                      d. stabilize

6. A life history pattern for a population is a set of traits such as the average _____ .
   a. longevity                     c. age at first reproduction
   b. fertility                     d. all of the above

7. True or false? Life history traits are shaped by natural selection.

8. The human population is now over 6.7 billion. It was about half that in _____ .
   a. 2004      b. 1960      c. 1802      d. 1350

9. Compared to the less developed countries, the highly developed ones have a higher _____ .
   a. death rate                c. total fertility rate
   b. birth rate                d. resource consumption rate

10. Match each term with its most suitable description.
   _____ carrying          a. change in birth and death rates
         capacity              with industrialization
   _____ logistic          b. group of individuals born
         growth                during the same period of time
   _____ exponential       c. population growth plots out
         growth                as an S-shaped curve
   _____ demographic       d. largest number of individuals
         transition            sustainable by the resources
   _____ limiting              in a given environment
         factor            e. population growth plots out
   _____ cohort               as a J-shaped curve
                           f. essential resource that restricts
                              population growth when scarce

Additional questions are available on CENGAGENOW™

# Critical Thinking

1. The age structure diagrams for two hypothetical human populations are shown at left. Describe the growth rate of each population and discuss the current and future social and economic problems that each is likely to face.

2. Each summer, the giant saguaro cactuses in deserts of the American Southwest produce tens of thousands of tiny black seeds apiece. Most die, but a few land in a sheltered spot and sprout the following spring. The saguaro is a CAM plant (Section 5.5) and it grows slowly. After 15 years, the saguaro may be only knee high, and it will not flower until it is about age 30. The cactus may survive to age 200. Saguaros share their desert habitat with annuals such as poppies, which sprout just after the seasonal rains, produce seeds, and die in just a few weeks. How would you describe these two life history patterns? How could such different life histories both be adaptive in this environment?

3. Most species consist of many populations. When determining whether a species need to be protected, the U.S. Fish and Wildlife Service holds hearings to determine whether or not specific populations are endangered. Imagine that you are a member of the panel at such a hearing. A biologist comes before you to discuss a population of whales that spend their summer in a nearby bay. What would you want to know about this whale population to decide whether it is threatened?

## Digging Into Data

### Monitoring Iguana Populations

In 1989, Martin Wikelski started a long-term study of marine iguana populations in the Galápagos Islands (Section 11.3). He marked the iguanas on two islands—Genovesa and Santa Fe—and collected data on how their body size, survival, and reproductive rates varied over time. The iguanas eat algae and have no predators, so deaths are usually the result of food shortages, disease, or old age. His studies showed that the iguana populations decline during El Niño events, when water surrounding the islands heats up.

In January 2001, an oil tanker ran aground and leaked a small amount of oil into the waters near Santa Fe. Figure 16.14 shows the number of marked iguanas that Wikelski and his team counted in their census of study populations just before the spill and about a year later.

1. Which island had more marked iguanas at the time of the first census?

2. How much did the population size on each island change between the first and second census?

3. Wikelski concluded that changes on Santa Fe were the result of the oil spill, rather than sea temperature or other climate factors common to both islands. How would the census numbers be different from those he observed if an adverse event had affected both islands?

**FIGURE 16.14**

Shifting numbers of marked marine iguanas on two Galápagos islands. An oil spill occurred near Santa Fe just before the January 2001 census (*blue* bars). A second census was carried out in December 2001 (*green* bars).

# 17 Communities and Ecosystems

A species takes part in a web of relationships with other species, while also interacting with its nonliving environment.

## Impacts/Issues: Fighting the Foreign Fire Ants

Accidentally step on a nest mound of red imported fire ants (RIFAs), and you will be sorry. When disturbed, these ants stream out from the ground and sting their attacker. Venom from the ant's stinger causes burning pain, and multiple stings can cause nausea, dizziness, and, in rare cases, lead to death.

RIFAs arrived in the United States from South America during the 1930s, as stowaways on a ship. The ants spread out from the Southeast and have been found as far west as California and as far north as Kansas and Delaware.

The species name of the most widespread RIFA is *Solenopsis invicta* (Figure 17.1**A**). Invicta means "invincible" in Latin, and *S. invicta* lives up to its name. So far, pesticides have not managed to slow the ants' spread. In fact, these chemicals might even be aiding the foreign ants by wiping out native ant populations.

*S. invicta* is an example of an **exotic species**, a species that evolved in one region but has been introduced to and become established in another. In its new home, an exotic species is often untroubled by competitors, predators, parasites, and diseases that kept it in check back home. Freed from these natural restrictions, the exotic species often outcompetes species native to its new habitat. For example, RIFAs outcompete and displace North America's native fire ants. As a result, the Texas horned lizard (a species that eats native ants but not RIFAs) is on the decline. A high population density of RIFAs also threatens some songbirds. The ants feed on defenseless nestlings, killing many of them.

Taking a cue from nature, biologists are now enlisting some of the ants' enemies. In South America, attacks of phorid flies (Figure 17.1**B**) help keep *S. invicta* populations in check. The flies kill the ants in a rather gruesome way. A female fly pierces the cuticle of an adult ant, then lays an egg in the ant's soft tissues. The egg hatches into a larva, which grows and eats its way through the body to the ant's head. After the larva gets big enough, it causes the ant's head to fall off (Figure 17.1**C**). The larva then develops into an adult within the detached head.

Phorid fly species have now been introduced in several southern states. The flies attack *S. invicta*, but ignore other ants. The flies are not expected to kill off all the *S. invicta* in affected areas, but they may reduce the density of colonies. When phorid flies are present, the exotic ants spend more time acting defensively, and less time foraging for food. The biologists hope that less food will lead to a reduction in *S. invicta* populations. Such a reduction may allow our native ants and the species that depend on them to recover.

A species takes part in a web of relationships with other species, and interacts with its nonliving environment. We refer to all the species that live and interact in a specific area as a **community**. A community together with its physical environment constitute an **ecosystem**. In this chapter, we consider interactions among species, as well as between species and the nonliving portion of their environment. In Chapter 18 we will take a closer look at the ways in which human activities alter these interactions, and the long-range implications of these changes.

**FIGURE 17.1** Off with her head! **A** Group of red imported fire ants. **B** Phorid fly that can inject its egg into an ant's body. The fly larva that hatches feeds on the ant's tissues. When ready to become an adult, the larva moves into the ant's head and **C** causes the head to fall off.

# 17.2 Factors That Shape Communities

Communities vary in size and often are nested one inside another. For example, we find a community of microbial organisms inside the gut of a termite. That termite is part of a larger community of organisms that live on a fallen log. This community is in turn part of a still larger forest community.

Even communities that are similar in scale differ in their species diversity. There are two components to species diversity. The first, species richness, refers to the number of species that are present. The second is species evenness, or the relative abundance of each species. For example, a pond in which five fish species occur in nearly equal numbers has a higher species diversity than a pond in which one fish species is abundant and four others are rare.

Community structure is dynamic. The array of species and their relative abundances change over time. Communities change over a long time span as they form and then age. They also change suddenly as a result of natural or human-induced disturbances.

**Nonbiological Factors**  The structure of a community is affected by geographic and climate variables. These variables include sunlight intensity, rainfall, and temperature along gradients in latitude, elevation, and—for aquatic habitats—depth. Species diversity varies with latitude. Tropical regions receive the most sunlight energy and have the most even temperature. For most plants and animal groups, the number of species is greatest in the tropical regions near the equator, and declines as you move toward the poles. For example, tropical rain forest communities are highly diverse (Figure 17.2), and forest communities in temperate regions are less so. Similarly, tropical reef communities are more diverse than comparable marine communities farther from the equator.

**Biological Factors**  The evolutionary history and adaptations of the various species in a community affect community structure. Each species is adapted to a specific **habitat**, the type of place where it typically occurs. All species of a community share the same habitat, the same "address," but each also has a unique ecological role that sets it apart. This role is the species' **niche**, which we describe in terms of the conditions, resources, and interactions necessary for survival and reproduction. Aspects of an animal's niche include temperatures it can tolerate, the kinds of foods it can eat, and the types of places where it can breed or hide. A description of a plant's niche would include its soil, water, light, and pollinator requirements.

Species in a community interact in ways that affect community structure. Any increase in the numbers of one species often affects the abundance of other species. In some cases, the effect is indirect. For example, when songbirds eat caterpillars, the birds indirectly benefit the trees that the caterpillars feed on, while directly reducing the abundance of caterpillars. The types of direct species interactions among members of a community are the focus of the next section.

**FIGURE 17.2** Two of the twelve or so fruit-eating pigeon species in New Guinea's tropical rain forests (*left*). *Top*, a Victoria crowned pigeon the size of a turkey. *Below*, the smaller superb crowned fruit pigeon.

## Take-Home Message  What factors shape a biological community?

- Communities vary in their species diversity as a result of nonbiological factors such as differences in sunlight and nutrient availability.
- Species' resource requirements and interactions among species also influence community structure.

**community**  All populations of all species in some area.
**ecosystem**  A community plus its physical environment.
**exotic species**  A species that evolved in one community and later became established in a different one.
**habitat**  The type of place in which a species lives.
**niche**  The role of a species in its community.

# 17.3 Species Interactions in Communities

We recognize five types of direct interactions among species in a community: commensalism, mutualism, competition, predation, and parasitism (Table 17.1). Three of these—parasitism, commensalism, and mutualism—can all be types of **symbiosis**, which means "living together." Symbiotic species, also known as symbionts, spend most or all of their life cycle in close association with each other. An **endosymbiont** is a species that lives inside its partner.

Regardless of whether one species helps or hurts another, two species that interact closely may coevolve over generations. In **coevolution**, each species is a selective agent that shifts the range of variation in the other (Section 12.6).

**Commensalism and Mutualism** **Commensalism** benefits one species and does not affect the other. For example, some ferns live attached to the trunk or branches of a tree (Figure 17.3**A**). The fern benefits by getting a perch in the sun, and the tree is unaffected. As another example, many animals have commensal bacteria inside their gut. The bacteria get a warm, nutrient-rich place to live, and their presence neither helps nor harms their host.

Other gut bacteria help their host by aiding in digestion or synthesizing vitamins. Such an interaction, which benefits both species, is a **mutualism**. Flowering plants take part in mutualistic relationships with animals that pollinate them or disperse their seeds. Plants also have a mutualistic relationship with fungi that live on or in their roots. The fungi absorb mineral ions from the soil and share them with the plant. In return the fungi get sugars from the plant.

Mutualism is not a cozy cooperative venture, but rather a case of mutual exploitation. If there is a cost to participating, individuals who lower that cost will be at a selective advantage. For example, a plant that lures a pollinator with a small nectar reward has an advantage over one that provides more nectar.

Mutualisms can be essential to one or both partners. A pink anemone fish will be eaten by a predator unless it has a sea anemone to hide in (Figure 17.3**B**). The anemone's tentacles are covered by stinging cells that do not affect the anemone fish, but help keep predatory fish at bay. The anemone can survive on its own, but benefits by having a partner that chases away the few fish species that are able to feed on anemone tentacles.

| Table 17.1 | Interspecific Interactions | |
|---|---|---|
| Type of Interaction | Direct Effect on Species 1 | Direct Effect on Species 2 |
| Commensalism | Benefits | None |
| Mutualism | Benefits | Benefits |
| Competition | Harmed | Harmed |
| Predation | Benefits | Harmed |
| Parasitism | Benefits | Harmed |

**FIGURE 17.3 A** Commensal fern growing on a tree trunk. **B** An anemone fish nestles among the tentacles of a sea anemone. In this mutualistic partnership, each species protects the other.

**FIGURE 17.4** Interspecific competition among scavengers. **A** A golden eagle and a red fox face off over a moose carcass. **B** The eagle attacks the fox with its talons. After this attack, the fox retreated, leaving the eagle to exploit the carcass.

As a final example, mitochondria probably evolved from aerobic bacteria that were endosymbionts inside early eukaryotes (Section 13.3). The bacteria entered host cells or were taken in as food. Over generations, the bacteria lost the ability to live on their own and their hosts came to rely on ATP produced by the symbionts. Similarly, chloroplasts probably evolved from photosynthetic bacteria.

**Competitive Interactions** Individuals of the same species compete for resources. As Malthus and Darwin understood, these interactions can be fierce and they are important driving forces for natural selection (Section 11.3). In this chapter, we focus on **interspecific competition**, the competition between different species. Usually interspecific competition is not as intense as competition among members of the same species. Members of two species may be similar, but never as similar as members of the same species.

Sometimes, members of one species actively prevent members of another species from using a resource. For example, scavengers such as eagles and foxes fight over carcasses (Figure 17.4). Plants interfere with their competitors as well. For example, a sagebrush plant secretes chemicals that taint the soil around it, thus preventing potential competitors from taking root.

In other cases, competing species do not actively interfere with one another. Instead, all scramble for a share of the resource pie. For example, blue jays, deer, and squirrels eat acorns in oak forests. The animals do not fight over acorns, but they do compete. By eating or storing acorns, each species reduces the number of acorns available to the others.

When species compete for a resource, each gets less of that resource than it would if it lived alone. In this way, competition has a negative impact on all competitors. The more alike two species are, the more intensely they compete. If both species require the same limiting resource, the superior competitor will drive the lesser competitor to extinction in their shared habitat. We refer to this outcome of competition as **competitive exclusion**.

> The more alike two species are, the more intensely they will compete.

**coevolution** The joint evolution of two closely interacting species; each species is a selective agent that shifts the range of variation in the other.

**commensalism** Species interaction that benefits one species and neither helps nor harms the other.

**competitive exclusion** When two species compete for a limiting resource, one drives the other to local extinction.

**endosymbiont** A species that lives in the body of another species in a commensal, mutualistic, or parasitic relationship.

**interspecific competition** Two species compete for a limited resource and both are harmed by the interaction.

**mutualism** Species interaction that benefits both species.

**symbiosis** One species lives in or on another in a commensal, mutualistic, or parasitic relationship.

**Parasites and Parasitoids** **Parasites** obtain nutrients from a living host. You already know about some examples from earlier chapters. Some bacteria, protists, and fungi are parasites. Tapeworms and flukes are parasitic annelid worms. Some roundworms, insects, and crustaceans are parasites, as are all ticks (Figure 17.8**A**). Even a few plants are parasitic. Nonphotosynthetic plants, such as dodders, obtain sugars and nutrients from other plants (Figure 17.8**B**). Other parasitic plants, including mistletoes, can carry out photosynthesis but tap into nutrients and water in a host plant's tissues.

Many parasites are pathogens, organisms that cause disease in their hosts. Even when a parasite does not cause obvious symptoms, infection can weaken the host, making it more vulnerable to predation or less attractive to potential mates. Some parasitic infections cause sterility. Others shift the sex ratio of the offspring that their host produces.

Like predators and prey, parasites and their hosts exert selective pressure on one another. Some parasites have evolved the ability to alter their host's behavior to their own benefit. For example, *Plasmodium*, the protist that causes malaria, needs a mosquito to convey it from one human host to the next. When the protist is in its infectious stage, it "calls for a ride" by making its human host smell especially appetizing to mosquitoes.

Hosts' defenses against parasites include immune responses (a topic we consider in detail in Chapter 22) and behavioral responses. For example, many primates take turns removing ticks and other parasites from one another. Birds kill external parasites by preening their feathers, and their bill shape reflects this function, as well as its role in feeding. In pigeons, even a slight experimental modification of bill shape that has no effect on feeding can result in an increase in parasite numbers.

**Parasitoids** are free-living insects that lay eggs in other insects. Larvae hatch and devour their host from the inside, eventually killing the host. As many as 15 percent of all insects may be parasitoids. The phorid flies described in Section 17.1 are one example.

Parasitoids usually are very particular about their host. This makes them useful as biological controls. Introducing a parasitoid that attacks a pest allows for a more targeted approach than use of pesticides, which often affect nonpest species.

**FIGURE 17.8** Two examples of parasites. **A** Bloodsucking ticks on the head of a finch. **B** Dodder (*Cuscuta*) is also known as strangleweed or devil's hair. This parasitic flowering plant lacks chlorophyll. It winds around a host plant during growth. Modified roots penetrate the host's vascular tissues and draw water and sugars from them.

## Take-Home Message How do species interactions affect a community?

- In commensalism, one species benefits and the other is unaffected.
- In mutualism, two species exploit one another in a way that benefits both.
- When two species compete for a limited resource, both are harmed. If both use the same resource in the same way, the stronger competitor drives the weaker one to local extinction, a process called competitive exclusion.
- Interspecific competition favors individuals of both species whose resource needs are most unlike those of the competing species. Over time, the competition acts as a selective pressure that alters traits related to resource use and leads to resource partitioning among species.
- Predators benefit at the expense of their prey, and parasites benefit at the expense of their hosts. As a result, predators and parasites select for defensive traits in prey and hosts. These defenses in turn select for new traits in the predators and parasites.

**parasite** A species that withdraws nutrients from another species (its host), usually without killing it.

**parasitoid** An insect that lays eggs in another insect, and whose young devour their host from the inside.

# 17.4 How Communities Change

**Ecological Succession** Community structure—the kinds of species and their relative abundance in a habitat—is in constant flux. In a process called **ecological succession**, the array of species gradually shifts over time as organisms alter their own habitat. One array of species is replaced by another, which is in turn replaced by another, and so on.

**Primary succession** is succession in habitats that lack soil and have few or no existing species (Figure 17.9). For example, a rocky area exposed by retreat of a glacier in Alaska undergoes primary succession. At first, no multicellular organisms are present, although there are prokaryotes and perhaps some single-celled algae ❶. The community begins to change as pioneer species gain a foothold ❷. **Pioneer species** are species that colonize new or vacated habitats. They often include lichens, mosses, and hardy annual plants with wind-dispersed seeds. As generations of pioneers live and die, they help build and improve the soil. In doing so, they set the stage for their own replacement. Seeds of shrubby species find shelter in mats of pioneers and take root ❸. Over time, organic wastes and remains build up and, by adding volume and nutrients to soil, this material allows tall trees to take hold ❹.

**Secondary succession** occurs after a natural or human disturbance removes the natural array of species, but not the soil. We observe this kind of succession after a fire destroys a forest or a plowed field is abandoned and wild species move in and take over.

The 1980 eruption of Mount Saint Helens, a volcano in Washington State, gave scientists an opportunity to observe primary succession in action (Figure 17.10). The eruption showered the area around the volcano with volcanic rock and ash, wiping out the existing plant life and covering the mature soil. Since then, plant life has colonized the area and succession is under way.

**FIGURE 17.9** Artist's depiction of how primary succession in a previously glaciated area can lead to establishment of a forest community.

**FIGURE 17.10** Example of ecological succession. **A** Mount Saint Helens erupted in 1980. Volcanic ash completely buried the community that previously existed at the base of this volcano. **B** In less than a decade, numerous pioneer species had become established. **C** Twelve years after the eruption, Douglas fir seedlings were taking hold in soils enriched with volcanic ash.

**ecological succession** A gradual change in a community in which one array of species replaces another.

**pioneer species** Species that can colonize a new habitat.

**primary succession** Ecological succession occurs in an area where there was previously no soil.

**secondary succession** Ecological succession occurs in an area where a community previously existed and soil remains.

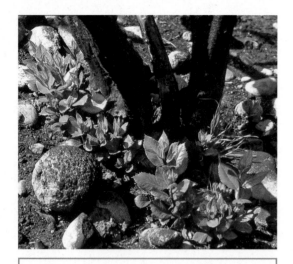

**FIGURE 17.11** Effect of fire on community structure. Some woody shrubs, such as this toyon, resprout from their roots after a fire. In the absence of occasional fire, they are outcompeted and displaced by faster-growing but less fire-resistant species.

**Random Factors and Disturbances** Communities are dynamic entities that are rarely, if ever, in a stable state. Disturbances such as windstorms, freezes, droughts, and fires alter community structure (Figure 17.11). It is often difficult to predict exactly how a community will change during succession or after a disturbance because of random factors. For example, the order in which the pioneer species arrive can have a dramatic effect on community structure.

The frequency and severity of disturbances influences the number of species in a community. Field studies and models indicate that species diversity is highest in communities where moderate disturbances occur with an intermediate frequency. Under these conditions, there are many opportunities for new species to enter the habitat after disturbances, but not enough time between disturbances for many species to become competitively excluded from it.

**The Role of Keystone Species** A **keystone species** has a disproportionately large effect on a community relative to its actual abundance. Robert Paine was the first to describe the importance of a keystone species on community structure. He studied interactions on the rocky shores of California's coast. Species in this rocky intertidal zone survive by clinging to rocks, and access to a space to hold onto is a limiting factor. Paine set up control plots with the sea star *Pisaster ochraceus* and its prey, which include snails, barnacles, and mussels. He removed all of the sea stars from his experimental plots.

With the sea stars gone, mussels took over in the experimental plots, crowding out seven other invertebrate species. The mussels are the preferred prey of the sea star, and the best competitors in its absence. Normally, predation by sea stars keeps the diversity of prey species high, because it restricts competitive exclusion by mussels. Remove all the sea stars, and the community shrinks from fifteen species down to eight. The mussels overgrow and crowd out many of their competitors.

Not all keystone species are predators. For example, beavers can be a keystone species. These large rodents cut down trees by gnawing through their trunks. The beaver then uses the felled trees to build a dam, thus creating a deep pool where a shallow stream would otherwise exist (Figure 17.12). By altering the physical conditions in a section of the stream, the beaver affects which types of fish and aquatic invertebrates can live there.

**FIGURE 17.12** A beaver dam. The beaver is a keystone species that modifies its environment in a way that affects community composition. A beaver gnaws through trunks of small trees and uses the logs and branches to dam a stream. The resulting pond holds aquatic species that would not be present in a fast-moving stream.

**Exotic Invaders** As Section 17.1 explained, an exotic species is a resident of an established community that has dispersed from its home range and become established elsewhere. Unlike most imports, which never take hold outside their home range, an exotic species becomes a permanent part of its new community. Here, with no coevolved parasites, pathogens, or predators to keep the species in check, its numbers may soar.

More than 4,500 exotic species have established themselves in the United States. The red imported fire ants are one example. A look at three others will give you an idea of some of their effects. One of the most notorious is the vine called kudzu (*Pueraria lobata*). Native to Asia, it was introduced to the American Southeast as a food for grazers and to control erosion, but it quickly became an invasive weed. Kudzu shoots overgrow trees, telephone poles, houses, and almost everything else in their path (Figure 17.13**A**).

Gypsy moths (*Lymantria dispar*) are an exotic species native to Europe and Asia. They entered the northeastern United States in the mid-1700s and have extended their range into the Southeast, Midwest, and Canada. Gypsy moth caterpillars (Figure 17.13**B**) prefer to feed on oaks. Loss of leaves to gypsy moths weakens the trees, making them more susceptible to parasites and less efficient competitors.

Nutrias (*Myocastor coypus*) are large semi-aquatic rodents that were imported from South America for their fur, and released into the wild in the 1940s. In the states near the Gulf of Mexico, they thrive in freshwater marshes, where they eat so much that they threaten the native vegetation (Figure 17.13**C**). In addition, their burrowing contributes to marsh erosion and damages levees, increasing the risk of flooding.

**FIGURE 17.13** Three exotic species that are altering natural communities in the United States.

**A** Kudzu vines overgrowing trees in South Carolina.

**B** A gypsy moth caterpillar feeding on oak leaves.

**C** A nutria in a freshwater marsh in Texas.

To learn more about invasive species in the United States, visit the National Invasive Species Information Center online at www.invasivespeciesinfo.gov.

## Take-Home Message What causes changes in community structure?

- In ecological succession, one array of species changes the habitat in a way that allows another array of species to take hold.

- Large and small disturbances shift community structure on an ongoing basis.

- A change in the presence or abundance of a keystone species has a big effect on other species in a habitat.

- An exotic species that leaves behind the predators, parasites, and competitors it evolved with can have dramatic effects on its adopted community.

**keystone species** A species that has a disproportionately large effect on community structure.

light
energy

Producers
plants, some protists
and prokaryotes

energy in
chemical
bonds

materials
cycling

Consumers
animals, fungi, some
protists and prokaryotes

heat energy

**FIGURE 17.14** Generalized model for the one-way flow of energy (*yellow* arrows) and the cycling of materials (*blue* arrows) in an ecosystem. Producers convert sunlight energy to heat energy and energy in chemical bonds. Consumers use the chemical bond energy and also give off energy as heat. Eventually, all light energy that entered the ecosystem is converted to heat energy in the environment.

# The Nature of Ecosystems

**Overview of the Participants** The organisms of a community interact with their environment as an ecosystem. In any ecosystem, there is a one-way flow of energy and a cycling of essential materials (Figure 17.14).

An ecosystem's **producers** capture energy and use it to make their own food from inorganic materials in the environment. Usually the producer's energy source is sunlight and the producers are plants and photosynthetic prokaryotes and protists. An ecosystem's **consumers** get energy and carbon by feeding on tissues, wastes, and remains of producers and one another. Herbivores (plant eaters), predators, and parasites are consumers that feed on living organisms. **Detritivores** such as crabs and earthworms eat tiny bits of organic matter, or detritus. Finally, wastes and remains of organisms are broken down into inorganic building blocks by bacterial, protist, and fungal **decomposers**.

Light energy captured by producers is converted to bond energy in organic molecules, which is then released by metabolic reactions that give off heat. This is a one-way process because heat energy is not recycled—producers cannot convert heat into chemical bond energy. In contrast, nutrients are cycled within an ecosystem. The cycle begins when producers take up hydrogen, oxygen, and carbon from inorganic sources such as the air and water. They also take up dissolved nitrogen, phosphorus, and other necessary minerals. Nutrients move from producers into the consumers who eat them. Decomposition returns nutrients to the environment, where producers take them up again.

**Food Chains and Webs** All organisms of an ecosystem take part in a hierarchy of feeding relationships referred to as **trophic levels** ("troph" means nourishment). When one organism eats another, energy and nutrients are transferred from the eaten to the eater. All organisms at the same trophic level are the same number of transfers away from the energy input into that system.

A **food chain** is the sequence of steps by which some energy captured by primary producers is transferred to higher trophic levels. For example, grasses and other plants are the main producers in a tallgrass prairie (Figure 17.15). They are at this ecosystem's first trophic level. In one food chain, energy flows from grasses to grasshoppers, to sparrows, and finally to hawks. Grasshoppers are primary consumers and are at the second trophic level. Sparrows that eat grasshoppers are second-level consumers and at the third trophic level. Hawks that eat sparrows are third-level consumers and at the fourth trophic level.

A number of food chains cross-connect with one another as a **food web**. Figure 17.16 shows just a small sample of the species that take part in an arctic food web. Nearly all food webs include two types of food chains. In a grazing

**FIGURE 17.15** One food chain in a tallgrass prairie. Species at the first trophic level capture sunlight energy. Arrows represent the transfer of nutrients and energy from one trophic level to the next.

| First Trophic Level | Second Trophic Level | Third Trophic Level | Fourth Trophic Level |
|---|---|---|---|
|  |  |  |  |
| Producer Grass | Primary Consumer Grasshopper | Second-Level Consumer Sparrow | Third-Level Consumer Hawk |

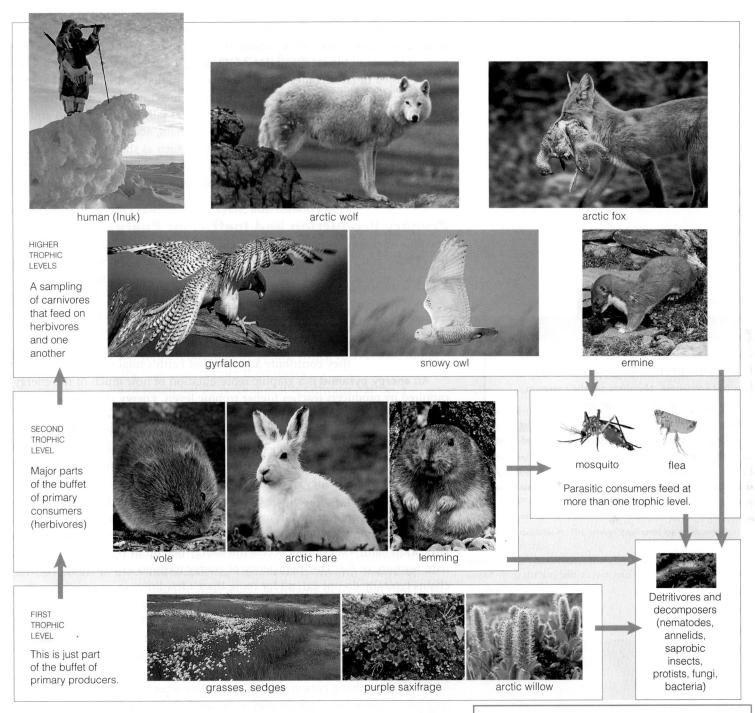

human (Inuk)  arctic wolf  arctic fox

**HIGHER TROPHIC LEVELS**

A sampling of carnivores that feed on herbivores and one another

gyrfalcon  snowy owl  ermine

**SECOND TROPHIC LEVEL**

Major parts of the buffet of primary consumers (herbivores)

vole  arctic hare  lemming

mosquito  flea

Parasitic consumers feed at more than one trophic level.

**FIRST TROPHIC LEVEL**

This is just part of the buffet of primary producers.

grasses, sedges  purple saxifrage  arctic willow

Detritivores and decomposers (nematodes, annelids, saprobic insects, protists, fungi, bacteria)

**FIGURE 17.16 Animated!** Arctic food web. Arrows point from eaten to eater.

food chain, the energy stored in producer tissues flows to herbivores, which tend to be relatively large animals. In a detrital food chain, the energy in producers flows to detritivores, which tend to be smaller animals, and to decomposers.

In most land ecosystems, the bulk of the energy that becomes stored in producer tissues moves through detrital food chains. For example, in an arctic ecosystem, grazers such as voles, lemmings, and hares eat some plant parts. However, far more plant matter becomes detritus that sustains soil-dwelling worms and insects, and decomposers such as soil bacteria and fungi.

Detrital food chains and grazing food chains interconnect to form the overall food web. For example, animals at higher trophic levels such as wolves eat both grazers and detritivores. Also, after grazers and their predators die, the energy in their tissues flows to detritivores and decomposers.

**consumers** Organisms that eat organisms or their remains.
**decomposers** Consumers that feed on remains and break them into their inorganic building blocks.
**detritivores** Consumers that feed on small bits of organic material (detritus).
**food chain** Linear description of who eats whom.
**food web** System of cross-connecting food chains.
**producers** Organisms that capture energy and make their own food from inorganic materials in the environment.
**trophic level** Position of an organism in a food chain.

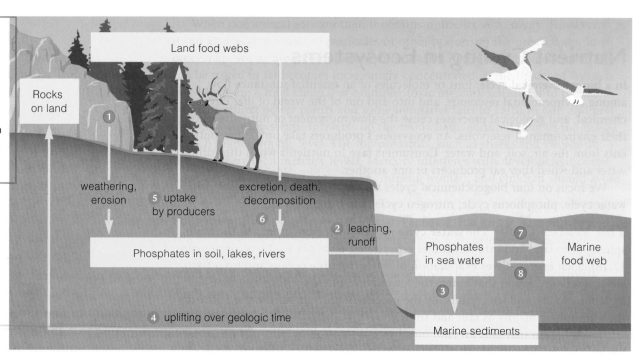

**FIGURE 17.19 Animated!** The phosphorus cycle. In this cycle, most of the phosphorus moves in the form of phosphate ions ($PO_4^{3-}$). The main phosphorus reservoir is rocks and sediments.

Rocks on land

Land food webs

weathering, erosion
5 uptake by producers
excretion, death, decomposition
6
2 leaching, runoff
7
Phosphates in soil, lakes, rivers
Phosphates in sea water
Marine food web
8
3
4 uplifting over geologic time
Marine sediments

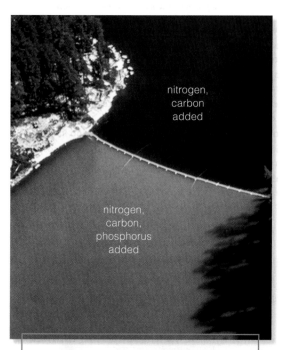

nitrogen, carbon added

nitrogen, carbon, phosphorus added

**FIGURE 17.20** Results of a nutrient enrichment experiment. Researchers put a plastic curtain across a channel between two basins of a lake. They added nitrogen, carbon, and phosphorus on one side of the curtain (here, the *lower* part of the lake) and added nitrogen and carbon on the other side. Within months, the phosphorus-rich basin had a dense layer of single-celled algae covering its surface.

All organisms need phosphorus. It is a component of the sugar–phosphate backbone of DNA, and the "P" in ATP stands for "phosphate." Your body's main store of phosphorus is your bones.

In the **phosphorus cycle**, phosphate moves among Earth's rocks, soil, and water, and into and out of food webs (Figure 17.19). Weathering and erosion move phosphate ions from rocks into soil, lakes, and rivers ❶. Leaching and runoff deliver phosphate ions to the ocean ❷, where most of the phosphorus comes out of solution and settles as deposits along the edges of continents ❸.

Over millions of years, movements of Earth's crust can uplift parts of the sea floor onto land ❹. Weathering releases phosphates from the rocks. Dissolved phosphates enter streams and rivers, and the environmental portion of the phosphorus cycle starts over again.

The biological portion of the phosphorus cycle begins when producers take up phosphorus. Roots of land plants take up dissolved phosphate from the soil water ❺. Land animals get phosphates by eating plants or one another. Phosphorus returns to the soil in wastes and remains ❻. In the seas, phosphorus enters food webs when producers take up dissolved phosphate from seawater ❼. As on land, wastes and remains replenish the supply ❽.

Vast quantities of phosphate-rich droppings from seabird or bat colonies are collected and used as fertilizer. Phosphate-rich rock is also mined for this purpose. Lack of phosphate commonly limits growth of aquatic producers. Figure 17.20 shows an experiment that demonstrated how adding phosphate to part of a lake basin can cause a population explosion of algae. Such algal blooms can pose a threat to other species that inhabit the lake. Humans cause the same problem when they allow phosphate-containing detergents, sewage, fertilizer runoff, and waste from stockyards to pollute aquatic environments.

**The Nitrogen Cycle** Gaseous nitrogen ($N_2$) makes up about 80 percent of Earth's atmosphere. In the **nitrogen cycle**, nitrogen moves among the atmosphere, reservoirs in the soil and water, and into and out of food webs (Figure 17.21). All organisms need nitrogen. Nucleotides such as those in DNA include nitrogen, as do the amino acids that make up proteins.

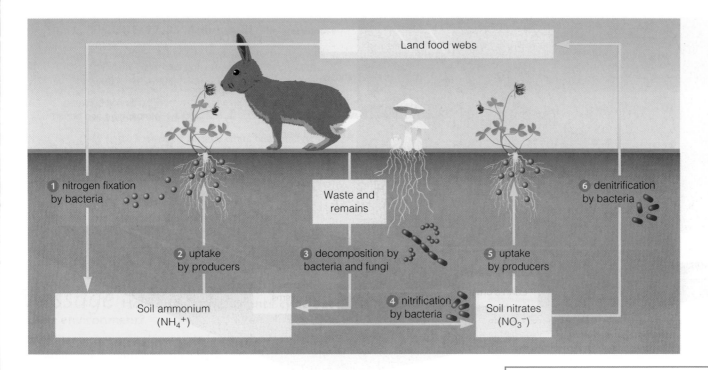

Land food webs

① nitrogen fixation by bacteria

② uptake by producers

Waste and remains

③ decomposition by bacteria and fungi

④ nitrification by bacteria

⑤ uptake by producers

⑥ denitrification by bacteria

Soil ammonium $(NH_4^+)$

Soil nitrates $(NO_3^-)$

**FIGURE 17.21** The nitrogen cycle. The main reservoir for nitrogen is the atmosphere. Activity of nitrogen-fixing bacteria makes gaseous nitrogen available to other living organisms.

Figure It Out: What are the two forms of nitrogen that can be taken up by plants?

Answer: Ammonium and nitrates

Plants cannot use gaseous nitrogen because they do not have an enzyme that breaks the triple covalent bond holding its two nitrogen atoms together. Some bacteria do have such an enzyme and can carry out **nitrogen fixation**. They break the bonds in $N_2$, then use the nitrogen atoms to form ammonia, which dissolves and forms ammonium ions $(NH_4^+)$ ①. Plant roots take up ammonium from the soil ② and use it in metabolic reactions. Consumers get nitrogen by eating plants or one another.

There is also another source of soil ammonium. Bacterial and fungal decomposers break down wastes and remains and form ammonium ③.

Other soil bacteria (nitrifying bacteria) obtain energy by converting ammonium to nitrates $(NO_3^-)$, a process called **nitrification** ④. Like ammonium, nitrates can be taken up from the soil and used by producers ⑤.

Ecosystems lose nitrogen by **denitrification**. Denitrifying bacteria use nitrate for energy and produce nitrogen gas that escapes into the atmosphere ⑥.

Humans alter the nitrogen cycle by industrial fixation of nitrogen to make synthetic fertilizers. Scientists estimate that use of synthetic fertilizers has doubled the amount of nitrogen that enters land ecosystems. Burning fossil fuels further alters the nitrogen cycle by producing nitrogen oxides. These pollutants cause problems when rain deposits them in habitats where plants are adapted to low nitrogen levels.

**The Carbon Cycle** Carbon occurs abundantly in the atmosphere, combined with oxygen as carbon dioxide $(CO_2)$. In the **carbon cycle**, carbon moves among rocks, water, and the atmosphere, and into and out of food webs. After water, carbon is the most abundant substance in living organisms. All organic molecules (carbohydrates, fats, lipids, and proteins) have a carbon backbone.

On land, plants take up and use carbon dioxide in photosynthesis. Plants and most other land organisms release carbon dioxide back to the atmosphere when they carry out aerobic respiration. Bicarbonate ions $(HCO_3^-)$ form when carbon dioxide dissolves in water. Aquatic producers take up bicarbonate and convert it to carbon dioxide for use in photosynthesis. As on land, most aquatic organisms carry out aerobic respiration and release carbon dioxide.

**carbon cycle** Movement of carbon among rocks, water, the atmosphere, and living organisms.

**denitrification** Conversion of nitrates or nitrites to gaseous forms of nitrogen.

**nitrogen cycle** Movement of nitrogen among the atmosphere, soil, and water, and into and out of food webs.

**nitrogen fixation** Conversion of nitrogen gas to ammonia.

**nitrification** Conversion of ammonium to nitrates.

**phosphorus cycle** Movement of phosphorus among rocks, water, soil, and living organisms.

# Summary

**Section 17.1** A species interacts with other species and its environment. All species in a defined area are a community. An exotic species evolved in one community, then became established in another. A community and its environment is an ecosystem.

**Section 17.2** Each species occupies a certain habitat, or type of place. Every species in the community has its own niche—the conditions and resources it requires, and the interactions it takes part in. The types of species in a community and their relative abundance is determined by nonbiological factors such as climate, as well as biological ones such as how species interact.

**Section 17.3** Species in an ecosystem interact with one another in a variety of ways. Commensalism benefits one species and neither helps nor harms the other. In mutualism, both participants exploit one another to their mutual benefit.

Interspecific competition harms both participants. When two (or more) species require identical resources, the superior competitor drives others to local extinction. Resource partitioning allows similar species to coexist by using different portions of shared resources.

Predators are free-living and typically kill their prey. Parasites live in or on their hosts and withdraw nutrients from them, usually without killing them. Parasitoids are free-living as adults, but their larvae develop inside and feed on a host, which they eventually kill. Predators, parasites, and parasitoids coevolve with their hosts.

CENGAGENOW™ Learn about competitive exclusion with the animation on CengageNow.

**Section 17.4** Ecological succession is the sequential replacement of arrays of species within a community. Primary succession occurs in new habitats. Secondary succession takes place in disturbed ones. The first species in a community are pioneer species. Their presence may help other potential colonists.

Community structure is not easily predicted. It is affected by random events and disturbances such as storms, droughts, and fires, and it rarely stabilizes.

The presence of a keystone species has a large effect on community structure. Arrival of an exotic species can drastically alter a community.

**Section 17.5** There is a one-way flow of energy through an ecosystem, and a cycling of materials among the organisms in it.

Sunlight is the initial energy source for almost all ecosystems. Producers convert sunlight energy to chemical bond energy and take up nutrients that they and the ecosystem's consumers require.

All organisms at the same trophic level in an ecosystem are the same number of steps away from the energy source for that ecosystem. Energy transfers are inefficient, so most ecosystems support no more than a few trophic levels.

The rate of primary production—the capture and storage of energy by producers—varies with climate, season, and other factors. Energy pyramids show how usable energy lessens as it flows through an ecosystem. Toxic chemicals also move up trophic levels and become increasingly concentrated in body tissues.

CENGAGENOW™ Learn about trophic levels with animation on CengageNow.

**Section 17.6** In a biogeochemical cycle, water or a nutrient moves through the environment, then through organisms, then back to an environmental reservoir.

In the water cycle, water moves from the ocean into the atmosphere, falls on land, and flows back to the ocean—its main reservoir.

Earth's rocks and sediments are the largest reservoir of phosphorus, which moves into dissolved forms, into living organisms, and back.

The atmosphere is the main reservoir for nitrogen, but plants cannot use gaseous forms of nitrogen. Bacteria and the fertilizer industry fix nitrogen (convert atmospheric nitrogen to forms that plants can take up).

The global carbon cycle moves carbon from its reservoirs in rocks and seawater, through its gaseous form ($CO_2$), and through living organisms.

Carbon dioxide and nitrogen oxides are among the greenhouse gases that trap heat in Earth's atmosphere and make life possible. An increase in their concentration in the atmosphere is causing global climate change.

CENGAGENOW™ Learn about biogeochemical cycles and the greenhouse effect with the animation and interactions on CengageNow.

## Self-Quiz   Answers in Appendix I

1. A species' habitat is like its address, and its _____ is like its occupation.

2. True or false? A symbiosis always benefits both partners.

3. Match the species interaction with a suitable description.
   _____ mutualism
   _____ competition
   _____ predation
   _____ parasitism

   a. A snake eats a mouse.
   b. A bee pollinates a flower while sipping its nectar.
   c. An owl and a wood duck both need a tree cavity to nest.
   d. A mosquito sucks your blood.

4. Interspecific competition favors individuals of both species who are most _____ the competing species in their resource needs.
   a. similar to          b. different from

5. The establishment of a biological community on a newly formed volcanic island is an example of _____ .
   a. primary succession        c. competitive exclusion
   b. secondary succession       d. bioaccumulation

# Digging Into Data

## Biological Control of Fire Ants

Ant-decapitating phorid flies are just one of the biological control agents used to battle imported fire ants. Researchers have also enlisted the help of a fungal parasite that infects ants and slows production of offspring. As a result of infection, a colony dwindles in numbers and eventually dies out.

Are these biological controls useful against imported fire ants? To find out, USDA scientists treated infested areas with either traditional pesticides or pesticides plus biological controls (both flies and the parasite). The scientists left some plots untreated as controls. Figure 17.24 shows the results.

1. How did population size in the control plots change during the first four months of the study?

2. How did population size in the two types of treated plots change during this same interval?

3. If this study had ended after the first year, would you conclude that biological controls had a major effect?

4. How did the two types of treatment (pesticide alone versus pesticide plus biological controls) differ in their longer-term effects? Which is most effective?

**FIGURE 17.24** Effects of two methods of controlling red imported fire ants. The graph shows the numbers of red imported fire ants over a 28-month period. *Orange* triangles represent untreated control plots. *Green* circles are plots treated with pesticides alone. *Black* squares are plots treated with pesticide and biological control agents (phorid flies and a fungal parasite).

---

6. Match the terms with suitable descriptions.

| | |
|---|---|
| _____ producers | a. feed on plants |
| _____ herbivores | b. feed on small bits of |
| _____ decomposers | organic matter |
| _____ detritivores | c. degrade organic wastes and |
| | remains to inorganic forms |
| | d. capture sunlight energy |

7. A chemical that bioaccumulates in a prairie food web would be found at highest concentrations in the tissues of _____ .
   a. grasses
   b. grasshoppers
   c. grasshopper-eating sparrows
   d. sparrow-eating hawks

8. In an energy pyramid diagram of a prairie food web, which of these organisms would be in the lowest (and largest) tier?
   a. grasses
   b. grasshoppers
   c. grasshopper-eating sparrows
   d. sparrow-eating hawks

9. Match each substance with its largest environmental reservoir. One reservoir choice will be used more than once.

| | |
|---|---|
| _____ carbon | a. seawater |
| _____ water | b. rocks and sediments |
| _____ phosphorus | c. the atmosphere |
| _____ nitrogen | |

10. Earth's largest reservoir of fresh water is _____ .
   a. lakes
   b. groundwater
   c. glacial ice
   d. water in living organisms

11. _____ convert nitrogen gas to a form producers can take up.
   a. Fungi
   b. Bacteria
   c. Carnivores
   d. Herbivores

12. Land plants take in _____ for photosynthesis from the air.
   a. carbon dioxide
   b. phosphate ions
   c. ammonium ions
   d. bicarbonate ions

13. Aquatic producers get carbon for photosynthesis from _____ .
   a. decaying organic matter
   b. phosphate ions
   c. ammonium ions
   d. bicarbonate ions

14. Greenhouse gases _____ .
   a. trap heat in the atmosphere
   b. are released by burning of fossil fuels
   c. may cause global climate change if they accumulate
   d. all of the above

15. True or false? Imbalances in both the carbon cycle and nitrogen cycle contribute to increases in greenhouse gases.

Additional questions are available on CENGAGENOW™

# Critical Thinking

1. With antibiotic resistance rising (Section 12.3), researchers are looking for ways to reduce use of these drugs. Some cattle once fed antibiotic-laced food now get feed that includes helpful bacteria that can live in the animal's gut. The idea is that if a large population of beneficial bacteria is in place, then harmful bacteria with the same resource needs are less likely to thrive. Explain why this idea makes sense in terms of species interactions.

2. Figure 17.6 shows a harmless fly that mimics a stinging wasp. Studies have shown that in such mimicry systems, mimics benefit most when they are rare relative to the well-protected model. Can you explain why?

3. Ectotherms, or "cold-blooded" animals, such as invertebrates and fish, convert more of the energy they eat into body tissues than endotherms, or "warm-blooded" animals. What allows the ectotherms to make more efficient use of food energy?

# 18 The Biosphere and Human Effects

*Even seemingly remote regions are no longer beyond*
*the reach of human explorers and human influence.*

## 18.1

## Impacts/Issues:  A Long Reach

We began this book with the story of biologists who ventured into a remote forest in New Guinea and found many previously unknown species. At the far end of the globe, a U.S. submarine surfaced in Arctic waters and found polar bears hunting on the ice-covered sea (Figure 18.1). The bears were 435 kilometers (270 miles) from the North Pole and 805 kilometers (500 miles) from the nearest land.

Even seemingly remote regions are no longer beyond the reach of human explorers and human influence. Increasing levels of greenhouse gases are raising the temperature of Earth's atmosphere and seas. In the Arctic, the warming is causing sea ice to thin and to break up earlier in the spring. This raises the risk that polar bears hunting far from land will become stranded, unable to return to solid ground before the ice thaws.

Polar bears are top predators and their tissues contain a high amount of mercury and organic pesticides. These pollutants enter the water and air far from the Arctic, in more temperate regions, and winds and ocean currents deliver them to polar realms. Migratory animals such as seabirds pick up pollutants in densely populated regions where they spend their winters, then carry them to the Arctic and release them in wastes and, if they die, remains.

In places less remote than the Arctic, human populations have a more direct effect. As we cover more and more of the world with our homes, factories, and farms, less habitat remains for other species. We also put species at risk by competing with them for resources, overharvesting them, and introducing nonnative competitors.

It would be presumptuous to think that humans alone have had a profound impact on the world of life.

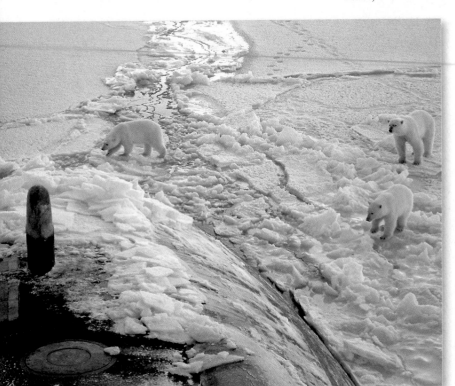

**FIGURE 18.1** Three polar bears investigate an American submarine that surfaced in ice-covered Arctic waters.

More than a billion years ago, the rise of oxygen-releasing photosynthetic cells changed the course of evolution by enriching the atmosphere with this gas (Section 5.6). Over life's long existence, the success of one species or group of organisms has often come at the expense of others. What is new is the increasing pace of change and the capacity of our own species to recognize and affect its role in this increase.

A century ago, Earth's physical and biological resources seemed inexhaustible. Now we know that many practices put into place when we were ignorant of how natural systems operate take a heavy toll on the biosphere. They threaten other species, ecosystem processes, and possibly our own long-term existence.

The **biosphere** is the sum of all places where we find life on Earth. With this chapter, we look at physical processes that affect the distribution of organisms through the biosphere. We also consider the ways that human activities are altering these processes and disrupting the world of life.

A

B

**FIGURE 18.2** Variation in intensity of solar radiation with latitude. For simplicity, we depict two equal parcels of incoming radiation on an equinox, a day when incoming rays are perpendicular to Earth's axis.

Rays that fall on high latitudes **A** pass through more atmosphere (*blue*) than those that fall near the equator **B**. Compare the length of the *green* lines. Atmosphere is not to scale.

Also, energy in the rays that fall at the high latitude is spread over a greater area than energy that falls on the equator. Compare the length of the *red* lines.

# 18.2 Factors Affecting Climate

**Global Air Circulation Patterns** **Climate** refers to average weather conditions, such as temperature, humidity, wind speed, cloud cover, and rainfall, over a long period. Many factors influence a region's climate, which in turn affects the types of species that can live there.

A region's latitude (how far north or south it is) determines how much light energy it receives. On any particular day, regions near the equator receive more sunlight than higher latitudes for two reasons (Figure 18.2). First, sunlight traveling to high latitudes passes through more atmosphere to reach Earth's surface than light traveling to the equator. Fine particles of dust, water vapor, and greenhouse gases absorb some solar radiation or reflect it back into space, so less light energy reaches the poles. Second, the energy in any incoming parcel of sunlight is spread out over a smaller surface area at the equator than at the higher latitudes. As a result of these factors, Earth's surface warms more at the equator than at the poles.

Latitudinal difference in surface warming, and the ways these differences affect air and water, cause global patterns of air circulation and rainfall (Figure 18.3). At the equator, intense sunlight warms the air and causes evaporation of water from the ocean. As the air heats up, it expands and rises ❶. The same effect causes a hot-air balloon to inflate and rise when the air inside it is heated. As the equatorial air mass rises, it flows north and south and begins to cool. Cool air can hold less moisture than warm air, so moisture leaves the air as rain that supports tropical rain forests.

By the time the air reaches about 30° north and south latitude, it has cooled and become dry. Being cool, the air sinks downward ❷. When it descends, it draws moisture from the soil. As a result, deserts often form at around 30° north and south latitude.

Air that continues flowing along Earth's surface toward the poles once again picks up heat and moisture. At a latitude of about 60° the air is warm and moist again and it rises, losing moisture as it does so ❸. In polar regions, cold air that holds little moisture descends ❹. Precipitation is sparse, and polar deserts form.

Landforms also affect rainfall. Deserts often form downwind of coastal mountains. Moisture-laden winds give up water as rain as they rise over mountains. The dry region beyond the mountains is referred to as a **rain shadow**.

**Ocean Currents** Like air, water expands when heated, and it is heated more at the equator than at higher latitudes. As a result, the sea level at the

❹ At the poles, cold, dry air sinks and moves toward lower latitudes.

❸ Air rises again at 60° north and south, where air flowing poleward meets air coming from the poles.

❷ At around 30° north and south latitude, the air—now cooler and dry—sinks.

❶ Warm, moist air rises at the equator. As the air flows north and south, it cools and loses moisture as rain.

**FIGURE 18.3 Animated!** Air circulation patterns that result from latitudinal differences in the amount of solar radiation reaching Earth.

**biosphere** All portions of the Earth where life exists.

**climate** Average weather conditions in a region over a long time period.

**rain shadow** Dry region on the downwind side of a coastal mountain range.

**FIGURE 18.4 Animated!** Major climate zones correlated with surface currents of the world ocean. Warm surface currents start moving from the equator toward the poles, but prevailing winds, Earth's rotation, gravity, the shape of ocean basins, and landforms influence the direction of flow. Water temperatures, which differ with latitude and depth, contribute to the regional differences in air temperature and rainfall.

warm surface current          cold surface current

equator is about 8 centimeters (3 inches) higher than at either pole. The volume of water in this "slope" starts sea surface water moving "downhill," from the equator toward the poles.

Enormous volumes of water circulate as ocean currents. The force of major winds, Earth's rotation, and underwater mountains and trenches determine the directional movement of these currents. Surface currents circulate clockwise in the Northern Hemisphere and counterclockwise in the Southern Hemisphere (Figure 18.4).

Ocean currents affect climates. Coasts in the Pacific Northwest are cool and foggy in summer because the cold California current chills the air, so water condenses out as droplets. Boston and Baltimore are humid in summer because air masses pick up heat and moisture from the warm Gulf Stream, then deliver it to these cities.

*Take-Home Message* **What causes prevailing winds and ocean currents and how do they affect climate?**

- Longitudinal differences in the amount of solar radiation reaching Earth produce global air circulation patterns.

- Surface ocean currents, set in motion by latitudinal differences in solar radiation, are also affected by winds and by Earth's rotation.

- Collective effects of air masses, oceans, and landforms determine regional temperature and moisture levels.

# 18.3 Types of Land Ecosystems

Different climates support different types of plant life, which in turn support different kinds of animals. A **biome** is a large-scale ecosystem characterized by particular climate conditions and its main type of vegetation. Each type of biome can typically be found on more than one continent.

**Deserts** **Deserts** cover about one-fifth of Earth's land. They receive little rainfall (less than 30 centimeters, or 11 inches, per year). The most common desert plants include cactuses or succulents that store water in their tissues, and shrubs with deep roots that tap water far underground (Figure 18.5**A**). Many desert animals have physiological adaptations that reduce their water needs.

As noted earlier, deserts tend to form at 30° north and south latitude, where dry air descends. In most biomes, moisture in the air has an insulating effect, slowing temperature increases during the day and heat loss at night. Deserts have low humidity, so they can heat up and cool off fast.

**Grasslands and Chaparral** **Grasslands** form in the interior of continents between deserts and temperate forests. Shortgrass and tallgrass prairie are North America's main types of grasslands (Figure 18.5**B**). Summers are warm, and winters are cold. Annual rainfall of 25 to 100 centimeters (10–40 inches) keeps desert from forming, but is too little water to support forest. Constant trimming by grazing animals, along with periodic fires, also keeps trees and most shrubs from taking hold. Low-growing plants tolerate strong winds and intervals of drought.

We find dry shrublands or **chaparral** in South Africa, Mediterranean regions, and California, where winters are mild and rainy but summers are dry (Figure 18.5**C**). Chaparral shrubs are adapted to survive lightning-ignited fires. Seeds of some species germinate only after exposure to heat or smoke. This ensures that they sprout when seedlings face little competition from established plants.

**biome** Type of ecosystem that can be characterized by its climate and dominant vegetation.

**chaparral** Biome where mild, rainy winters and hot, dry summers support shrubs adapted to periodic fires.

**desert** Biome where little rain falls, humidity is low, and the main plants store water in their tissues or tap into water sources deep underground.

**grasslands** Biome in the interior of continents, where grasses and other low-growing plants are adapted to warm summers, cold winters, periodic fires, and grazing animals.

**FIGURE 18.5** Examples of three low-moisture biomes in the United States. **A** The Sonoran Desert in Arizona. **B** Tallgrass prairie in Kansas. **C** Chaparral in California.

Deserts

Grassland, shrublands, and woodlands

Broadleaf forests

FIGURE 18.6 Broadleaf forests.
**A** Tropical rain forest in Southeast Asia.
**B** Temperate deciduous forest in New England.

**Tropical Rain Forests** There are a variety of forest biomes. For example, **tropical rain forests** are found in parts of Southeast Asia, Africa, and South America where temperatures are high and rain is plentiful throughout the year (Figure 18.6**A**). The broadleaf (angiosperm) trees that dominate this biome remain leafy year-round. Tropical rain forests have a complex, layered structure with many vines and epiphytes (plants that grow on another plant, but do not take nutrients from it). Animal species are similarly diverse and abundant. By some estimates, about half of all animal species live in tropical rain forests.

**Deciduous Broadleaf Forests** Deciduous broadleaf forests occur in regions where trees can only grow during part of the year. Such habitats are dominated by **deciduous trees** that shed all their leaves at once and become dormant during a season when conditions are not favorable. For example, the main plants in New England's **temperate deciduous forests** are maples and other trees that shed their leaves in the fall (Figure 18.6**B**). The trees then remain dormant during the winter when cold temperatures would slow photosynthesis and frozen soil would limit water uptake.

**Coniferous Forests** Conifers (evergreen gymnosperms with seed-bearing cones) are the main plants in coniferous forests (Figure 18.7). Conifer leaves are typically needle-shaped, with a thick cuticle and stomata below the leaf surface. These adaptations help conifers conserve water during drought or times when soil water is frozen. As a group, conifers tolerate poorer soils and drier habitats than broadleaf trees.

The most extensive land biome is the coniferous forest that sweeps across northern Asia, Europe, and North America (Figure 18.7). It is known as boreal forest, or **taiga**, which means "swamp forest" in Russian. Rain falls in the summer, and winters are long, cold, and dry. Conifers also dominate temperate lowlands along the Pacific coast from Alaska into northern California. These forests hold the world's tallest trees, Sitka spruce to the north and coast redwoods to the south. Pine forest covers about one-third of the southeastern United States. The pines survive periodic fires that kill most hardwood species. If fires are suppressed, hardwoods will replace the pines.

Coniferous forests

FIGURE 18.7 Coniferous forest.
Aerial view of Siberian taiga.

**Tundra** **Arctic tundra** forms between the polar ice cap and the belts of boreal forests in the Northern Hemisphere. Most is in northern Russia and Canada. It is Earth's youngest biome, having appeared about 10,000 years ago, when glaciers retreated at the end of the last ice age.

Arctic tundra is blanketed with snow for as long as nine months of the year. Annual snow and rain is usually less than 25 centimeters (10 inches). During a brief summer, plants grow fast under nearly continuous sunlight (Figure 18.8). Lichens and shallow-rooted, low-growing plants are a base for food webs. Many migratory birds nest here in summer, when the air is thick with insects.

Only the surface layer of tundra soil thaws during summer. Below that lies **permafrost**, a frozen layer that can be 500 meters (1,600 feet) thick in places. Permafrost acts as a barrier that prevents drainage, so the soil above it remains perpetually waterlogged. Cool, anaerobic conditions slow decay, so organic remains can build up. Organic matter in the permafrost makes the arctic tundra one of Earth's greatest stores of carbon.

**Alpine tundra** occurs at high altitudes around the world. At lofty elevations, where night temperatures usually fall below freezing, trees cannot grow. The soil is thin, nutrient-poor, and—unlike that of arctic tundra—fast draining, because there is no permafrost. The growing season is short and, even in summer, patches of snow persist. Strong winds whip the vegetation. Lichens, mosses, grasses, and small-leafed shrubs that form ground-hugging cushions and mats dominate the community.

Arctic tundra

**FIGURE 18.8** Arctic tundra. Soil just below the surface remains frozen even during the summer.

## Take-Home Message   What are the major biomes?

- Low rainfall produces deserts at latitudes between 30° north and south. Latitudes with somewhat higher rainfall are covered by grasslands or chaparral.

- At the equator, high rainfall and temperature support tropical rain forests with broadleaf trees that remain green year-round. Deciduous broadleaf trees are adapted to regions that support trees, but cannot sustain year-round growth.

- Forests of hardy conifers dominate high latitudes in the Northern Hemisphere, as well as other regions where drought, poor soil, or periodic fires prevent broadleaf trees from taking hold.

- The most northerly and youngest biome is arctic tundra, where low plants are adapted to a short growing season and soil with a layer of permafrost. Alpine tundra is low-growing plants that live at high altitudes.

# 18.4 Types of Aquatic Ecosystems

We can distinguish between types of aquatic ecosystems, just as we do biomes on land. Temperature, salinity, rate of water movement, and depth influence the composition of aquatic communities.

**Freshwater Ecosystems**   A lake is a body of standing fresh water. All but the shallowest lakes have zones that differ in their physical characteristics and species composition. Near shore, where sunlight penetrates all the way to the lake bottom, rooted aquatic plants and algae that attach to the bottom are primary producers. A lake's open waters include an upper well-lit zone and, if a lake is deep or cloudy, a zone where light does not penetrate. Producers in the well-lit water include photosynthetic protists and bacteria. In the deeper dark zone, consumers feed on organic debris that drifts down from above.

**alpine tundra**  High-altitude biome dominated by low plants.

**arctic tundra**  Northernmost biome dominated by low plants that grow over a layer of permafrost.

**deciduous tree**  A tree that drops all its leaves annually just before a season that does not favor growth.

**permafrost**  Layer of permanently frozen soil in the Arctic.

**taiga**  Extensive northern biome dominated by conifers. Also called boreal forest.

**temperate deciduous forest**  Biome dominated by trees that drop all their leaves and go dormant during a cold winter.

**tropical rain forest**  Species-rich tropical biome in which continual warmth and rainfall allows the dominant broadleaf trees to grow all year.

Streams are flowing-water ecosystems. They typically originate from runoff or melting snow or ice. As they flow downslope, they grow and merge to form rivers. Properties of a stream or river vary along its length. The type of rocks a stream flows over can affect its solute concentration, as when limestone rocks dissolve and add calcium to the water. Shallow water that flows rapidly over rocks mixes with air and holds more oxygen than slower-moving, deeper water. Also, cold water holds more oxygen than warm water. As a result, different parts of a stream or river support species with different oxygen needs. For example, rainbow trout can only live in cool, well-oxygenated water.

**Marine Ecosystems** An **estuary** is a mostly enclosed coastal region where seawater mixes with nutrient-rich fresh water from rivers and streams. Water inflow continually replenishes nutrients, so estuaries have a high primary productivity. Estuaries serve as marine nurseries for many invertebrates and fishes. Migratory ducks and geese often use them as rest stops. Estuaries need a constant inflow of unpolluted, fresh water to remain healthy, so they are threatened by the diversion of fresh water for human uses and contamination by pollutants.

Along ocean shores, organisms are adapted to the mechanical force of the waves and to tidal changes. Many species are underwater during high tide, but are exposed to the air when the tide is low. Along rocky shores, where waves prevent detritus from piling up, algae that cling to rocks are the producers in grazing food chains. In contrast, waves continually rearrange loose sediments along sandy shores, and make it difficult for algae to take hold. Here, detrital food chains start with organic debris from land or offshore.

Warm, shallow, well-lit tropical seas hold **coral reefs**, formations made primarily of calcium carbonate secreted by generations of corals, which are invertebrate animals. Like tropical rain forests, tropical coral reefs are home to an extraordinary assortment of species (Figure 18.9**A**).

The main producers in a coral reef community are photosynthetic dinoflagellates that live inside the tissues of reef-building corals. These protists provide their coral hosts with sugars. If a coral becomes stressed by environmental change such as a shift in temperature, it expels its protistan symbionts in a response called **coral bleaching**. If conditions improve fast, the symbiont population in the coral can recover. But when adverse conditions persist, the symbionts will not be restored, and the coral will die, leaving only its bleached skeletons behind (Figure 18.9**B**).

The open waters of the ocean are the **pelagic province** (Figure 18.10**A**). These open waters include the water over continental shelves and the more extensive waters farther offshore. In the oceanic zone's upper, brightly lit waters, photosynthetic microorganisms such as algae and bacteria are the primary producers, and grazing food chains predominate. Depending on the region, some light may penetrate as far as 1,000 meters (more than a half mile) beneath the sea surface. Below that, organisms live in continual darkness, and organic material that drifts down from above is the basis of detrital food chains.

The **benthic province** is the ocean bottom, its rocks and sediments. Species richness is greatest on the edges of continents, or the continental shelves. The benthic province also includes some largely unexplored species-rich regions, including seamounts and at hydrothermal vents.

**FIGURE 18.9** Coral reefs. **A** In Fiji, a healthy reef teems with life. **B** A "bleached" reef near Australia.

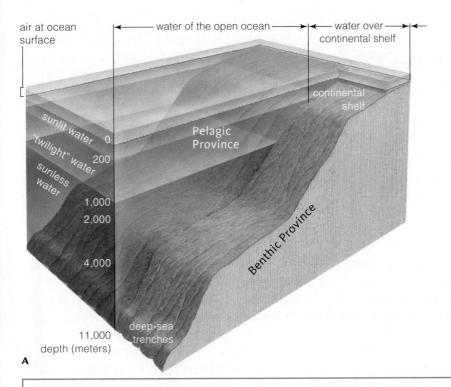

air at ocean surface

water of the open ocean

water over continental shelf

continental shelf

sunlit water 0

"twilight" water 200

sunless water

1,000

2,000

4,000

Pelagic Province

Benthic Province

11,000

deep-sea trenches

depth (meters)

A

B

C

**FIGURE 18.10 Animated!** The deep ocean. **A** Oceanic zones. Zone dimensions are not drawn to scale. **B** Computer model of three seamounts on the sea floor off the coast of Alaska. Patton Seamount, at the rear, stands 3.6 kilometers (about 2 miles) tall, with its peak about 240 meters (800 feet) below the sea surface. **C** Tube worms (annelids) and crabs of a hydrothermal vent community on the sea floor.

**Seamounts** are underwater mountains that stand 1,000 meters or more tall, but are still below the sea surface (Figure 18.10**B**). They attract large numbers of fishes and are home to many marine invertebrates. Like islands, seamounts often are home to species that evolved there and live nowhere else.

Superheated water that contains dissolved minerals spews out from the ocean floor at **hydrothermal vents**. When this heated, mineral-rich water mixes with cold seawater, the minerals settle out as extensive deposits. Some prokaryotes can get energy from these deposits. The prokaryotes serve as primary producers for food webs that include diverse invertebrates such as tube worms and crabs (Figure 18.10**C**). As explained in Section 13.2, one hypothesis holds that life originated near hydrothermal vents.

## Take-Home Message  **What factors shape aquatic ecosystems?**

■ Fast-flowing, cooler water holds more oxygen than warmer, slower-moving water, and the amount of available light decreases with the water's depth.

■ In well-lit upper waters, producers such as aquatic plants, algae, and photosynthetic microbes are the base for grazing food chains. On coral reefs, the main producers are photosynthetic protists that live inside the coral's tissues.

■ Detritus drifting down from above sustains most deep-water communities in lakes and oceans. However, hydrothermal vent communities on the ocean floor are sustained by energy that prokaryotes harvest from minerals.

**benthic province**  The ocean's rocks and sediments.

**coral bleaching**  Stress response in which a coral expels the photosynthetic protists in its tissues.

**coral reef**  In tropical sunlit seas, a formation composed of secretions of coral polyps that serves as home to many other species.

**estuary**  A highly productive ecosystem where nutrient-rich water from a river mixes with seawater.

**hydrothermal vent**  Place where hot, mineral-rich water streams out from an underwater opening in Earth's crust.

**pelagic province**  The ocean's open waters.

**seamount**  An undersea mountain.

**FIGURE 18.11** Living or extinct? Colorized photo of an ivory-billed woodpecker (*Campephilus principalis*). It is, or was, North America's largest woodpecker and a native of the southeastern states.

# Human Effects on the Biosphere

The rising size of the human population and its increasing industrialization have far-reaching effects on the biosphere. We begin by discussing how human activities affect individual species, then turn to activities with wider impacts.

**Increased Species Extinctions** Extinction, like speciation, is a natural process. Species arise and become extinct on an ongoing basis. The rate of extinction picks up dramatically during a mass extinction, when many kinds of organisms in many different habitats all become extinct in a relatively short period. We are currently in the midst of such an event. Unlike historical mass extinctions, this one cannot be blamed on some natural catastrophe such as an asteroid impact. Rather, this mass extinction is the outcome of the success of a single species—humans—and their effect on Earth.

Consider, for example, the ivory-billed woodpecker. This spectacular bird is native to swamp forests of the American Southeast (Figure 18.11). The species declined when these forests were cut for lumber. Until recently, the bird was thought to have become extinct in the 1940s. A possible sighting in Arkansas in 2004 led to an extensive hunt for evidence of the bird. By the end of 2007, this search had produced some blurry photos, snippets of video, and a few recordings of what may or may not be ivory-bill calls and knocks. Definitive proof that the bird still lives remains elusive.

If the ivory-billed woodpecker is still around, it is an **endangered species**, a species that faces extinction in all or part of its range. A **threatened species** is one that is likely to become endangered in the near future. Keep in mind that not all rare species are threatened or endangered. Some species have always been uncommon. If their numbers remain stable, they are not at risk of extinction.

Nearly all currently endangered or threatened species owe their precarious position to human actions. When European settlers first arrived in North America, they found billions of passenger pigeons. In the 1800s, commercial hunting caused a steep decline in the bird's numbers. The last wild passenger pigeon was shot in 1900. The last captive bird died in 1914.

We continue to overharvest species. The crash of the Atlantic codfish population (described in Section 16.4), is a recent example. It is a sad commentary on human nature that the rarer a species becomes, the higher the price it fetches on the black market. Globalization means that species can be sold to high bidders anywhere in the world. For example, rhino horn from endangered animals in Africa ends up as a traditional medicine in Asia and as knife handles in Yemen.

Each species requires a specific type of habitat, and any loss, degradation, or fragmentation of that habitat reduces population numbers. An **endemic species**, one that is confined to the limited area in which it evolved, is more likely to go extinct than a species with a more widespread distribution. For example, giant pandas are endemic to China's bamboo forests. As China's human population soared, bamboo was cut for building materials and to make room for farms. As the bamboo forests disappeared, so did pandas. Their numbers, which may once have been as high as 100,000, have fallen to 1,000 or so animals in the wild.

In the United States, habitat loss affects nearly all of the more than 700 species of threatened or endangered flowering plants. For example, widespread destruction of prairies and meadows threaten prairie fringed orchids (Figure 18.12**A**). Humans also degrade habitats in less direct ways. For example, Edwards Aquifer in Texas consists of water-filled, underground limestone formations that supply drinking water to the city of San Antonio. Excessive withdrawals of water from this aquifer, along with pollution of the water that recharges it, endanger species that live in the aquifer's depths. The Texas blind salamander (Figure 18.12**B**) is one of these endangered species.

Species introductions also pose a threat, because exotic species often outcompete native ones. For example, rats that reached islands by stowing away on ships attack and endanger many island species. As another example, European brown trout and eastern brook trout were introduced into California's mountain streams for sport fishing. Both exotic species threaten native golden trout.

A species most often becomes endangered because of number of simultaneous threats. Often, the decline or ~~loss~~ of one species endangers another. For example, running buffalo clover and the buffalo that grazed on it were ~~once~~ common in the Midwest. The plants thrived in the ~~open~~ woodlands that the buffalo favored. Here, the soil was ~~enr~~iched by buffalo droppings and periodically disturbed by ~~the~~ animals' hooves. Buffalo helped to disperse the clover's ~~seeds~~, which survive passage through digestive systems.

~~When~~ buffalo were hunted to near extinction, buffalo clover populations declined. Now listed as endangered, the clover is further threatened by conversion of its habitat to housing developments, competition from introduced plants, and attacks by introduced insects.

Endangered species listings have historically focused on vertebrates. We have just begun to consider threatened invertebrates and plants. Our impact on protists and fungi is mostly unknown, and the World Conservation Union's IUCN Red List of Threatened Species (Table 18.1) does not address prokaryotes.

| Table 18.1 | Global List of Threatened Species (2007)* | | |
|---|---|---|---|
| | Described Species | Evaluated for Threats | Found to Be Threatened |
| **Vertebrates** | | | |
| Mammals | 5,416 | 4,863 | 1,094 |
| Birds | 9,956 | 9,956 | 1,217 |
| Reptiles | 8,240 | 1,385 | 422 |
| Amphibians | 6,199 | 5,915 | 1,808 |
| Fishes | 30,000 | 3,119 | 1,201 |
| **Invertebrates** | | | |
| Insects | 950,000 | 1,255 | 623 |
| Mollusks | 81,000 | 2,212 | 978 |
| Crustaceans | 40,000 | 553 | 460 |
| Corals | 2,175 | 13 | 5 |
| Others | 130,200 | 83 | 42 |
| **Land Plants** | | | |
| Mosses | 15,000 | 92 | 79 |
| Ferns and allies | 13,025 | 211 | 139 |
| Gymnosperms | 980 | 909 | 321 |
| Angiosperms | 258,650 | 10,771 | 7,899 |
| **Protists** | | | |
| Green algae | 3,715 | 2 | 0 |
| Red algae | 5,956 | 58 | 9 |
| Brown algae | 2,849 | 15 | 6 |
| **Fungi** | | | |
| Lichens | 10,000 | 2 | 2 |
| Mushrooms | 16,000 | 1 | 1 |

\* IUCN–WCU Red List, available online at www.iucnredlist.org

**FIGURE 18.12** Species under threat. **A** Habitat destruction threatens the eastern prairie fringed orchid. **B** Aquifer depletion and pollution endanger Texas blind salamanders. Generations of life in a dark aquifer, where there is no selection against mutations that impair eye development, have reduced this species' eyes to tiny black spots.

**endangered species** A species that faces extinction in all or part of its range.

**endemic species** A species that evolved in one place and is found nowhere else.

**threatened species** A species likely to become endangered in the near future.

**Desertification** Some human activities can threaten entire ecosystems. For example, natural grasslands often are plowed under for farming or used to graze livestock. **Desertification**, a conversion of grasslands or woodlands to desertlike conditions, is one result. It begins when loss of plant cover allows wind to blow away topsoil, the nutrient-rich, upper soil layer.

Drought encourages desertification, which encourages drought. Normally, plant roots take up water, which then evaporates from leaves into the air. However, plants cannot thrive where topsoil has blown away. With fewer plants, less water enters the air and local humidity and rainfall decrease.

During the mid-1930s, large portions of prairie on the southern Great Plains were plowed under to plant crops. This plowing exposed the prairie topsoil to the force of the region's constant winds. Coupled with a drought, the result was an economic and ecological disaster. Winds lifted up more than a billion tons of topsoil as huge dust clouds, and the region came to be known as the Dust Bowl. A similar situation now exists in Africa, where the Sahara Desert is expanding south into the Sahel region. Overgrazing and poor farming practices in this region strip grasslands of their vegetation and allow winds to erode the soil. Winds carry the soil aloft and westward (Figure 18.13). African soil particles land as far away as the southern United States and the Caribbean.

**Deforestation** **Deforestation**, the removal of trees, threatens forest ecosystems. The amount of forested land is currently stable or increasing in North America, Europe, and China, but this increase is overshadowed by the staggering losses of tropical forests (Figure 18.14). Southeast Asia, Africa, and Latin America stretch across the tropical latitudes. Developing nations on these continents have the world's fastest-growing populations and high demands for food, fuel, and lumber. Of necessity, people turn to forests.

Cutting down forests puts forest species at risk of extinction. It also encourages flooding. When trees are cut down, more water flows into streams and rivers, raising the risk of downstream floods. In hilly areas, deforestation raises the risk of landslides because with no tree roots to keep the soil in place, waterlogged soil becomes more likely to slide.

Loss of tropical forests is not merely a regional concern. People in highly developed nations use most of the world's resources, including products from tropical forests. In addition, the disappearance of tropical forests could alter the global atmosphere. Trees take up and store carbon, and they release oxygen. Fewer forests means less carbon storage and less oxygen production. Also, burn-

**FIGURE 18.13** A symptom of desertification. Increasing amounts of dust blow from Africa's Sahara Desert into and across the Atlantic Ocean.

**acid rain** Rainfall contaminated by acidic pollutants.

**deforestation** Removal of all trees from a large tract of land.

**desertification** Conversion of grassland or woodlands to desertlike conditions.

**pollutant** A natural or man-made substance that is released into the environment in greater than natural amounts and that damages the health of organisms.

**FIGURE 18.14**
Deforestation. Aerial view (*left*) and ground view (*right*) of a region in Mato Grosso, Brazil, where a tropical forest is being cleared for pasture and industrial-scale soybean, sugarcane, and corn plantations.

50 km

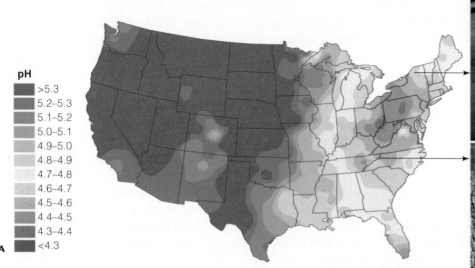

pH
- >5.3
- 5.2–5.3
- 5.1–5.2
- 5.0–5.1
- 4.9–5.0
- 4.8–4.9
- 4.7–4.8
- 4.6–4.7
- 4.5–4.6
- 4.4–4.5
- 4.3–4.4
- <4.3

A

B

C

ing enormous tracts of tropical forest to make way for agriculture releases carbon dioxide. Ironically, concern about greenhouse gases released by the burning of fossil fuels may be encouraging some rain forest destruction. Areas of rain forest in the Amazon and Indonesia are being cleared to make way for plantations that grow soybeans or palms. Oils from these plants are exported, mainly to Europe, where they are used to produce biodiesel fuel.

## Acid Rain

**Pollutants** can harm forests and other ecosystems. A pollutant is a natural or man-made substance released into soil, air, or water in greater than natural amounts. It disrupts the physiological processes of organisms that evolved in its absence, or that are adapted to lower levels of it.

For example, coal-burning power plants, smelters, and factories emit sulfur dioxides into the air. Vehicles, power plants that burn gas and oil, and nitrogen-rich fertilizers emit nitrogen oxides. In dry weather, airborne sulfur and nitrogen oxides coat dust particles and fall as dry acid deposition. In moist air, they form nitric acid vapor, sulfuric acid droplets, and sulfate and nitrate salts. Winds typically disperse these pollutants far from their source. They fall to Earth in rain and snow. We call this a wet acid deposition, or **acid rain**.

The pH of typical rainwater is about 5 (Section 2.5). Acid rain can be 10 to 100 times more acidic. In much of eastern North America, rain is now thirty to forty times more acidic than it was even a few decades ago (Figure 18.15**A**). Most aquatic organisms cannot tolerate a dramatic change in pH. As one result, acid rain has caused fish to vanish from more than 200 lakes in New York's Adirondack Mountains (Figure 18.15**B**).

Acid rain contributes to the decline of forests by burning the leaves of trees. It also changes the composition of the soil by raising the level of nitrates and removing other nutrients. Plants weaken or die as a result (Figure 18.15**C**).

## Other Sources of Water Pollution

In addition to acid rain, aquatic ecosystems receive an onslaught of other pollutants. Industrial chemicals, oil, fertilizers, animal wastes, sewage, excreted prescription drugs, and sediments flow into lakes, streams, rivers, and the sea. Some of these pollutants come from a point source, an easily identifiable source, such as a factory or a sewage treatment facility that discharges wastes into a river. Pollutants that

**FIGURE 18.15 Animated!** Acid rain.

**A** Average precipitation acidities in the United States in 2006. The lower the pH, the more acidic the rain.

**B** A biologist tests the pH of water in New York's Woods Lake. In 1979, the lake's pH was 4.8. Since then, experimental addition of calcite to soil around the lake has raised the pH to more than 6.

**C** Dying trees in Great Smoky Mountains National Park, where acid rain harms leaves and soil.

**Figure It Out:** Is rain more acidic on the East Coast or the West Coast of the United States?

Answer: The East Coast

# Two-thirds of plastic soft drink bottles and three-quarters of glass bottles are not recycled.

come from a point source are the easiest to control. Identify the source, and you can take action to halt the pollution.

Dealing with pollution from nonpoint sources is more challenging. Such pollution stems from widespread release of a pollutant. For example, oil from vehicles is a nonpoint source of water pollution. The oil drips from cars and trucks while they move along roads and are parked in parking lots. During rains, the accumulated oil washes from pavement into natural waterways or storm drains. In many places, water that flows into storm drains is discharged into a body of water without any sort of treatment. Halting nonpoint source pollution is difficult because it requires the cooperative action of many people.

Chemical pollutants such as oil, pesticides, or mercury cause harm by disrupting the metabolism of aquatic organisms. For example, the herbicide atrazine is widely used to control weeds. When atrazine gets into water, it disrupts the sexual development of amphibians, causing males to develop ovaries. We discuss the effects of atrazine and other endocrine-disrupting chemicals more in Chapter 25. Section 17.5 explained the process of **bioaccumulation**, in which mercury and some other toxins become increasingly concentrated as they move up through food chains.

**Eutrophication**, the nutrient enrichment of aquatic ecosystems, is another menace to aquatic life. Fertilizer runoff, sewage, and animal waste that enter water can encourage population explosions of photosynthetic protists. Such events are commonly called algal blooms. They are also known as red tides, because red dinoflagellates are often involved. Some protists involved in algal blooms make toxins that kill aquatic organisms. Even a bloom of nontoxic protists can deplete the water of oxygen, because after the protists die, aerobic bacteria that feed on their remains use up all the oxygen in the water.

Sediments in runoff from deforested areas, construction sites, and other places where soil is exposed can also damage aquatic organisms. Soil particles that wash into the water can clog gills and choke filter-feeders. In addition, suspended particles prevent light from penetrating the water, thus interfering with photosynthesis. Reef-building corals are especially vulnerable to damage from sediments. These corals filter food from the water and also rely on sugars produced by photosynthetic protists that live inside their tissues.

## The Trouble With Trash

Trash is a menace to water supplies and ocean life. Historically, humans buried unwanted material in the ground or dumped it out at sea. Trash was out of sight, and also out of mind. We now understand that chemicals seeping from buried trash can contaminate groundwater. Waste dumped into the sea disturbs marine ecosystems. For example, seabirds frequently eat floating bits of plastic or feed them to their chicks, with deadly results (Figure 18.16).

In 2006, the United States generated 251 million tons of garbage, which averages out to 2.1 kilograms (4.6 pounds) per person per day. By weight, about a third of that material was recycled, but there is plenty of room for improve-

**FIGURE 18.16 A** Recently deceased Laysan albatross chick, dissected to reveal the contents of its gut. **B** Scientists found more than 300 pieces of plastic inside the bird. One of the pieces had punctured its gut wall, resulting in the chick's death. The chick was fed this junk by its parents, who gathered floating plastic from the ocean surface, mistaking it for food.

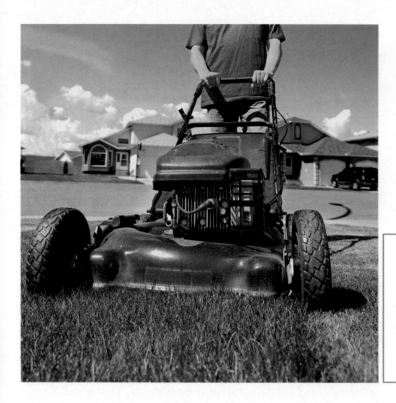

**FIGURE 18.17** Contributing to ground-level ozone pollution. Exhaust from gasoline-powered lawn mowers, chain saws, weed whackers, and other appliances contains pollutants that combine in the presence of sunlight to produce ozone. Postponing use of these appliances until evening helps keep ground-level ozone concentration low.

To find out the current status of ground-level ozone and particle pollution in your area, visit http://airnow.gov/.

ment. Two-thirds of plastic soft drink bottles and three-quarters of glass bottles are not recycled. Foam packaging from fast-food outlets, plastic shopping bags, and other material discarded as litter ends up in storm drains. From there it enters streams and rivers that can carry it to the sea. Seawater sampled near the mouth of the San Gabriel River in southern California had 128 times more plastic than plankton by weight. Once in the ocean, trash persists for a surprisingly long time. Components of a disposable diaper will last for more than 100 years, as will fishing line. A plastic bag will be around for more than 50 years, and a cigarette filter for more than 10.

**Air Quality** Just as sediments can clog the respiratory organs of aquatic organisms, airborne particles can harm the respiratory organs of air-breathers. Particles most dangerous to human health are smaller in diameter than a human hair. These particles are most likely to be inhaled all the way into the lungs.

Burning nearly anything produces particle pollution. Forest fires can cause a temporary rise in the amount of particles in the air. However, burning of fossil fuel and industrial processes sends a constant stream of particles skyward.

Release and burning of fossil fuels also causes an increase in the concentration of ozone ($O_3$) in the air near the ground. Ozone irritates the eyes and increases the effects of allergens on sensitive people. It also slows plant growth.

Ozone forms when nitrogen oxides and volatile organic compounds released by the burning or evaporation of fossil fuels are exposed to sunlight. Warm temperatures speed the reaction. Thus, ground-level ozone tends to vary daily (being higher during the daytime) and seasonally (being higher during the summer). You can help reduce ozone pollution by avoiding actions that put fossil fuels or their combustion products into the air at times that favor ozone production. On hot, sunny, still days, postpone filling your gas tank or using gasoline-powered appliances until the evening, when there is less sunlight to power the conversion of pollutants to ozone (Figure 18.17).

**bioaccumulation** A substance becomes more concentrated in organisms at increasingly higher levels of a food chain.

**eutrophication** Increase in nutrients in an aquatic ecosystem; may lead to oxygen depletion.

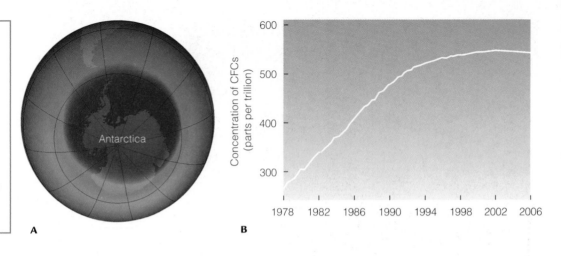

**FIGURE 18.18 Animated!**
Ozone and CFCs. **A** Ozone levels in September 2007, the Antarctic spring. *Purple* indicates the least ozone, with *blue, green,* and *yellow* indicating increasingly higher levels. Check current status of the ozone hole at NASA's web site: http://ozonewatch.gsfc.nasa.gov/.

**B** Concentration of CFCs high in the atmosphere. These pollutants encourage ozone destruction. A worldwide ban on CFCs successfully halted the rise.

A

B

**The Ozone Hole** Ozone is sometimes said to be "bad nearby, but good up high." You just learned why ozone is bad near the ground. The "good" ozone is high in Earth's atmosphere. Between 17 and 27 kilometers above sea level (10.5 and 17 miles), the ozone concentration is so great that scientists refer to this region as the **ozone layer**. The ozone layer benefits us by absorbing most of the ultraviolet (UV) radiation in incoming sunlight. UV radiation, remember, is a mutagen. It can damage DNA and cause mutations.

In the mid-1970s, scientists noticed that the ozone layer was thinning. Its thickness had always varied a bit with the season, but now there was steady decline from year to year. By the mid-1980s, the spring ozone thinning over Antarctica was so pronounced that people were referring to the low-ozone region as an "ozone hole" (Figure 18.18**A**).

Declining ozone quickly became an international concern. The ozone hole over the South Pole was a sign that the ozone layer was thinning worldwide. With a thinner ozone layer, people would be exposed to more UV radiation, the main cause of skin cancers. Higher UV levels also harm wildlife, which do not have the option of avoiding sunlight. In addition, exposure to higher-than-normal UV levels affects plants and other producers, slowing the rate of photosynthesis and the release of oxygen into the atmosphere.

Chlorofluorocarbons, or CFCs, are the main ozone destroyers. These odorless gases were once widely used as propellants in aerosol cans, as coolants, and in solvents and plastic foam. CFCs interact with ice crystals and UV light in the atmosphere. These reactions release chlorine radicals that degrade ozone. A single chlorine radical can break apart thousands of ozone molecules. Ozone thins the most at the poles because swirling winds concentrate CFCs in this region during dark, cold polar winters. In the spring, increasing daylight and the presence of ice clouds allow a surge in the formation of chlorine radicals from the highly concentrated CFCs.

In response to the potential threat posed by ozone thinning, countries worldwide agreed in 1987 to phase out the production of CFCs and other ozone-destroying chemicals. As a result of that agreement (the Montreal Protocol), the concentrations of CFCs in the atmosphere are no longer rising dramatically (Figure 18.18**B**). However, CFCs break down quite slowly, so scientists expect them to remain at a level that significantly impairs the ozone layer for several decades.

**A** Muir Glacier 1941

**B** Muir Glacier 2004

**C** Arctic perennial sea ice 1979

**D** Arctic perennial sea ice 2003

**FIGURE 18.19** Dramatic evidence of a warming world. **A** Muir Glacier in south-eastern Alaska in 1941. **B** By 2004, the ice in the foreground of the earlier photo had melted. **C,D** The extent of perennial sea ice in the Arctic in 1979 and in 2003. Decreases in the amount of glacial ice and sea ice are expected to accelerate the warming trend. Ice reflects sunlight, whereas the water and land exposed by melting ice absorbs light and then radiates the absorbed energy as heat.

**Global Climate Change** Like ozone depletion, climate change affects ecosystems worldwide. How is the climate changing? Most notably, average temperatures are getting hotter. The effects of the temperature rise are illustrated by recent changes in the extent of glaciers and sea ice (Figure 18.19). However, global warming is just one aspect of **global climate change**. As you learned earlier in this chapter, the temperature of the land and seas affects evaporation, winds, and currents. As a result, many weather patterns are expected to change as temperature rises. For example, warmer temperatures are correlated with extremes in rainfall patterns, with periods of drought interrupted by unusually heavy rains. Also, warmer seas tend to increase the intensity of hurricanes.

**global climate change** Global warming and other changes in the current climate and weather patterns.

**ozone layer** Atmospheric layer with a high concentration of ozone that prevents much ultraviolet radiation from reaching Earth's surface.

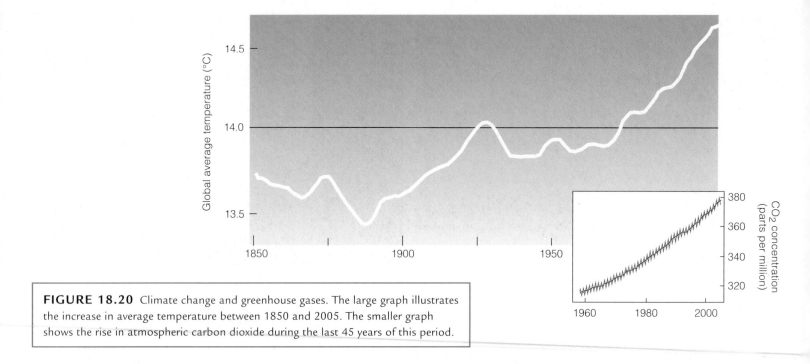

**FIGURE 18.20** Climate change and greenhouse gases. The large graph illustrates the increase in average temperature between 1850 and 2005. The smaller graph shows the rise in atmospheric carbon dioxide during the last 45 years of this period.

**Causes of Climate Change** Earth's climate has varied greatly over its long history. There have been ice ages, when much of the planet was covered by glaciers, and unusually hot periods, when tropical plants and coral reefs thrived at what are now cool latitudes. Scientists can correlate past large-scale temperature changes with shifts in Earth's orbit, which varies in a regular fashion over 100,000 years, and Earth's tilt, which varies over 40,000 years. Changes in solar output and volcanic eruptions also affect Earth's temperature. However, most scientists do not see evidence that these natural factors have a major role in the rise in temperature that we are currently experiencing.

In 2007, the Intergovernmental Panel on Climate Change reviewed the results of many scientific studies related to climate change. The panel, which includes hundreds of scientists from all over the world, concluded that the warming in recent decades is very likely due to a human-induced increase in atmospheric greenhouse gases.

Unlike other possible factors, the rise in greenhouse gases does correlate with the rise in temperature. Figure 18.20 shows the average global temperature between 1850 and 2005, and the rise in atmospheric carbon dioxide during the latter part of this interval. As Section 17.6 explained, greenhouse gases such as carbon dioxide act like insulation. They keep heat near Earth's surface from escaping into space. Burning of fossil fuels is the main source of the excess carbon dioxide entering the atmosphere (Figure 18.21).

**Effects of Climate Change** As temperatures rise, so does the sea level. Meltwater from glaciers and sea ice runs into the ocean, increasing its volume. In addition, water expands as it warms. A rising sea level puts coastal communities at risk for increased erosion and flooding. It also allows salt water to seep into aquifers that supply drinking water to coastal regions. Global sea level rose 10 to 20 centimeters (4 to 8 inches) during the twentieth century. Scientists predict that if the current warming trend continues, sea level could rise as much as 0.6 meter (2 feet) over the next century. That may not sound like much of a change, but in the United States it would put about 13,000 square kilometers (5,000 square miles) of land underwater at high tide.

The warming climate is already having effects on biological systems. Temperature changes are important cues for many temperate-zone species, and warming has been more pronounced at temperate and polar latitudes than at the equator. Warmer-than-normal springs are causing deciduous trees to put leaves out earlier, and spring-blooming flowers to flower earlier. Animal migration times and breeding seasons are also shifting. Species arrays in biological communities are changing as warmer temperatures allow some species to move to higher latitudes or elevations. Of course, not all species can move, and warmer temperatures will certainly drive some of them to extinction. For example, warming of tropical waters is already stressing reef-building corals and increasing the frequency of coral bleaching events.

Reducing levels of greenhouse gases will be a challenge. Fossil fuels are in more widespread use than CFCs ever were. Still, efforts are under way to increase the efficiency of processes that require fossil fuels, shift to alternative energy sources such as solar and wind power, and develop innovative ways to store excess carbon dioxide.

**FIGURE 18.21** Fueling global climate change. Burning of fossil fuels is the greatest source of excess carbon dioxide by far.

## Take-Home Message   How do human activities affect the biosphere?

- Humans are increasing the rate of species extinctions by degrading, destroying, and fragmenting natural habitats, overharvesting species, and introducing exotic species.

- Human activities turn grasslands into deserts, strip woodlands of trees, and generate pollutants and trash that kill animals and damage ecosystems.

- Some pollutants have global effects, as when CFCs cause thinning of the ozone layer, and rising levels of greenhouse gases bring about climate change.

# Maintaining Biodiversity

**The Value of Biodiversity**   Every nation enjoys several forms of wealth: material wealth, cultural wealth, and biological wealth, or biodiversity. We measure a region's **biodiversity** at three levels: the genetic diversity within its species, its species diversity, and its ecosystem diversity.

Why should we protect biodiversity? From a purely selfish standpoint, doing so is an investment in our future. Healthy ecosystems are essential to the survival of our own species. Other organisms produce the oxygen we breathe and the food we eat. They also remove waste carbon dioxide from the air and decompose and detoxify other wastes. Plants take up rain and hold soil in place, preventing erosion and reducing the risk of flooding.

Compounds discovered in wild species often serve as medicines. Two widely used chemotherapy drugs, vincristine and vinblastine, were extracted from the rosy periwinkle, a low-growing plant native to Madagascar's rain forests. Cone snails that live in tropical seas are the source of a highly potent pain reliever.

Wild relatives of crop plants are reservoirs of genetic diversity that plant breeders can draw on to protect and improve crops. Wild plants often have genes that make them more resistant to disease or adverse conditions than their domesticated relatives. Plant breeders can use traditional cross-breeding methods or biotechnology to introduce genes from wild species into domesticated ones, thus creating improved varieties.

**biodiversity** Of a region, the genetic diversity within its species, variety of species, and variety of ecosystems.

# The extinction of a species removes its unique collection of traits from the world of life forever.

A decline in biodiversity warns us that the natural support system we depend on is in trouble. **Indicator species**, species that are particularly sensitive to environmental change, can be monitored as indicators of environmental health. For example, a decline in lichens tells us that air quality is deteriorating. The loss of mayflies from a stream tells us that the quality of water in a stream is declining.

In addition, there are ethical reasons to preserve biodiversity. As we have emphasized many times, all living species are the result of an ongoing evolutionary process that stretches back billions of years. Each species has a unique combination of traits. The extinction of a species removes its unique collection of traits from the world of life forever.

**Conservation Biology** Biodiversity is currently in decline at all three levels and in all regions. **Conservation biology** addresses these declines. The goals of this relatively new field of biology are to survey the range of biodiversity and find ways to maintain and use biodiversity in a manner that benefits human populations. The aim is to conserve as much biodiversity as possible by encouraging people to value it and use it in ways that do not destroy it.

With so many species and ecosystems at risk, conservation biologists are often forced to make difficult choices about which should be targeted for protection first. The biologists are working to identify the so-called **hot spots**, places that are richest in endemic species and under the greatest threat. Once identified, hot spots can take priority in worldwide conservation efforts. The goal of prioritizing is to save representative examples of all of Earth's existing biomes. By focusing on hot spots, rather than on individual species, scientists hope to maintain ecosystem processes that naturally sustain biological diversity.

Conservation scientists of the World Wildlife Fund have defined 867 distinctive land ecoregions that are considered the top priority for conservation efforts. Each has a large number of endemic species and is under threat. The Klamath-Siskiyou forest in southwestern Oregon and northwestern California is one hot spot. This forest is home to many rare conifers. Two endangered birds, the northern spotted owl and the marbled murrelet, nest in old-growth portions of the forest. Endangered coho salmon breed in streams that run through it. Logging is the main threat to this region, but a newly introduced pathogen that affects conifers is another concern.

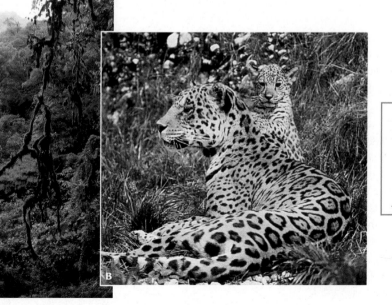

**FIGURE 18.22** Protecting a biodiversity hotspot. **A** Costa Rica's Monteverde Cloud Forest Reserve is a protected area that is home to many endangered species, including jaguars **B**.

**FIGURE 18.23** Ecological restoration. **A** Marsh restoration project in Louisiana's Sabine National Wildlife Refuge. In places where marshland has become open water, sediments are barged in and marsh grasses are planted on them. The marsh shelters migratory waterbirds during the winter, and is a nesting ground for roseate spoonbills **B** in summer.

Protecting biological diversity is often a tricky proposition. Even in developed countries, people often oppose environmental protections because they fear such measures will have adverse economic consequences. However, taking care of the environment can make good economic sense. With a bit of planning, people can both preserve and profit from their biological wealth.

Worldwide, many ecologically important regions are now protected and are providing benefits to local people. For example, during the 1970s, George Powell was studying birds in the Monteverde Cloud Forest in Costa Rica. This forest was rapidly being cleared and Powell got the idea to buy part of it as a nature sanctuary. His efforts inspired individuals and conservation groups to donate funds, and much of the forest is now protected as a private nature reserve (Figure 18.22). The reserve's plants and animals include more than 100 mammal species, 400 bird species, and 120 species of amphibians and reptiles. The reserve is one of the few habitats left for the jaguar, ocelot, puma, and their relatives. More than 50,000 tourists now visit the Monteverde Cloud Forest Reserve each year. A tourism industry centered on this reserve provides much-needed employment to local people.

**Ecological Restoration** Sometimes, an ecosystem is already damaged or there is so little of it left that conservation alone is not enough. **Ecological restoration** is work designed to bring about the renewal of a natural ecosystem that has been degraded or destroyed, fully or in part.

For example, more than 40 percent of the coastal wetlands in the United States are in Louisiana. These marshes, known locally as bayous, are an ecological and economic treasure. Millions of migratory birds overwinter in Louisiana's bayous and billions of dollars' worth of fish, shrimp, and shellfish are harvested from them. Despite their importance, the marshes are in trouble. Dams and levees built upstream of the marshes keep back sediments that would normally replenish sediments lost to the sea. Channels cut through the marshes for oil exploration and production have encouraged erosion, and the rising sea level threatens to flood the existing plants. Since the 1940s, Louisiana has lost an area of marshland the size of Rhode Island. Restoration efforts now under way aim to reverse some of those losses (Figure 18.23).

**conservation biology** Field of applied biology that surveys biodiversity and seeks ways to maintain and use it.

**ecological restoration** Actively altering an area in an effort to restore or create a functional ecosystem.

**hot spots** Threatened regions with great biodiversity that are considered a high priority for conservation efforts.

**indicator species** A species that is particularly sensitive to environmental changes and can be monitored to assess whether an ecosystem is threatened.

FIGURE 18.24 Resource extraction. Bingham copper mine near Salt Lake City, Utah. The mine is 4 kilometers (2.5 miles) wide and 1,200 meters (0.75 miles) deep.

**Living Sustainably** Ultimately, the health of our planet depends on our ability to recognize that the principles of energy flow and of resource limitation, which govern the survival of all systems of life, do not change. We must take note of these principles and find a way to live within our limits. The goal is **sustainable development**, meeting the needs of the present generation without reducing the ability of future generations to meet their own needs.

Promoting sustainability begins with recognizing the environmental consequences of our own life-style. People in industrial nations use enormous quantities of resources, and the extraction and delivery of these resources has negative effects on biodiversity. In the United States, the size of the average family has declined since the 1950s, while the size of the average home has doubled. All the materials used to build and furnish those larger homes come from the environment. For example, an average new home contains about 500 pounds of copper in its wiring and plumbing. Where does copper come from? Like most other mineral elements used in manufacturing, most of it is mined from the ground (Figure 18.24). Most mines generate pollution and are ecological dead zones.

Nonrenewable mineral resources are also used in electronic devices such as phones, computers, televisions, and MP3 players. Constantly trading up to the newest device may be good for the ego and the economy, but it is bad for the environment. Reducing consumption by fixing existing products promotes sustainability, as does recycling. Obtaining nonrenewable materials by recycling reduces the need for extraction of those resources from the environment and helps keep pollutants out of ecosystems.

Reducing your energy use is another way to promote sustainability. Fossil fuels such as petroleum, natural gas, and coal supply most of the energy used by developed countries. You already know that use of these nonrenewable fuels contributes to global warming and acid rain. In addition, extraction and transportation of these fuels have negative impacts. Oil harms many species when it leaks from pipelines or from ships. Renewable energy sources do not produce

**sustainable development** Using resources to meet current human needs in a way that takes into account the needs of future generations.

greenhouse gases, but they have their own drawbacks. For example, dams in rivers of the Pacific Northwest generate renewable hydroelectric power, but they also prevent endangered salmon from returning to streams above the dam to breed. Similarly, wind turbines can harm birds and bats. Panels used to collect solar energy are made using nonrenewable mineral resources, and manufacturing the panels generates pollutants.

In short, all commercially produced energy has some kind of negative environmental impact, so the best way to minimize that impact is to use less energy. Shop for energy-efficient appliances, use fluorescent bulbs instead of incandescent ones, and do not leave lights on in empty rooms. Walking, bicycling, and using public transportation are energy-efficient alternatives to driving. Shopping locally and purchasing locally produced goods also saves energy.

If you want to make a difference, learn about the threats to ecosystems in your own area. Are species threatened? If so, what are the threats? How can you help reduce those threats? Support efforts to preserve and restore local biodiversity. Many ecological restoration projects are supervised by trained biologists but carried out primarily through the efforts of volunteers (Figure 18.25).

Keep in mind that unthinking actions of billions of individuals are the greatest threat to biodiversity. Each of us may have little impact on our own, but our collective behavior, for good or for bad, will determine the future of the planet.

**FIGURE 18.25** Volunteers restoring the Little Salmon River in Idaho so that salmon can migrate upstream to their breeding grounds.

## Take-Home Message  What is biodiversity and how can we sustain it?

- Biodiversity is the genetic diversity of individuals of a species, the variety of species, and the variety of ecosystems. Worldwide, biodiversity is declining at all of these levels.

- Conservation biologists are working to identify threatened regions with high biodiversity and prioritize which receive protection.

- Ecological restoration is the process of re-creating or renewing a diverse natural ecosystem that has been destroyed or degraded.

- Individuals can help maintain biodiversity by using resources in a sustainable fashion.

# 18.7
# Impacts/Issues Revisited:
# A Long Reach

The Arctic is not a separate continent like Antarctica, but rather a region that encompasses the northernmost parts of several continents. Eight countries, including the United States, Canada, and Russia, control parts of the Arctic and have rights to its extensive oil, gas, and mineral deposits. Until recently, ice sheets that covered the Arctic Ocean made it difficult for ships to move to and from the Arctic land mass, but those sheets are breaking up as a result of global climate change. At the same time, ice that covered the Arctic land mass is melting. These changes will make it easier for people to remove minerals and fossil fuels from the Arctic. With the world supply of fuel and minerals dwindling, pressure to exploit Arctic resources is rising. However, conservationists warn that extracting these resources will harm Arctic species such as the polar bear that are already threatened by global climate change.

**How Would**
**YOU**
**☑ Vote ?**

The Arctic has extensive deposits of minerals and fossil fuel, but tapping into these resources might pose a risk to species already threatened by global climate change. Should the United States exploit its share of the Arctic resources? **See CengageNow for details, then vote online (cengagenow.com).**

# Summary

**Section 18.1** Humans and the chemical pollutants that their activities produce have reached even remote parts of the biosphere.

**Section 18.2** Climate refers to average weather conditions over time. Variations in climate depend largely upon differences in the amount of solar radiation reaching different parts of the Earth. The closer a region is to the equator, the more solar energy it receives. Warming of air at the equator is the start of global patterns of air circulation and ocean currents.

CENGAGENOW™ Learn how sunlight energy drives patterns of air circulation and observe major ocean currents with the animation on CengageNow.

**Section 18.3** Biomes are categories of major ecosystems on land. They are maintained largely by regional variations in climate and are described mainly in terms of their dominant plant life.

Deserts occur at latitudes about 30° north and south, where dry air descends and annual rainfall is sparse. Grasslands form at midlatitudes in the interior of continents. Fire helps maintain grasslands. Chaparral, a biome dominated by shrubby plants, takes hold in places with cool, wet winters and hot, dry summers. Like grasses, chaparral plants are adapted to periodic fires.

Near the equator, high rainfall and mild temperatures support tropical rain forests dominated by trees that remain leafy and active all year. Deciduous broadleaf forests grow in temperate regions with warm summers and cold winters. The trees lose their leaves and become dormant during the winter.

Conifers tend to be more resistant to dryness and cold than broadleaf trees. Taiga, a biome dominated by conifers, extends across high latitudes where a cold, dry season alternates with a cool, rainy season. Coniferous forests also occur in other regions.

Tundra forms at high latitudes and high altitudes. Arctic tundra is the youngest biome and lies over permafrost.

CENGAGENOW™ Explore the distribution of Earth's biomes with the interaction on CengageNow.

**Section 18.4** Aquatic ecosystems have gradients of sunlight penetration, water temperature, salinity, and dissolved gases. Lakes are standing bodies of water. Different communities of organisms live at different depths and distances from the shore.

Streams and rivers are flowing bodies of water. Physical characteristics of a stream or river that vary along its length influence the types of organisms that live in it. A semi-enclosed area where nutrient-rich water from a river mixes with seawater is an estuary, a highly productive habitat. Seashores may be rocky or sandy. Grazing food chains based on algae form on rocky shores. Detrital food chains dominate sandy shores.

Coral reefs are species-rich ecosystems that form in warm, well-lit tropical waters. The main producers on reefs are photosynthetic protists that live inside the coral's tissues.

The open ocean's upper waters hold photosynthetic organisms that form the basis for grazing food chains. Deeper water communities usually subsist on material that drifts down from above. However, prokaryotes that can strip energy from minerals serve as the producers at hydrothermal vent ecosystems.

CENGAGENOW™ Use the animation on CengageNow to learn about the oceanic zones.

**Section 18.5** Humans are increasing the rate of species extinctions by overharvesting species, degrading and destroying habitat, and introducing exotic species.

Human activities can also threaten entire ecosystems, as when poor agricultural practices turn grasslands or woodlands into desert. Deforestation and pollutants such as those that cause acid rain threaten forest ecosystems. Acid rain also threatens freshwater ecosystems. Trash that gets into fresh water can make its way into the oceans, where it degrades marine ecosystems.

Ozone is a pollutant near the ground, but depletion of the ozone layer is a global threat caused by use of chemicals called CFCs. Global agreement to phase out CFC use lessens this threat. Climate change caused by rising concentrations of greenhouse gases is another global threat.

CENGAGENOW™ Learn how acid rain affects forests and how CFCs destroy ozone with the animation on CengageNow.

**Section 18.6** Biodiversity includes the diversity of genes, species, and ecosystems. All three levels of biodiversity are threatened. A decrease in biodiversity can harm humans. We rely on ecosystems to produce oxygen and decompose waste. We also benefit from many compounds produced by wild species, and by tapping their genetic diversity to enhance our crops.

Conservation biologists document the extent of biodiversity and look for ways to preserve it, while benefiting humans. They give priority to hot spots, areas with high biodiversity that are most threatened.

Ecological restoration is the work of actively renewing an ecosystem that has been damaged or destroyed.

Ordinary individuals can help maintain biodiversity and ensure that resources remain for future generations by cutting their consumption, reusing and recycling materials, and reducing energy use.

## Self-Quiz     Answers in Appendix I

1. The most solar radiation reaches the ground at _____ .
   a. the equator            c. midlatitudes
   b. the North Pole         d. the South Pole

2. When air is heated, it _____ and can hold _____ water.
   a. sinks, less            c. rises, less
   b. sinks, more            d. rises, more

3. In what direction do ocean currents circulate water in the Northern Hemisphere?
   a. clockwise                        b. counterclockwise

4. Air circulation patterns cause dry air to descend and deserts to form at _____ degrees north and south latitude.

5. Plants in _____ are adapted to periodic fires.
   a. deserts                        c. arctic tundra
   b. taiga                          d. chaparral

6. Permafrost underlies _____ .
   a. grasslands                     c. temperate deciduous forests
   b. arctic tundra                  d. coniferous forests

7. The taiga is a broad northern biome dominated by _____ .
   a. conifers                       c. grasses
   b. mosses and lichens             d. deciduous broadleaf trees

8. Prokaryotes that can obtain energy from minerals are the main producers at _____ .
   a. hydrothermal vents             c. coral reefs
   b. estuaries                      d. sandy shores

9. Which would hold more oxygen?
   a. a fast-moving, cool stream   b. a warm pond

10. Match the terms with their most suitable description.
   _____ tundra          a. freshwater and seawater mix
   _____ chaparral       b. low humidity, and little rainfall
   _____ desert          c. North American grassland
   _____ prairie         d. fire-adapted shrubs
   _____ estuary         e. low-growing plants at high
   _____ taiga              latitudes or high elevations
   _____ tropical rain   f. northern coniferous forest
          forest          g. broadleaf trees are active all year

11. An _____ species has population levels so low it is at great risk of extinction in the near future.
   a. endemic                        c. indicator
   b. endangered                     d. exotic

12. An _____ species can be monitored to gauge the health of its environment.
   a. endemic                        c. indicator
   b. endangered                     d. exotic

13. The 1930s environmental disaster known as the Dust Bowl is an example of _____ .
   a. deforestation                  c. ecological restoration
   b. desertification                d. species extinction

14. The main threat to the ozone layer is _____ .
   a. use of CFCs                    c. burning of fossil fuels
   b. acid rain                      d. deforestation

15. Acid rain _____ .
   a. harms aquatic ecosystems   c. is a type of pollution
   b. kills trees                    d. all of the above

Additional questions are available on CENGAGENOW™

# Critical Thinking

1. Conifers have evergreen leaves and maintain a higher rate of photosynthesis than broadleaf trees at low temperatures. Conifers also are less likely to get flow-stopping bubbles in their tissues during spring thaws. How do these traits help them survive in taiga?

## Digging Into Data

### Arctic PCB Pollution

Winds carry chemical contaminants produced and released at temperate latitudes to the Arctic, where the chemicals enter food webs. By the process of bioaccumulation (Section 17.5), top carnivores in arctic food webs, including polar bears and people, end up with high concentrations of these chemicals in their body. Arctic people who eat a lot of local wildlife tend to have unusually high levels of polychlorinated biphenyls, or PCBs. The Arctic Monitoring and Assessment Programme studies the effects of these industrial chemicals on the health and reproduction of Arctic people. Figure 18.26 shows the average PCB levels for women in native populations in the Russian Arctic and the sex ratios at birth for each PCB level.

1. Which sex was more common in offspring of women with less than 1 microgram per milliliter of PCB in serum?

2. At what PCB concentrations were women more likely to have daughters?

3. In some villages in Greenland, nearly all recent newborns are female. Would you expect PCB levels in those villages to be above or under 4 micrograms per milliliter?

**FIGURE 18.26** Effect of maternal PCB concentration on sex ratio of newborns in indigenous populations in the Russian Arctic. *Blue* bars indicate the relative number of males born per one female (*pink* bars).

2. In one seaside community in New Jersey, the U.S. Fish and Wildlife Service suggested trapping and removing feral cats (domestic cats that live in the wild). The goal was to protect some endangered wild birds (plovers) that nested on the town's beaches. Many residents were angered by the proposal, arguing that the cats have as much right to be there as the birds. Do you agree? Why or why not?

3. Burning fossil fuel puts excess carbon dioxide into the atmosphere, but deforestation and desertification also affect carbon dioxide concentration. Explain why a global decrease in the amount of vegetation is contributing to the rise in carbon dioxide.

# 19 Animal Tissues and Organs

# Summary

**Section 19.1** Stem cells can divide to form more stem cells or differentiate to become specialized cells. All body parts develop from stem cells present in the embryo. Use of embryonic stem cells or of adult stem cells made to behave like embryonic ones could one day help treat diseases and disorders.

mitosis → differentiation → or

**Section 19.2** Animal bodies are structurally and functionally organized on several levels. A tissue is a group of cells and intercellular substances that perform a common task. Tissues make  up organs, which interact as organ systems. Activities at all levels contribute to homeostasis, the process of maintaining conditions inside the body within tolerable limits.

Animal structure and function have a genetic basis and are shaped by natural selection. However, because evolution modifies existing structures, body parts often are less than optimal for a task.

**Section 19.3** Most animals are constructed of four types of tissue.

 Epithelial tissues cover external body surfaces and line internal cavities and tubes. Epithelium has one free surface exposed to some body fluid or the environment. Gland cells and glands are derived from epithelial tissue.

 Connective tissues bind, support, protect, and insulate other tissues. Soft connective tissues have different proportions and arrangements of protein fibers, fibroblasts, and other cells in an extracellular matrix. Specialized connective tissues include cartilage, bone tissue, adipose tissue, and blood.

 Muscle tissues contract (shorten) when stimulated. They help move the body or parts of it. The three types of muscle tissue are skeletal muscle, smooth muscle, and cardiac muscle.

Neurons are communication lines of nervous tissue. They relay signals along their plasma membrane and send and receive chemical signals. Cells called neuroglia support neurons.

CENGAGENOW™ Use the interaction on CengageNow to investigate the different types of tissues.

**Section 19.4** An organ is a structural unit of different tissues combined in definite proportions and patterns that allow them to perform a common task. Skin is an organ composed of all four tissue types. It functions in protection, temperature control, detection of shifts in the environment, vitamin D production, and defense. An organ system consists of two or more organs interacting in tasks that keep individual cells as well as the whole body functioning.

CENGAGENOW™ Explore the structure of skin and survey the organ systems of the vertebrate body with animation on CengageNow.

**Section 19.5** Temperature regulation is an aspect of homeostasis. Human temperature regulation involves sensory receptors that detect changes, a brain that receives signals from receptors and coordinates responses, and muscles and glands that carry out responses. Temperature regulation involves negative feedback in which a change brings about a response that reverses the change.

CENGAGENOW™ Learn how a body regulates temperature with the animation on CengageNow.

## Self-Quiz     Answers in Appendix I

1. _____ tissues are sheetlike with one free surface.
   a. Epithelial            c. Nervous
   b. Connective            d. Muscle

2. A _____ connects epithelium to underlying connective tissue.
   a. gap junction          c. keratinocyte
   b. basement membrane     d. plasma membrane

3. Most animals have glands derived from _____ tissue.
   a. epithelial            c. muscle
   b. connective            d. nervous

4. Only _____ cells have cilia or microvilli at their surface.
   a. epithelial            c. muscle
   b. connective            d. nervous

5. The most abundant protein in the human body is _____ , made by fibroblasts.
   a. collagen              c. melanin
   b. keratin               d. hemoglobin

6. _____ is mostly plasma.
   a. Irregular connective tissue   c. Cartilage
   b. Blood                 d. Bone

7. Your body converts excess carbohydrates and proteins to fats, which accumulate in _____ .
   a. fibroblasts           c. adipose tissue cells
   b. neurons               d. melanocytes

8. _____ tissues are the body's most abundant and widely distributed tissue.
   a. Epithelial            c. Nervous
   b. Connective            d. Muscle

9. Cells of _____ can shorten (contract).
   a. epithelial tissue     c. muscle tissue
   b. connective tissue     d. nervous tissue

10. _____ muscle tissue has a striated appearance.
    a. Skeletal             c. Cardiac
    b. Smooth               d. a and c

11. _____ detects and integrates information about changes and controls responses to those changes.
    a. Epithelial tissue    c. Muscle tissue
    b. Connective tissue    d. Nervous tissue

# Digging Into Data

### Growing Skin To Heal Wounds

Diabetes is a disorder in which the blood sugar level is not properly controlled. Among other complications, this disorder reduces blood flow to the lower legs and feet. As a result, about 3 million diabetes patients have ulcers—open wounds that do not heal—on their feet. Each year, about 80,000 diabetics require amputations.

Fibroblasts and keratinocytes can be grown to produce a cultured skin substitute (Figure 19.13A). The cultured skin is placed over wounds to help them heal (Figure 19.13B). Figure 19.13C shows the results of a clinical experiment that tested the effect of the cultured skin product versus standard treatment for diabetic foot wounds. Patients were randomly assigned either to the experimental treatment group or to the control group. Their progress was monitored for 12 weeks.

1. What percentage of wounds had healed at 8 weeks when treated the standard way? When treated with cultured skin?

2. What percentage of wounds had healed at 12 weeks when treated the standard way? When treated with cultured skin?

3. How early was the healing difference between the control and treatment groups obvious?

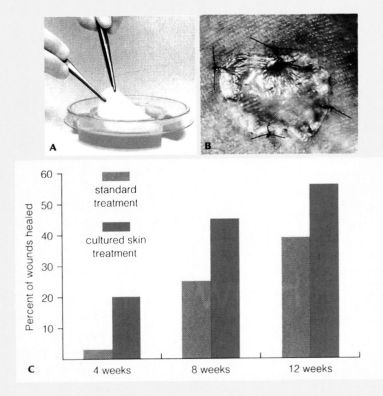

FIGURE 19.13 Cultured skin. **A** Cultured skin ready for use and **B** in place over a wound. **C** Results of a study comparing standard treatment for diabetic foot ulcers to use of a cultured cell product. Bars show the percentage of foot ulcers that had completely healed.

---

12. Thin cytoplasmic projections from cells called _____ carry signals between your spinal cord and your toes.

13. The functions of skin include _____ .
   a. defense against pathogens
   c. production of vitamin D
   b. helping to cool the body
   d. all of the above

14. When the level of sugar in your blood falls too low, your body senses this decline and converts glycogen to sugar, putting more sugar into your blood. This is an example of _____ .
   a. differentiation    c. homeostasis
   b. negative feedback    d. b and c

15. Match the terms with the most suitable description.
   _____ exocrine gland    a. outermost skin layer
   _____ endocrine gland    b. secretes through duct
   _____ epidermis    c. in heart only
   _____ cardiac muscle    d. support in ears and nose
   _____ cartilage    e. contracts, not striated
   _____ smooth muscle    f. darkens skin
   _____ blood    g. plasma, platelets, and cells
   _____ melanin    h. ductless hormone secretor

Additional questions are available on CENGAGENOW

# Critical Thinking

1. Leukemia is a cancer in which the body makes too many white blood cells. Affected people are sometimes treated with a bone marrow transplant. Radiation or chemotherapy drugs are used to kill the existing bone marrow, then a bone marrow transplant replaces it. Why would a bone marrow transplant affect the production of white blood cells?

2. Radiation and chemotherapy drugs preferentially kill cells that divide frequently, most notably cancer cells. These cancer treatments also cause hair to fall out. Why?

3. Each level of biological organization has emergent properties that arise from the interaction of its component parts. For example, cells have a capacity for inheritance that the molecules making up the cell do not. Can you think of an emergent property of a tissue? Of an organ that contains that tissue?

4. The micrograph to the *right* shows cells from the lining of an airway leading to the lungs. The *gold* cells are ciliated and the *darker brown* ones secrete mucus. What type of tissue is this? How can you tell?

# 26 Reproduction and Development

26.1

**Impacts/Issues:  Mind-Boggling Births**

In December of 1998, Nkem Chukwu of Houston, Texas, gave birth to six girls and two boys. They were the first set of human octuplets to be born alive. The births were premature. In total, all eight newborns weighed a bit more than 4.5 kilograms (10 pounds). Odera, the smallest, weighed about 300 grams (less than 1 pound). She died six days after birth, when her heart and lungs gave out. Two others required surgery. The seven survivors had to spend months in the hospital before going home (Figure 26.1). However, all are now in good health.

FIGURE 26.1 Outcome of fertility-enhancing drugs, seven survivors of a set of octuplets.

Why did octuplets form in the first place? Chukwu had trouble getting pregnant. Her doctors gave her hormone injections, which caused many of her eggs to mature and be released at the same time. When the doctors realized that she was carrying a large number of embryos, they suggested reducing the number. Chukwu chose instead to try to carry all of them to term. Her first child was thirteen weeks premature. The others were surgically delivered two weeks later.

Over the past two decades, the number of multiple births has increased by almost 60 percent. There have been four times as many higher-order multiple births (triplets or more). Increased use of fertility drugs is one cause for these increases. A woman's fertility peaks in her midtwenties. By thirty-nine, her chance of conceiving naturally has declined by about half. Yet the number of first-time mothers more than forty years old doubled in the past decade. Many of these women required fertility drugs to become pregnant, and such drugs raise the likelihood of multiple births.

Carrying more than one embryo increases the risk of miscarriage, premature delivery, or stillbirth. Multiple-birth newborns weigh less than normal and are more likely to have birth defects. For these reasons, many doctors consider the rise in multiple births a troubling trend.

In this chapter, we turn to one of life's most amazing dramas, animal reproduction and development. How does a single fertilized egg of a human—or frog or bird or any other animal—give rise to so many specialized kinds of cells? How does development yield an adult with all the complex tissues and organs discussed throughout this unit?

Answers to these questions will emerge as we consider the developmental processes common to all animals. We will also delve into the story of human reproduction, learning how humans develop from a single cell to an adult body with trillions of specialized cells.

# 26.2 How Animals Reproduce and Develop

**Asexual Reproduction** With **asexual reproduction**, a single individual makes offspring that are genetically identical to the parent and one another. As a result, the parent has all its genes represented in each offspring. Asexual reproduction can be advantageous in a stable environment. Gene combinations that make the parent successful can be expected to do the same for offspring. However, being locked into a particular gene combination may be a disadvantage if the environment is not stable.

Many invertebrates reproduce asexually. Some do this by fragmentation—a piece breaks off and grows into a new individual. In others, new individuals bud from existing ones (Figure 26.2**A**). Offspring of insects, fish, amphibians, and lizards develop from unfertilized eggs by a process called **parthenogenesis**. No mammals reproduce asexually.

**Sexual Reproduction** With **sexual reproduction**, two parents produce gametes that combine at fertilization. Each resulting offspring has a unique combination of paternal and maternal genes (Section 8.8).

Sexual reproducers have higher genetic and energetic costs than asexual reproducers. On average, only half of a sexually reproducing parent's genes end up in each offspring. However, most animals live where resources and threats change over time. In such environments, production of offspring that differ from both parents and from one another can be advantageous. By reproducing sexually, a parent increases the likelihood that some offspring will inherit a combination of genetic traits that suits them to a newly changed environment.

Some species switch between sexual and asexual reproduction. Plant-sucking insects called aphids offer one example. During the summer, a female aphid settles on a plant and gives birth to many wingless daughters that have developed inside the mother's body from unfertilized eggs. An aphid's daughters live on the same plant as their mother, or on an adjacent one, so they all experience more or less similar conditions. In autumn, males are produced and sexual reproduction yields genetically variable females. These females spend the winter in a resting state. In the spring, they seek out new plants on which to raise the new generation of genetically identical daughters.

**Variations on Sexual Reproduction** Sexually reproducing animals that produce both eggs and sperm are **hermaphrodites**. Tapeworms and some roundworms are simultaneous hermaphrodites. They produce eggs and sperm at the same time, and can fertilize themselves. Earthworms and slugs are simultaneous hermaphrodites too, but they swap gametes with a partner. So do barred hamlets, a type of marine fish (Figure 26.2**B**). During a bout of mating, hamlet partners take turns in the "male" and "female" roles. Other fishes are sequential hermaphrodites. They switch from one sex to another during the course of a lifetime. More typically, vertebrates have separate sexes that remain fixed for life. Each individual is either male or female.

Most aquatic invertebrates, fishes, and amphibians release gametes into the water, where they combine during external fertilization. As Section 15.6 explained, the amniotes have internal fertilization, meaning sperm and egg meet inside the female's body. In most reptiles and mammals, a specialized organ (a penis) delivers sperm into a female's reproductive tract (Figure 26.2**C**). Internal fertilization reduces the number of gametes that must be produced and, in some groups, allows offspring to develop inside the mother's body.

**FIGURE 26.2** Animal reproduction. **A** Hydra reproducing asexually by budding. **B** Mating barred hamlets. The fish are hermaphrodites that fertilize eggs externally. During mating, each fish alternates between laying eggs and fertilizing its partner's eggs. **C** Male elephant inserting his penis into his female partner. Eggs will be fertilized inside the mother's body, and offspring will develop there.

**asexual reproduction** Reproductive mode by which offspring arise from one parent and inherit that parent's genes only.

**hermaphrodite** Individual animal that produces both eggs and sperm.

**parthenogenesis** Process by which individuals develop from unfertilized eggs.

**sexual reproduction** Reproductive mode by which offspring arise from two parents and inherit genes from both.

**A** Eggs form and mature in female reproductive organs. Sperm form and mature in male reproductive organs.

Gamete Formation

**B** A sperm penetrates an egg. Their nuclei fuse. A zygote has formed.

Fertilization

**C** Mitotic cell divisions form a ball of cells, a blastula. Each cell gets regionally different parts of the egg cytoplasm.

Cleavage

**D** A gastrula, an early embryo that has primary tissue layers, forms by cell divisions, cell migrations, and rearrangements.

Gastrulation

**E** Details of the body plan fill in as different cell types interact and form tissues and organs in predictable patterns.

Organ Formation

**F** Organs grow in size, take on mature form, and gradually assume specialized functions.

Growth, Tissue Specialization

**FIGURE 26.3** Overview of reproductive and developmental processes that occur in animals with tissues and organs.

**blastula** Hollow ball of cells that forms early in animal development.

**cleavage** Mitotic division of an animal cell.

**differentiation** Process by which cells become specialized; occurs as different cell lineages express different subsets of their genes.

**ectoderm** Outermost tissue layer of an animal embryo.

**endoderm** Innermost tissue layer of an animal embryo.

**fertilization** Egg and sperm combine and form a zygote.

**gastrula** Three-layered developmental stage formed by gastrulation in an animal.

**gastrulation** Animal developmental process by which cell movements produce a three-layered gastrula.

**mesoderm** Middle tissue layer of a three-layered animal embryo.

**yolk** Nutritious material in many animal eggs.

**zygote** Cell formed by fusion of gametes; first cell of a new individual.

## Stages in Reproduction and Development

Animals develop through a series of stages. Figure 26.3 is an overview of the six stages of reproduction and development that occur in animals that have tissues and organs.

Reproduction begins with gamete formation. Gametes (eggs or sperm) form by meiosis of germ cells in primary reproductive organs (gonads). A sperm consists of paternal DNA and a bit of cellular equipment that helps it reach and penetrate an egg. There is little cytoplasm. An egg is much larger than a sperm and more complex internally. As it matures, enzymes, mRNA transcripts, and other materials are stored in its cytoplasm. Most animal eggs also include **yolk**, a mixture of lipids and proteins that nourishes a developing individual.

**Fertilization** begins when a sperm penetrates an egg. It ends when sperm and egg nuclei fuse, forming a **zygote**, the first cell of the new individual. A zygote's cytoplasm is almost entirely derived from the egg.

Developmental processes transform a single-celled zygote to an adult animal. Figure 26.4 show the development of one vertebrate, a frog. Development begins with **cleavage**, during which mitotic cell divisions increase the number of cells without adding to a zygote's original volume ❶. Because materials are not randomly distributed in the egg cytoplasm, cleavage distributes different mRNAs to different cells. Which of these "maternal messages" are inherited helps determine the fate of a cell lineage. For example, cells of one lineage alone might receive maternal mRNA for a regulatory protein that turns on the embryo's gene for a particular hormone.

Cleavage ends with the formation of the **blastula**, a hollow ball of cells around a fluid-filled center ❷. After the blastula forms, cell divisions slow and the blastula undergoes **gastrulation**. This is a process of structural organization, during which some cells on the blastula's surface move inward. These cellular movements produce a **gastrula**, an embryonic form with three primary tissue layers (also called germ layers) ❸. Cellular descendants of these primary tissues give rise to all tissues and organs of the adult.

**Ectoderm**, the outermost primary tissue, emerges first. It is the source of the nervous system and outer portions of the body coverings. Inner **endoderm** is the source of the gut's inner lining and organs derived from it. In most animals, **mesoderm** forms between the outer and inner primary tissue layers. It gives rise to muscles, most of the skeleton, the circulatory, reproductive, and excretory systems, and connective tissues of the gut and skin.

Because all cells of an embryo are descended from the same zygote, they all have the same number and kinds of genes. How then, do different kinds of cells arise? From gastrulation onward, different cell lineages express some groups of genes and not others. As Section 7.7 explained, selective gene expression begins the process of **differentiation**. By this process, cell lineages become specialized. For example, all cells use genes for enzymes that carry out glycolysis. However, only cells that will become the lens of the eye turn on a gene for crystallin, a transparent protein. Thus, the end of gastrulation and the beginning of cell differentiation marks the onset of organ formation ❹. Growth and tissue specialization is the sixth and final stage of animal development ❺. This stage usually continues into early adulthood.

Tissues and organs develop in a genetically programmed, orderly sequence. The body takes on its characteristic form as cells of various lineages divide, migrate, alter their size and shape, and die at specific times and in specific locations. For example, a frog larva (a tadpole) has a tail. During metamorphosis to the adult form, the death of cells in the tail makes the tail disappear. A similar process shapes a human hand. The hand starts out as a paddlelike structure with digits connected by webs of flesh. Death of cells in the webbing sculpts a five-fingered hand.

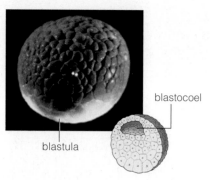

gray crescent

blastocoel

blastula

**①** Here we show the first three divisions of cleavage, a process that carves up the zygote's cytoplasm. In this species, cleavage results in a blastula, a ball of cells with a fluid-filled cavity.

**②** Cleavage is over when the blastula forms.

   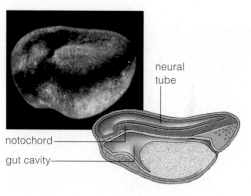

ectoderm
dorsal lip
future gut cavity

yolk plug

neural plate

ectoderm
mesoderm
endoderm

neural tube

notochord

gut cavity

**③** The blastula becomes a three-layered gastrula by a process called gastrulation. At the dorsal lip, a fold of ectoderm above the first opening that appears in the blastula, cells migrate inward and start rearranging themselves.

**④** Organs begin to form as a primitive gut cavity opens up. A neural tube, then a notochord and other organs form from the primary tissue layers.

Tadpole, a swimming larva with segmented muscles and a notochord extending into a tail.

Limbs grow and the tail is absorbed during metamorphosis to the adult form.

Sexually mature, four-legged adult leopard frog.

**⑤** The frog's body form changes as it grows and its tissues specialize. The embryo becomes a tadpole, which metamorphoses into an adult.

**FIGURE 26.4 Animated!**
Stages in the development of a vertebrate, the leopard frog.

## Take-Home Message *How do animals reproduce and develop?*

- Some animals reproduce asexually, producing offspring identical to one another and to their parents. Most animals reproduce sexually, and so produce genetically variable offspring.

- In sexually reproducing animals, gametes combine and form a zygote. Cleavage (mitotic divisions) produces a blastula. This hollow ball of cells undergoes gastrulation, a series of cellular rearrangement that yields a three-layered gastrula. Cells of the gastrula differentiate to form specialized tissues.

- Cell divisions, migrations, shape changes, and deaths shape organs and give rise to the final body form.

# The Human Reproductive System

We turn now to details of reproduction and development in our own species. In humans, as in other sexually reproducing animals, reproduction begins with gamete formation. Gametes form by meiosis inside a special pair of organs called gonads. Sperm form inside male gonads, the **testes** (singular, testis). Eggs form inside female gonads, the **ovaries**. The male reproductive tract also has components that store sperm and move them from the male's body into the female reproductive tract. A female's reproductive system has components that receive sperm and sustain developing offspring.

**Male Reproductive System** In both males and females, the gonads form deep inside the body. Before a male is born, the testes typically descend into the **scrotum**, a pouch suspended below the pelvic girdle (Figure 26.5). Smooth muscle inside this pouch encloses the testes. Reflexive contraction and relaxation of this muscle adjusts the position of the testes. When a man is cold or frightened, muscle contractions draw the testes closer to his body. When he feels warm, relaxation of muscle in the scrotum allows his testes to hang lower, so the sperm-making cells do not overheat. These cells function best just a bit below normal body temperature.

A male enters puberty (the stage of development when reproductive organs mature) sometime between the ages of 11 and 16 years. Testes enlarge and sperm production begins. Secretion of testosterone increases and leads to development of secondary sexual traits: thickened vocal cords that deepen the voice; increased growth of hair on the face, chest, armpits, and pubic region; and an altered distribution of fat and muscle.

Immature sperm formed in a testis are moved into the epididymis (plural, epididymides), a coiled duct perched on a testis. The Greek *epi–* means upon and *didymos* means twins. In this context, the "twins" refers to the two testes. Secretions from the epididymis wall nourish the sperm and help them mature.

The last region of each epididymis stores mature sperm and is continuous with the first portion of a **vas deferens** (plural, vasa deferentia). In Latin, *vas* means vessel, and *deferens*, to carry away. A vas deferens is a duct that carries sperm away from an epididymis, and to a short ejaculatory duct. Ejaculatory ducts deliver sperm to the urethra, the duct that extends through a male's penis to an opening at the body surface.

Beneath the skin of the penis, connective tissue encloses three elongated cylinders of spongy tissue. When a male becomes sexually excited, signals from the nervous system cause blood to flow into the spongy tissue faster than it flows out. As fluid pressure rises, the normally limp penis becomes erect.

Sperm stored in the epididymides typically continue their journey toward the body surface only when a male reaches the peak of sexual excitement and ejaculates. During **ejaculation**, smooth muscle in the walls of the epididymides and vasa deferentia undergoes rhythmic contractions that propel sperm and accessory gland secretions out of the body as a thick, white fluid called semen.

**Semen** is a complex mixture of sperm, proteins, nutrients, ions, and signaling molecules. Sperm constitute less than 5 percent of semen's volume; accessory glands secretions make up the other 95 percent. **Seminal vesicles**, exocrine glands near the base of the bladder, secrete fructose-rich fluid into the vasa deferentia. Sperm use fructose (a sugar) as their energy source. The **prostate gland**, an exocrine gland that encircles the urethra and secretes fluid into it, is the other major contributor to semen volume. Its secretions help raise the pH of

**ejaculation** Smooth muscle contractions that propel semen through the penis and out of the body.

**ovary** Organ in which eggs form.

**prostate gland** Exocrine gland that encircles a male's urethra; its secretions contribute to semen.

**scrotum** Pouch that holds the testes.

**semen** Sperm mixed with fluid secreted by exocrine glands.

**seminal vesicles** Exocrine glands that secrete fluid into the vasa deferentia; main source of semen volume.

**testes** In animals, organs that produce sperm.

**vas deferens** Main duct that conveys mature sperm toward the urethra.

**Prostate Gland**
An exocrine gland that contributes some fluid to the semen

urinary bladder

**Urethra**
Duct with dual functions: channel for ejaculation of sperm during sexual arousal and for excretion of urine at other times

**Ejaculatory Duct**
One pair of ducts that carry sperm to the penis

**Seminal Vesicle**
One of a pair of exocrine glands that contributes fructose-rich fluid to semen

**Bulbourethral Gland**
One of a pair of exocrine glands that secrete mucus

anus

**Vas Deferens**
One of a pair of ducts that carry sperm to the penis

**Epididymis**
One of a pair of ducts in which sperm mature and are stored

scrotum

cylinders of spongy tissue that swell with blood during an erection

urethra

**Penis**
Male organ of sexual intercourse

**Testis**
One of a pair of gonads, packed with small, sperm-producing tubes (seminiferous tubules) and cells that secrete testosterone and other sex hormones

**A**

bladder

**B**

**FIGURE 26.5 Animated!** Male reproductive structures and their functions. **A** Cutaway side view, with cross-section of penis. **B** Frontal view, showing position of reproductive organs relative to the pelvic girdle and bladder.

Figure It Out: Which glandular structure do sperm travel past first during ejaculation: a seminal vesicle, the bulbourethral gland, or the prostate gland?

Answer: A seminal vesicle

the female reproductive tract, so sperm can swim more efficiently. Two pea-sized bulbourethral glands secrete mucus into the urethra. The mucus helps clear the urethra of urine prior to ejaculation.

In a young, healthy man, the prostate gland is about the size of a walnut. However, the prostate often enlarges with age. Because the urethra runs through the prostate gland, prostate enlargement can squeeze this tube and cause difficulty urinating. Medication, laser treatments, and surgery are used to shrink the prostate or create a tunnel through it and make room for the urethra.

Prostate enlargement can be a symptom of prostate cancer, the second most common fatal cancer in men (surpassed only by lung cancer). Many prostate cancers grow relatively slowly, but some grow fast and spread to other parts of the body. Risk factors for prostate cancer include advancing age, a diet rich in animal fats, smoking, and obesity. Genes also play a role. If a man has an affected father or brother, his own risk of prostate cancer doubles.

Doctors can diagnose prostate cancer by blood tests that detect increases in prostate-specific antigen (PSA) and by physical examination. Surgery and radiation therapy can cure cancers that are detected early.

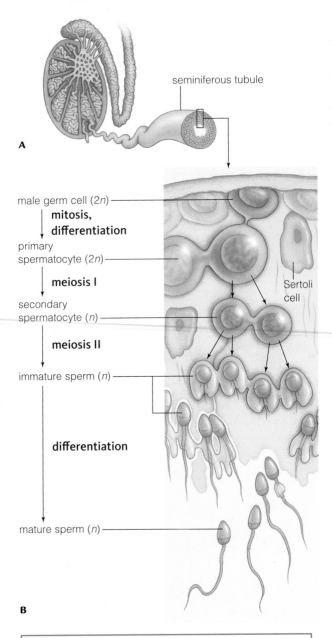

male germ cell (2n)

↓ **mitosis, differentiation**

primary spermatocyte (2n)

↓ **meiosis I**

secondary spermatocyte (n)

↓ **meiosis II**

immature sperm (n)

↓ **differentiation**

mature sperm (n)

seminiferous tubule

Sertoli cell

**B**

---

**FIGURE 26.6 Animated!** Sperm formation.
**A** Location of seminiferous tubules in a testis.
**B** Steps in sperm formation inside a tubule.
**C** *Below,* a mature sperm.

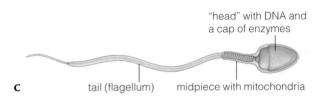

"head" with DNA and a cap of enzymes

**C**  tail (flagellum)  midpiece with mitochondria

---

**How Sperm Form**  Although smaller than a golf ball, a testis holds coiled seminiferous tubules that would extend for 125 meters (longer than a football field) if stretched out (Figure 26.6**A**). Cells between the tubules secrete the hormone testosterone. Diploid male germ cells line the inner wall of the tubule (Figure 26.6**B**). These cells divide repeatedly by mitosis, and their offspring differentiate to become primary spermatocytes. Primary spermatocytes undergo meiosis I, forming secondary spermatocytes. Completion of meiosis yields immature sperm, which differentiate to form mature sperm. Sertoli cells, also in the tubules, metabolically support the developing sperm.

A mature sperm is a haploid, flagellated cell (Figure 26.6**C**). It uses the flagellum, or "tail," to swim toward an egg. Mitochondria in an adjacent midpiece supply the energy required for movement. A sperm's "head" is packed full of DNA and has an enzyme-containing cap. The enzymes in the cap help the sperm penetrate an egg during fertilization. Sperm formation takes about 100 days, from start to finish. An adult male makes sperm continually, so on any given day he has millions of them in various stages of development.

Hormones control gamete formation. Gonadotropin-releasing hormone (GnRH) is one of the hypothalamic hormones that targets the pituitary gland (Section 25.3). GnRH stimulates anterior pituitary cells to secrete luteinizing hormone (LH) and follicle-stimulating hormone (FSH). These two hormones have a role in both male and female reproductive function.

In males, LH and FSH target cells inside the testes. LH stimulates cells that lie between the seminiferous tubules to secrete testosterone. FSH targets Sertoli cells inside seminiferous tubules. In combination with testosterone, FSH causes Sertoli cells to produce substances that encourage sperm formation, development, and maturation.

**Female Reproductive System**  A female's ovaries lie deep inside her body (Figure 26.7). Each is about the size of an almond. A ciliated **oviduct** connects each ovary to the **uterus**, a hollow, pear-shaped organ above the urinary bladder. The uterus is commonly called the womb. If fertilization occurs, an embryo forms and develops in the uterus. A thick layer of smooth muscle makes up most of the uterine wall. The uterine lining consists of glandular epithelium, connective tissues, and blood vessels. The lowest portion of the uterus narrows, forming the **cervix**, which connects to the vagina.

The **vagina** is a muscular tube that extends from the cervix to the body's surface. The vagina functions as the female organ of intercourse and also as the birth canal in childbirth. Two pairs of skin folds enclose the surface openings of the vagina and urethra. Fatty tissue fills the pair of outer folds (the labia majora). Thin inner folds (the labia minora) have a rich blood supply and swell during sexual arousal.

The tip of the clitoris, a highly sensitive sex organ, is positioned between the two inner folds, just in front of the urethra. The clitoris and penis develop from the same embryonic tissue. Both have an abundance of highly sensitive touch receptors, and both swell with blood and become erect during sexual arousal.

**Egg Formation and the Ovarian Cycle**  Unlike male germ cells, female germ cells do not divide after birth. A girl is born with about 2 million primary oocytes in her ovaries. An **oocyte** is a general term for an immature egg. A primary oocyte is an immature egg that has entered meiosis but stopped in prophase I. When a female reaches puberty, her primary oocytes begin to mature, one at a time, in an approximately 28-day ovarian cycle.

Figure 26.8 shows how an oocyte matures over the course of this cycle. A primary oocyte and the cells around it constitute an **ovarian follicle** ❶. In the

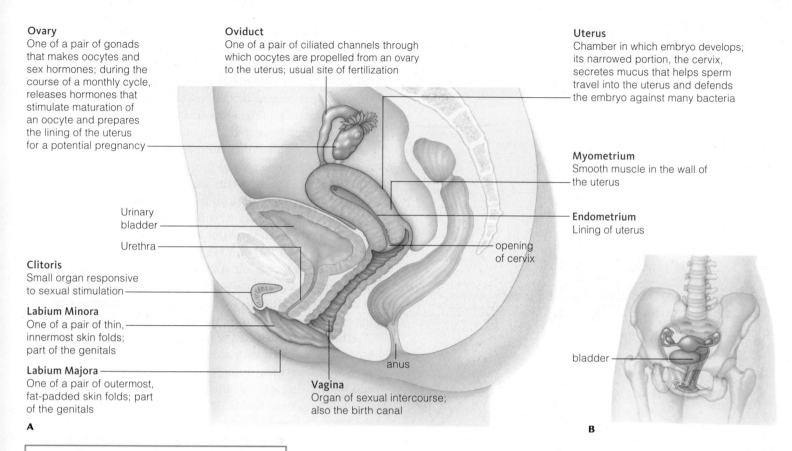

**Ovary**
One of a pair of gonads that makes oocytes and sex hormones; during the course of a monthly cycle, releases hormones that stimulate maturation of an oocyte and prepares the lining of the uterus for a potential pregnancy

**Oviduct**
One of a pair of ciliated channels through which oocytes are propelled from an ovary to the uterus; usual site of fertilization

**Uterus**
Chamber in which embryo develops; its narrowed portion, the cervix, secretes mucus that helps sperm travel into the uterus and defends the embryo against many bacteria

**Myometrium**
Smooth muscle in the wall of the uterus

Urinary bladder

Urethra

**Endometrium**
Lining of uterus

opening of cervix

**Clitoris**
Small organ responsive to sexual stimulation

**Labium Minora**
One of a pair of thin, innermost skin folds; part of the genitals

**Labium Majora**
One of a pair of outermost, fat-padded skin folds; part of the genitals

anus

**Vagina**
Organ of sexual intercourse; also the birth canal

bladder

**A**

**B**

**FIGURE 26.7 Animated!** Components of the human female reproductive system and their functions. **A** Cutaway side view. **B** Frontal view, showing position of reproductive organs relative to the pelvic girdle and bladder.

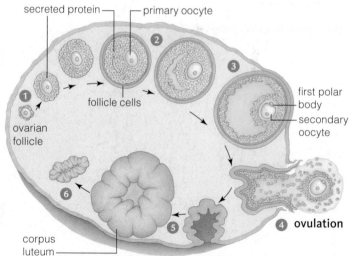

**FIGURE 26.8 Animated!** Changes in a follicle during one ovarian cycle.

first part of the ovarian cycle, cells around the oocyte divide repeatedly as the oocyte enlarges and secretes a layer of proteins ❷. As the follicle matures, a fluid-filled cavity opens around the oocyte. Often more than one follicle begins to develop, but typically only one becomes fully mature. In that follicle, the primary oocyte completes meiosis I and undergoes unequal cytoplasmic division. The result is a large secondary oocyte and a tiny polar body ❸. The secondary oocyte starts meiosis II, then halts in metaphase II. The polar body has no reproductive function and will later disintegrate.

About two weeks after the cycle began, the follicle wall ruptures and **ovulation** occurs: The secondary oocyte and polar body are ejected into the adjacent oviduct ❹. Once in the oviduct, an oocyte must meet up with sperm within 12 to 24 hours for fertilization to occur. The secondary oocyte will not complete meiosis until it has been penetrated by a sperm.

Meanwhile, back in the ovary, the cells of the ruptured follicle develop into a hormone-secreting structure called the **corpus luteum** ❺. (The name means "yellow body" in Latin and refers to its yellowish color.) If pregnancy does not occur, the corpus luteum breaks down ❻. Once the corpus luteum is gone, a new follicle can begin to mature.

**cervix** Narrowed region of uterus; connects to vagina.
**corpus luteum** Hormone-secreting structure that forms from follicle cells after ovulation.
**oocyte** Immature egg.
**ovarian follicle** Immature egg and surrounding cells.
**oviduct** Ciliated tube connecting an ovary to the uterus.
**ovulation** Release of a secondary oocyte from an ovary.
**uterus** Muscular chamber where offspring develop; womb.
**vagina** Female organ of intercourse and birth canal.

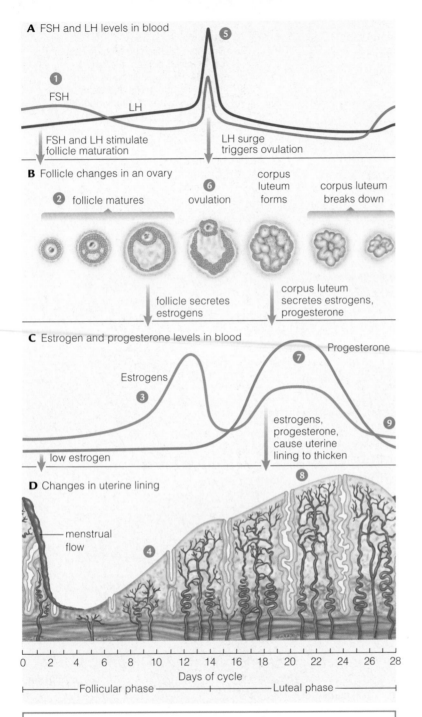

**A** FSH and LH levels in blood

**1** FSH

LH

FSH and LH stimulate follicle maturation

LH surge triggers ovulation

**5**

**B** Follicle changes in an ovary

**2** follicle matures

**6** ovulation

corpus luteum forms

corpus luteum breaks down

follicle secretes estrogens

corpus luteum secretes estrogens, progesterone

**C** Estrogen and progesterone levels in blood

Progesterone

**7**

Estrogens

**3**

low estrogen

estrogens, progesterone, cause uterine lining to thicken

**9**

**D** Changes in uterine lining

menstrual flow

**4**

**8**

0  2  4  6  8  10  12  14  16  18  20  22  24  26  28

Days of cycle

Follicular phase — Luteal phase

**FIGURE 26.9 Animated!** Changes in a human ovary and uterus correlated with changing hormone levels. Onset of menstrual flow is considered Day 1 of the approximately 28-day menstrual cycle.

**A,B** Prompted by GnRH from the hypothalamus, the anterior pituitary secretes FSH and LH, which stimulate a follicle to grow and an oocyte to mature in an ovary. A midcycle surge of LH triggers ovulation and the formation of a corpus luteum. A decline in FSH after ovulation stops more follicles from maturing.

**C,D** Early on, estrogen from a maturing follicle encourages repair and rebuilding of uterine lining. After ovulation, the corpus luteum secretes some estrogen and more progesterone that primes the uterus for pregnancy. If pregnancy occurs, the corpus luteum will persist, and its secretions will stimulate the maintenance of the uterine lining.

## Hormones and the Menstrual Cycle

Cyclic events in the ovaries are coordinated with cyclic changes in the uterus. We refer to the approximately monthly changes in the uterus as the **menstrual cycle**. The first day of the menstrual cycle is marked by the onset of **menstruation**: the flow of bits of uterine lining and a small amount of blood from the uterus, through the cervix, and out of the vagina.

Figure 26.9 shows how hormone levels and the thickness of the uterine lining change during the menstrual cycle. It also shows how those events are tied to the ovarian cycle.

Like testes, ovaries are under the control of GnRH. As the menstrual cycle begins, GnRH from the hypothalamus is making cells in the anterior lobe of the pituitary increase their secretion of FSH and LH **1**. As its name implies, follicle-stimulating hormone stimulates an ovarian follicle to begin maturing **2**. As a follicle matures, cells surrounding the oocyte secrete estrogens (a type of female sex hormone). Rising estrogens **3** encourage the uterine lining to thicken **4**.

The pituitary detects the rising level of estrogens in the blood and responds with an outpouring of LH **5**. The LH surge encourages the primary oocyte to complete meiosis I and undergo cytoplasmic division. The LH surge also causes the follicle to swell and burst. Thus, a midcycle surge of LH is the trigger for ovulation **6**.

Immediately after ovulation, the estrogen level declines until the corpus luteum forms. The corpus luteum secretes some estrogen and a lot of progesterone (another type of female sex hormone) **7**. Estrogens and progesterone cause the uterine lining to thicken and encourage blood vessels to grow through it. The uterus is now ready for a pregnancy **8**.

If a pregnancy does not occur, the corpus luteum persists for about twelve days. The estrogen and progesterone it secretes keep the hypothalamus from secreting FSH, so no other follicles start to mature. When the corpus luteum begins to break down, estrogen and progesterone levels fall **9**. The hypothalamus senses this decline, and stimulates the pituitary to begin secreting FSH and LH once again. In the uterus, the decline in estrogens and progesterone causes thickened lining to break down, and menstruation begins.

## Menstruation-Related Disorders

Many women occasionally experience some discomfort a week or so before they menstruate. Body tissues swell because premenstrual changes influence aldosterone secretion. This adrenal gland hormone stimulates reabsorption of sodium and, indirectly, water (Section 25.6). Breasts may become tender because hormonal changes cause the milk ducts inside them to enlarge. Cycle-induced hormonal changes can also cause depression, irritability, or anxiety. Headaches and sleeping problems are also common.

Regular recurrence of these symptoms is known as premenstrual syndrome (PMS). A balanced diet and exercise make PMS less likely and less severe. Taking oral contraceptives minimizes hormone swings and usually prevents PMS.

During menstruation, local signaling molecules (prostaglandins) stimulate contractions of smooth muscle in the uterine wall. Many women barely notice these contractions, but others experience a dull ache or sharp pain, commonly called menstrual cramps.

Menstruation usually lasts for five to seven days. Unusually heavy or persistent menstrual flow can be caused by fibroids. About one-third of women over age thirty have these benign tumors of the uterus. Most fibroids cause no symptoms, but some result in pain, long menstrual periods, and excessive bleeding. A woman who needs to change pads or tampons on an hourly basis should discuss this condition with her doctor. Fibroids can be surgically removed, usually without impairing fertility.

Excessive exercise or malnutrition can halt menstrual cycling. Usually, the cycle starts up again when physical activity lessens or diet improves. Menstrual cycles halt permanently and fertility ends when a woman completes **menopause**, usually at about age 50. Hormonal changes related to menopause cause many women to have hot flashes. A woman gets abruptly and uncomfortably hot, flushed, and sweaty as blood surges to her skin. Hormone replacement therapy (taking estrogen and in some cases progesterone) can relieve symptoms, but raises some health risks.

## Take-Home Message  What are the roles of human reproductive organs?

- A male's testes produce sperm and secrete the sex hormone testosterone. Sperm and secretions from accessory glands form semen. Semen is propelled through a series of ducts and leaves the body through an opening in the penis.

- A woman's ovaries make eggs and secrete sex hormones (estrogens and progesterone). Oviducts connect the ovaries to the uterus, where offspring develop. The vagina is the organ of intercourse and also the birth canal.

- In men, germ cells divide continually to produce sperm. By contrast, a woman is born with all the immature eggs she will ever have.

- From puberty until menopause, a woman's eggs mature—one at a time—in an approximately monthly cycle. During each cycle, the uterine lining thickens in preparation for pregnancy. If pregnancy does not occur, the woman sheds the uterine lining (menstruates), and the cycle begins again.

# 26.4 How Pregnancy Happens

**Sexual Intercourse**  For males, intercourse requires an **erection**. Cylinders of spongy tissue make up the bulk of the penis. When a male is not sexually aroused, his penis remains limp, because the large blood vessels that transport blood to the spongy tissue are constricted. When a male becomes aroused, signals from the parasympathetic nervous system induce arteries supplying the spongy tissue to widen. Inward flow of blood now exceeds outward flow, and the increase in fluid pressure expands the internal chambers. As a result, the penis enlarges and stiffens, so it can be inserted into a female's vagina.

The ability to achieve and sustain an erection peaks during the late teens. As a man ages, he may have episodes of erectile dysfunction. With this disorder, the penis cannot stiffen enough for intercourse. Men who have circulatory problems are most often affected. Smoking also increases risk. The National Institutes of Health estimates that 30 million men are affected in the United States alone.

**erection**  Penis becomes erect as a result of increased fluid pressure inside its spongy tissue.

**menopause**  Of a human female, the end of fertility and of menstrual cycles.

**menstrual cycle**  Approximately monthly cycle in which the uterine lining thickens in preparation for pregnancy, then is shed if pregnancy does not occur.

**menstruation**  Flow of blood and bits of shed uterine lining out through the vagina.

Viagra and similar drugs prescribed for erectile dysfunction cause blood vessels that carry blood into the penis to widen and deliver more blood. Such drugs can cause headaches and (rarely) sudden hearing loss. They also interact with other drugs, and should never be taken without a prescription.

In a sexually excited female, the vaginal wall, labia, and clitoris swell with blood. Her cervix and glands near the entrance to the vagina increase their secretion of mucus.

During intercourse, mechanical stimulation of the male's penis and the female's clitoris and vaginal wall may lead to **orgasm**, or sexual climax. During orgasm, neurotransmitters flood the brain, causing sensations of release and pleasure. In females, muscles of the vaginal wall and pelvis contract rhythmically. In males, similar reflexive contractions force sperm and contents of seminal vesicles and the prostate gland into the urethra. These substances mix, forming semen, which is ejaculated in the vagina.

You may have heard that a female cannot become pregnant unless she reaches orgasm. Don't believe it!

**Fertilization** On average, an ejaculation will put 150 million to 350 million sperm into the vagina. Within thirty minutes some have made their way into the female's oviducts. Just a few hundred will survive the long journey to the upper region of the oviduct, where eggs usually are fertilized (Figure 26.10).

If sperm and oocyte meet, receptors in the plasma membrane of the sperm's head bind to proteins in the secreted layer that encloses the oocyte. The sperm's entry causes granules in the oocyte cortex (the region just beneath the plasma membrane) to move to the cell's surface. The granules contain enzymes that digest the outer portion of the protein coat. With this outer coat gone, other sperm have nothing to attach to and are unable to enter the oocyte.

Once inside the oocyte, a sperm breaks down, but its nucleus remains intact. Sperm entry prompts the secondary oocyte to complete meiosis II, forming a mature egg, or **ovum** (plural, ova), and a second polar body. The egg nucleus and sperm nucleus fuse, restoring the diploid number for the zygote, the first cell of the new individual.

Sometimes two eggs mature and are released at the same time, and each is fertilized by a different sperm. The result is fraternal twins. Such twins are no more similar than any other siblings.

**FIGURE 26.10 Animated!** Fertilization.

❶ Sperm surround a secondary oocyte and release enzymes that digest their way through the protein layer around the oocyte.

❷ When a sperm penetrates the oocyte, granules in the egg cortex move to the surface and follicle cells are shed. Penetration of a sperm into the oocyte stimulates meiosis II in the oocyte's nucleus.

❸ The sperm tail degenerates; its nucleus enlarges and fuses with the oocyte nucleus.

❹ At nuclear fusion, a zygote forms and fertilization is completed.

## Take-Home Message  How does a pregnancy occur?

■ In preparation for intercourse, a male's penis becomes inflated by the inflow of blood and a female's reproductive tract becomes lubricated with mucus.

■ During orgasm, smooth muscles of the reproductive tract undergo rhythmic contractions. In males, ejaculation forces sperm out of the penis.

■ Fertilization usually occurs in the oviduct. Usually an oocyte changes after one sperm penetrates it, preventing other sperm from binding. The result of fertilization is a zygote, the first cell of the new individual.

# 26.5

# Fertility and Reproductive Health

**Contraception** Methods used to prevent pregnancy are termed **contraception**. Table 26.1 lists common options and compares their effectiveness. The most effective option is abstinence—no sex— which is 100 percent effective. However, it can take great self-discipline. Rhythm methods are forms of abstinence; a woman simply avoids sex during her fertile period. She calculates when she is ovulating by recording how long her menstrual cycles last, checking her temperature each morning, monitoring the thickness of her cervical mucus, or by checking some combination of these indicators.

| Table 26.1 | Common Methods of Contraception | |
|---|---|---|
| Method | Description | Pregnancy Rate* |
| Abstinence | No intercourse | 0% per year |
| Rhythm method | Avoid intercourse in female's fertile period | 25% per year |
| Withdrawal | End intercourse before male ejaculates | 27% per year |
| Douche | Wash semen from vagina after intercourse | 60% per year |
| Vasectomy | Cut or close off male's vasa deferentia | >1% per year |
| Tubal ligation | Cut or close off female's oviducts | >1% per year |
| Condom | Enclose penis, block sperm entry to vagina | 15% per year |
| Diaphragm, cervical cap | Cover cervix, block sperm entry to uterus | 16% per year |
| Spermicides | Kill sperm | 29% per year |
| Intrauterine device | Prevent sperm entry to uterus or prevent implantation of embryo | >1% per year |
| Oral contraceptives | Prevent ovulation | >1% per year |
| Hormone patches, implants, or injections | Prevent ovulation | >1% per year |
| Emergency contraception pill | Prevent ovulation | 15–25% per use** |

\* Percent of users who become pregnant with consistent, correct usage.

\*\* Not meant for regular use. 15–25 percent of users become pregnant despite use of pill.

Withdrawal, or removing the penis from the vagina before ejaculation, requires great willpower. It also may be ineffective because sperm can be in pre-ejaculation fluids. Similarly, rinsing out the vagina (douching) immediately after intercourse is unreliable. Typically, some sperm swim through the cervix within seconds of ejaculation.

Surgical methods are highly effective, but are meant to make a person permanently sterile. Men may opt for a vasectomy. A doctor makes a small incision into the scrotum, then cuts and ties off each vas deferens. A tubal ligation blocks or cuts a woman's oviducts.

Other fertility control methods use physical and chemical barriers to stop sperm from reaching an egg. Spermicidal foams and jellies poison sperm. They are not always reliable, but their use with a condom or diaphragm reduces the chance of pregnancy. A diaphragm is a flexible, dome-shaped device that is positioned inside the vagina so it covers the cervix. A diaphragm is relatively effective if it is first fitted by a doctor and used correctly with a spermicide. A cervical cap is a similar but smaller device. Condoms are thin, tight-fitting sheaths worn over the penis during intercourse. Latex ones have the advantage of also protecting against sexually transmitted diseases (STDs). However, all condoms can tear or leak.

An intrauterine device, or IUD, is inserted into the uterus by a physician. Some IUDs thicken cervical mucus so sperm cannot swim through it. Others shed copper, which keeps an early embryo from implanting in the uterus.

The birth control pill is the most common fertility control method in developed countries. "The Pill" is a mix of synthetic estrogens and progesterone-like hormones that prevents both maturation of oocytes and ovulation. When taken consistently, it is highly effective. Its use lowers risk of ovarian and uterine cancer but raises risk of breast, cervical, and liver cancer. A birth control patch is a small, flat adhesive patch applied to skin. It delivers the same mixture of hormones as an oral contraceptive, and it blocks ovulation the same way.

Both birth control pills and the birth control patch raise the risk of stroke and other serious cardiovascular disorders. The risk of these complications is greatest in older women and women who smoke.

> Typically, some sperm swim through the cervix within seconds of ejaculation.

**contraception** Methods used to prevent pregnancy.
**orgasm** Sexual climax during which neurotransmitter release causes smooth muscle contractions accompanied by a feeling of release and pleasure.
**ovum** Mature egg.

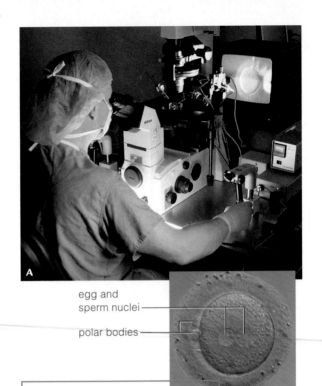

**FIGURE 26.11**

Assisted reproduction. **A** Doctor using a micromanipulator to inject a human sperm into an egg. The monitor shows what he sees in the microscope. **B** Fertilized human egg produced by *in vitro* fertilization.

egg and sperm nuclei

polar bodies

Hormone injections or implants prevent ovulation. Each injection acts for several months, whereas the implant lasts for three years. Both methods are quite effective, but may cause sporadic, heavy bleeding.

Some women turn to emergency contraception after a condom tears, or after unprotected consensual sex or rape. "Morning-after pills" are now available without a prescription to women over age 18. They prevent ovulation and work best if taken immediately after intercourse. However, they can be effective up to three days later. The pills are not meant to be used on a regular basis. Nausea, vomiting, abdominal pain, headache, and dizziness are side effects. Insertion of a copper IUD can also be used as a form of emergency contraception. Like any other use of an IUD, this requires the assistance of a physician.

**Abortion** About 10 percent of women who learn that they are pregnant suffer a spontaneous abortion, or miscarriage. The risk is higher for women older than age 35. Many more pregnancies end without ever being detected. It is estimated that about 50 percent of fertilized eggs are spontaneously aborted, most often because they have genetic defects.

An induced abortion is the deliberate dislodging and removal of an embryo or a fetus from the uterus. In the United States, about half of unplanned pregnancies end in induced abortion. From the clinical standpoint, abortion usually is a brief, safe, and relatively painless procedure, especially in the first trimester.

The drug mifepristone (RU-486) together with a prostaglandin can be used to induce abortion during the first nine weeks of pregnancy. The two chemicals interfere with progesterone receptors in the uterus. The uterine lining cannot be maintained, and neither can pregnancy.

**Assisted Reproduction** About 15 percent of couples in the United States are infertile; the woman either does not become pregnant or repeatedly miscarries. When a couple make normal sperm and oocytes but cannot conceive naturally they may turn to *in vitro* **fertilization**. By this process, an egg and sperm are combined outside the body. The process was first carried out in 1978, and has since produced about 45,000 pregnancies in the United States alone.

In preparation for *in vitro* fertilization, a woman receives injections of a drug that increases the number of oocytes that mature during a cycle. The physician then harvests mature oocytes from the woman's body. Often sperm are injected into the harvested oocytes (Figure 26.11). This overcomes any problems with sperm motility. The zygotes that result from fertilization are allowed to divide, forming small cell clusters. One or more of these clusters are then transferred to a woman's uterus to undergo development.

Assisted reproduction attempts are costly and most fail. In 30-year-old women, about one-third of *in vitro* attempts result in a birth. In 40-year-olds, only one in six attempts succeeds.

**Overview of Sexually Transmitted Disease** Each year, pathogens that cause **sexually transmitted diseases**, or STDs, infect about 15 million Americans (Table 26.2). Two-thirds of those infected are under age twenty-five; one-quarter are teenagers. More than 65 million Americans have a viral STD that cannot be cured. The social consequences of STDs are enormous. Women are more easily infected than men, and they develop more complications. For example, pelvic inflammatory disease (PID), a secondary outcome of bacterial STDs, scars the female reproductive tract and can cause infertility, chronic pain, and tubal pregnancies (Figure 26.12**A**). Infected women commonly pass chlamydia on to their newborn (Figure 26.12**B**). Besides causing skin sores, type 2 herpes virus kills half of infected fetuses and causes neural defects in one-fourth of the rest.

| Table 26.2 | New STD Cases Annually | |
|---|---|---|
| STD | In the U.S. | Worldwide |
| HPV infection | 6,200,000 | 400,000,000 |
| Trichomoniasis | 7,400,000 | 174,000,000 |
| Chlamydia | 3,000,000 | 92,000,000 |
| Genital herpes | 1,000,000 | 24,000,000 |
| Gonorrhea | 650,000 | 62,000,000 |
| Syphilis | 70,000 | 12,000,000 |
| HIV infection | 56,000 | 2,500,000 |

**Common STDs** Infection by human papillomaviruses (HPV) is one of the most widespread and fastest spreading STDs in the United States. Of about 100 HPV strains, a few cause genital warts. In women, the bumplike growths form on the vagina, cervix, and genitals. In men, they form on the penis and scrotum. A few strains of HPV are the main cause of cervical cancer. Sexually active females should have an annual Pap smear, in which cells from the cervix are examined using a microscope. A recently approved vaccine can prevent HPV infection if given before viral exposure (Section 22.1).

Trichomoniasis is caused by the flagellated protozoan *Trichomonas vaginalis*. Symptoms in women include a yellowish discharge, soreness, and itching of the vagina. Men are usually symptom-free. In both sexes, untreated infections cause infertility. A single dose of an antiprotozoal drug can quickly cure the infection. Both sexual partners must receive treatment to prevent reinfection.

Chlamydial infection is primarily a young person's disease, because 40 percent of those infected are still in their teens. A bacterium, *Chlamydia trachomatis*, causes the disease, and antibiotics quickly kill it. Most infected women have no symptoms and are not even diagnosed. Half of infected men have discharge from the penis and painful urination. Untreated men risk inflammation of the epididymides and infertility.

About 45 million Americans have genital herpes, which is caused by type 2 herpes simplex virus. An initial infection commonly causes small sores at the site of infection. The sores heal, but once a person has been infected, he or she harbors the virus for life. In most people, the infection periodically becomes reactivated, causing tingling or itching, which may or may not be accompanied by visible sores. Antiviral drugs can promote healing of sores caused by an active infection and lessen the likelihood of viral reactivation.

The bacterium *Neisseria gonorrhoeae* is the cause of gonorrhea. Less than one week after a male is infected, yellow pus oozes from the penis. Urination becomes frequent and painful. An infected woman usually has few symptoms at first, but the pathogen can infect oviducts, causing cramps, scarring, and sterility. Oral contraceptives promote infection by altering vaginal pH. Altered pH causes the number of resident bacteria in the vagina to decline, allowing *N. gonorrhoeae* to move in. Even though antibiotic treatment quickly cures gonorrhea, the disease remains common. One reason may be a tendency of women to overlook the slight symptoms that arise in the early stages of the disease.

Syphilis is caused by a spiral-shaped bacteria (*Treponema pallidum*). Painless chancres (skin ulcers) appear in the primary stage. They heal, but the bacteria multiply inside the spinal cord, brain, eyes, bones, joints, and mucous membranes. More chancres form in the infectious secondary stage (Figure 26.12**C**). Continued infection can damage the liver, bones, and other internal organs. Chronic immune reactions to the bacteria may severely damage the brain and spinal cord, leading to blindness and paralysis. The incidence of syphilis declined in the 1990s, but began rising in 2000 and continues to increase.

Infection by HIV (or human immune deficiency virus) can cause AIDS (acquired immunodeficiency syndrome), in which the immune system weakens and infectious organisms take hold. Section 13.6 described the HIV virus and Section 22.8 explained how its effects on the immune system lead to AIDS. With regard to sexual transmission, oral sex is least likely to transmit an infection. Unprotected anal sex is 5 times more dangerous than unprotected vaginal sex and 50 times more dangerous than oral sex. To reduce the risk of HIV transmission during vaginal or anal sex, doctors recommend use of a latex condom and a lubricant. The lubricant helps prevent small abrasions that could allow the virus to enter the body. If you think you could have been exposed to HIV, get tested as soon as possible. Early treatment may prevent development of AIDS.

**FIGURE 26.12** A few consequence of STDs.

**A** Increased risk of tubal pregnancy. Scarring caused by STDs can cause an embryo to implant itself in an oviduct. Untreated tubal pregnancies can rupture an oviduct and cause bleeding, infection, and death.

**B** An infant with chlamydia-inflamed eyes. The bacterial pathogen passed from mother to child during the birth process.

**C** Chancres (open sores) caused by syphilis.

*in vitro* **fertilization** Infertility treatment in which gametes are combined outside the body.

**sexually transmitted disease** Infectious disease caused by a pathogen that can live in the reproductive tract.

Week 4

Weeks 5–6

yolk sac
connecting stalk
embryo

forebrain

future lens

pharyngeal
arches

developing heart

upper limb bud

somites

neural tube
forming

lower limb
bud

tail

actual length

head growth exceeds
growth of other regions

retinal pigment

future external ear

upper limb differentiation
(hand plates develop, then
digital rays of future fingers;
wrist, elbow start forming)

umbilical cord formation
between weeks 4 and 8
(amnion expands, forms
tube that encloses the
connecting stalk and a
duct for blood vessels)

foot plate

actual length

**FIGURE 26.14** Human embryonic
and fetal development.

Figure It Out: Is a human embryo ever
as big as your fist?

Answer: No. By the time the developing
individual is as big as a fist, it is a fetus.

**Embryonic Development** Gastrulation occurs about two weeks after
fertilization. Cells from the outer layer of the embryonic disk migrate inward
and form a three-layered embryo.

By the fourth week, the neural tube and notochord that characterize all
vertebrate embryos have formed (Figure 26.14). Multiple paired bumps of mesoderm called somites become visible. These are the embryonic sources of most
bones, of skeletal muscles of the head and trunk, and of the dermis overlying
these regions. Pharyngeal arches appear at an embryo's head end. They look like
the arches that give rise to fish gills, but they do not ever support gills. They
develop into bone, cartilage, and muscles of the face, ears, larynx, and pharynx.

When the fourth week ends, the embryo is 500 times its starting size. Now
the pace slows as details of the embryo's organs begin to fill in. Limbs form as
toes and fingers are sculpted from paddles.

Week 8                    Week 16

placenta

final week of embryonic
period; embryo looks
distinctly human
compared to other
vertebrate embryos

upper and lower limbs well
formed; fingers and then
toes have separated

primordial tissues of
all internal, external
structures now developed

tail has become stubby

actual length

Length:  16 centimeters
         (6.4 inches)
Weight:  200 grams
         (7 ounces)

**WEEK 29**
Length:  27.5 centimeters
         (11 inches)
Weight:  1,300 grams
         (46 ounces)

**WEEK 38** (full term)
Length:  50 centimeters
         (20 inches)
Weight:  3,400 grams
         (7.5 pounds)

During fetal period, length
measurement extends
from crown to heel (for
embryos, it is the longest
measurable dimension, as
from crown to rump).

## Fetal Development

At the end of the eighth week, all organ systems have formed and the developing individual is now considered a **fetus**. A fetal heartbeat can be detected at about five months, and a mother usually begins to feel reflexive fetal movements about five to six months after fertilization. Soft, fuzzy hair, the lanugo, covers the fetus. The fetal skin is wrinkled, reddish, and protected from abrasion by a thickened, cheeselike coating. Eyelids form and the eyes open in the seventh month.

The optimal birthing time is about 38 weeks after the estimated time of fertilization. A fetus born prematurely (before 22 weeks) cannot survive. Births before 28 weeks (7 months) are risky, mainly because the lungs have not fully developed. The risks start to drop after this. By 36 weeks, the survival rate is 95 percent. However, a fetus born between 36 and 38 weeks still has some trouble breathing and maintaining a normal body temperature.

**fetus** Developing human between 9 weeks of age and birth.

amniotic fluid

umbilical cord

pool of maternal blood

placenta

fetal blood vessels inside umbilical cord

chorionic villus, with fetal blood vessels inside it

maternal blood in uterine lining

**FIGURE 26.15 Animated!** The life-support system of a developing human. *Left*, artist's depiction of the view inside the uterus, showing a fetus connected by an umbilical cord to the pancake-shaped placenta. *Right*, the structure of the placenta. It consists of maternal and fetal tissue. Fetal blood flowing in vessels of chorionic villi exchanges substances by diffusion with maternal blood around the villi. However, the bloodstreams do not mix.

**Functions of the Placenta** All exchange of materials between an embryo and its mother takes place by way of the placenta, a pancake-shaped, blood-engorged organ made of uterine lining and extraembryonic membranes (Figure 26.15).

The placenta begins forming early in pregnancy. By the third week, maternal blood has begun to pool in spaces in the lining of the uterus tissue. Chorionic villi—the tiny fingerlike projections from the chorion—grow into the pools of maternal blood. Embryonic blood vessels extend through the umbilical cord to the placenta, and into the chorionic villi, where they are surrounded by the pooled maternal blood. The maternal and embryonic bloodstreams never mix. Instead, substances move between maternal and embryonic blood by diffusing across the walls of the embryonic vessels in the chorionic villi. Oxygen and nutrients diffuse from pooled maternal blood into embryonic vessels in the villi. Wastes diffuse the other way, and the mother's body disposes of them.

The placenta also has a hormonal role. From the third month on, it produces large amounts of HCG, progesterone, and estrogens. These hormones encourage the ongoing maintenance of the uterine lining.

**Maternal Effects on Prenatal Development** An embryo or fetus depends on its mother to supply nutrients. It is also exposed to pathogens and toxins that enter the mother's body.

A pregnant woman must eat enough to gain 20 to 25 pounds, on average. If she does not, her newborn may be seriously underweight. A low birth weight is correlated with a higher risk of postdelivery complications and impaired brain function. Supplements of some minerals and vitamins can help ensure that development proceeds normally. For example, taking B-complex vitamins during early pregnancy helps reduce the risk of severe neural tube defects in the embryo. Folate (folic acid) is especially important in this regard.

Some pathogens can cross the placenta. Diseases are especially dangerous in the first six weeks after fertilization, when organ systems are still forming. For example, if a pregnant woman gets rubella (German measles) in this critical period, there is a 50 percent chance that some of her child's organs will not form properly. For instance, if she is infected while embryonic ears are forming, her newborn may be deaf. If she is infected from the fourth month of pregnancy onward, the disease will have no notable effect. A woman can avoid risks associates with rubella by getting vaccinated against the virus before pregnancy.

Another pathogen that can affect development is a protist that sometimes lurks in garden soil, cat feces, and undercooked meat. It causes toxoplasmosis. The disease often does not cause symptoms, so a pregnant woman may become infected and not realize it. If the parasite crosses the placenta, it can infect her child and lead to developmental problems, a miscarriage, or stillbirth. To minimize the risk, pregnant women should eat well-cooked meat and avoid cat feces. Let someone else change that litter box.

Alcohol passes across the placenta, so when a pregnant woman drinks alcohol, her embryo or fetus feels the effects. Alcohol exposure can cause fetal alcohol syndrome, or FAS. A small head and brain, facial abnormalities, slow growth, mental impairment, heart problems, and poor coordination characterize affected infants (Figure 26.16). The damage is permanent. Children affected by FAS never catch up, physically or mentally. As a result, most doctors now advise women who are pregnant or attempting to become pregnant to avoid alcohol.

Caffeine interferes with nervous system development in animals, and may also harm human embryos. A recent study showed that women who took in 200 milligrams a day of caffeine (the amount in one and a half cups of coffee) had twice as many miscarriages as those who avoided caffeine. The study's authors advise pregnant women to chose decaffeinated or caffeine-free beverages.

Smoking or exposure to secondhand smoke increases the risk of miscarriage and adversely affects fetal growth and development. Carbon monoxide in the smoke can outcompete oxygen for the binding sites on hemoglobin, so the embryo or fetus of a smoker gets less oxygen than that of a nonsmoker. In addition, levels of the addictive stimulant nicotine in amniotic fluid can be even higher than those in the mother's blood.

Some medications cause birth defects. Isotretinoin (Accutane), a highly effective treatment for severe acne, is often prescribed for young women. If taken early in a pregnancy, it can cause heart problems or facial and cranial deformities in the embryo. Some antidepressants also increase the risk of birth defects. Paroxetine (Paxil) and related drugs inhibit the reuptake of serotonin. Use of these drugs during early pregnancy increases the likelihood of heart malformations. Taking them later in pregnancy increases risk that an infant will have fatal heart and lung disorders.

Highly addictive drugs such as methamphetamine and cocaine also cross the placenta. They increase the risk of a prenatal stroke and decrease birth weight.

FIGURE 26.16 Child with fetal alcohol syndrome. Obvious symptoms are low and prominently positioned ears, improperly formed cheekbones, and an abnormally wide, smooth upper lip. Growth-related complications, heart problems, and nervous system abnormalities are also common.

# Take-Home Message  How does a human develop?

- Cleavage produces a blastocyst, which implants in the uterus. Projections from its surface invade maternal tissue and form a placenta. The placenta permits exchanges between a mother and embryo without intermingling bloodstreams. Pathogens and toxins, as well as nutrients, can cross the placenta.

- Gastrulation occurs about two weeks after fertilization, and produces a three-layered embryo. Chordate features such as a neural tube, notochord, and pharyngeal arches form later in the embryonic period.

- The fetal period begins at the end of the eighth week. Heartbeats are detected at about five months, and limb movements are felt at five to six months.

- Lungs are not fully formed until about 28 weeks (7 months), so births before this point are highly risky. A fetus born before 22 weeks will not survive.

**FIGURE 26.17** Childbirth.

**1** The fetal head puts pressure on the cervix, stimulating hormone (oxytocin) release that causes muscle contractions.

**2** Muscle contractions propel the fetus out of the uterus and through the vagina.

**3** The placenta detaches and is also expelled.

**labor** Expulsion of a placental mammal from its mother's uterus by muscle contractions.

# 26.7 From Birth Onward

**The Process of Birth** Properties of the cervix are altered as a fetus nears full term. Up to this point, the cervix has remained firm and has helped keep the fetus from slipping out of the uterus prematurely. In the final weeks of pregnancy, the connective tissue of the cervix weakens. Collagen fibers become less tightly linked and the cervix gets thinner, softer, and more flexible. This prepares it to stretch enough to allow the passage of the fetus.

The birth process is known as **labor**, or parturition. Often a women finds she is about to begin labor when "her water breaks." This common phrase describes the rupturing of the amnion, which causes a large amount of amniotic fluid to drain out of the vagina. During labor, the cervix dilates and the fetus moves through it into the vagina, and then into the outside world (Figure 26.17).

The hormone oxytocin stimulates smooth muscle contractions during labor. As the fetus nears full term, it usually "drops," or shifts down, so the head touches the cervix. Receptors in the cervix sense mechanical pressure and signal the hypothalamus, which calls for oxytocin secretion by the posterior pituitary.

The binding of oxytocin to smooth muscle of the uterus increases the strength of contractions, which causes more mechanical pressure. This leads to more oxytocin secretion, and so on. The result is a positive feedback cycle—stretching of the cervix triggers more oxytocin secretion, which results in more stretching. This continues until the fetus has been expelled and there is no longer any mechanical pressure on the cervix. Synthetic oxytocin is sometimes given intravenously to induce or increase contractions.

Strong contractions help detach the placenta from the uterus and expel it as the afterbirth. Contractions also help to stop the bleeding where the placenta was attached to the wall of the uterus, by causing blood vessels at this ruptured attachment site to constrict. The umbilical cord is cut and tied off. A few days after shriveling up, the cord's stump has become the navel.

**Nourishing the Newborn** Once the lifeline to the mother is severed, a newborn enters the extended time of dependency and learning that is typical of all primates. Early survival requires an ongoing supply of milk or a nutritional equivalent. Lactation, or milk production, occurs in mammary glands inside a mother's breasts (Figure 26.18). Before pregnancy, breast tissue is largely adipose tissue and a system of undeveloped ducts. During pregnancy, estrogens and progesterone stimulate the development of a glandular system for milk production. Prolactin, a hormone secreted by the anterior pituitary gland, stimulates the growth of cells that will produce milk proteins.

After birth, the mechanical stimulus of suckling by a newborn increases maternal secretion of prolactin and oxytocin. The prolactin stimulates the production of milk proteins. For the first few days after birth, mammary glands produce a clear fluid rich in proteins and lactose (milk sugar). Then, milk production begins. Oxytocin causes smooth muscle contractions that force fluid into milk ducts. It also causes smooth muscle contractions in the uterus, which helps this organ shrink to its pre-pregnancy size.

In addition to its nutrients, human breast milk has antibodies that enhance resistance to infection. Other components of breast milk stimulate the growth of symbiotic bacteria in an infant's gut. Alcohol, drugs, mercury, and other toxins in a mother's body can also be secreted in milk. HIV and some other viruses are carried by milk as well.

**Postnatal Development** Like many animals, humans change in size and proportion until reaching sexual maturity. Postnatal growth is most rapid between years thirteen and nineteen. Sex hormone secretions increase and bring about development of secondary sexual traits as well as sexual maturity. Not until adulthood are the bones fully mature. Body tissues are usually well maintained into early adulthood. As more years pass, they slowly deteriorate through processes collectively described as aging.

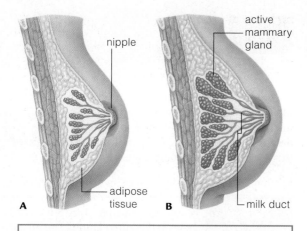

**FIGURE 26.18 A** Breast of a woman who is not lactating. **B** Breast of a lactating woman. Her mammary glands have been activated by exposure to prolactin and are producing milk. Milk ducts are lined with smooth muscle, which contracts to force milk out of the breast through ducts in the nipple.

## Take-Home Message  What happens during and after birth?

- Hormonal changes prepare a woman's body for labor and nursing.
- During labor, hormone-stimulated contraction of uterine smooth muscle forces the fetus out of the body.
- Milk secreted by mammary glands provides nutrition and also has antibodies that protect the newborn from infection. Some pathogens and toxins can be transmitted in breast milk.
- Growth and development continues after birth. Bones are not fully mature until early adulthood.

# 26.8

# Impacts/Issues Revisited: Mind-Boggling Births

A high level of FSH, the hormone that stimulates egg maturation, increases the likelihood of fraternal twins and other multiple births. FSH level and the prevalence of fraternal twinning varies among families and among ethnic groups. A woman who is herself a fraternal twin has double the average chance of giving birth to fraternal twins. If a woman has one set of fraternal twins, her odds of having a second set triples. Fraternal twins are most common among women of African descent, less common among Caucasians, and rare among Asians.

Age also has an effect. A woman's FSH levels rise from puberty through her midthirties, causing her likelihood of having fraternal twins to rise. Thus, a trend toward later childbearing is contributing to a rise in fraternal twinning.

FSH level does not influence formation of identical twins. Such twins arise when a zygote or early embryo splits, and two genetically identical individuals develop. A split is a chance event; a tendency to produce identical twins does not run in families and such twins occur with equal frequency among women of all ethnic groups and ages.

**How Would**

YOU ☑ Vote ?

Should use of fertility drugs, which increase the risk of multiple births, be discouraged?

See CengageNow for details, then vote online (cengagenow.com).

# Summary

**Section 26.1** Multiple births are on the increase, largely as a result of fertility treatments. The increase is a matter of concern because multiple births are more likely than single births to have complications.

**Section 26.2** Asexual reproduction produces genetic copies of the parent. Sexual reproduction is energetically more costly, and a parent does not have as many of its genes represented among the offspring. However, sexual reproduction produces variable offspring, which may be advantageous in environments where conditions change from one generation to the next.

Most animals reproduce sexually and have separate sexes, but some are hermaphrodites that produce both eggs and sperm. With external fertilization, gametes are released into water. Most animals on land have internal fertilization; gametes meet in a female's body.

Sexual reproduction begins with the formation of gametes—sperm and eggs—that combine at fertilization to form a zygote. During cleavage, mitosis increases the number of cells but not the original volume of the zygote. Cleavage yields a blastula, a hollow, fluid-filled cluster of cells (*right*).

During gastrulation, cells become organized into primary tissue layers. Organs start to form as cells in these layers differentiate. The development of body form involves cell migrations, cell shape changes, and cell death. In the final stage, growth and tissue specialization, organs enlarge and develop specialized properties.

CENGAGENOW‑ Watch a frog develop and see how the neural tube is formed with the animation on CengageNow.

**Section 26.3** Testes are primary male reproductive organs (Table 26.3). They produce sperm and the sex hormone testosterone. Accessory glands produce the other components of semen. These components are added as the sperm pass through a series of ducts that convey them out of the body. Ovaries are the female's primary reproductive organs (Table 26.3). They produce eggs and sex hormones: estrogens and progesterone. Pituitary hormones (LH, FSH) control production of both sperm and eggs.

Males produce sperm continually. A female is born with immature eggs. After puberty, the eggs mature one at a time in an

approximately monthly cycle. In this cycle, FSH encourages follicle maturation, then a surge of LH near the midpoint of the cycle triggers ovulation. After ovulation, the remains of a follicle become a hormone-secreting corpus luteum.

Hormones secreted by the maturing follicle and the corpus luteum encourage thickening of the uterine lining. If pregnancy does not occur, the corpus luteum breaks down, and the uterine lining is shed during menstruation.

CENGAGENOW‑ Use the animation and interaction on CengageNow to learn about human reproductive structures, sperm formation, egg formation, and the cyclic changes in the ovary and uterus.

**Section 26.4** Hormones and nerves govern physiological changes that occur during arousal and intercourse. Millions of sperm are ejaculated, but usually only one penetrates the secondary oocyte. Fertilization usually occurs in an oviduct.

CENGAGENOW‑ Observe fertilization with the animation on CengageNow.

**Section 26.5** Pregnancy can be avoided by behavior, or through diverse methods that prevent ovulation, fertilization, or implantation. *In vitro* fertilization brings sperm and eggs together for fertilization outside the body. An abortion ends a pregnancy.

Sexually transmitted diseases (STDs) are caused by protozoal, bacterial, and viral pathogens and are spread by unsafe sex. Viral STDs are incurable. Bacterial and protozoal STDs can be cured. If untreated, they can cause sterility and harm the health of parents and their offspring.

**Section 26.6** After fertilization, a blastocyst forms by cleavage and burrows into the wall of the uterus. Membranes form around the blastocyst. Some combine with the maternal tissue to form a placenta that passes oxygen and nutrients between mother and embryo. The placenta can also deliver toxins.

By the end of the eighth week, when the embryo becomes a fetus, all organ systems have formed. After 7 months it can survive if born prematurely.

CENGAGENOW‑ Observe fertilization and implantation and learn how the placenta forms and functions with the animation on CengageNow.

**Section 26.7** Hormones prepare a woman's body for pregnancy, labor, and nursing. During labor, uterine contractions expel the fetus and placenta. Milk secreted by mammary glands supplies nutrients and also contains antibodies that help a newborn resist infection. Development and growth continue until adulthood.

| Table 26.3 | Organs of the Human Reproductive Tracts |
|---|---|
| **Male Reproductive Tract** | |
| Testes | Sperm production; sex hormone production |
| Epididymides | Sperm maturation and storage |
| Vasa deferentia | Convey sperm from epididymides to ejaculatory ducts |
| Ejaculatory ducts | Convey sperm from vasa deferentia to the urethra |
| Urethra | Conveys sperm through penis and out of the body |
| Penis | Organ of sexual intercourse |
| **Female Reproductive Tract** | |
| Ovaries | Egg production, maturation; sex hormone production |
| Oviducts | Convey oocyte from ovary to uterus |
| Uterus | Chamber in which new individual develops |
| Cervix | Entrance into uterus; mucus secretion |
| Vagina | Organ of sexual intercourse; birth canal |

## Self-Quiz     Answers in Appendix I

1. _____ reproduction produces genetic copies of a parent.

2. A(n) _____ produces both eggs and sperm.
   a. hermaphrodite          c. ovary
   b. asexual organism       d. testis

3. A _____ is a hollow ball of cells that becomes a _____ by the process of gastrulation.

4. Meiotic divisions of germ cells in the _____ give rise to sperm.
   a. seminiferous tubule    c. penis
   b. prostate gland         d. epididymis

5. True or false? A female's germ cells do not divide after birth.

6. During a menstrual cycle, a midcycle surge of _____ secreted by the pituitary triggers ovulation.
   a. estrogen    b. progesterone    c. LH    d. FSH

7. After ovulation, the corpus luteum secretes _____ .
   a. LH                      c. progesterone
   b. FSH                     d. prolactin

8. A _____ implants in the lining of the uterus.
   a. zygote                  c. blastocyst
   b. gastrula                d. fetus

9. Number these events in human development in the correct order.
   _____ gastrulation occurs
   _____ blastocyst forms
   _____ zygote forms
   _____ neural tube forms
   _____ heart starts beating

10. Which of the following STDs are caused by bacteria?
    a. chlamydia              d. trichomoniasis
    b. gonorrhea              e. a and b
    c. genital warts          f. all of the above

11. The placenta includes _____ .
    a. maternal tissue        c. mesoderm
    b. chorion tissue         d. a and b

12. Secretion of oxytocin stimulates _____ .
    a. contraction of uterine smooth muscle
    b. expulsion of milk from mammary glands
    c. ovulation              e. a and b
    d. blastocyst implantation    f. all of the above

13. Match each human reproductive structure with the most suitable description.
    _____ testis          a. maternal and fetal tissues
    _____ cervix          b. adds fluid to sperm in semen
    _____ placenta        c. produces testosterone
    _____ vagina          d. produces estrogen and
    _____ ovary               progesterone
    _____ oviduct         e. usual site of fertilization
    _____ prostate gland  f. secretes milk
    _____ mammary gland   g. birth canal
                          h. entrance to uterus

Additional questions are available on CENGAGENOW™

# Digging Into Data

### Multiple Births and Birth Defects

People considering fertility treatments should be aware that such treatments raise the risk of multiple births, and that multiple pregnancies are associated with an increased risk of some birth defects.

Figure 26.19 shows the results of Yiwei Tang's study of birth defects reported in Florida from 1996 to 2000. Tang compared the incidence of various defects among single and multiple births. She calculated the relative risk for each type of defect based on type of birth, and corrected for other differences that might increase risk such as maternal age, income, race, and medical care during pregnancy. A relative risk of less than 1 means a defect occurs less often with multiple births than single births. A relative risk greater than 1 means that multiples are more likely to have a defect.

1. What was the most common type of birth defect in the single-birth group?

2. Was that type of defect more or less common among multiple-birth newborns than among single births?

3. Tang found that multiples have more than twice the risk of single newborns for one type of defect. Which type?

4. Does a multiple pregnancy increase the relative risk of chromosomal defects in offspring?

| | Prevalence of Defect | | Relative Risk |
|---|---|---|---|
| | Multiples | Singles | |
| Total birth defects | 358.50 | 250.54 | 1.46 |
| Central nervous system defects | 40.75 | 18.89 | 2.23 |
| Chromosomal defects | 15.51 | 14.20 | 0.93 |
| Gastrointestinal defects | 28.13 | 23.44 | 1.27 |
| Genital/urinary defects | 72.85 | 58.16 | 1.31 |
| Heart defects | 189.71 | 113.89 | 1.65 |
| Musculoskeletal defects | 20.92 | 25.87 | 0.92 |
| Fetal alcohol syndrome | 4.33 | 3.63 | 1.03 |
| Oral defects | 19.84 | 15.48 | 1.29 |

**FIGURE 26.19** Prevalence, per 10,000 live births, of various types of birth defects among multiple and single births. Relative risk for each defect is given after researchers adjusted for mother's age, race, previous adverse pregnancy experience, education, Medicaid participation during pregnancy, and the infant's sex and number of siblings.

# Critical Thinking

1. Signals from parasympathetic nerves are necessary for a male to have an erection. Explain why fear or anxiety can make it difficult for a man to achieve an erection.

2. Of all birds, the flightless kiwi has the highest proportion of yolk in its eggs and the longest incubation time. Explain why yolk increases with the length of time a bird spends inside an egg.

# 27 Plant Form and Function

# Phytoremediation uses the ability of plants to take up toxic chemicals dissolved in soil water.

## 27.1 Impacts/Issues: Leafy Cleanup Crews

From World War I until the 1970s, the United States Army tested and disposed of weapons at J-Field, Aberdeen Proving Ground in Maryland (Figure 27.1**A**). Obsolete chemical weapons and explosives were burned in open pits, together with plastics, solvents, and other wastes. Lead, arsenic, mercury, and other metals heavily contaminated the soil and groundwater. So did highly toxic organic compounds, including trichloroethylene (TCE). TCE damages the nervous system, lungs, and liver, and exposure to large amounts can be fatal. Today, the toxic groundwater is seeping toward nearby marshes and the Chesapeake Bay.

To protect the bay and clean up the soil, the Army and the Environmental Protection Agency turned to phytoremediation: the use of plants to take up and concentrate or degrade environmental contaminants. They planted poplar trees that cleanse groundwater by taking up TCE and other organic pollutants from it (Figure 27.1**B**).

Like other vascular plants, poplar trees take up soil water through their roots. Along with the water come nutrients and chemical contaminants, including TCE. Although TCE is toxic to animals, it does not harm the trees. The poplars break down some of it, but they release most of the toxin into the atmosphere. Airborne TCE is the lesser of two evils: It breaks down much more quickly in air than it does in groundwater.

**FIGURE 27.1**
Toxic waste cleanup.
**A** J-Field during its use as a testing site for weapons.
**B** J-Field today. Poplar trees are helping to remove toxic waste left behind in the soil.

Phytotoremediation uses the ability of plants to take up toxic chemicals dissolved in soil water. Plants have this capacity not for our benefit, but rather to meet their own needs for water and nutrients. Scientists who know about plant physiology are finding ways to put plants to work as leafy cleanup crews. Compared to other methods of cleaning up toxic waste sites, phytoremediation is usually less expensive—and it is more appealing to neighbors.

In this chapter and the next, we look at the structure and function of plants. We focus on seed-bearing vascular plants, especially the flowering types that are integral to our lives. These plants are adapted to life on land, where they must obtain water from soil, hold their bodies upright, and keep themselves from drying out. The anatomy of stems, leaves, flowers, and roots are adaptations to these challenges. So are the physiological processes that plants use to obtain nutrients, distribute materials through their body, and reproduce.

# Organization of the Plant Body

With 260,000 species, flowering plants dominate the plant kingdom. Its major groups are the magnoliids, eudicots (true dicots), and monocots (Section 14.7). We focus on eudicots and monocots, many of which have a body plan similar to the one in Figure 27.2. Aboveground shoots consist of plant stems together with their leaves. Stems provide a structural framework for plant growth, and pipelines inside of them conduct water and nutrients between leaves and roots. Roots are structures that absorb water and dissolved minerals as they grow down and outward through the soil. They often anchor the plant. Root cells store food for their own use, and some types also store it for the rest of the plant body.

**Three Plant Tissue Systems**  All plant parts consist of the same three types of tissues (Figure 27.3). The **ground tissue system**, which makes up the bulk of the plant, has many essential functions such as photosynthesis and food storage. Pipelines of the **vascular tissue system** thread through ground tissue. They distribute water and nutrients to all parts of the plant body. The **dermal tissue system** covers and protects the plant's exposed surfaces.

All three plant tissue systems consist of cells that are organized into simple and complex tissues. Simple tissues consist primarily of one type of cell; examples include parenchyma, collenchyma, and sclerenchyma. Complex tissues have two or more cell types. Xylem, phloem, and epidermis are examples.

**Simple Tissues**  Parenchyma tissue makes up most of the soft primary growth of roots, stems, leaves, and flowers, and it also has storage and secretion functions. **Parenchyma** is a simple tissue that consists mainly of parenchyma cells, which are typically thin-walled, flexible, and many-sided. These cells are alive in mature tissue, and they can continue

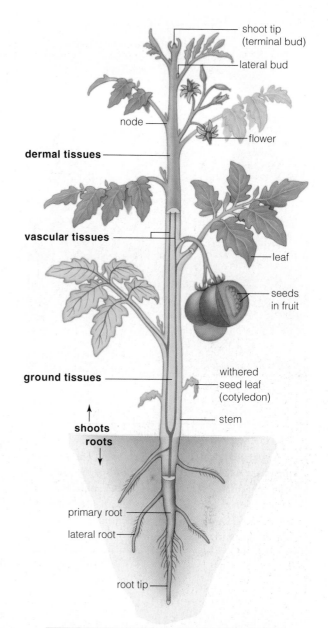

**FIGURE 27.2 Animated!** Body plan of a tomato plant. Vascular tissues (*purple*) conduct water and solutes. They thread through ground tissues that make up most of the plant body. Epidermis, a type of dermal tissue, covers root and shoot surfaces.

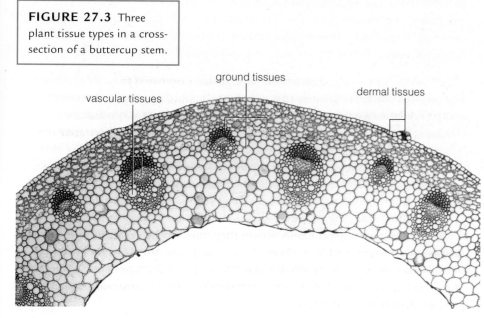

**FIGURE 27.3** Three plant tissue types in a cross-section of a buttercup stem.

**dermal tissue system**  Tissue system that covers and protects the plant body.

**ground tissue system**  Tissue system that makes up the bulk of the plant body; includes most photosynthetic cells.

**parenchyma**  Simple plant tissue made up of living cells; the main component of the ground tissue system.

**vascular tissue system**  Tissue system that distributes water and nutrients through a plant body.

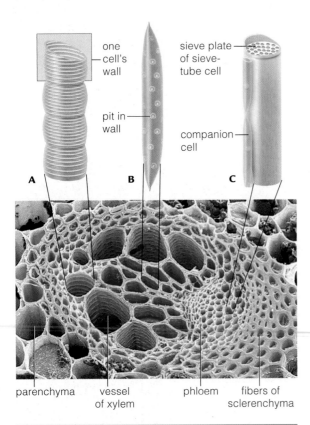

one cell's wall

pit in wall

sieve plate of sieve-tube cell

companion cell

A      B      C

parenchyma    vessel of xylem    phloem    fibers of sclerenchyma

**FIGURE 27.4** Simple and complex tissues in a stem. In xylem, a part of a column of vessel members **A**, and a tracheid **B**. **C** One of the living cells that interconnect as sieve tubes in phloem. Companion cells closely associate with sieve tubes. Fibers of sclerenchyma and parenchyma cells are also visible in the micrograph.

| Table 27.1 | Overview of Flowering Plant Tissues | |
|---|---|---|
| **Tissue Type** | **Main Components** | **Main Functions** |
| **Simple Tissues** | | |
| Parenchyma | Parenchyma cells | Photosynthesis, storage, secretion, tissue repair, other tasks |
| Collenchyma | Collenchyma cells | Pliable structural support |
| Sclerenchyma | Fibers or sclereids | Structural support |
| **Complex Tissues** | | |
| Vascular | | |
| Xylem | Tracheids, vessel members; parenchyma cells; sclerenchyma cells | Water-conducting tubes and reinforcing components |
| Phloem | Sieve-tube members, parenchyma cells; sclerenchyma cells | Tubes of living cells that distribute sugars; supporting cells |
| Dermal | | |
| Epidermis | Undifferentiated cells and specialized cells (e.g., guard cells) | Secretion of cuticle; protection; control of gas exchange and water loss |
| Periderm | Cork cambium; cork cells; parenchyma | Forms protective cover on older stems, roots |

**collenchyma** Simple plant tissue composed of living cells with unevenly thickened walls; provides flexible support.

**companion cell** In phloem, parenchyma cell that loads sugars into sieve tubes.

**cotyledon** Seed leaf; part of a flowering plant embryo.

**epidermis** Outer tissue layer.

**phloem** Complex vascular tissue that distributes sugars through a plant body.

**sclerenchyma** Simple plant tissue; dead at maturity, its lignin-reinforced cell walls structurally support plant parts.

**vascular bundle** Multistranded, sheathed cord of primary xylem and phloem in a stem or leaf.

**xylem** Complex vascular tissue; distributes water and solutes through tubes that consist of interconnected walls of dead cells.

to divide. Plant wounds are repaired by dividing parenchyma cells. Mesophyll, the only photosynthetic ground tissue, is a type of parenchyma.

**Collenchyma** is a simple tissue that consists mainly of collenchyma cells, which are elongated and alive in mature tissue. This stretchable tissue supports rapidly growing plant parts, including young stems and leaf stalks. A polysaccharide called pectin imparts flexibility to a collenchyma cell's primary wall, which is thickened where three or more of the cells abut.

Cells of **sclerenchyma** are variably shaped and dead at maturity, but the lignin-containing walls that remain help this tissue resist compression. Lignin, an organic compound, protects and structurally supports upright plants, and helped them evolve on land (Section 14.2). Fibers and sclereids are typical sclerenchyma cells. Fibers are long, tapered cells that structurally support the vascular tissues in some stems and leaves. They flex and twist, but resist stretching. We use certain fibers as materials for cloth, rope, paper, and other commercial products. The stubbier and often branched sclereids strengthen hard seed coats, such as peach pits, and make pear flesh gritty.

**Vascular Tissues** Xylem and phloem are vascular tissues. Both consist of elongated conducting tubes that are often sheathed in sclerenchyma fibers and parenchyma. **Xylem**, the vascular tissue that conducts water and mineral ions, consists of two types of cells: tracheids and vessel members (Figure 27.4**A,B**). Both cell types are dead at maturity, but their walls, which are stiffened and waterproofed with lignin, remain. These walls interconnect to form conducting tubes, and they lend structural support to the plant. The perforations in adjoining cell walls align, so water moves laterally between the tubes as well as upward through them.

**Phloem** conducts sugars and other organic solutes. Its main cells, sieve-tube members, are alive in mature tissue. They connect end to end at sieve plates, forming sieve tubes that transport sugars from photosynthetic cells to all parts of the plant (Figure 27.4**C**). Phloem's **companion cells** are parenchyma cells that load sugars into the tubes.

**Dermal Tissues** The first dermal tissue to form on a plant is **epidermis**, which is usually a single layer of cells. Epidermal cells secrete substances such as cutin, a polymer of fatty acids, on their outward-facing cell walls. The waxy deposits form a cuticle that helps the plant conserve water and repel pathogens. The epidermis of leaves and young stems also has specialized cells. For example, pairs of specialized epidermal cells form stomata (small gaps across the epidermis) when the cells swell with water. Plants control the diffusion of water vapor, oxygen, and carbon dioxide gases across their epidermis by opening and closing stomata.

**Eudicots and Monocots** Table 27.1 lists the main types of flowering plant tissues, their components, and their functions. The same tissues form in all flowering plants, but they do so in different patterns. Monocots and eudicots are named after their **cotyledons**, which are leaf-like structures that contain food for a plant embryo. These "seed leaves" wither after the seed germinates and the developing plant begins to make its own food by photosynthesis. Cotyledons consist of the same types of tissues in all plants that have them, but the seeds of eudicots have two cotyledons and those of monocots have only one.

Figure 27.5 shows some other differences between monocots and eudicots. Most shrubs and trees, such as rose bushes and maple trees, are eudicots. Lilies, orchids, and corn are examples of typical monocots.

## Take-Home Message What is the basic structure of a flowering plant?

- Plants typically have aboveground shoots and stems, and belowground roots, all of which consist of ground, vascular, and dermal tissues.

- Ground tissues make up most of a plant. Cells of parenchyma have diverse roles, including photosynthesis. Collenchyma and sclerenchyma support and strengthen plant parts.

- Vascular tissues that thread through ground tissue distribute water and solutes. In xylem, water and ions flow through tubes of dead tracheid and vessel member cells. In phloem, sieve tubes that consist of living cells distribute sugars.

- Dermal tissues cover and protect plant surfaces. Epidermis covers young plant surfaces.

- The patterns in which plant tissues are organized differ between eudicots and monocots.

# 27.3 Primary Shoots and Roots

**Inside a Stem** Inside stems and leaves, the ground, vascular, and dermal tissue systems are organized in predictable patterns. In most flowering plants, the cells of primary xylem and phloem are bundled together as long, multistranded cords called **vascular bundles**. Vascular bundles thread lengthwise through the ground tissue system of all stems, leaves, and roots, but the arrangement of the bundles in these structures differs between eudicots and monocots. The vascular bundles of most eudicot

| **A** Eudicots | **B** Monocots |
|---|---|

In seeds, two cotyledons (seed leaves of embryo) | In seeds, one cotyledon (seed leaf of embryo)

Flower parts in fours or fives (or multiples of four or five) | Flower parts in threes (or multiples of three)

Leaf veins usually forming a netlike array | Leaf veins usually running parallel with one another

Pollen grains with three pores or furrows | Pollen grains with one pore or furrow

Vascular bundles organized in a ring in ground tissue of stem | Vascular bundles throughout ground tissue of stem

**FIGURE 27.5 Animated!** Comparing some of the characteristics of eudicots **A** and monocots **B**.

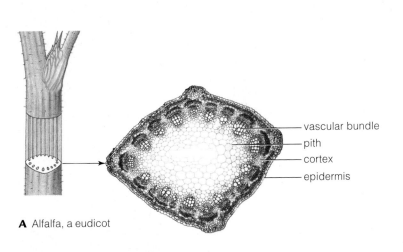

**A** Alfalfa, a eudicot

vascular bundle
pith
cortex
epidermis

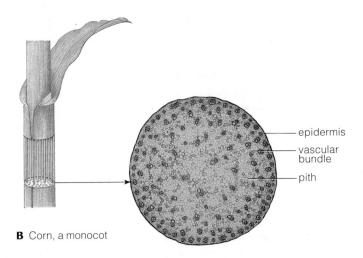

**B** Corn, a monocot

epidermis
vascular bundle
pith

**FIGURE 27.6 Animated!**
Stem structure.

petiole
axillary bud
node
blade
stem
node
blade
sheath

**A** A eudicot leaf    **B** A monocot leaf

**FIGURE 27.7** Typical leaf forms of eudicots and monocots.

**apical meristem** In shoot and root tips, mass of undifferentiated cells, the division of which lengthens plant parts.

**guard cell** One of a pair of cells that define a stoma across the epidermis of a leaf or stem.

**meristem** Zone of undifferentiated plant cells that can divide rapidly.

**primary growth** Plant growth from apical meristems in root and shoot tips.

stems form a cylinder that runs parallel with the long axis of the shoot. Figure 27.6**A** shows how the cylinder divides the parenchyma of ground tissue into cortex (parenchyma between the vascular bundles and the epidermis) and pith (parenchyma inside the cylinder of vascular bundles). Stems of monocots have a different arrangement. Their vascular bundles are distributed all throughout the ground tissue (Figure 27.6**B**).

**Leaf Structure**  A leaf is a sugar factory that has many photosynthetic cells. A typical leaf has a flat blade and, in eudicots, a petiole (stalk) attached to the stem (Figure 27.7**A**). The leaves of most monocots are flat blades, the base of which forms a sheath around the stem (Figure 27.7**B**). Grasses are examples.

Leaf shapes and orientations are adaptations that help a plant intercept sunlight and exchange gases. Most leaves are thin, with a high surface-to-volume ratio; many reorient themselves during the day so that they stay perpendicular to the sun's rays. Typically, adjacent leaves project from a stem in a pattern that allows sunlight to reach them all. However, the leaves of plants native to arid regions may stay parallel to the sun's rays, reducing heat absorption and thus conserving water. Thick or needlelike leaves of some plants also conserve water.

Epidermis covers every leaf surface exposed to the air (Figure 27.8). This surface tissue may be smooth, sticky, or slimy, with hairs, scales, spikes, hooks, and other specializations. A translucent, waxy secreted cuticle slows water loss from the sheetlike array of epidermal cells **1**.

The bulk of the leaf consists of mesophyll, a photosynthetic parenchyma with air spaces between cells **2**. Leaves oriented perpendicular to the sun have two layers of mesophyll. Palisade mesophyll is attached to the upper epidermis. The elongated parenchyma cells of this tissue have more chloroplasts than cells of the spongy mesophyll layer below. Blades of grass and other monocot leaves that grow vertically can intercept light from all directions. The mesophyll in such leaves is not divided into two layers.

Leaf veins are vascular bundles typically strengthened with fibers **3**. Inside the bundles, continuous strands of xylem rapidly transport water and dissolved ions to mesophyll. Continuous strands of phloem rapidly transport the products of photosynthesis (sugars) away from mesophyll. In most eudicots, large veins branch into a network of minor veins embedded in mesophyll. In most monocots, all veins are similar in length and run parallel with the leaf's long axis.

Most leaves have stomata mainly on their lower surface **4**. The **guard cells** on either side of each stoma are the only photosynthetic cells in the leaf epider-

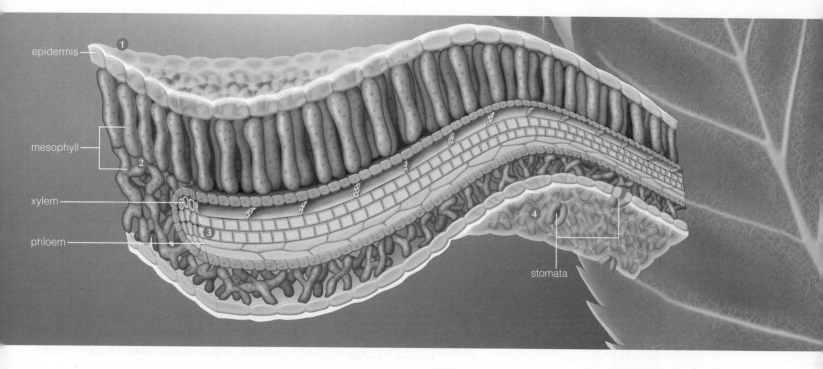

epidermis
mesophyll
xylem
phloem
stomata

**FIGURE 27.8 Animated!**
Anatomy of a eudicot leaf.

**1** The upper leaf surface is epidermis with a secreted layer of cuticle.

**2** The bulk of the leaf is mesophyll, a type of photosynthetic parenchyma.

**3** Vascular bundles of xylem (*gold*) and phloem (*pink*) form veins that thread through the leaf.

**4** The lower leaf surface is also covered with cuticle. Gas exchanges between air inside and outside of the leaf occur at stomata in the lower leaf epidermis.

mis. As you will see in Section 27.6, shape changes of the guard cells close the stomata to prevent water loss, or open the stomata to allow gases to cross the epidermis. Carbon dioxide needed for photosynthesis enters the leaf through stomata, then through air in the spaces between mesophyll cells. Oxygen released by photosynthesis diffuses in the opposite direction.

**Primary Growth of a Shoot** In animals, growth occurs as cells throughout the body divide. In plants, growth occurs only in localized regions called **meristems**, where cells continually divide. **Primary growth** is the lengthening of roots or shoots. It occurs at **apical meristems**—masses of undifferentiated cells that can divide rapidly in the tips of roots and shoots. Terminal buds at shoot tips are the main zone of primary growth (Figure 27.9). Just beneath a terminal bud's surface, cells of apical meristem divide continually during the growing season. Populations of cells that form here are the immature forerunners of dermal tissues, primary vascular tissues, and ground tissue.

Buds may be naked or encased in modified leaves called bud scales. Small regions of tissue that bulge out near the sides of a bud's apical meristem will become new leaves. As the stem lengthens, the leaves form and mature in orderly tiers, one after the next. A region of stem where one or more leaves form is called a node; the region between two successive nodes is called an internode.

A lateral bud is a dormant shoot of mostly meristematic tissue. Each bud forms inside a leaf axil, the point at which the leaf is attached to the stem. Division of cells in an axillary bud can give rise to a branch, leaf, or flower.

**Structure and Development of Primary Roots** The underground portion of a plant, the root system, is just as extensive and essential as the shoot system. Roots grow through the soil and take up water and mineral nutrients. Root primary growth results in one of two kinds of root systems. The taproot system of eudicots consists of a primary root and its lateral branchings. Carrots, oak trees, and poppies are among the plants with a taproot system

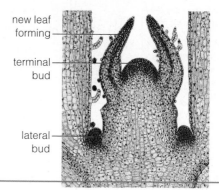

new leaf forming
terminal bud
lateral bud

**FIGURE 27.9** Cross-section through a shoot tip. Division of meristem cells in the terminal bud gives rise to primary growth.

epidermis

cortex

pith

vascular
cylinder

primary
xylem

primary
phloem

**B** Eudicot root cross-section

**C** Monocot root cross-section

a taproot
system

a fibrous
root system

**FIGURE 27.10** Comparing different types of root systems.

VASCULAR
CYLINDER

pericycle

xylem

phloem

cortex

epidermis

root
hair

Vessel members
are mature; root
hairs are about
to form.

New root cells
lengthen, sieve
tubes mature,
vessel members
start forming.

Most cells have
stopped dividing.

Meristem cells
are dividing fast.

No cell division is
occurring here.

root
tip

root cap

**A** Organization of a primary root

**FIGURE 27.11 Animated!** Tissue organization in typical roots. **Figure It Out:** Where does most cell division occur in a primary root? *Answer: At the apical meristem*

(Figure 27.10). By comparison, the primary root of most monocots is replaced by adventitious roots that grow outward from the stem. Lateral roots that are similar in diameter and length branch from adventitious roots. Together, adventitious and lateral roots of such plants form a fibrous root system.

Look at the root tip in Figure 27.11**A**. Some descendants of root apical meristem give rise to a root cap, a dome-shaped mass of cells that protects the soft, young root as it grows through soil. Other descendants give rise to lineages of cells that lengthen, widen, or flatten when they differentiate as part of the dermal, ground, and vascular tissue systems.

Ongoing divisions push cells away from the active root apical meristem. Some of their descendants form epidermis. The root epidermis is the plant's absorptive interface with soil. Many of its specialized cells send out fine extensions called **root hairs**, which collectively increase the surface area available for taking up soil water along with dissolved oxygen and mineral ions.

Descendants of meristem cells also form the root's **vascular cylinder**, a central column of conductive tissue. The root vascular cylinder of typical eudicots is mainly primary xylem and phloem (Figure 27.11**B**). In a typical monocot, the vascular cylinder divides the ground tissue into two zones, cortex and pith (Figure 27.11**C**). The vascular cylinder is sheathed by a pericycle, an array of parenchyma cells one or more layers thick. These cells divide repeatedly in a direction perpendicular to the axis of the root. Masses of cells erupt through the cortex and epidermis as the start of new lateral roots.

## Take-Home Message  How are primary roots and shoots organized?

- The arrangement of vascular bundles, which are multistranded cords of vascular tissue, differs between eudicot and monocot stems and roots.

- Leaves are structurally adapted to intercept sunlight and distribute water and nutrients. Components include mesophyll (photosynthetic cells), veins (bundles of vascular tissue), and cuticle-secreting epidermis.

- A shoot lengthens as cells of apical meristem tissue in a terminal bud divide and differentiate. New leaves or branches develop from lateral buds.

- Roots provide a plant with a tremendous surface area for absorbing water and solutes. Inside each root is a vascular cylinder, with long strands of primary xylem and phloem.

**FIGURE 27.12 Animated!** Secondary growth. **A** Secondary growth occurs at two lateral meristems: Vascular cambium gives rise to secondary vascular tissues, and cork cambium gives rise to periderm. **B** Pattern of growth at vascular cambium. **C** Divisions of meristem cells in vascular cambium expand the inner core of xylem, displacing the vascular cambium (*orange*) toward the surface.

# 27.4 Secondary Growth

Roots and shoots of many plants thicken and become woody over time. Such thickening is called **secondary growth**. Cell divisions in lateral meristems give rise to secondary growth. **Lateral meristems** are cylindrical layers of meristem that run lengthwise through stems and roots (Figure 27.12**A**). Woody plants have two types of lateral meristems: vascular cambium and cork cambium (*cambium* is the Latin word for change).

The **vascular cambium** is the lateral meristem that produces secondary vascular tissue, a few cells thick, inside older stems and roots. Divisions of vascular cambium cells produce secondary xylem on the cylinder's inner surface, and secondary phloem on its outer surface (Figure 27.12**B**). As the core of xylem thickens, it also displaces the vascular cambium toward the surface of the stem or root. The displaced cells of the vascular cambium divide in a widening circle (Figure 27.12**C**).

A core of secondary xylem, or **wood**, contributes up to 90 percent of the weight of some plants. As seasons pass, the expanding inner core of xylem continues to put pressure on the stem or root surface. In time, the pressure ruptures the cortex and the outer secondary phloem. Then, another lateral meristem, the **cork cambium**, forms and gives rise to periderm. **Periderm** is a dermal tissue that consists of parenchyma and cork, as well as the cork cambium that produces them. What we call **bark** is secondary phloem and periderm. Bark consists of all of the living and dead tissues outside of the vascular cambium. The **cork** component of bark has densely packed rows of dead cells, the walls of which are thickened with a waxy substance. Cork protects, insulates, and waterproofs the stem or root surface. Cork also forms over wounded tissues. When leaves drop from the plant, cork forms at the places where petioles had attached to stems.

**bark** In woody plants, secondary phloem and periderm.
**cork** Component of bark; waterproofs, insulates, and protects the surfaces of woody stems and roots.
**cork cambium** In plants, a lateral meristem that gives rise to periderm.
**lateral meristem** Sheetlike cylinder of meristem inside older stems and roots; vascular cambium or cork cambium.
**periderm** Plant dermal tissue that replaces epidermis on older stems and roots.
**root hairs** Hairlike, absorptive extensions of a young cell of root epidermis.
**secondary growth** A thickening of older stems and roots at lateral meristems.
**vascular cambium** Ring of meristematic tissue that produces secondary xylem and phloem.
**vascular cylinder** Sheathed, cylindrical array of primary xylem and phloem in a root.
**wood** Accumulated secondary xylem.

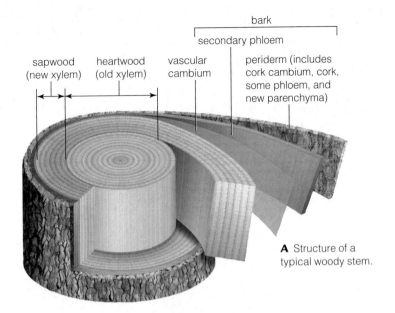

sapwood (new xylem)    heartwood (old xylem)    vascular cambium

bark

secondary phloem

periderm (includes cork cambium, cork, some phloem, and new parenchyma)

**A** Structure of a typical woody stem.

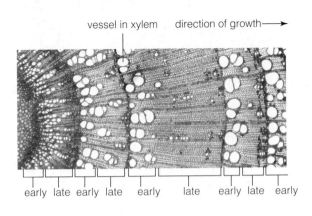

vessel in xylem    direction of growth→

early late early late early late early late early

**B** Early and late wood in an ash tree. Early wood forms during wet springs. Late wood indicates that a tree did not waste energy making large-diameter xylem cells for water uptake during a dry summer or drought.

**FIGURE 27.13 Animated!** Structure of a woody stem. The rings visible in the heartwood and sapwood are regions of early and late wood. In most temperate zone trees, one ring forms each year.

Wood's appearance and function change as a stem or root ages. Metabolic wastes, such as resins, tannins, gums, and oils, clog and fill the oldest xylem so much that it no longer is able to transport water and solutes. These substances darken and strengthen the wood, which is called heartwood.

Sapwood is moist, still-functional xylem between heartwood and vascular cambium. In trees of temperate zones, dissolved sugars travel from roots to buds through sapwood's secondary xylem in spring. The sugar-rich fluid is sap. Each spring, New Englanders collect maple tree sap to make maple syrup.

Vascular cambium is inactive during cool winters or long dry spells. When the weather warms or moisture returns, the vascular cambium gives rise to early wood, with large-diameter, thin-walled cells. Late wood, with small-diameter, thick-walled xylem cells, forms in dry summers. A cross-section through an older trunk reveals alternating bands of early and late wood (Figure 27.13). Each band is a growth ring, or "tree ring."

Trees in regions where growth slows or is suspended during the winter tend to add one growth ring each year. In tropical regions where rainfall is continuous, trees grow at the same rate year-round and do not have growth rings.

## Take-Home Message   What is secondary growth in plants?

- Secondary growth thickens the stems and roots of older plants.
- Divisions of cells in vascular cambium and cork cambium give rise to secondary growth. These lateral meristems form in cylinders that run horizontally through older roots and shoots.
- Secondary vascular tissues form at vascular cambium. Cork cambium gives rise to periderm, which is part of a protective covering of bark.
- Wood is mainly accumulated secondary xylem.

**humus** Decaying organic matter in soil.

# 27.5 Plant Nutrition

**Plant Nutrients and Properties of Soil** Plant growth requires the sixteen elements listed in Table 27.2. Nine elements are macronutrients, which means they are required in amounts above 0.5 percent of the plant's dry weight (its weight after all the water has been removed from the plant body). Seven other elements are micronutrients, which make up traces—typically a few parts per million—of dry weight. Carbon, oxygen, and hydrogen are abundant in air and water. Plants obtain the other nutrients when their roots take up minerals dissolved in soil water.

Some soils are better for plant growth than others. Most plants do best in soil with some decaying organic matter, or **humus**. Humus provides nutrients and also retains water. The amounts and proportions of mineral particles also matters. Sand, silt, and clay—mineral particles that form by the weathering of rocks—differ in size and chemical properties. The biggest sand grains are big enough to see with the naked eye, about one millimeter in diameter. Silt particles are hundreds or thousands of times smaller than sand grains, so they are too small to see. Clay particles are even smaller. A clay particle consists of thin, stacked layers of negatively charged crystals with sheets of water alternating between the layers. Because clay is negatively charged, it attracts positively charged mineral ions dissolved in the soil water. Thus, clay retains dissolved nutrients that would otherwise trickle past roots too quickly to be absorbed.

Even though they do not bind mineral ions as well as clay, sand and silt are also necessary for growing plants. Water and air occupy spaces between the particles and organic bits in soil. Without enough sand and silt to intervene between tiny particles of clay, soil packs so tightly that it excludes air, and without air, root cells cannot secure enough oxygen for aerobic respiration.

| Table 27.2 | Plant Nutrients and Symptoms of Deficiencies | | | | |
|---|---|---|---|---|---|
| Macronutrient | Functions | Symptoms of Deficiency | Micronutrient | Functions | Symptoms of Deficiency |
| Carbon Hydrogen Oxygen | Raw materials for second stage of photosynthesis | None; all are abundantly available in water and carbon dioxide | Chlorine | Role in root and shoot growth and photolysis | Wilting; chlorosis; some leaves die |
| Nitrogen | Component of proteins, coenzymes, chlorophyll, nucleic acids | Stunted growth; light-green older leaves; older leaves yellow and die (these are symptoms of a condition called chlorosis) | Iron | Roles in chlorophyll synthesis and in electron transport | Chlorosis; yellow and green striping in leaves of grass species |
| Potassium | Activation of enzymes; contributes to water–solute balances that influence osmosis* | Reduced growth; curled, mottled, or spotted older leaves; burned leaf edges; weakened plant | Boron | Roles in germination, flowering, fruiting, cell division, nitrogen metabolism | Terminal buds, lateral branches die; leaves thicken, curl, become brittle |
| Calcium | Component in control of many cell functions; cementing cell walls | Terminal buds wither, die; deformed leaves; poor root growth | Manganese | Chlorophyll synthesis; coenzyme action | Dark veins, but leaves whiten and fall off |
| Magnesium | Chlorophyll component; activation of enzymes | Chlorosis; drooped leaves | Zinc | Role in forming auxin, chloroplasts, starch; enzyme component | Chlorosis; mottled or bronzed leaves; root abnormalities |
| Phosphorus | Component of nucleic acids, ATP, phospholipids | Purplish veins; stunted growth; fewer seeds, fruits | Copper | Component of several enzymes | Chlorosis; dead spots in leaves; stunted growth |
| Sulfur | Component of most proteins, two vitamins | Light-green or yellowed leaves; reduced growth | Molybdenum | Part of enzyme used in nitrogen metabolism | Pale green, rolled or cupped leaves |

\* All mineral elements contribute to water–solute balances.

FIGURE 27.14 Examples of root specializations that help plants take up nutrients.

**A** The hairs on this root of a white clover plant are about 0.2 mm long. **B** Mycorrhizae (*white* hairs) extending from the tip of these roots (*tan*) greatly enhance their surface area for absorbing scarce minerals from the soil.

**C** Root nodules on this soybean plant fix nitrogen from air, and share it with the plant. **D** Soybean plants growing in nitrogen-poor soil show how root nodules affect growth. Only the plants in the rows at *right* were infected with nitrogen-fixing bacteria.

**Root Adaptations for Nutrient Uptake** Certain root specializations help plants take up water and nutrients from soil and air. For example, as a plant adds primary growth, its root system may develop billions of tiny root hairs (Figure 27.14**A**). Collectively, these thin extensions of root epidermal cells enormously increase the surface area available for absorbing water and nutrients. Root hairs are fragile and no more than a few millimeters long. They do not develop into new roots; each lasts only a few days.

You already know something about "fungus–roots," or **mycorrhizae** (singular, mycorrhiza). A mycorrhiza is a symbiotic interaction between a young root and a fungus (Section 14.9). Hyphae—filaments of the fungus—form a velvety cover around roots or penetrate the root cells. Collectively, the hyphae have a large surface area, so they absorb mineral ions from a larger volume of soil than roots alone (Figure 27.14**B**). The fungus absorbs some sugars and nitrogen-rich compounds from root cells. The root cells get some scarce minerals that the fungus is better able to absorb.

Some types of anaerobic bacteria in soil are mutualists with clover, peas, and other legumes. Like all other plants, legumes require nitrogen for growth. Nitrogen gas (N≡N, or $N_2$) is abundant in the air, but plants do not have an enzyme that can break it apart. The bacteria do. The enzyme uses ATP to convert nitrogen gas to ammonia ($NH_3$). The metabolic conversion of gaseous nitrogen to ammonia is called **nitrogen fixation**. Other soil bacteria convert ammonia to nitrate ($NO_3^-$), a form of nitrogen that plants readily absorb. Nitrogen-fixing bacteria infect roots and thus become symbionts in localized swellings called **root nodules** (Figure 27.14**C,D**). The bacteria get an oxygen-free environment and sugars from the plant. The plant gets some fixed nitrogen from the bacteria.

## Take-Home Message How do plants get the nutrients they need?

- Nutrients are essential elements for plant growth. Plants require nine macronutrients and seven micronutrients. All are available in air, water, and soil.

- Humus (decaying organic matter) is rich in nutrients. Clay in soil attracts water and nutrients, but can pack tightly, excluding air. Most plants do best in soil with a mixture of particle sizes and a moderate amount of humus.

- Root hairs, root nodules that contain bacteria, and mycorrhizae greatly enhance the uptake of water and dissolved nutrients.

**cohesion–tension theory** Explanation of how transpiration creates a tension that pulls a cohesive column of water through xylem, from roots to shoots.
**mycorrhiza** Fungus–plant root partnership.
**nitrogen fixation** Conversion of nitrogen gas to ammonia.
**root nodules** Swellings of some plant roots that contain nitrogen-fixing bacteria.

# 27.6 Water and Solute Movement in Plants

Water that enters a root moves into xylem of the root vascular cylinder. From there, it travels through pipelines of the xylem to the rest of the plant body. Tracheids and vessel members of xylem are dead at maturity; only their lignin-impregnated walls remain. Being dead, these cells cannot expend any energy to pump water upward against gravity. So how does water move from roots to leaves that may be more than 100 meters (330 feet) above the soil? Figure 27.15 illustrates the **cohesion–tension theory**. By this theory, water in xylem is pulled upward by air's drying power, which creates a continuous negative pressure called tension. The tension extends all the way from leaves to roots.

**FIGURE 27.15 Animated!** Cohesion–tension theory of water transport in vascular plants.

**1** Water evaporates from aboveground plant parts.

**2** The evaporation exerts tension (pulls) on the narrow columns of water that fill xylem tubes. The tension extends from leaves to roots. Hydrogen bonds hold water molecules together inside xylem tubes (cohesion).

**3** As long as evaporation continues, the tension it creates drives the uptake of water molecules from soil.

stoma     cuticle

A

guard cell     guard cell

B

C

10 µm

**FIGURE 27.16** Water-conserving structures in plants. **A** Stomata and cuticle in a cross-section of basswood leaf.

**B** Open stoma. When guard cells swell with water, they bend so that a gap opens between them. The gap allows the plant to exchange gases with air. Guard cells are the only type of epidermal cell with chloroplasts (round structures inside the cells).

**C** Closed stoma. The guard cells, which are not plump with water, are collapsed against each other so there is no gap between them. A closed stoma limits water loss, but it also limits gas exchange.

The evaporation of water from aboveground plant parts, particularly at stomata, is called **transpiration**. Its effect on water inside a plant is a bit like what happens when you suck a drink through a straw. Transpiration puts negative pressure (pulls) on continuous columns of water that fill the narrow conductive tubes of xylem. The water resists breaking into droplets because its molecules are all connected to one another by hydrogen bonds (Section 2.4). A pull on one also pulls on the others. Thus, the negative pressure created by transpiration (tension) pulls on the entire column of water that fills a xylem tube. Because of water's cohesion, the tension extends from leaves, down through stems, into young roots where water is being absorbed from the soil.

The movement of water through plants is driven mainly by transpiration. However, evaporation is only one of many processes in plants that involve the loss of water molecules. Photosynthesis and many other processes contribute to the negative pressure that results in water movement.

**Controlling Water Loss** Even mildly water-stressed plants would wilt and die without a cuticle. This water-impermeable layer coats the walls of all plant cells exposed to air (Figure 27.16**A**). It consists of the waxy, waterproof secretions of epidermal cells. The cuticle is translucent, so it does not prevent light from reaching photosynthetic tissues.

Only about 2 percent of the water that enters a root is used in metabolism. Despite the water-conserving cuticle, most of the rest evaporates right out of the plant, through stomata. A pair of guard cells defines each stoma. When these two cells swell with water, they bend slightly so a gap forms between them (Figure 27.16**B**). The gap is the stoma. When the cells lose water, they collapse against each other, so the gap closes (Figure 27.16**C**).

Environmental cues such as water availability, the level of carbon dioxide inside the leaf, and light intensity affect whether stomata open or close. These cues trigger osmotic pressure changes in the cytoplasm of guard cells. For example, when the sun comes up, the light causes guard cells to begin pumping potassium ions into their cytoplasm. The resulting buildup of potassium ions causes water to enter the cells by osmosis. The guard cells plump up, so the gap between them opens. Carbon dioxide from the air diffuses into the plant's tissues, and photosynthesis begins.

**Distribution of Sugars** Unlike conducting tubes of xylem, sieve tubes in phloem consist of living cells. Sieve-tube cells are positioned side by side and

**pressure flow theory** Explanation of how flow of fluid through phloem is driven by differences in pressure and sugar concentration between a source and a sink.

**translocation** Process that moves organic compounds through phloem.

**transpiration** Evaporation of water from plant parts.

end to end, and their abutting end walls (sieve plates) are porous. Dissolved organic compounds flow through the tubes.

Companion cells that are pressed against the sieve tubes actively transport the organic products of photosynthesis into them. Some of the molecules are used in the cells that make them, but the rest travel through the sieve tubes to all other parts of the plant.

**Translocation** is the formal name for the process that moves organic molecules through phloem. The molecules flow from a source to a sink. A source is any region of the plant where companion cells are loading organic compounds into the sieve tubes. Photosynthetic tissues in leaves are usually a plant's main source region. A sink is any region where molecules are being used or stored. Roots are sink regions, as are growing fruits.

Why do organic compounds flow from a source to a sink? According to the **pressure flow theory**, internal pressure builds up at the source end of the sieve tube. The pressure pushes the solute-rich fluid toward a sink (Figure 27.17). By energy-requiring reactions, companion cells in leaf veins load sugars into sieve-tube members ❶. The sugars increase the solute concentration of the fluid inside the tubes, so water also moves into the tubes, by osmosis ❷. The water increases the fluid volume, which in turn increases the internal pressure (turgor) inside the sieve tubes ❸. Pressure in phloem can be five times higher than the pressure in an automobile tire. That high pressure pushes the sugar-laden fluid toward sink regions, which have a lower internal pressure ❹. The sugars are unloaded at sink regions, and water diffuses out of phloem there, again by osmosis ❺.

## Take-Home Message  How do substances move through a plant body?

- Open stomata allow gas exchange between the air and the plant, but they also allow water loss by transpiration.

- Transpiration puts water in xylem into a continuous state of negative tension from roots to leaves to roots. The tension pulls columns of water in xylem upward through the plant.

- Concentration and pressure gradients move organic compounds inside sieve tubes of phloem, from sources to sinks.

**Translocation**

interconnected sieve tubes

SOURCE (e.g., mature leaf cells)

WATER

❶ Solutes move into a sieve tube against their concentration gradients by active transport.

❷ As a result of increased solute concentration, the fluid in the sieve tube becomes hypertonic. Water moves in from surrounding xylem, increasing phloem turgor.

❸ The pressure difference pushes the fluid from the source to the sink. Water moves into and out of the sieve tube along the way.

flow

❹ Both pressure and solute concentrations gradually decrease as the fluid moves from source to sink.

❺ Solutes are unloaded into sink cells, which then become hypertonic with respect to the sieve tube. Water moves from the sieve tube into sink cells.

SINK (e.g., developing root cells)

**FIGURE 27.17 Animated!** Translocation.

## 27.7

# Impacts/Issues Revisited:
# Leafy Cleanup Crews

With elemental pollutants such as lead or mercury, the best phytoremediation strategies use plants that take up toxins and store them in aboveground tissues. The toxin-laden plant parts can then be harvested for safe disposal. Researchers have genetically modified some plants to enhance their absorptive and storage capacity. Dr. Kuang-Yu Chen, pictured at *left*, is analyzing zinc and cadmium levels in plants that can take up these elements. In the case of organic toxins such as TCE, the best phytoremediation strategies use plants with biochemical pathways that break down the compounds to less toxic molecules. Researchers are beefing up these pathways in many plants. Some are transferring genes from bacteria or animals into plants; others are enhancing expression of genes that encode molecular participants in the plants' own detoxification pathways.

**How Would**

# YOU
☑ **Vote?**

Plants can be genetically engineered to take up toxins more effectively. Do you support the use of such plants to help clean up toxic waste sites? See CengageNow for details, then vote online (cengagenow.com).

# Summary

 **Section 27.1** The ability of plants to take up substances from soil and water is the basis for phytoremediation (the removal of toxic substances from a contaminated area with the help of plants).

**Section 27.2** A plant consists of shoots and roots. The vascular tissue system distributes nutrients and water through the plant. The dermal system protects plant surfaces. The ground tissue system makes up the bulk of the plant body.

Simple plant tissues have only one type of cell. Complex plant tissues have two or more. Monocots and eudicots (true dicots) have the same tissues organized in different ways.

Water and dissolved mineral ions flow through conducting tubes of xylem. The interconnected, perforated walls of tracheids and vessel members (cells that are dead at maturity) form the tubes.

CENGAGENOW™ Explore the body plan of a tomato plant, compare monocot and eudicot tissues, and learn more about ground and vascular tissues with the animations and interactions on CengageNow.

**Section 27.3** Stems support upright growth and conduct water and solutes through vascular bundles. Most eudicot stems have a ring of bundles dividing the ground tissue into cortex and pith. Monocot stems often have vascular bundles distributed throughout their ground tissue.

Leaves have mesophyll (photosynthetic parenchyma) and veins (vascular bundles) between their upper and lower epidermis. Water vapor, oxygen, and carbon dioxide cross the cuticle-covered epidermis at stomata. Roots absorb water and dissolved mineral ions, which become distributed to aboveground parts. Eudicots typically have a taproot system, and many monocots have a fibrous root system.

Lengthening of roots and shoots (primary growth) occurs when cells of apical meristems at root tips or shoot tips divide.

CENGAGENOW™ Look inside plant stems and examine the structure of a leaf and a root with the animations on CengageNow.

**Section 27.4** Woody plants thicken (add secondary growth) by cell divisions at lateral meristems. Divisions at vascular cambium add secondary xylem (wood) and secondary phloem. Divisions at cork cambium add periderm. Bark is periderm and secondary phloem of a woody stem.

CENGAGENOW™ Learn about secondary growth and the structure of a woody stem with the animations on CengageNow.

 **Section 27.5** Plant nutrition requires water, mineral ions, and carbon dioxide. Plants obtain nine macronutrients (such as carbon, oxygen, hydrogen, nitrogen, and phosphorus) and seven micronutrients (such as iron) from air, water, and soil. The properties of soil affect accessibility of water, oxygen, and nutrients to plants. Root hairs increase the surface area for absorption of water and nutrients. Mycorrhizae and bacterial symbionts in root nodules help many plants take up nutrients.

 **Section 27.6** Transpiration is the evaporation of water from plant parts, mainly at stomata, into air. By the cohesion–tension theory, transpiration pulls water upward by creating a continuous negative pressure (or tension) inside xylem from leaves to roots. Hydrogen bonds among water molecules keep the columns of fluid continuous inside the narrow vessels.

A cuticle and stomata balance a plant's loss of water with its needs for gas exchange. Stomata are gaps across the cuticle-covered epidermis of leaves and other plant parts. Each is defined by a pair of guard cells. Closed stomata limit the loss of water, but also prevent the gas exchange required for photosynthesis and aerobic respiration. Water moving into guard cells plumps them, which opens the stoma between them. Water diffusing out of the cells causes them to collapse against each other, so the gap closes.

The movement of sugars and other organic compounds through sieve tubes of phloem is driven by pressure and concentration gradients between source and sink regions. Companion cells load sugars from photosynthetic cells into sieve tubes. The sugars are unloaded at actively growing regions or in areas used for storage.

CENGAGENOW™ See how stomata work, and how vascular plants transport water and organic compounds with the animations on CengageNow.

## Self-Quiz    Answers in Appendix I

1. Roots and shoots lengthen through activity at _____ .
   a. apical meristems          c. vascular cambium
   b. lateral meristems          d. cork cambium

2. _____ conducts mainly water and mineral ions, and _____ conducts mainly sugars.
   a. Phloem; xylem              b. Xylem; phloem

3. The bulk of a leaf is made up of mesophyll, a type of _____ .
   a. sclerenchyma              c. collenchyma
   b. parenchyma                d. dermal tissue

4. Which of the following cell types are alive in mature tissue? Choose all that apply.
   a. collenchyma cells     c. vessels       e. companion cells
   b. sieve tubes            d. tracheids     f. sclerenchyma cells

5. Division of cells of the vascular cambium produces _____ .
   a. epidermis                 c. cork
   b. secondary phloem          d. all of the above

6. Water evaporation from plant parts is called _____ .
   a. translocation             c. transpiration
   b. cohesion                  d. tension

7. When guard cells swell, _____ .
   a. transpiration ceases      c. a stoma opens
   b. sugars enter phloem       d. root cells die

8. A waxy cuticle is secreted by _____ .
   a. ground tissue             c. a stoma
   b. epidermal cells           d. root hairs

9. Plants obtain carbon, hydrogen, and oxygen from _____ .
   a. soil                    c. air
   b. water                   d. b and c

10. Decomposing matter in soil is called _____ .

11. In many plant species, older roots and stems thicken by activity at _____ .
    a. apical meristems        c. vascular cambium
    b. lateral meristems       d. both b and c

12. Water transport from roots to leaves occurs by _____ .
    a. pressure flow
    b. differences in source and sink solute concentrations
    c. the pumping force of xylem vessels
    d. transpiration, tension, and cohesion of water

13. Sugar transport from leaves to roots occurs by _____ .
    a. pressure flow
    b. differences in source and sink solute concentrations
    c. the pumping force of xylem vessels
    d. transpiration, tension, and cohesion of water

14. Match the plant parts with the suitable description.
    _____ apical meristem       a. mass of secondary xylem
    _____ lateral meristem      b. source of primary growth
    _____ xylem                 c. distribution of sugars
    _____ phloem                d. source of secondary growth
    _____ vascular cylinder     e. distribution of water
    _____ wood                  f. central column in roots

Additional questions are available on CENGAGENOW™

# Critical Thinking

1. Suppose you hammer a nail into an oak tree trunk five feet above the ground. If you return 15 years later, after the tree has grown 20 feet taller, how high will the nail be?

2. Iron and manganese are components of chlorophyll. How does a plant obtain these minerals? What effect would you expect a deficiency in one of these minerals to have on plant growth?

3. Farmers sometimes plant clovers or other legumes in fields during the season when they are not growing crops. When crop-planting season approaches, the "cover crop" is plowed under. Explain how this procedure enhances soil fertility.

4. Is the plant with the yellow flower *below* a eudicot or a monocot? What about the plant with the purple flower?

# Digging Into Data

### Transgenic Plants for Phytoremediation

Plants used for phytoremediation take up organic pollutants from the soil or air, then transport the chemicals to plant tissues, where they are stored or broken down. Researchers are now designing transgenic plants that have enhanced ability to take up or break down toxins.

   In 2007, Sharon Doty and her colleagues published the results of their efforts to design plants useful for phytoremediation of soil and air containing organic solvents. The researchers used *Agrobacterium tumefaciens* (Section 10.4) to deliver a mammalian gene into poplar plants. The gene encodes cytochrome P450, an enzyme involved in the metabolism of a range of organic molecules, including solvents such as TCE. The results of one of the researchers' tests on these transgenic plants are shown in Figure 27.18.

1. How many transgenic plants did the researchers test?

2. In which group did the researchers see the slowest rate of TCE uptake? The fastest?

3. On day 6, what was the difference between the TCE content of air around transgenic plants and that around vector control plants?

4. Assuming no other experiments were done, what two explanations are there for the results of this experiment? What other control might the researchers have used?

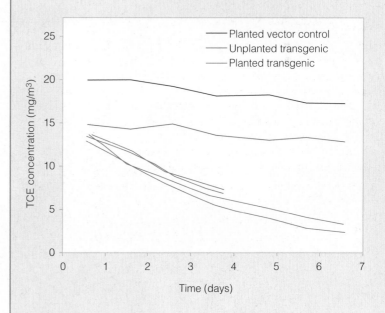

**FIGURE 27.18** Results of tests on transgenic poplar trees. Planted trees were incubated in sealed containers with an initial 15,000 micrograms of TCE (trichloroethylene) per cubic meter of air. Samples of the air in the containers were taken daily and measured for TCE content. Controls included a tree transgenic for a Ti plasmid with no cytochrome P450 in it (vector control), and a bare-root transgenic tree (one that was not planted in soil).

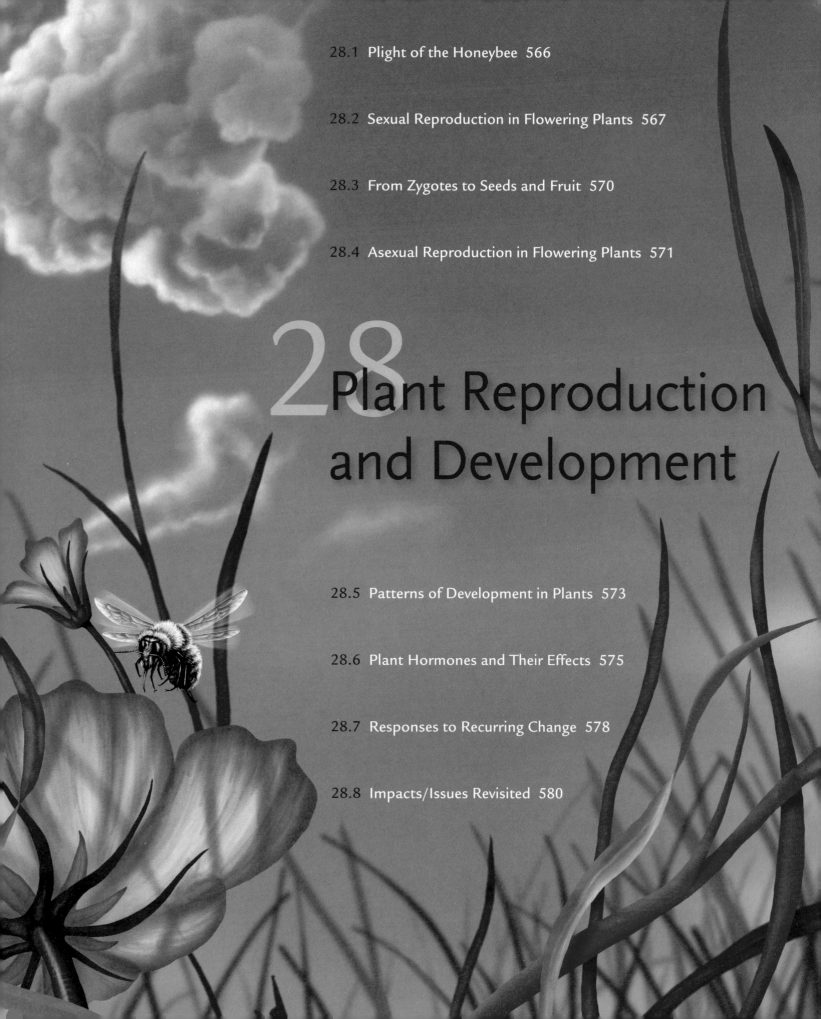

# 28 Plant Reproduction and Development

Most flowers are specialized to attract and be pollinated by
a specific type of pollinator or even a specific species.

## Impacts/Issues:  Plight of the Honeybee

In the fall of 2006, commercial beekeepers in Europe, India, and North America began to notice something was amiss in their honeybee hives. The bees were dying off in unusually high numbers. Many colonies did not survive through the following winter. By spring, the phenomenon had a name: colony collapse disorder. Farmers and biologists began to worry about what would happen if the honeybee populations continued to decline. Honey production would suffer, but many commercial crops would fail too.

Nearly all of our crops are flowering plants. These plants make pollen grains that consist of a few cells, one of which produces sperm. Honeybees are **pollinators**; they carry pollen from one plant to another, pollinating flowers as they do. Typically, a flower will not develop into a fruit unless it receives pollen from another flower. Even plants with flowers that can self-pollinate tend to make bigger fruits and more of them when they are cross-pollinated (Figure 28.1).

Many types of insects pollinate plants, but honeybees are especially efficient pollinators of a variety of plant species. They are also the only ones that tolerate living in man-made hives that can be loaded onto trucks and carted wherever crops require pollination. Loss of their portable pollination service is a huge threat to our agricultural economy.

We still do not know what causes colony collapse disorder. Honeybees can be infected by a variety of parasites and diseases that may be part of the problem. Parasitic mites and Israeli acute paralysis virus have been detected in many affected hives, and pesticides may also be taking a toll. In the past few years, neonicotinoids have become the most widely used insecticides in the United States. These chemicals are systemic insecticides, which means they are taken up by all plant tissues, including the nectar and pollen that honeybees collect. Neonicotinoids are highly toxic to honeybees.

Colony collapse disorder is currently in the spotlight because it affects our food supply. However, other pollinator populations are also dwindling. Habitat loss is probably the main factor, but pesticides that harm honeybees also harm other pollinators.

Flowering plants rose to dominance in part because they coevolved with animal pollinators. Most flowers are specialized to attract and be pollinated by a specific type of pollinator or even a specific species. Those adaptations put the plants at risk of extinction if coevolved pollinator populations decline. Wild animal species that depend on the plants for fruits and seeds will also be affected. Recognizing the prevalence and importance of these interactions is our first step toward finding workable ways to protect them.

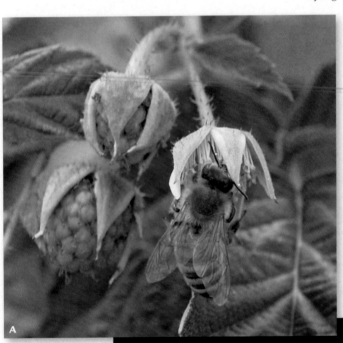

**FIGURE 28.1** Importance of insect pollinators. **A** Honeybees are efficient pollinators of a variety of flowers, including berries. **B** Raspberry flowers can pollinate themselves, but the fruit that forms from a self-fertilized flower is of lower quality than that of a cross-pollinated flower. The two berries on the *left* formed from self-pollinated flowers. The one on the *right* formed from an insect-pollinated flower.

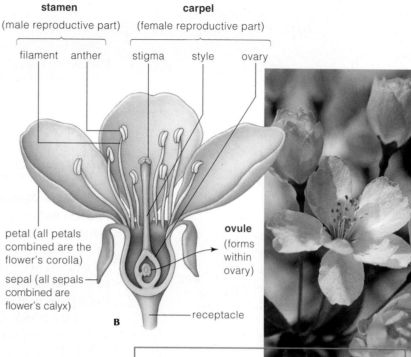

# Sexual Reproduction in Flowering Plants

28.2

**Regarding Flowers** A sporophyte (Section 14.2) is a diploid plant body that grows by mitotic divisions of a fertilized egg. Flowers are the specialized reproductive shoots of sporophytes. Haploid reproductive bodies (spores) form by meiosis in flowers. Spores develop into haploid gametophytes, which make eggs or sperm (Figure 28.2**A**).

A flower forms when a lateral bud along a stem develops into a short, modified branch called a receptacle. The petals and other parts of a typical flower are modified leaves that form in four spirals or rings (whorls) at the end of the floral shoot. The outermost whorl develops into a calyx, which is a ring of leaf-like sepals (Figure 28.2**B**). The sepals of most flowers are photosynthetic and inconspicuous; they protect the flower's reproductive parts. Just inside the calyx, petals form in a whorl called the corolla (from the Latin *corona*, or crown). Petals are usually the largest and most brightly colored parts of a flower. They function mainly to attract pollinators.

A whorl of stamens forms inside the ring of petals. **Stamens** are the male parts of a flower. In most flowers, they consist of a thin filament with an anther at the tip. Inside a typical anther are two pairs of elongated pouches called pollen sacs. Meiosis of diploid cells in each sac produces haploid, walled spores. The spores differentiate into pollen grains, which are immature male gametophytes.

The innermost whorl of modified leaves are folded and fused into **carpels**, the female parts of a flower. Carpels are sometimes called pistils. Many flowers have one carpel; others have several carpels, or several groups of carpels, that may be fused. The upper region of a carpel is a sticky or hairy stigma that is specialized to trap pollen grains. Typically, the stigma sits on top of a slender stalk called a style. The lower, swollen region of a carpel is the **ovary**, which contains one or more ovules. An **ovule** is a tiny bulge of tissue inside the ovary. A cell in the ovule undergoes meiosis and develops into the haploid female gametophyte.

At fertilization, a diploid zygote forms when male and female gametes meet inside an ovary. The ovule then matures into a seed. The life cycle is completed when the seed sprouts, and a new sporophyte forms and matures.

**FIGURE 28.2 Animated!** Sexual reproduction in flowering plants. **A** Life cycle of a typical angiosperm. **B** Like many flowers, a cherry blossom has several stamens and one carpel. The male reproductive parts are stamens, which consist of pollen-bearing anthers atop slender filaments. The female reproductive part is the carpel, which consists of stigma, style, and ovary.

**carpel** Female reproductive structure of a flower; a sticky or hairlike stigma above a chamber (ovary) that contains one or more ovules.

**ovary** In flowering plants, the enlarged base of a carpel, inside which one or more ovules form and eggs are fertilized.

**ovule** In a seed-bearing plant, structure in which a haploid, egg-producing female gametophyte forms; after fertilization, matures into a seed.

**pollinator** An organism that moves pollen grains from one plant to another.

**stamen** The male reproductive part of a flowering plant; consists of a pollen-producing anther on a filament.

**From Spores to Zygotes** Figure 28.3 zooms in on a flowering plant life cycle. On the male side, masses of diploid, spore-producing cells form by mitosis in the anthers. Typically, walls develop around the cell masses to form four pollen sacs ❶. Each cell inside the sacs undergoes meiosis, forming four haploid **microspores** ❷.

Mitosis and differentiation of microspores produce pollen grains. Each pollen grain consists of a coat that surrounds two cells, one inside the cytoplasm of the other ❸. A pollen grain's durable coat is a bit like a suitcase that carries and protects the cells inside on their journey to meet an egg. After a period of arrested growth, or **dormancy**, the pollen sacs split open and release pollen from the anther ❹.

**Pollination** refers to the arrival of a pollen grain on a receptive stigma. Interactions between the two structures stimulate the pollen grain to resume metabolic activity. One of the two cells in the pollen grain then develops into a tubular outgrowth called a pollen tube. The other cell undergoes mitosis and cytoplasmic division, producing two sperm cells (the male gametes) within the pollen tube. A pollen tube together with its contents of male gametes constitutes the mature male gametophyte ❺.

On the female side, a mass of tissue—the ovule—starts growing on the inner wall of an ovary ❻. One cell in the middle of the mass undergoes meiosis and cytoplasmic division, forming four haploid **megaspores** ❼.

Three of the four megaspores typically disintegrate. The remaining megaspore undergoes three rounds of mitosis without cytoplasmic division. The outcome is a single cell with eight haploid nuclei ❽. The cytoplasm of this cell divides unevenly, and the result is a seven-celled embryo sac that constitutes the female gametophyte ❾. The gametophyte is enclosed and protected by cell layers, called integuments, that developed from the outer layers of the ovule. One of the cells in the gametophyte, the **endosperm mother cell**, has two nuclei ($n + n$). Another cell is the egg.

The pollen tube grows from its tip down through the carpel and ovary toward the ovule, carrying with it the two sperm cells. Chemical signals secreted by the female gametophyte guide the tube's growth to the embryo sac within the ovule. Many pollen tubes may grow down into a carpel, but only one typically penetrates an embryo sac. The sperm cells are then released into the sac ❿. Flowering plants undergo **double fertilization**: One of the sperm cells from the pollen tube fuses with (fertilizes) the egg and forms a diploid zygote. The other fuses with the endosperm mother cell, forming a triploid ($3n$) cell. This cell gives rise to triploid **endosperm**, a nutritious tissue that forms only in seeds of flowering plants. When a seed sprouts, endosperm sustains rapid growth of the sporophyte seedling until true leaves form and photosynthesis begins.

## Take-Home Message  How does sexual reproduction work in angiosperms?

- The male parts of flowers are stamens, which typically consist of a filament with an anther at the tip. Pollen forms inside anthers. Pollen gives rise to the male gametophytes.

- The female parts of flowers are carpels, which typically consist of stigma, style, and ovary. Haploid, egg-producing female gametophytes form in an ovule inside the ovary. Pollination occurs when pollen arrives on a receptive stigma.

- A pollen grain germinates on a stigma as a pollen tube containing male gametes. The pollen tube grows into the carpel and enters an ovule. Double fertilization occurs when one of the male gametes fuses with the egg, the other with the endosperm mother cell.

**dormancy** Period of arrested growth.
**double fertilization** Mode of fertilization in flowering plants in which one sperm cell fuses with the egg, and a second sperm cell fuses with the endosperm mother cell.
**endosperm** Nutritive tissue in the seeds of flowering plants.
**endosperm mother cell** A cell with two nuclei ($n + n$) that is part of the female gametophyte of a flowering plant.
**megaspore** Haploid spore that forms in ovary of seed plants; gives rise to a female gametophyte with an egg cell.
**microspore** Walled haploid spore of seed plants; gives rise to a pollen grain.
**pollination** The arrival of pollen on a receptive stigma.

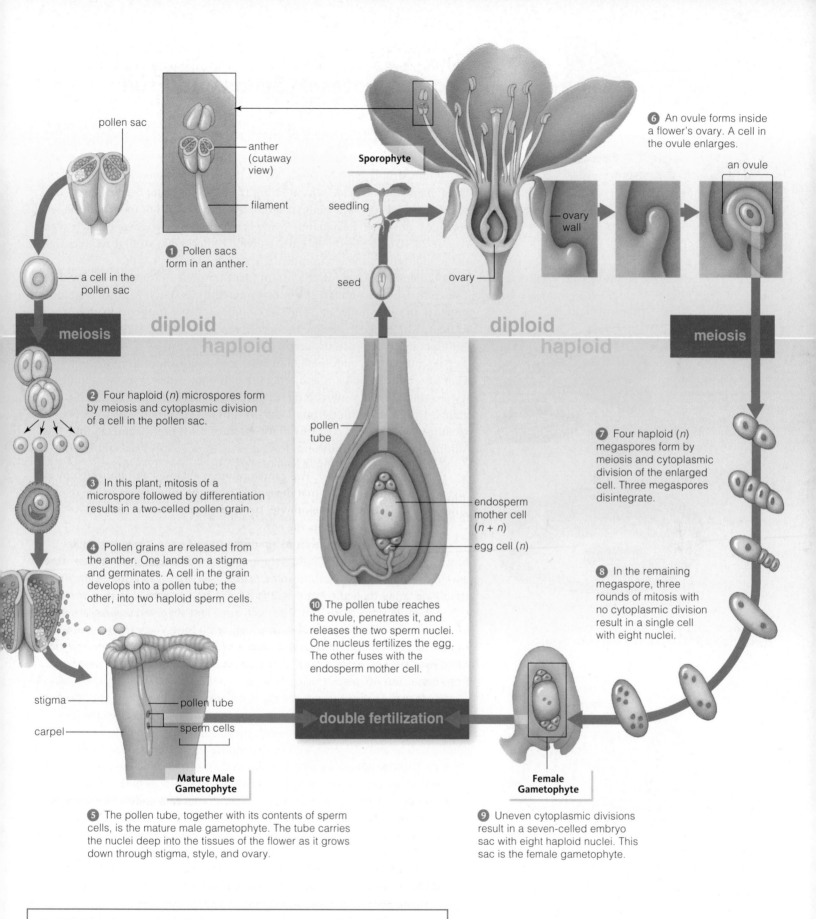

pollen sac

anther (cutaway view)

filament

**1** Pollen sacs form in an anther.

Sporophyte

seedling

seed

ovary wall

ovary

**6** An ovule forms inside a flower's ovary. A cell in the ovule enlarges.

an ovule

a cell in the pollen sac

**meiosis**

**diploid**

**haploid**

**diploid**

**haploid**

**meiosis**

**2** Four haploid (*n*) microspores form by meiosis and cytoplasmic division of a cell in the pollen sac.

pollen tube

**7** Four haploid (*n*) megaspores form by meiosis and cytoplasmic division of the enlarged cell. Three megaspores disintegrate.

**3** In this plant, mitosis of a microspore followed by differentiation results in a two-celled pollen grain.

endosperm mother cell (*n* + *n*)

egg cell (*n*)

**4** Pollen grains are released from the anther. One lands on a stigma and germinates. A cell in the grain develops into a pollen tube; the other, into two haploid sperm cells.

**8** In the remaining megaspore, three rounds of mitosis with no cytoplasmic division result in a single cell with eight nuclei.

**10** The pollen tube reaches the ovule, penetrates it, and releases the two sperm nuclei. One nucleus fertilizes the egg. The other fuses with the endosperm mother cell.

stigma

carpel

pollen tube

sperm cells

**Mature Male Gametophyte**

**double fertilization**

**Female Gametophyte**

**5** The pollen tube, together with its contents of sperm cells, is the mature male gametophyte. The tube carries the nuclei deep into the tissues of the flower as it grows down through stigma, style, and ovary.

**9** Uneven cytoplasmic divisions result in a seven-celled embryo sac with eight haploid nuclei. This sac is the female gametophyte.

**FIGURE 28.3 Animated!** Life cycle of cherry tree, a eudicot. **Figure It Out:** What structure gives rise to a pollen grain by mitosis?

*Answer: A microspore*

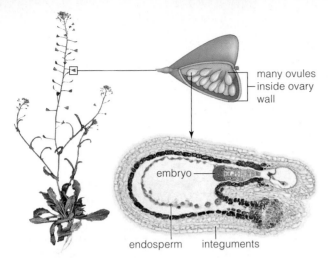

many ovules
inside ovary
wall

embryo

endosperm    integuments

**A** After fertilization, the flower's ovary develops into a fruit. An embryo surrounded by integuments forms inside each of the ovary's many ovules.

**B** The embryo is heart-shaped when cotyledons start forming. Endosperm tissue expands as the parent plant transfers nutrients into it.

embryo

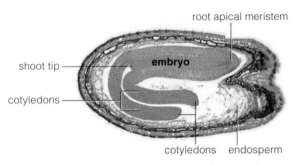

root apical meristem

shoot tip

**embryo**

cotyledons

cotyledons    endosperm

**C** The developing embryo becomes torpedo-shaped when the enlarging cotyledons bend inside the ovule.

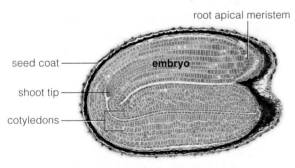

root apical meristem

seed coat

**embryo**

shoot tip

cotyledons

**D** A layered seed coat that formed from the layers of integuments surrounds the mature embryo sporophyte. In eudicots like shepherd's purse, nutrients have been transferred from endosperm into two cotyledons.

**FIGURE 28.4 Animated!** Embryonic development of shepherd's purse, a eudicot.

# From Zygotes to Seeds and Fruit

**The Embryo Sporophyte Forms** In flowering plants, double fertilization produces a zygote and a triploid ($3n$) cell. By mitotic cell divisions, the zygote develops into an embryo sporophyte, and the triploid cell develops into endosperm (Figure 28.4**A–C**). When the embryo approaches maturity, the integuments of the ovule separate from the ovary wall and become layers of a protective seed coat. The embryo sporophyte, its reserves of food, and the seed coat have now become a mature ovule, a self-contained package called a **seed** (Figure 28.4**D**). The seed may enter a period of dormancy until it receives signals that conditions in the environment are appropriate for growth.

As an embryo develops, the parent plant transfers nutrients to the ovule. These nutrients accumulate in endosperm mainly as starch with some lipids, proteins, or other molecules. Eudicot embryos transfer nutrients in endosperm to their two cotyledons before the seed sprouts. The embryos of monocots tap endosperm only after seeds sprout.

The nutrients in endosperm and cotyledons nourish seedling sporophytes. They also nourish humans and other animals. Rice, wheat, rye, oats, and barley are among the grasses commonly cultivated for their nutritious seeds, or grains. The embryo (the germ) of a grain contains most of the seed's protein and vitamins, and the seed coat (the bran) contains most of the minerals and fiber. Milling removes bran and germ, leaving only the starch-packed endosperm.

Maize, or corn, is the most widely grown grain crop. Popcorn pops because the moist endosperm steams when heated; pressure builds inside the seed until it bursts. Cotyledons of bean and pea seeds are valued for their starch and protein; those of coffee and cacao, for their stimulants.

**Fruits** Only flowering plants form seeds in ovaries, and only they make fruits. A **fruit** is a seed-containing mature ovary, often with fleshy tissues that develop from the ovary wall. In some plants, fruit tissues develop from parts of the flower other than the ovary wall (such as petals, sepals, stamens, or receptacles). Simple fruits, such as pea pods, acorns, and shepherd's purse, are derived from one ovary. Strawberries and other aggregate fruits form from separate ovaries of one flower; they mature as a cluster of fruits. Multiple fruits form from fused ovaries of separate flowers. The pineapple is a multiple fruit that forms from fused ovary tissues of many flowers.

An embryo or seedling can use the nutrients stored in endosperm or cotyledons, but not in fruit. The function of fruit is to protect and disperse seeds. Dispersal increases reproductive success by minimizing competition for resources among parent and offspring, and by expanding the area colonized by the species. Thus, fruits have adaptations that facilitate their dispersal by environmental factors such as water or wind, or by mobile organisms such as birds or insects.

Water-dispersed fruits have water-repellent outer layers. The fruits of sedges native to American marshlands have seeds encased in a bladderlike envelope that floats (Figure 28.5**A**). Buoyant fruits of the coconut palm have thick, tough husks that can float for thousands of miles in seawater.

Many plant species use wind as a dispersal agent. Part of a maple fruit is a dry outgrowth of the ovary wall that extends like a pair of thin, lightweight wings (Figure 28.5**B**). The fruit breaks in half when it drops from the tree; as the halves drop to the ground, wind currents that catch the wings spin the attached seeds away. Tufted fruits of thistle, cattail, dandelion, and milkweed may be blown as far as 10 kilometers (6 miles) from the parent plant (Figure 28.5**C**).

The fruits of cocklebur, bur clover, and many other plants have hooks or spines that stick to the feathers, feet, fur, or clothing of more mobile species (Figure 28.5**D**). The dry, podlike fruit of plants such as California poppy propel their seeds through the air when they pop open explosively (Figure 28.5**E**).

Colorful, fleshy, fragrant fruits attract insects, birds, and mammals that disperse seeds (Figure 28.5**F**). The animal may eat the fruit and discard the seeds, or eat the seeds along with the fruit. Abrasion of the seed coat by digestive enzymes in an animal's gut can help the seed sprout after it departs in feces.

## Take-Home Message   How do seeds and fruits develop?

- After fertilization, the zygote develops into an embryo, the endosperm becomes enriched with nutrients, and the ovule's integuments develop into a seed coat.

- A seed is a mature ovule. It contains an embryo sporophyte.

- A mature ovary, with or without accessory tissues that develop from other parts of a flower, is a fruit.

- Seeds and fruits are adapted for dispersal by specific environmental factors.

**FIGURE 28.5** Examples of adaptations that aid fruit dispersal. **A** Air-filled bladders that encase the seeds of certain sedges allow the fruits to float in their marshy habitats.

**B** Wind lifts the "wings" of maple (*Acer*) fruits, which spin the seeds away from the parent tree.

**C** Wind that catches the hairy modified sepals of a dandelion fruit (*Taraxacum*) lifts the seed away from the parent plant.

**D** Curved spines make cocklebur (*Xanthium*) fruits stick to the fur of animals (and clothing of humans) that brush past it.

**E** The fruits of the California poppy (*Eschscholzia californica*) are long, dry pods that split open suddenly. The movement jettisons the seeds.

**F** The red, fleshy fruit of crabapples attracts birds such as cedar waxwings.

# 28.4 Asexual Reproduction in Flowering Plants

Unlike most animals, most flowering plants can reproduce asexually. New roots and shoots can grow from extensions or pieces of a parent plant, a process called **vegetative reproduction**. Each new plant is a clone, a genetic replica of its parent. As long as conditions in the environment favor growth, such clones are as close as any organism gets to being immortal. The oldest known plant is a clone: the one and only population of King's holly, which consists of several hundred stems growing along 1.2 kilometers (0.7 miles) of a river gully in Tasmania. Radiometric dating of the plant's fossilized leaf litter show that the clone is at least 43,600 years old—predating the last ice age!

The ancient King's holly is triploid. With three sets of chromosomes, it is sterile—it can only reproduce asexually. Why? During meiosis, an odd number of chromosome sets cannot be divided equally between the two spindle poles. If meiosis does not fail entirely, unequal segregation of chromosomes during meiosis results in aneuploid offspring, which rarely survive.

**fruit** Mature ovary, often with accessory parts, from a flowering plant.

**seed** The mature ovule of a seed plant; contains an embryo sporophyte.

**vegetative reproduction** Growth of new roots and shoots from extensions or fragments of a parent plant; form of asexual reproduction in plants.

**FIGURE 28.6** Examples of asexual reproduction in plants.

**A** Strawberry plants can propagate themselves by sending out stolons. New plants develop at nodes in the stolons.

**B** Potatoes are tubers that grow on stolons. New plants sprout from their nodes, or "eyes."

**C** New plants form at nodes on the leaflike cladodes of many succulents such as this devil's backbone plant.

King's holly probably arose by a chance genetic event. Many other types of plants reproduce asexually when new roots and shoots sprout from an existing plant. For example, "forests" of quaking aspen are actually stands of clones that grew from root suckers, which are shoots that sprout from the aspens' shallow, cordlike lateral roots. Suckers sprout after aboveground parts of the aspens are damaged or removed. One stand in Utah consists of about 47,000 shoots and stretches for 107 acres.

In other species, new plants sprout from modified stems. Stolons, often called runners, are stems that branch from the main stem of the plant, typically on or near the surface of the soil. Stolons may look like roots, but they have nodes, and roots do not have nodes. Adventitious roots and leafy shoots that sprout from the nodes develop into new plants (Figure 28.6**A**). A corm is a thickened underground stem that stores nutrients. It has nodes from which new plants develop. Tubers are thickened portions of underground stolons; they serve as the plant's primary storage tissue. Tubers have nodes from which new shoots and roots sprout. Potatoes are tubers; their "eyes" are nodes (Figure 28.6**B**). Cactuses and other succulents have flattened photosynthetic stems called cladodes. New plants form at nodes on the cladodes (Figure 28.6**C**).

**Cuttings and Grafts** For thousands of years, we humans have been taking advantage of the natural capacity of plants to reproduce asexually. Almost all houseplants, woody ornamentals, and orchard trees are clones that have been grown from stem fragments (cuttings) of a parent plant.

Propagating some plants from cuttings may be as simple as jamming a broken stem into the soil. This method uses the plant's natural ability to form roots and new shoots from stem nodes. Other plants must be grafted. Grafting means inducing a cutting to fuse with the tissues of another plant. Often, the stem of a desired plant is spliced onto the roots of a hardier one.

Propagating a plant from cuttings ensures that offspring will have the same desirable traits as the parent plant. For example, domestic apple trees (*Malus*) are typically grafted because they do not breed true for fruit color, flavor, size, or texture. Even trees grown from seeds of the same fruit produce fruits that vary, sometimes dramatically so. The genus is native to central Asia, where apple trees grow wild in forests. Apples do not breed true from seeds, so each wild tree is different from the next, and very few of the fruits are palatable (Figure 28.7).

In the early 1800s, the eccentric humanitarian John Chapman (known as Johnny Appleseed) planted millions of apple seeds in the midwestern United States. He sold the trees to homesteading settlers, who would plant orchards and make hard cider from the apples. About one of every hundred trees produced fruits that could be eaten out of hand. Its lucky owner would graft the tree and patent it. Most of the apple varieties sold in American grocery stores are clones of these trees, and they are still propagated by grafting.

Grafting is also used to increase the hardiness of a desirable plant. In 1862, the plant louse *Phylloxera* was accidentally introduced into France via imported American grapevines. European grapevines had little resistance to this tiny insect, which attacks and kills the root systems of the vines. By 1900, *Phylloxera* had destroyed two-thirds of the vineyards in Europe, and devastated the winemaking industry. Today, French vintners routinely graft their prized grapevines onto the roots of *Phylloxera*-resistant American vines.

**Tissue Culture** An entire plant may be cloned from a single cell. By a method called **tissue culture propagation**, a body cell is coaxed to divide and form an embryo. The technique, which can yield millions of genetically identical offspring from a single plant, is currently being used to improve food crops and to propagate rare or hybrid ornamental plants such as orchids.

**FIGURE 28.7** Apples (*Malus*). **A** Commercial growers plant grafted apple trees in order to reap consistent crops. **B** Diverse fruit of 21 wild apple trees. **C** Gennaro Fazio (*left*) and Phil Forsline (*right*) are trying to maintain the genetic diversity of apple trees in the United States. They are breeding new apples with the palatability of commercial varieties and the disease resistance of wild ones.

**Seedless Fruits** In some plants such as figs, blackberries, and dandelions, fruits may form even in the absence of fertilization. In other species, fruit may continue to form after ovules or embryos abort. Seedless grapes and navel oranges are the result of mutations that result in arrested seed development. These plants are sterile, so they are propagated by grafting.

Seedless bananas are triploid (3*n*), so they are sterile. They are propagated by adventitious shoots that sprout from corms. Despite the ubiquity of polyploid plants in nature (Section 12.5), they rarely arise spontaneously. Plant breeders can speed up the process by treating plants with colchicine, a microtubule poison that increases the frequency of polyploidy. Tetraploid (4*n*) offspring of colchicine-treated plants are then backcrossed with diploid parent plants. The resulting triploid offspring are sterile. They make seedless fruit after pollination (but not fertilization) by a diploid plant, or on their own. Seedless watermelons are produced this way.

## Take-Home Message How do plants reproduce asexually?

- Many plants propagate asexually when new shoots grow from a parent plant or pieces of it. Offspring of such vegetative reproduction are clones.
- Humans propagate plants asexually for agricultural or research purposes by grafting, tissue culture, or other methods.

# 28.5 Patterns of Development in Plants

In Section 28.3, we left the embryo sporophyte after its dispersal from the parent plant. What happens next? An embryonic plant complete with shoot and root apical meristems formed as part of the embryo. However, a seed typically dries out as it matures. Drying out causes the embryo's cells to stop dividing, and the embryo enters a period of temporarily suspended development (dormancy).

**tissue culture propagation** Laboratory method in which body cells are induced to divide and form an embryo.

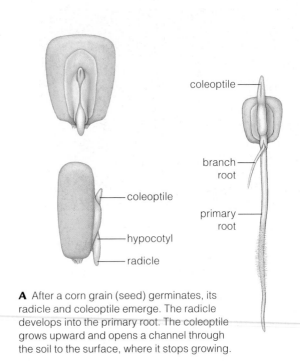

coleoptile

branch root

primary root

coleoptile

hypocotyl

radicle

**A** After a corn grain (seed) germinates, its radicle and coleoptile emerge. The radicle develops into the primary root. The coleoptile grows upward and opens a channel through the soil to the surface, where it stops growing.

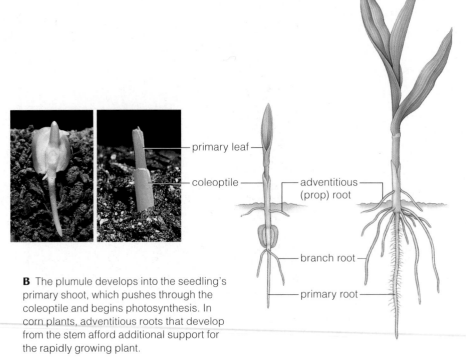

primary leaf

coleoptile

adventitious (prop) root

branch root

primary root

**B** The plumule develops into the seedling's primary shoot, which pushes through the coleoptile and begins photosynthesis. In corn plants, adventitious roots that develop from the stem afford additional support for the rapidly growing plant.

**FIGURE 28.8 Animated!** Early growth of corn, a monocot. *Below,* anatomy of a corn seed.

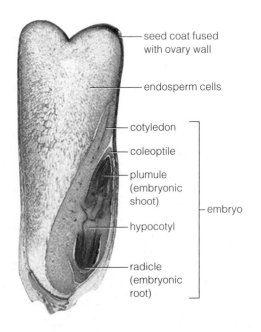

seed coat fused with ovary wall

endosperm cells

cotyledon

coleoptile

plumule (embryonic shoot)

embryo

hypocotyl

radicle (embryonic root)

An embryo may idle in its protective seed coat for years before it resumes metabolic activity. **Germination** is the process by which a mature embryo sporophyte resumes growth. The process begins with water seeping into a seed. The water activates enzymes that break down stored starches into sugars (Section 2.7). It also swells tissues inside the seed, so the coat splits open and oxygen enters. Meristem cells in the embryo use the sugars and the oxygen for aerobic respiration as they start dividing rapidly. The embryonic plant begins to grow from the meristems. Germination ends when the first part of the embryo—the embryonic root, or radicle—breaks out of the seed coat.

Seed dormancy is a climate-specific adaptation that allows germination to occur when conditions in the environment are most likely to support the growth of a seedling. For example, the weather in regions near the equator does not vary by season, so seeds of most plants native to such regions do not enter dormancy; they can germinate as soon as they are mature. By contrast, the seeds of many annual plants native to colder regions are dispersed in autumn. If they germinated immediately, the tender seedlings would not survive the coming winter. Instead, the seeds stay dormant until spring, when milder temperatures and longer daylength are more suitable for seedlings.

How does a dormant embryo sporophyte "know" when to germinate? The triggers, other than the presence of water, differ by species, and all have a genetic basis. For example, some seed coats are so dense that they must be abraded or broken (by being chewed, for example) before water can even enter the seed. Seeds of some species of lettuce must be exposed to bright light. The germination of wild California poppy seeds is inhibited by light and enhanced by smoke. The seeds of some species of pine will not germinate unless they have been previously burned. The seeds of many cool-climate plants require exposure to freezing temperatures.

Germination is just one of many patterns of development in plants. As a sporophyte grows and matures, its tissues and parts develop in other patterns characteristic of its species (Figures 28.8 and 28.9). Leaves form in predictable

**A** After a bean seed germinates, its radicle emerges and bends in the shape of a hook. Sunlight causes the hypocotyl to straighten, which pulls the cotyledons up through the soil.

**B** Photosynthetic cells in the cotyledons make food for several days. Then, the seedling's leaves take over the task and the cotyledons wither and fall off.

**FIGURE 28.9 Animated!** Early growth of the common bean plant, a eudicot.

shapes and sizes, stems lengthen and thicken in particular directions, flowering occurs at a certain time of year, and so on. As in germination, these patterns have a genetic basis, but they also have an environmental component.

Development includes growth, which is an increase in cell number and size. Plant cells are interconnected by shared walls, so they cannot move about within the organism. Thus, plant growth occurs primarily in the direction of cell division—and cell division occurs primarily at meristems. Behind meristems, cells differentiate and form specialized tissues. However, unlike animal cell differentiation, plant cell differentiation is often reversible, as when new shoots form on mature roots, or when new roots sprout from a mature stem.

## Take-Home Message  **What is plant development?**

- In plants, development includes growth and differentiation. It results in the formation of tissues and parts in predictable patterns.
- Germination and other patterns of plant development are an outcome of gene expression and environmental influences.

Plant development depends on extensive coordination among individual cells, just as it does in animals.

## 28.6  Plant Hormones and Their Effects

You may be surprised to learn that plant development depends on extensive coordination among individual cells, just as it does in animals. A plant is an organism, not just a collection of cells, and as such it develops as a unit. Cells in different parts of a plant coordinate their activities by communicating with one

**germination** The resumption of growth after a period of dormancy.

| Table 28.1 | Major Plant Hormones and Some of Their Effects | | |
|---|---|---|---|
| Hormone | Primary Source | Effect | Site of Effect |
| **Gibberellins** | | | |
| | Stem tip, young leaves | Stimulates cell division, elongation | Stem internode |
| | Embryo | Stimulates germination | Seed |
| | Embryo (grass) | Stimulates starch hydrolysis | Endosperm |
| **Auxins** | | | |
| | Stem tip, young leaves | Stimulates cell elongation | Growing tissues |
| | | Initiates formation of lateral roots | Roots |
| | | Inhibits growth (apical dominance) | Lateral buds |
| | | Stimulates differentiation of xylem | Cambium |
| | | Inhibits abscission | Leaves, fruits |
| | Developing embryos | Stimulates fruit development | Ovary |
| **Abscisic acid** | | | |
| | Leaves | Closes stomata | Guard cells |
| | | Stimulates formation of dormant buds | Stem tip |
| | Ovule | Inhibits germination | Seed coat |
| **Cytokinins** | | | |
| | Root tip | Stimulates cell division | Stem tip, lateral buds |
| | | Inhibits senescence (aging) | Leaves |
| **Ethylene** | | | |
| | Damaged or aged tissue | Inhibits cell elongation | Stem |
| | | Stimulates senescence (aging) | Leaves |
| | | Stimulates ripening | Fruits |

**FIGURE 28.10** Effect of gibberellins. The three tall cabbage plants were treated with gibberellins. Two untreated cabbage plants are under the ladder.

**abscisic acid** Plant hormone that stimulates stomata to close in response to water stress; induces dormancy in buds and seeds.

**apical dominance** Growth-inhibiting effect on lateral buds, mediated by auxin produced in shoot tips.

**auxin** Plant hormone; stimulates cell division, elongation.

**cytokinin** Plant hormone that promotes cell division. Releases lateral buds from apical dominance.

**ethylene** Gaseous plant hormone that inhibits cell division in stems and roots; also promotes fruit ripening.

**gibberellin** Plant hormone; induces stem elongation, helps seeds break dormancy. Role in flowering in some species.

**gravitropism** Plant growth in a direction influenced by gravity.

**phototropism** Change in the direction of cell movement or growth in response to a light source.

**tropism** In plants, directional growth response to an environmental stimulus.

another. Such communication means, for example, that roots and shoots can be triggered to grow at the same time.

Plant cells use hormones to communicate with one another. Plant hormones are signaling molecules that can stimulate or inhibit plant development, including growth. Environmental cues such as the availability of water, length of night, temperature, and gravity influence plants by triggering the production and dispersal of hormones. When a plant hormone binds to a target cell, it may modify gene expression, change solute concentrations, affect enzyme activity, or activate another molecule in the cytoplasm.

Five types of plant hormones—gibberellins, auxins, abscisic acid, cytokinins, and ethylene—all interact to orchestrate plant development (Table 28.1).

Growth and other processes of development in all flowering plants, gymnosperms, mosses, ferns, and some fungi are regulated in part by **gibberellins**. These hormones induce cell division and elongation in stem tissue; thus, they cause stems to lengthen between the nodes. This effect can be demonstrated by application of gibberellin to the leaves of young plants (Figure 28.10). The short stems of Mendel's dwarf pea plants (Section 9.2) are the result of a mutation that reduces the rate of gibberellin synthesis in these plants. Gibberellins are also involved in breaking dormancy of seeds, seed germination, and the induction of flowering in biennials and some other plants.

**Auxins** are plant hormones that promote or inhibit cell division and elongation, depending on the target tissue. Auxins produced in apical meristems result in elongation of shoots (Figure 28.11**A,B**). They also induce cell division and differentiation in vascular cambium, fruit development in ovaries, and lateral root formation in roots. Auxins also have inhibitory effects. For example, auxin produced in a shoot tip prevents the growth of lateral buds along a lengthening stem, an effect called **apical dominance**. Gardeners routinely pinch off shoot tips to make a plant bushier. Pinching the tips ends the supply of auxin in a main stem, so lateral buds give rise to branches. Auxins also inhibit abscission, which is the dropping of leaves, flowers, and fruits from the plant.

**Abscisic acid** (ABA) is a hormone that was misnamed; it inhibits growth, and has little to do with abscission. ABA is part of a stress response that causes stomata to close (Section 27.6). It also diverts photosynthetic products from leaves to seeds, an effect that overrides growth-stimulating effects of other hormones as the growing season ends. ABA inhibits seed germination in some species, such as apple. Such seeds do not germinate before most of the ABA they contain has been broken down, for example by a long period of cold, wet conditions.

Plant **cytokinins** form in roots and travel via xylem to shoots, where they induce cell divisions in the apical meristems. These hormones also release lateral buds from apical dominance, and inhibit the normal aging process in leaves. Cytokinins signal to shoots that roots are healthy and active. When roots stop growing, they stop producing cytokinins, so shoot growth slows and leaves begin to deteriorate.

The only gaseous hormone, **ethylene**, is produced by damaged cells. It is also produced in autumn in deciduous plants, or near the end of the life cycle as part of a plant's normal process of aging. Ethylene inhibits cell division in stems and roots. It also induces fruit and leaves to mature and drop. Ethylene is widely used to artificially ripen fruit that has been harvested while still green.

**Adjusting the Direction and Rate of Growth** Plants respond to environmental stimuli by adjusting the growth of roots and shoots. These responses are called **tropisms**, and they are typically mediated by hormones. For example, a root or shoot "bends" because of differences in auxin concentration. Auxin that accumulates in cells on one side of a shoot causes the cells to elongate more than the cells on the other side (Figure 28.11**C**). The result is that the shoot bends away from the side with more auxin. Auxin has the opposite effect in roots: It inhibits elongation of root cells. Thus, a root will bend toward the side that contains more auxin.

No matter how a seed is positioned in the soil when it germinates, the radicle always grows down, and the primary shoot always grows up. Even if a seedling is turned upside down just after germination, the primary root and shoot will curve so the root grows down and the shoot grows up. A growth response to gravity is called **gravitropism**.

How does a plant "know" which direction is up? Gravity-sensing mechanisms of many organisms are based on organelles called statoliths. Statoliths stuffed with starch grains occur in root cap cells, and also in specialized cells at the periphery of vascular tissues in the stem. Starch grains are heavier than cytoplasm, so statoliths tend to sink to the lowest region of the cell, wherever that is. The shift causes a redistribution of auxin so that this hormone is transported to the downward-facing side of roots and shoots.

Light streaming in from one direction causes a stem to curve toward its source. This response, **phototropism**, orients certain parts of the plant in the direction that will maximize the amount of light intercepted by its photosynthetic cells. Phototropism in plants occurs in response to blue light. Nonphotosynthetic pigments called phototropins absorb blue light, and translate its energy into a cascade of intracellular signals. The ultimate effect of this

**A** A coleoptile stops growing after its tip has been removed.

*time*

**B** A block of agar will absorb auxin from the cut tip. Growth of a de-tipped coleoptile will resume when the agar block with absorbed auxin is placed on top of it.

*time*

**C** If the agar block is placed to one side of the shaft, the coleoptile will bend as it grows.

*time*

**FIGURE 28.11 Animated!** A coleoptile lengthens in response to auxin produced in its tip.

**A** Sunlight strikes only one side of a coleoptile.

**B** Auxin is transported to the shaded side, where it causes cells to lengthen.

**FIGURE 28.12 Animated!** Phototropism. **A,B** Auxin-mediated differences in cell elongation between two sides of a coleoptile induce bending toward light. The photo shows a shamrock plant's response to a directional light source.

cascade is that auxin is redistributed to the shaded side of a shoot or coleoptile. As a result, cells on the shaded side elongate faster than cells on the illuminated side. Differences in growth rates between cells on opposite sides of a shoot or coleoptile cause the entire structure to bend toward the light (Figure 28.12).

A plant's contact with a solid object may result in a change in the direction of its growth, a response called **thigmotropism**. The mechanism that gives rise to this response is not well understood, but it involves calcium ions and the products of at least five genes called *TOUCH*.

We see thigmotropism when a vine's tendril touches an object. The cells near the area of contact stop elongating, and the cells on the opposite side of the shoot keep elongating. The unequal growth rates of cells on opposite sides of the shoot cause it to curl around the object. A similar mechanism causes roots to grow away from contact, so they "feel" their way around rocks and other impassable objects in the soil. Mechanical stress, such as by wind exposure, inhibits stem lengthening in a touch response related to thigmotropism.

## Take-Home Message **What regulates growth and development in plants?**

- Plant hormones are signaling molecules that influence plant development.
- The five main classes of plant hormones are gibberellins, auxins, abscisic acid, cytokinins, and ethylene.
- Via hormones, plants adjust the direction and rate of growth in response to environmental stimuli that include gravity, light, contact, and mechanical stress.

# 28.7 Responses to Recurring Change

Most organisms have a **biological clock**—an internal mechanism that governs the timing of rhythmic cycles of activity. A cycle of activity that starts anew every twenty-four hours or so is called a **circadian rhythm** (Latin *circa*, about; *dies*, day). In the circadian response called solar tracking, a leaf or flower changes position in response to the changing angle of the sun throughout the day. For example, a buttercup stem swivels so the flower on top of it always faces the sun. Unlike a phototropic response, solar tracking does not involve redistribution of auxin and differential growth. Instead, the absorption of blue light by photoreceptor proteins increases fluid pressure in cells on the sunlit side of a stem or petiole. The cells change shape, which bends the stem.

Similar mechanisms cause flowers of some plants to open only at certain times of day. For example, the flowers of many bat-pollinated plants unfurl, secrete nectar, and release fragrance only at night. Closing flowers periodically protects the delicate reproductive parts when the likelihood of pollination is low.

Like a mechanical clock, a biological one can be reset. Sunlight resets biological clocks in plants by activating and inactivating photoreceptors called **phytochromes**. These blue-green pigments are sensitive to red light (660 nanometers) and far-red light (730 nanometers). The relative amounts of these wavelengths in sunlight that reaches a given environment vary during the day and with the season. Red light causes phytochromes to change from an inactive form to an active form. Far-red light causes them to change back to their inactive form (Figure 28.13**A**). Active phytochromes bring about transcription of many genes, including some that encode components of rubisco, photosystems,

**A** Red light changes the structure of a phytochrome from inactive (Pr) to active (Pfr) form; far-red light changes it back to the inactive form. Activated phytochromes control important processes such as germination and flowering.

**B** A flash of red light interrupting a long night activates phytochrome. It causes plants to respond as if the night were short, and long-day plants flower. A pulse of far-red light, which inactivates phytochrome, cancels the effect of the red flash, and short-day plants flower. *Blue* bars indicate night length; *yellow* bars, day length.

---

**FIGURE 28.13 Animated!** Phytochrome and flowering. **Figure It Out:** What is the critical length of night that triggers a short-day plant's flowering response in the experiments shown in **B**?

*Answer: 12 hours*

---

ATP synthase, and other proteins used in photosynthesis; phototropin for phototropic responses; and molecules involved in flowering, gravitropism, and germination.

**Photoperiodism** is an organism's response to changes in the length of night relative to the length of day. Except at the equator, night length varies with the season. Nights are longer in winter than in summer, and the difference increases with latitude. Flowering is photoperiodic in many species of plants. *Long-day* plants such as irises flower only when the hours of darkness fall below a critical value (Figure 28.13**B**). Chrysanthemums and other *short-day* plants flower only when the hours of darkness are greater than some critical value (Figure 28.13**C**). Sunflowers and other *day-neutral* plants flower when they mature, regardless of night length.

The length of night is not the only cue for flowering. Some biennials and perennials flower only after exposure to cold winter temperatures. This process is called **vernalization** (from Latin *vernalis*, which means "to make springlike").

**Senescence and Dormancy** **Senescence** is the phase of a plant life cycle between full maturity and the death of plant parts or the whole plant. In many species of flowering plants, recurring cycles of growth and inactivity are responses to conditions that vary seasonally. Such plants are typically native to regions that are too dry or too cold for optimal growth during part of the year. Plants may drop leaves during such unfavorable intervals. The process by which plant parts are shed is **abscission**. It occurs in deciduous plants in response to shortening daylight hours, and year-round in evergreen plants. Abscission may also be induced by injury, water or nutrient deficiencies, or high temperatures.

Let's use deciduous plants as an example. As leaves and fruits grow in early summer, their cells produce auxin. The auxin moves into the stems, where it helps maintain growth. By midsummer, the nights are longer. Plants begin to divert nutrients away from their leaves, stems, and roots, and into flowers, fruits, and seeds. As the growing season comes to a close, nutrients are routed to twigs, stems, and roots, and auxin production declines in leaves and fruits.

**abscission** Process by which plant parts are shed in response to seasonal change, drought, injury, or nutrient deficiency.

**biological clock** Internal time-measuring mechanism by which individuals adjust their activities seasonally, daily, or both in response to environmental cues.

**circadian rhythm** A biological activity repeated about every 24 hours.

**photoperiodism** Biological response to seasonal changes in the relative lengths of day and night.

**phytochrome** A light-sensitive pigment that helps set plant circadian rhythms based on length of night.

**senescence** Phase in a life cycle from maturity until death; also applies to death of parts, such as plant leaves.

**thigmotropism** Redirected growth of a plant in response to contact with a solid object.

**vernalization** Stimulation of flowering in spring by low temperature in winter.

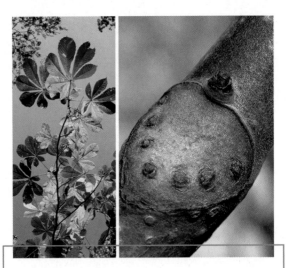

**FIGURE 28.14** Abscission in the horse chestnut tree. *Left*, leaves change color in autumn before dropping. *Right*, the horseshoe-shaped leaf scar is all that remains of an abscission zone that formed before a leaf detached from the stem.

The auxin-deprived structures release ethylene that diffuses into nearby abscission zones—twigs, petioles, and fruit stalks. The ethylene is a signal for cells in the zone to produce enzymes that digest their own walls. The cells bulge as their walls soften, and separate from one another as the extracellular matrix that cements them together dissolves. Tissue in the zone weakens, and the structure above it drops (Figure 28.14).

For many species, growth stops in autumn as a plant enters dormancy, a period of arrested growth that is triggered by (and later ended by) environmental cues. Long nights, cold temperatures, and dry, nitrogen-poor soil are strong cues for dormancy in many plants. Dormancy-breaking cues usually operate between fall and spring. Dormant plants do not resume growth until certain conditions in the environment occur. A few species require exposure of the dormant plant to many hours of cold temperature. More typical cues include the return of milder temperatures and plentiful water and nutrients. With the return of favorable conditions, life cycles begin to turn once more as seeds germinate and buds resume growth.

## Take-Home Message **Do plants have biological clocks?**

- Flowering plants respond to recurring cues from the environment with recurring cycles of development.

- The main environmental cue for flowering is the length of night relative to the length of day, which varies by the season in most places. Low winter temperatures stimulate the flowering of many plant species in spring.

- Abscission and dormancy are triggered by environmental cues such as seasonal changes in temperature or daylength.

# 28.8

# Impacts/Issues Revisited:
# Plight of the Honeybee

Sexual reproduction in plants involves the transfer of pollen, typically from one plant to another. Unlike animals, plants cannot move about to find a mate, so they depend on factors in the environment that can move pollen around for them. The diversity of flower form in part reflects that dependence.

A **pollination vector** is any agent that delivers pollen from an anther to a compatible stigma. Many plants are pollinated by wind, which is entirely nonspecific in where it dumps pollen. Such plants often release pollen grains by the billions, insurance in numbers that some of their pollen will reach a receptive stigma.

Other plants enlist the help of pollinators—living pollination vectors—to transfer pollen among individuals of the same species. An insect, bird, or other animal that is attracted to a particular flower often picks up pollen on a visit, then inadvertently transfers it to the flower of a different plant on a later visit. The more specific the attraction, the more efficient the transfer of pollen among plants of the same species. Given the selective advantage for flower traits that attract specific pollinators, it is not surprising that about 90 percent of flowering plants have coevolved animal pollinators.

**nectar** Sweet fluid exuded by some flowers; attracts pollinators.
**pollination vector** Any agent that moves pollen grains from one plant to another.

A flower's shape, pattern, color, and fragrance are adaptations that attract certain animal pollinators (Figure 28.15). For example, the petals of many flowers pollinated by bees usually are bright white, yellow, or blue, typically with pigments that reflect ultraviolet light. Such UV-reflecting pigments are often distributed in patterns that bees can recognize as visual guides to nectar. We can see the patterns only with special camera filters; our eyes do not have receptors that respond to UV light.

Pollinators such as bats and moths have an excellent sense of smell, and can follow concentration gradients of airborne chemicals to a flower that is emitting them. Not all flowers smell sweet; odors like dung or rotting flesh beckon beetles and flies.

An animal's reward for a visit to the flower may be **nectar** (a sweet fluid exuded by flowers), oils, nutritious pollen, or even the illusion of having sex. Nectar is the only food for most adult butterflies ❶, and it is the food of choice for hummingbirds ❷. Honeybees collect nectar ❸ and convert it to honey, which helps feed the bees through the winter. Pollen is an even richer food, with more vitamins and minerals than nectar.

Many flowers have specializations that exclude nonpollinators. For example, nectar at the bottom of a long floral tube or spur is often accessible only to a certain pollinator that has a matching feeding device. Often, stamens adapted to brush against a pollinator's body or lob pollen onto it will function only when triggered by that pollinator. Such relationships are to both species' mutual advantage: A flower that captivates the attention of an animal has a pollinator that spends its time seeking out (and pollinating) only those flowers; the animal receives an exclusive supply of the reward offered by the plant.

**How Would**
# YOU
☑ **Vote ?**

Besides targeting pests, microencapsulated pesticides also wipe out populations of important pollinators. Should their use be restricted? See CengageNow for details, then vote online (cengagenow.com).

# Summary

**Section 28.1** Declines in populations of pollinators such as honeybees affect coevolved plant populations as well as other animal species that depend on the plants.

**Section 28.2** Flowers consist of modified leaves (sepals, petals, stamens, and carpels) at the ends of specialized branches of angiosperm sporophytes. An ovule develops from a mass of ovary wall tissue inside carpels. Spores produced by meiosis in ovules develop into female gametophytes; those produced in anthers develop into immature male gametophytes (pollen grains).

Pollination is the arrival of pollen grains on a receptive stigma. A pollen grain germinates and forms a pollen tube that contains two sperm cells. Species-specific molecular signals guide the tube's growth down through carpel tissues to the egg. In double fertilization, one of the sperm cells in the pollen tube fertilizes the egg, forming a zygote; the other fuses with the endosperm mother cell and gives rise to endosperm.

CENGAGENOW™ Take a closer look at the life cycle of a eudicot, and investigate the plant life cycle and the structure of a flower, with the animations on CengageNow.

**Section 28.3** An embryo sporophyte develops inside an ovule. A seed is a mature ovule. It consists of the embryo and its food reserves inside a protective seed coat. Fruits function in seed dispersal.

CENGAGENOW™ See how an embryo sporophyte develops inside a eudicot seed with the animation on CengageNow.

**Section 28.4** Many flowering plants can reproduce asexually by sending out runners or by other types of vegetative reproduction. Many agriculturally valuable plants are produced by grafting or tissue culture propagation.

**Section 28.5** Gene expression and cues from the environment coordinate plant development, which is the formation and growth of tissues and parts in predictable patterns. Germination is one pattern of development in plants.

CENGAGENOW™ Compare the growth and development of a monocot and a eudicot with the animation on CengageNow.

**Section 28.6** Like animal hormones, plant hormones secreted by one cell alter the activity of a different cell. Plant hormones can promote or arrest growth of a plant by stimulating or inhibiting cell division, differentiation, elongation, and reproduction. The main plant hormones are gibberellins, auxins, cytokinins, ethylene, and abscisic acid. In addition to controlling patterns of growth and development, hormones also trigger adjustments in the direction and rate of growth in response to environmental stimuli.

CENGAGENOW™ Observe the effect of auxin on plant growth and investigate plant tropisms with the animations on CengageNow.

**Section 28.7** Internal timing mechanisms such as biological clocks (including circadian rhythms) are set by daily and seasonal varia-

tions in environmental conditions. Photoperiodism is a response to changes in length of night relative to length of day. Light detection in plants involves nonphotosynthetic pigments called phytochromes (in photoperiodism) and phototropins (in phototropism).

Dormancy is a period of arrested growth that does not end until specific environmental cues occur. Dormancy is typically preceded by abscission. Senescence is the part of the plant life cycle between maturity and death of the plant or plant parts.

CENGAGENOW™ Learn how plants respond to night length with the animation on CengageNow.

**Section 28.8** A flower's shape, pattern, color, and fragrance typically reflect an evolutionary relationship with a particular pollination vector, often a coevolved animal. Coevolved pollinators receive nectar, pollen, or another reward for visiting a flower.

## Self-Quiz    Answers in Appendix I

1. The _____ of a flower contains one or more ovaries in which eggs develop, fertilization occurs, and seeds mature.
   a. pollen sac            c. receptacle
   b. carpel                d. sepal

2. Seeds are mature _____ ; fruits are mature _____ .
   a. ovaries; ovules       c. ovules; ovaries
   b. ovules; stamens       d. stamens; ovaries

3. Meiosis of cells in pollen sacs forms haploid _____ .
   a. megaspores            c. stamens
   b. microspores           d. sporophytes

4. Cotyledons develop as part of _____ .
   a. carpels               c. embryo sporophytes
   b. accessory fruits      d. petioles

5. The seed coat forms from the _____ .
   a. integuments           c. endosperm
   b. coleoptile            d. sepals

6. A new plant forms from a stem that broke off of the parent plant and fell to the ground. This is an example of _____ .
   a. parthenogenesis       c. vegetative reproduction
   b. exocytosis            d. nodal growth

7. Plant hormones _____ .
   a. may have multiple effects
   b. are influenced by environmental cues
   c. are active in plant embryos within seeds
   d. are active in adult plants
   e. all of the above

8. In some plants, flowering is a _____ response.
   a. phototropic           c. photoperiodic
   b. gravitropic           d. thigmotropic

9. Name one reward that a pollinator may receive in return for a visit to a flower of its coevolved plant partner.

# Digging Into Data

## Searching for Pollinators

*Massonia depressa* is a low-growing succulent plant native to the desert of South Africa. The dull-colored flowers of this monocot develop at ground level, have tiny petals, emit a yeasty aroma, and produce a thick, jelly-like nectar. These features led researchers to suspect that desert rodents such as gerbils pollinate this plant (Figure 28.16).

To test their hypothesis, the researchers trapped rodents in areas where *M. depressa* grows and checked them for pollen. They also put some plants in wire cages that excluded mammals, but not insects, to see whether fruits and seeds would form in the absence of rodents. The results are shown in Figure 28.17.

1. How many of the 13 captured rodents showed some evidence of pollen from *M. depressa*?

2. Would this evidence alone be sufficient to conclude that rodents are the main pollinators for this plant?

3. How did the average number of seeds produced by caged plants compare with that of control plants?

4. Do these data support the hypothesis that rodents are required for pollination of *M. depressa*? Why or why not?

**FIGURE 28.17** *Right*, results of experiments testing rodent pollination of *M. depressa*. **A** Evidence of visits to *M. depressa* by rodents. **B** Fruit and seed production of *M. depressa* with and without visits by mammals. Mammals were excluded from plants by wire cages with openings large enough for insects to pass through. 23 plants were tested in each group.

**FIGURE 28.16** The dull, petal-less, ground-level flowers of *Massonia depressa* are accessible to rodents, who push their heads through the stamens to reach the nectar at the bottom of floral cups. Note the pollen on the gerbil's snout.

**A**

| Type of rodent | Number caught | # with pollen on snout | # with pollen in feces |
|---|---|---|---|
| Namaqua rock rat | 4 | 3 | 2 |
| Cape spiny mouse | 3 | 2 | 2 |
| Hairy-footed gerbil | 4 | 2 | 4 |
| Cape short-eared gerbil | 1 | 0 | 1 |
| African pygmy mouse | 1 | 0 | 0 |

**B**

| | Mammals allowed access to plants | Mammals excluded from plants |
|---|---|---|
| Percent of plants that set fruit | 30.4 | 4.3 |
| Average number of fruits per plant | 1.39 | 0.47 |
| Average number of seeds per plant | 20.0 | 1.95 |

10. Which of the following statements is false?
   a. Auxins and gibberellins promote stem elongation.
   b. Cytokinins promote cell division, retard leaf aging.
   c. Abscisic acid promotes water loss and dormancy.
   d. Ethylene promotes fruit ripening and abscission.

11. Match the observation with the hormone most likely to be its cause.

| | |
|---|---|
| _____ ethylene | a. Your cabbage plants bolt (they form elongated flowering stalks). |
| _____ cytokinin | |
| _____ auxin | b. The philodendron in your room is leaning toward the window. |
| _____ gibberellin | |
| _____ abscisic acid | c. The last of your apples is getting really mushy. |
| | d. The seeds of your roommate's marijuana plant do not germinate no matter what he does to them. |
| | e. Lateral buds on your *Ficus* plant are sprouting branch shoots. |

Additional questions are available on CENGAGENOW™

# Critical Thinking

1. The following oat coleoptiles have been modified: either cut or placed in a light-blocking tube. Which ones will still bend toward a light source?

a    b    c    d

# Appendix I

## Chapter 1

| | | |
|---|---|---|
| 1. b | | *1.2* |
| 2. c | | *1.2* |
| 3. c | | *1.4* |
| 4. energy, nutrients | | *1.3* |
| 5. c | | *1.3* |
| 6. b | | *1.4* |
| 7. d | | *1.3* |
| 8. a, d, e | | *1.2, 1.4* |
| 9. a, d, f | | *1.2, 1.4* |
| 10. d | | *1.3* |
| 11. a | | *1.3* |
| 12. b | | *1.5* |
| 13. b | | *1.7* |
| 14. c | | *1.2* |
| b | | *1.4* |
| d | | *1.6* |
| e | | *1.6* |
| a | | *1.6* |

## Chapter 2

| | | |
|---|---|---|
| 1. tracer | | *2.2* |
| 2. compound | | *2.3* |
| 3. polar covalent | | *2.3* |
| 4. hydrophobic | | *2.4* |
| 5. d | | *2.2, 2.5* |
| 6. acid | | *2.5* |
| 7. buffer | | *2.5* |
| 8. four | | *2.6* |
| 9. e | | *2.7, 2.10* |
| 10. double bonds | | *2.8* |
| 11. False: *trans* fats are unsaturated and unhealthy | | *2.1, 2.8* |
| 12. e | | *2.8* |
| 13. d | | *2.9, 2.10* |
| 14. d | | *2.9* |
| 15. d | | *2.10* |
| 16. i | | *2.9* |
| e | | *2.10* |
| b | | *2.8* |
| d | | *2.10* |
| h | | *2.7* |
| f | | *2.8* |
| a | | *2.4* |
| g | | *2.2* |
| c | | *2.4* |

## Chapter 3

| | | |
|---|---|---|
| 1. cell | | *3.2* |
| 2. c | | *3.2* |
| 3. False | | *3.6* |
| 4. c | | *3.4* |
| 5. c | | *3.5* |
| 6. c | | *3.4* |
| 7. lysosomes | | *3.6* |
| 8. c, b, d, a | | *3.6* |
| 9. lipids; proteins | | *3.6* |
| 10. False; e.g., many cells have walls on the outside of the plasma membrane | | *3.5, 3.7* |
| 11. a | | *3.4* |
| 12. d | | *3.7* |
| 13. a | | *3.7* |
| 14. c, f, a, e, d, b | | *3.6* |

## Chapter 4

| | | |
|---|---|---|
| 1. c | | *4.2* |
| 2. d | | *4.2* |
| 3. d | | *4.3* |
| 4. c, d | | *4.3, 4.4* |
| 5. d | | *4.4, 4.5* |
| 6. e | | *4.2, 4.4* |
| 7. more, less | | *4.5* |
| 8. water, gases, or small nonpolar molecules | | *4.5* |
| 9. b | | *4.6* |
| 10. a | | *4.5* |
| 11. osmotic pressure or turgor | | *4.5* |
| 12. e | | *4.6* |
| 13. c | | *4.3* |
| d | | *4.4* |
| e | | *4.2* |
| b | | *4.3* |
| a | | *4.4* |
| f | | *4.5* |
| g | | *4.6* |
| i | | *4.6* |
| h | | *4.6* |

## Chapter 5

| | | |
|---|---|---|
| 1. cat, bird, caterpillar are heterotrophs; weed is an autotroph | | *5.1* |
| 2. carbon dioxide, sunlight | | *5.1* |
| 3. a | | *5.3, 5.4* |
| 4. b | | *5.3, 5.4* |
| 5. c | | *5.4* |
| 6. c | | *5.5* |
| 7. b | | *5.3, 5.5* |
| 8. oxygen | | *5.6* |
| 9. False | | *5.6* |
| 10. c | | *5.6* |
| 11. d | | *5.6* |
| 12. b | | *5.6* |
| 13. d | | *5.7* |
| 14. c | | *5.6* |
| 15. b | | *5.6* |
| c | | *5.7* |
| a | | *5.6* |
| d | | *5.4, 5.6* |
| e | | *5.5* |

## Chapter 6

| | | |
|---|---|---|
| 1. b | | *6.2* |
| 2. d | | *6.3* |
| 3. c | | *6.3* |
| 4. a | | *6.4* |
| 5. d | | *6.4* |
| 6. d | | *6.4* |
| 7. b | | *6.4* |
| 8. CCAAAGAAGTTCTCT | | *6.4* |
| 9. d | | *6.5* |
| 10. d | | *6.3* |
| b | | *6.5* |
| c | | *6.4* |
| a | | *6.4* |

## Chapter 7

| | | |
|---|---|---|
| 1. c | | *7.2* |
| 2. b | | *7.3* |
| 3. d | | *7.3* |
| 4. a | | *7.2* |
| 5. c | | *7.2* |
| 6. 15 | | *7.4* |
| 7. c | | *7.4* |
| 8. a | | *7.4* |
| 9. c | | *7.5* |
| 10. a | | *7.3* |
| 11. d | | *7.5* |
| 12. gly-phe-leu-lys-arg | | *7.4* |
| 13. val-ser-[stop] | | *7.4* |
| 14. b | | *7.7* |
| 15. b | | *7.7* |
| 16. c | | *7.7* |
| 17. c | | *7.4* |
| d | | *7.2* |
| e | | *7.5* |
| g | | *7.7* |
| f | | *7.4* |
| a | | *7.7* |
| b | | *7.6* |

## Chapter 8

| | | |
|---|---|---|
| 1. 2 | | *8.3* |
| 2. d | | *8.2* |
| 3. a | | *8.2* |
| 4. d | | *8.3, 8.7* |
| 5. a | | *8.3* |
| 6. c | | *8.3* |
| 7. a | | *8.3, 8.4* |
| 8. b | | *8.3* |
| 9. c | | *8.2* |
| 10. sister chromatids have just been pulled apart | | *8.7* |
| 11. b | | *8.6* |
| 12. alleles | | *8.6* |
| 13. d | | *8.4* |
| e | | *8.4* |
| a | | *8.7* |
| c | | *8.4* |
| b | | *8.7* |
| g | | *8.7* |
| h | | *8.7* |
| f | | *8.7* |

## Chapter 9

| | | |
|---|---|---|
| 1. b | | *9.2* |
| 2. a | | *9.2* |
| 3. c | | *9.2* |
| 4. d | | *9.2* |
| 5. c | | *9.2* |
| 6. d | | *9.5* |
| 7. b | | *9.6* |
| 8. c | | *9.5* |
| 9. d | | *9.6* |
| 10. c | | *9.7, 9.8* |
| 11. False | | *9.6* |
| 12. True | | *9.7* |
| 13. a | | *9.5* |
| 14. b, d, a, c | | *9.2* |
| 15. b | | *9.7* |
| a | | *9.5* |
| e | | *9.7* |
| c | | *9.7* |
| d | | *9.3* |

## Chapter 10

| | | |
|---|---|---|
| 1. c | | *10.2* |
| 2. a | | *10.2* |
| 3. b | | *10.2* |
| 4. b | | *10.2* |
| 5. c | | *10.2* |
| 6. d | | *10.2* |
| 7. b | | *10.3* |
| 8. d | | *10.3* |
| 9. b | | *10.5* |
| d | | *10.2* |
| e | | *10.5* |
| f | | *10.4* |
| 10. b | | *10.4* |
| 11. b | | *10.5* |
| 12. c | | *10.3* |
| g | | *10.4* |
| d | | *10.2* |
| e | | *10.5* |
| b | | *10.2* |
| a | | *10.1, 10.4* |
| f | | *10.1, 10.4* |

## Chapter 11

| | | |
|---|---|---|
| 1. c | | *11.3* |
| 2. b | | *11.2* |
| 3. c | | *11.2* |
| 4. d | | *11.3* |
| 5. d | | *11.4* |
| 6. d | | *11.4* |
| 7. a | | *11.5* |
| 8. 65.5 | | *11.5* |
| 9. a, c, e, f, g, h | | *11.2, 11.5* |
| 10. d | | *11.6* |
| 11. d | | *11.6* |
| 12. c | | *11.7* |
| 13. b | | *11.6* |
| 14. a | | *11.3* |
| i | | *11.4* |
| e | | *11.3* |
| f | | *11.4* |
| c | | *11.3* |
| b | | *11.3* |
| g | | *11.6* |
| d | | *11.4* |
| h | | *11.6* |

## Chapter 12

| | | |
|---|---|---|
| 1. b | | *12.2* |
| 2. c | | *12.2, 12.4* |
| 3. a, d | | *12.3* |
| 4. b, c | | *12.3* |
| 5. e | | *12.3* |
| 6. d | | *12.5* |
| 7. balanced polymorphism | | *12.4* |
| 8. gene flow | | *12.4* |
| 9. allopatric speciation | | *12.5* |
| 10. c | | *12.7* |
| 11. c | | *12.7* |
| 12. b | | *12.7* |
| 13. c | | *12.4* |
| e | | *12.3* |
| g | | *12.2* |
| b | | *12.4* |
| f | | *12.6* |
| a | | *12.6* |
| d | | *12.7* |
| h | | *12.7* |

## Chapter 13

| | | |
|---|---|---|
| 1. oxygen | | *13.2* |
| 2. b | | *13.2* |
| 3. d | | *13.3* |
| 4. b | | *13.3* |
| 5. c | | *13.4* |
| 6. b | | *13.3* |
| 7. True | | *13.5* |
| 8. contractile vacuole | | *13.5* |
| 9. b | | *13.5* |
| 10. c | | *13.5* |
| 11. c | | *13.5* |
| 12. red | | *13.5* |
| 13. b | | *13.5* |
| 14. d | | *13.6* |
| 15. g | | *13.5* |
| d | | *13.6* |
| c | | *13.4* |
| e | | *13.5* |
| i | | *13.4* |
| f | | *13.5* |
| a | | *13.5* |
| j | | *13.5* |
| b | | *13.5* |
| h | | *13.3* |

## Chapter 14

| | | |
|---|---|---|
| 1. a | | *14.2* |
| 2. c | | *14.5* |
| 3. b | | *14.3* |
| 4. c | | *14.4* |
| 5. a | | *14.4* |
| 6. d | | *14.5* |
| 7. b | | *14.5* |
| 8. ferns | | *14.4* |
| 9. c | | *14.6* |
| d | | *14.2* |
| f | | *14.4* |
| e | | *14.3* |
| a | | *14.2* |
| b | | *14.7* |
| g | | *14.7* |
| 10. c | | *14.8* |
| 11. a | | *14.8* |
| 12. c | | *14.8* |
| 13. mycorrhiza | | *14.9* |
| 14. lichen | | *14.9* |
| 15. False | | *14.9* |

## Chapter 15

| | | |
|---|---|---|
| 1. True | | *15.2* |
| 2. a | | *15.2* |
| 3. coelom | | *15.2* |
| 4. bilateral | | *15.2* |
| 5. c | | *15.3* |
| 6. e | | *15.3* |

| | |
|---|---|
| 7. pharynx with gill slits, notochord, dorsal nerve cord, tail extending beyond anus | 15.4 |
| 8. pharynx with gill slits | 15.4 |
| 9. False | 15.5 |
| 10.b | 15.4 |
| 11.f | 15.6 |
| 12.False | 15.5 |
| 13.d | 15.6 |
| 14.b | 15.3 |
| g | 15.3 |
| l | 15.3 |
| j | 15.3 |
| e | 15.3 |
| c | 15.3 |
| d | 15.3 |
| f | 15.3 |
| k | 15.5 |
| a | 15.5 |
| h | 15.6 |
| i | 15.6 |
| 15.2 | 15.2 |
| 1 | 15.2 |
| 4 | 15.4 |
| 5 | 15.6 |
| 6 | 15.7 |
| 3 | 15.5 |

## Chapter 16

| | |
|---|---|
| 1. a | 16.2 |
| 2. f | 16.3 |
| 3. a | 16.3 |
| 4. d | 16.3 |
| 5. a | 16.3 |
| 6. d | 16.4 |
| 7. True | 16.4 |
| 8. b | 16.5 |
| 9. d | 16.5 |
| 10.d | 16.3 |
| c | 16.3 |
| e | 16.3 |
| a | 16.5 |
| f | 16.3 |
| b | 16.4 |

## Chapter 17

| | |
|---|---|
| 1 niche | 17.2 |
| 2. False | 17.3 |
| 3. b, c, a, d | 17.3 |
| 4. b | 17.3 |
| 5. a | 17.4 |
| 6. d, a, c, b | 17.5 |
| 7. d | 17.5 |
| 8. a | 17.5 |
| 9. b, a, b, c | 17.6 |
| 10.c | 17.6 |
| 11.b | 17.6 |
| 12.a | 17.6 |
| 13.d | 17.6 |
| 14.d | 17.6 |
| 15.True | 17.6 |

## Chapter 18

| | |
|---|---|
| 1. a | 18.2 |
| 2. d | 18.2 |
| 3. a | 18.2 |
| 4. 30 | 18.3 |
| 5. d | 18.3 |
| 6. b | 18.3 |
| 7. a | 18.3 |
| 8. a | 18.4 |
| 9. a | 18.4 |
| 10.e | 18.3 |
| d | 18.3 |
| b | 18.3 |
| c | 18.3 |
| a | 18.4 |
| f | 18.3 |
| g | 18.3 |
| 11.b | 18.5 |
| 12.c | 18.6 |
| 13.b | 18.5 |
| 14.a | 18.5 |
| 15.d | 18.5 |

## Chapter 19

| | |
|---|---|
| 1. a | 19.3 |
| 2. b | 19.3 |
| 3. a | 19.3 |
| 4. a | 19.3 |
| 5. a | 19.3 |
| 6. b | 19.3 |
| 7. c | 19.3 |
| 8. b | 19.3 |
| 9. c | 19.3 |
| 10.d | 19.3 |
| 11.d | 19.3 |
| 12.neurons | 19.3 |
| 13.d | 19.4 |
| 14.d | 19.5 |
| 15.b | 19.3 |
| h | 19.3 |
| a | 19.4 |
| c | 19.3 |
| d | 19.3 |
| e | 19.3 |
| g | 19.3 |
| f | 19.4 |

## Chapter 20

| | |
|---|---|
| 1. a | 20.2 |
| 2. d | 20.2 |
| 3. d | 20.2 |
| 4. b | 20.3 |
| 5. a | 20.2 |
| 6. b | 20.4 |
| 7. d | 20.4 |
| 8. c | 20.4 |
| 9. d | 20.4 |
| 10.d | 20.5 |
| 11.b | 20.3 |
| 12.myosin | 20.4 |
| 13.a | 20.2 |
| 14.b, e, c, d, a | 20.2 |
| 15.d | 20.5 |
| f | 20.5 |
| g | 20.5 |
| a | 20.5 |
| c | 20.2 |
| e | 20.2 |
| j | 20.2 |
| i | 20.2 |
| h | 20.4 |
| b | 20.4 |

## Chapter 21

| | |
|---|---|
| 1. b | 21.2 |
| 2. b | 21.4 |
| 3. a | 21.5 |
| 4. c | 21.4 |
| 5. c | 21.5 |
| 6. d | 21.5 |
| 7. pulmonary | 21.3 |
| 8. a | 21.4 |
| 9. c | 21.7 |
| 10.d | 21.7 |
| 11.a | 21.7 |
| 12.a | 21.7 |
| 13.2, 1, 3, 4, 5 | 21.7 |
| 14.b | 21.5 |
| e | 21.7 |
| i | 21.5, 21.7 |
| h | 21.5 |
| c | 21.4 |
| g | 21.7 |
| d | 21.7 |
| f | 21.4 |
| a | 21.4 |

## Chapter 22

| | |
|---|---|
| 1. e | 22.2, 22.3 |
| 2. g | 22.4 |
| 3. c | 22.5–22.7 |
| 4. d | 22.4 |
| 5. d | 22.2 |
| 6. e.g., immediate; fixed (does not change much over a lifetime); can recognize about 1,000 pathogen-associated molecular patterns; inborn | 22.2, 22.4 |
| 7. e.g., recognizes self and nonself; targets specific antigens; changes over the course of the individual's lifetime; can recognize billions of antigens; provides lasting protection; consists of cell-mediated and antibody-mediated responses | 22.2, 22.5 |
| 8. d | 22.6 |
| 9. b | 22.5 |
| 10.e | 22.5 |
| 11.b | 22.7 |
| 12.c | 22.8 |
| 13.e, g, c, d a, f, b | 22.2 |
| 14.g | 22.8 |
| b | 22.6 |
| a | 22.2 |
| e | 22.5 |
| d | 22.8 |
| f | 22.6 |
| c | 22.4 |

## Chapter 23

| | |
|---|---|
| 1. d | 23.2 |
| 2. b | 23.3 |
| 3. c | 23.3 |
| 4. b | 23.3 |
| 5. b | 23.3 |
| 6. f, b, a, d, e, c | 23.3 |
| 7. d | 23.4 |
| 8. no | 23.4 |
| 9. b | 23.4 |
| 10.d | 23.6 |
| 11.a | 23.7 |
| 12.a | 23.7 |
| 13.b | 23.7 |
| 14.c | 23.7 |
| 15.c | 23.6 |
| a | 23.6 |
| b | 23.6 |
| e | 23.7 |
| d | 23.7 |

## Chapter 24

| | |
|---|---|
| 1. a | 24.2 |
| 2. c | 24.2 |
| 3. a | 24.2 |
| 4. b | 24.2 |
| 5. b | 24.4 |
| 6. c | 24.4 |
| 7. reflex | 24.5 |
| 8. c | 24.5 |
| 9. b | 24.5 |
| 10.c | 24.6 |
| 11.c | 24.6 |
| 12.b | 24.6 |
| 13.a | 24.6 |
| 14.c | 24.6 |
| 15.j | 24.6 |
| c | 24.6 |
| i | 24.5 |
| b | 24.5 |
| h | 24.5 |
| f | 24.6 |
| e | 24.3 |
| g | 24.2 |
| d | 24.5 |
| a | 24.6 |

## Chapter 25

| | |
|---|---|
| 1. a | 25.2 |
| 2. b | 25.3 |
| 3. c | 25.2 |
| 4. c, b, a, d | 25.3 |
| 5. growth hormone | 25.3 |
| 6. d | 25.4 |
| 7. b | 25.5 |
| 8. b | 25.4 |
| 9. b | 25.5 |
| 10.b | 25.4 |
| 11. False | 25.7 |
| 12.b | 25.4 |
| 13.d | 25.6 |
| 14.c | 25.7 |
| 15.e | 25.6 |
| g | 25.4 |
| d | 25.4 |
| c | 25.4 |
| h | 25.5 |
| f | 25.7 |
| b | 25.3 |
| a | 25.7 |

## Chapter 26

| | |
|---|---|
| 1. asexual | 26.2 |
| 2. a | 26.2 |
| 3. blastula, gastrula | 26.2 |
| 4. a | 26.3 |
| 5. True | 26.3 |
| 6. c | 26.3 |
| 7. c | 26.3 |
| 8. c | 26.6 |
| 9. 3, 2, 1, 4, 5 | 26.2, 26.6 |
| 10.e | 26.5 |
| 11.d | 26.6 |
| 12.e | 26.7 |
| 13.c | 26.3 |
| h | 26.3 |
| a | 26.6 |
| g | 26.3 |
| d | 26.3 |
| e | 26.3 |
| b | 26.3 |
| f | 26.7 |

## Chapter 27

| | |
|---|---|
| 1. a | 27.3 |
| 2. b | 27.2, 27.6 |
| 3. b | 27.3 |
| 4. a, b, e | 27.2 |
| 5. b | 27.4 |
| 6. c | 27.6 |
| 7. c | 27.6 |
| 8. b | 27.3 |
| 9. d | 27.5 |
| 10.humus | 27.5 |
| 11.d | 27.4 |
| 12.d | 27.6 |
| 13.b | 27.6 |
| 14.b | 27.3 |
| d | 27.4 |
| e | 27.2, 27.6 |
| c | 27.2, 27.6 |
| f | 27.3 |
| a | 27.4 |

## Chapter 28

| | |
|---|---|
| 1. b | 28.2 |
| 2. c | 28.3 |
| 3. b | 28.2 |
| 4. c | 28.3 |
| 5. a | 28.3 |
| 6. c | 28.4 |
| 7. e | 28.6 |
| 8. c | 28.7 |
| 9. nectar, pollen, oils, and the illusion of sex are mentioned in the text | 28.8 |
| 10.c | 28.6 |
| 11.c, e, b, a, d | 28.6 |

# Appendix II

**Answers to Genetics Problems**

1. a. *AB*
   b. *AB, aB*
   c. *Ab, ab*
   d. *AB, Ab, aB, ab*

2. a. All offspring will be *AaBB*.
   b. 1/4 *AABB* (25% each genotype)
      1/4 *AABb*
      1/4 *AaBB*
      1/4 *AaBb*
   c. 1/4 *AaBb* (25% each genotype)
      1/4 *Aabb*
      1/4 *aaBb*
      1/4 *aabb*
   d. 1/16 *AABB* (6.25% of genotype)
      1/8 *AaBB* (12.5%)
      1/16 *aaBB* (6.25%)
      1/8 *AABb* (12.5%)
      1/4 *AaBb* (25%)
      1/8 *aaBb* (12.5%)
      1/16 *AAbb* (6.25%)
      1/8 *Aabb* (12.5%)
      1/16 *aabb* (6.25%)

3. A mating between a mouse from a true-breeding, white-furred strain and a mouse from a true-breeding, brown-furred strain would provide you with the most direct evidence. Because true-breeding strains of organisms typically are homozygous for a trait being studied, all $F_1$ offspring from this mating should be heterozygous. Record the phenotype of each $F_1$ mouse, then let them mate with one another. Assuming only one gene locus is involved, these are possible outcomes for the $F_1$ offspring:

   a. All $F_1$ mice are brown, and their $F_2$ offspring segregate: 3 brown : 1 white. *Conclusion*: Brown is dominant to white.

   b. All $F_1$ mice are white, and their $F_2$ offspring segregate: 3 white : 1 brown. *Conclusion*: White is dominant to brown.

   c. All $F_1$ mice are tan, and the $F_2$ offspring segregate: 1 brown : 2 tan : 1 white. *Conclusion*: The alleles at this locus show incomplete dominance.

4. a. Both parents are heterozygotes (*Aa*). Their children may be albino (*aa*) or unaffected (*AA* or *Aa*).

   b. All are homozygous recessive (*aa*).

   c. Homozygous recessive (*aa*) father, and heterozygous (*Aa*) mother. The albino child is *aa*, the unaffected children *Aa*.

5. A daughter could develop this muscular dystrophy only if she inherited two X-linked recessive alleles—one from each parent. Males who carry the allele are unlikely to father children because they develop the disorder and die early in life.

# Appendix III

## Annotations to A Journal Article

This journal article reports on the movements of a female wolf during the summer of 2002 in northwestern Canada. It also reports on a scientific process of inquiry, observation and interpretation to learn where, how and why the wolf traveled as she did. In some ways, this article reflects the story of "how to do science" told in section 1.5 of this textbook. These notes are intended to help you read and understand how scientists work and how they report on their work.

**(1)** ARCTIC

**(2)** VOL. 57, NO. 2 (JUNE 2004) P. 196–203

## (3) Long Foraging Movement of a Denning Tundra Wolf

**(4)** Paul F. Frame,[1,2] David S. Hik,[1] H. Dean Cluff,[3] and Paul C. Paquet[4]

**(5)** (Received 3 September 2003; accepted in revised form 16 January 2004)

**(6)** ABSTRACT. Wolves (*Canis lupus*) on the Canadian barrens are intimately linked to migrating herds of barren-ground caribou (*Rangifer tarandus*). We deployed a Global Positioning System (GPS) radio collar on an adult female wolf to record her movements in response to changing caribou densities near her den during summer. This wolf and two other females were observed nursing a group of 11 pups. She traveled a minimum of 341 km during a 14-day excursion. The straight-line distance from the den to the farthest location was 103 km, and the overall minimum rate of travel was 3.1 km/h. The distance between the wolf and the radio-collared caribou decreased from 242 km one week before the excursion to 8 km four days into the excursion. We discuss several possible explanations for the long foraging bout.

**(7)** Key words: wolf, GPS tracking, movements, *Canis lupus*, foraging, caribou, Northwest Territories

**(8)** RÉSUMÉ. Les loups (*Canis lupus*) dans la toundra canadienne sont étroitement liés aux hardes de caribous des toundras (*Rangifer tarandus*). On a équipé une louve adulte d'un collier émetteur muni d'un système de positionnement mondial (GPS) afin d'enregistrer ses déplacements en réponse au changement de densité du caribou près de sa tanière durant l'été. On a observé cette louve ainsi que deux autres en train d'allaiter un groupe de 11 louveteaux. Elle a parcouru un minimum de 341 km durant une sortie de 14 jours. La distance en ligne droite de la tanière à l'endroit le plus éloigné était de 103 km, et la vitesse minimum durant tout le voyage était de 3,1 km/h. La distance entre la louve et le caribou muni du collier émetteur a diminué de 242 km une semaine avant la sortie à 8 km quatre jours après la sortie. On commente diverses explications possibles pour ce long épisode de recherche de nourriture.

Mots clés: loup, repérage GPS, déplacements, *Canis lupus*, recherche de nourriture, caribou, Territoires du Nord-Ouest

Traduit pour la revue *Arctic* par Nésida Loyer.

### (9) Introduction

Wolves (*Canis lupus*) that den on the central barrens of mainland Canada follow the seasonal movements of their main prey, migratory barren-ground caribou (*Rangifer tarandus*) (Kuyt, 1962; Kelsall, 1968; Walton et al., 2001). However, most wolves do not den near caribou calving grounds, but select sites farther south, closer to the tree line (Heard and Williams, 1992). Most caribou migrate beyond primary wolf denning areas by mid-June and do not return until mid-to-late July (Heard et al., 1996; Gunn et al., 2001). Conse-quently, caribou density near dens is low for part of the summer.

During this period of spatial separation from the main caribou herds, wolves must either search near the homesite for scarce caribou or alternative prey (or **(10)** both), travel to where prey are abundant, or use a combination of these strategies.

Walton et al. (2001) postulated that the travel of tundra wolves outside their normal summer ranges is **(11)** a response to low caribou availability rather than a pre-dispersal exploration like that observed in terri-torial wolves (Fritts and Mech, 1981; Messier, 1985). The authors postulated this because most such travel was directed toward caribou calving grounds. We report details of such a long-distance excursion by a breeding female tundra wolf wearing a GPS radio collar. We discuss the relationship of the excursion to movements of satellite-collared caribou (Gunn et al., 2001), supporting the hypothesis that tundra wolves make directional, rapid, long-distance movements in response to seasonal prey availability.

[1] Department of Biological Sciences, University of Alberta, Edmonton, Alberta T6G 2E9, Canada
[2] Corresponding author: pframe@ualberta.ca
[3] Department of Resources, Wildlife, and Economic Development, North Slave Region, Government of the Northwest Territories, P.O. Box 2668, 3803 Bretzlaff Dr., Yellowknife, Northwest Territories X1A 2P9, Canada; Dean_Cluff@gov.nt.ca
[4] Faculty of Environmental Design, University of Calgary, Calgary, Alberta T2N 1N4, Canada; current address: P.O. Box 150, Meacham, Saskatchewan S0K 2V0, Canada

196

**1** Title of the journal, which reports on science taking place in Arctic regions.

**2** Volume number, issue number and date of the journal, and page numbers of the article.

**3** Title of the article: a concise but specific description of the subject of study—one episode of long-range travel by a wolf hunting for food on the Arctic tundra.

**4** Authors of the article: scientists working at the institutions listed in the footnotes below. Note #2 indicates that P. F. Frame is the *corresponding author*—the person to contact with questions or comments. His email address is provided.

**5** Date on which a draft of the article was received by the journal editor, followed by date one which a revised draft was accepted for publication. Between these dates, the article was reviewed and critiqued by other scientists, a process called peer review. The authors revised the article to make it clearer, according to those reviews.

**6** ABSTRACT: A brief description of the study containing all basic elements of this report. First sentence summarizes the *background* material. Second sentence encapsulates the *methods* used. The rest of the paragraph sums up the *results*. Authors introduce the main *subject* of the study—a female wolf (#388) with pups in a den—and refer to later *discussion* of possible explanations for her behavior.

**7** Key words are listed to help researchers using computer databases. Searching the databases using these key words will yield a list of studies related to this one.

**8** RÉSUMÉ: The French translation of the abstract and key words. Many researchers in this field are French Canadian. Some journals provide such translations in French or in other languages.

**9** INTRODUCTION: Gives the background for this wolf study. This paragraph tells of known or suspected wolf behavior that is important for this study. Note that (a) major species mentioned are always accompanied by scientific names, and (b) statements of fact or *postulations* (claims or assumptions about what is likely to be true) are followed by references to studies that established those facts or supported the postulations.

**10** This paragraph focuses directly on the wolf behaviors that were studied here.

**11** This paragraph starts with a statement of the *hypothesis* being tested, one that originated in other studies and is supported by this one. The hypothesis is restated more succinctly in the last sentence of this paragraph. This is the *inquiry* part of the scientific process—asking questions and suggesting possible answers.

**12** This map shows the study area and depicts wolf and caribou locations and movements during one summer. Some of this information is explained below.

**13** STUDY AREA: This section sets the stage for the study, locating it precisely with latitude and longitude coordinates and describing the area (illustrated by the map in Figure 1).

**14** Here begins the story of how prey (caribou) and predators (wolves) interact on the tundra. Authors describe movements of these nomadic animals throughout the year.

**15** We focus on the denning season (summer) and learn how wolves locate their dens and travel according to the movements of caribou herds.

**Figure 1.** Map showing the movements of satellite radio-collared caribou with respect to female wolf 388's summer range and long foraging movement, in summer 2002.

## 13 Study Area

Our study took place in the northern boreal forest–low Arctic tundra transition zone (63° 30′ N, 110° 00′ W; Figure 1; Timoney et al., 1992). Permafrost in the area changes from discontinuous to continuous (Harris, 1986). Patches of spruce (*Picea mariana, P. glauca*) occur in the southern portion and give way to open tundra to the northeast. Eskers, kames, and other glacial deposits are scattered throughout the study area. Standing water and exposed bedrock are characteristic of the area.

### 14 Details of the Caribou-Wolf System

The Bathurst caribou herd uses this study area. Most caribou cows have begun migrating by late April, reaching calving grounds by June (Gunn et al., 2001;

Figure 1). Calving peaks by 15 June (Gunn et al., 2001), and calves begin to travel with the herd by one week of age (Kelsall, 1968). The movement patterns of bulls are less known, but bulls frequent areas near calving grounds by mid-June (Heard et al., 1996; Gunn et al., 2001). In summer, Bathurst caribou cows generally travel south from their calving grounds and then, parallel to the tree line, to the northwest. The rut usually takes place at the tree line in October (Gunn et al., 2001). The winter range of the Bathurst herd varies among years, ranging through the taiga and along the tree line from south of Great Bear Lake to southeast of Great Slave Lake. Some caribou spend the winter on the tundra (Gunn et al., 2001; Thorpe et al., 2001).

In winter, wolves that prey on Bathurst caribou do **15** not behave territorially. Instead, they follow the herd throughout its winter range (Walton et al., 2001; Musiani, 2003). However, during denning (May–

**Table 1.** Daily distances from wolf 388 and the den to the nearest radio-collared caribou during a long excursion in summer 2002.

| Date (2002) | Mean distance from caribou to wolf (km) | Daily distance from closest caribou to den |
|---|---|---|
| 12 July | 242 | 241 |
| 13 July | 210 | 209 |
| 14 July | 200 | 199 |
| 15 July | 186 | 180 |
| 16 July | 163 | 162 |
| 17 July | 151 | 148 |
| 18 July | 144 | 137 |
| 19 July[1] | 126 | 124 |
| 20 July | 103 | 130 |
| 21 July | 73 | 130 |
| 22 July | 40 | 110 |
| 23 July[2] | 9 | 104 |
| 29 July[3] | 16 | 43 |
| 30 July | 32 | 43 |
| 31 July | 28 | 44 |
| 1 August | 29 | 46 |
| 2 August[4] | 54 | 52 |
| 3 August | 53 | 53 |
| 4 August | 74 | 74 |
| 5 August | 75 | 75 |
| 6 August | 74 | 75 |
| 7 August | 72 | 75 |
| 8 August | 76 | 75 |
| 9 August | 79 | 79 |

[1] Excursion starts.
[2] Wolf closest to collared caribou.
[3] Previous five days' caribou locations not available.
[4] Excursion ends.

August, parturition late May to mid-June), wolf movements are limited by the need to return food to the den. To maximize access to migrating caribou, many wolves select den sites closer to the tree line than to caribou calving grounds (Heard and Williams, 1992). Because of caribou movement patterns, tundra denning wolves are separated from the main caribou herds by several hundred kilometers at some time during summer (Williams, 1990:19; Figure 1; Table 1).

**16** Muskoxen do not occur in the study area (Fournier and Gunn, 1998), and there are few moose there (H.D. Cluff, pers. obs.). Therefore, alternative prey for wolves includes waterfowl, other ground-nesting birds, their eggs, rodents, and hares (Kuyt, 1972; Williams, 1990:16; H.D. Cluff and P.F. Frame, unpubl. data). During 56 hours of den observations, we saw no ground squirrels or hares, only birds. It appears that the abundance of alternative prey was relatively low in 2002.

## **17** Methods

### Wolf Monitoring

**18** We captured female wolf 388 near her den on 22 June 2002, using a helicopter net-gun (Walton et al., 2001). She was fitted with a releasable GPS radio collar (Merrill et al., 1998) programmed to acquire locations at 30-

**198** *P.F. Frame, et al*

minute intervals. The collar was electronically released (e.g., Mech and Gese, 1992) on 20 August 2002. From 27 June to 3 July 2002, we observed 388's den with a 78 mm spotting scope at a distance of 390 m.

### Caribou Monitoring

In spring of 2002, ten female caribou were captured by helicopter net-gun and fitted with satellite radio collars, bringing the total number of collared Bathurst cows to 19. Eight of these spent the summer of 2002 south of Queen Maud Gulf, well east of normal Bathurst caribou range. Therefore, we used 11 caribou for this analysis. The collars provided one location per day during our study, except for five days from 24 to 28 July. Locations of satellite collars were obtained from Service Argos, Inc. (Landover, Maryland).

### Data Analysis

Location data were analyzed by ArcView GIS software (Environmental Systems Research Institute Inc., Redlands, California). We calculated the average distance from the nearest collared caribou to the wolf and the den for each day of the study. **19**

Wolf foraging bouts were calculated from the time 388 exited a buffer zone (500 m radius around the den) until she re-entered it. We considered her to be traveling when two consecutive locations were spatially separated by more than 100 m. Minimum distance traveled was the sum of distances between each location and the next during the excursion.

We compared pre- and post-excursion data using Analysis of Variance (ANOVA; Zar, 1999). We first tested for homogeneity of variances with Levene's test (Brown and Forsythe, 1974). No transformations of these data were required.

## Results **20**

### Wolf Monitoring

**Pre-Excursion Period:** Wolf 388 was lactating when captured on 22 June. We observed her and two other females nursing a group of 11 pups between 27 June and 3 July. During our observations, the pack consisted of at least four adults (3 females and 1 male) and 11 pups. On 30 June, three pups were moved to a location 310 m from the other eight and cared for by an uncollared female. The male was not seen at the den after the evening of 30 June. **21**

Before the excursion, telemetry indicated 18 foraging bouts. The mean distance traveled during these bouts was 25.29 km (± 4.5 SE, range 3.1–82.5 km). Mean greatest distance from the den on foraging

**16** Other variables are considered—prey other than caribou and their relative abundance in 2002.

**17** METHODS: There is no one scientific method. Procedures for each and every study must be explained carefully.

**18** Authors explain when and how they tracked caribou and wolves, including tools used and the exact procedures followed.

**19** This important subsection explains what data were calculated (average distance ...) and how, including the software used and where it came from. (The calculations are listed in Table 1.) Note that the behavior measured (traveling) is carefully defined.

**20** RESULTS: The heart of the report and the *observation* part of the scientific process. This section is organized parallel to the Methods section.

**21** This subsection is broken down by periods of observation. Pre-excursion period covers the time between 388's capture and the start of her long-distance travel. The investigators used visual observations as well as telemetry (measurements taken using the global positioning system (GPS)) to gather data. They looked at how 388 cared for her pups, interacted with other adults, and moved about the den area.

**22** The key in the lower right-hand corner of the map shows areas (shaded) within which the wolves and caribou moved, and the dotted trail of 388 during her excursion. From the results depicted on this map, the investigators tried to determine when and where 388 might have encountered caribou and how their locations affected her traveling behavior.

**23** The wolf's excursion (her long trip away from the den area) is the focus of this study. These paragraphs present detailed measurements of daily movements during her two-week trip—how far she traveled, how far she was from collared caribou, her time spent traveling and resting, and her rate of speed. Authors use the phrase "minimum distance traveled" to acknowledge they couldn't track every step but were measuring samples of her movements. They knew that she went at least as far as they measured. This shows how scientists try to be exact when reporting results. Results of this study are depicted graphically in the map in Figure 2.

**Figure 2.** Details of a long foraging movement by female wolf 388 between 19 July and 2 August 2002. Also shown are locations and movements of three satellite radio-collared caribou from 23 July to 21 August 2002. On 23 July, the wolf was 8 km from a collared caribou. The farthest point from the den (103 km distant) was recorded on 27 July. Arrows indicate direction of travel.

bouts was 7.1 km (± 0.9 SE, range 1.7–17.0 km). The average duration of foraging bouts for the period was 20.9 h (± 4.5 SE, range 1–71 h).

The average daily distance between the wolf and the nearest collared caribou decreased from 242 km on 12 July, one week before the excursion period, to 126 km on 19 July, the day the excursion began (Table 1).

**23** **Excursion Period:** On 19 July at 2203, after spending 14 h at the den, 388 began moving to the northeast and did not return for 336 h (14 d; Figure 2). Whether she traveled alone or with other wolves is unknown. During the excursion, 476 (71%) of 672 possible locations were recorded. The wolf crossed the southeast end of Lac Capot Blanc on a small land bridge, where she paused for 4.5 h after traveling for 19.5 h (37.5

km). Following this rest, she traveled for 9 h (26.3 km) onto a peninsula in Reid Lake, where she spent 2 h before backtracking and stopping for 8 h just off the peninsula. Her next period of travel lasted 16.5 h (32.7 km), terminating in a pause of 9.5 h just 3.8 km from a concentration of locations at the far end of her excursion, where we presume she encountered caribou. The mean duration of these three movement periods was 15.7 h (± 2.5 SE), and that of the pauses, 7.3 h (± 1.5). The wolf required 72.5 h (3.0 d) to travel a minimum of 95 km from her den to this area near caribou (Figure 2). She remained there (35.5 km2) for 151.5 h (6.3 d) and then moved south to Lake of the Enemy, where she stayed (31.9 km²) for 74 h (3.1 d) before returning to her den. Her greatest distance from the den, 103 km, was recorded 174.5 h (7.3 d) after the excursion began, at 0433 on 27 July. She was 8 km from a collared caribou on 23 July, four days after the excursion began (Table 1).

The return trip began at 0403 on 2 August, 318 h (13.2 d) after leaving the den. She followed a relatively direct path for 18 h back to the den, a distance of 75 km.

The minimum distance traveled during the excursion was 339 km. The estimated overall minimum travel rate was 3.1 km/h, 2.6 km/h away from the den and 4.2 km/h on the return trip.

 **Post-Excursion Period:** We saw three pups when recovering the collar on 20 August, but others may have been hiding in vegetation.

Telemetry recorded 13 foraging bouts in the post-excursion period. The mean distance traveled during these bouts was 18.3 km (+ 2.7 SE, range 1.2–47.7 km), and mean greatest distance from the den was 7.1 km (+ 0.7 SE, range 1.1–11.0 km). The mean duration of these post-excursion foraging bouts was 10.9 h (+ 2.4 SE, range 1–33 h).

When 388 reached her den on 2 August, the distance to the nearest collared caribou was 54 km. On 9 August, one week after she returned, the distance was 79 km (Table 1).

*Pre- and Post-Excursion Comparison*

**25** We found no differences in the mean distance of foraging bouts before and after the excursion period (F = 1.5, df = 1, 29, p = 0.24). Likewise, the mean greatest distance from the den was similar pre- and post-excursion (F = 0.004, df = 1, 29, p = 0.95). However, the mean duration of 388's foraging bouts decreased by 10.0 h after her long excursion (F = 3.1, df = 1, 29, p = 0.09).

**26** *Caribou Monitoring*

**Summer Movements:** On 10 July, 5 of 11 collared caribou were dispersed over a distance of 10 km, 140 km south of their calving grounds (Figure 1). On the same day, three caribou were still on the calving grounds, two were between the calving grounds and the leaders, and one was missing. One week later (17 July), the leading radio-collared cows were 100 km farther south (Figure 1). Two were within 5 km of each other in front of the rest, who were more dispersed. All radio-collared cows had left the calving grounds by this time. On 23 July, the leading radio-collared caribou had moved 35 km farther south, and all of them were more widely dispersed. The two cows closest to the leader were 26 km and 33 km away, with 37 km between them. On the next location (29 July), the most southerly caribou were 60 km

farther south. All of the caribou were now in the areas where they remained for the duration of the study (Figure 2).

A Minimum Convex Polygon (Mohr and Stumpf, 1966) around all caribou locations acquired during the study encompassed 85 119 km².

**Relative to the Wolf Den:** The distance from the nearest collared caribou to the den decreased from 241 km one week before the excursion to 124 km the day it began. The nearest a collared caribou came to the den was 43 km away, on 29 and 30 July. During the study, four collared caribou were located within 100 km of the den. Each of these four was closest to the wolf on at least one day during the period reported.

**28** **Discussion**

*Prey Abundance*

Caribou are the single most important prey of tundra wolves (Clark, 1971; Kuyt, 1972; Stephenson and James, 1982; Williams, 1990). Caribou range over vast areas, and for part of the summer, they are scarce or absent in wolf home ranges (Heard et al., 1996). Both the long distance between radio-collared caribou and the den the week before the excursion and the increased time spent foraging by wolf 388 indicate that caribou availability near the den was low. Observations of the pups' being left alone for up to 18 h, presumably while adults were searching for food, provide additional support for low caribou availability locally. Mean foraging bout duration decreased by 10.0 h after the excursion, when collared caribou were closer to the den, suggesting an increase in caribou availability nearby.

*Foraging Excursion*

One aspect of central place foraging theory (CPFT) deals with the optimality of returning different-sized food loads from varying distances to dependents at a central place (i.e., the den) (Orians and Pearson, 1979). Carlson (1985) tested CPFT and found that the predator usually consumed prey captured far from the central place, while feeding prey captured nearby to dependants. Wolf 388 spent 7.2 days in one area near caribou before moving to a location 23 km back towards the den, where she spent an additional 3.1 days, likely hunting caribou. She began her return trip from this closer location, traveling directly to the den. While away, she may have made one or more successful kills and spent time meeting her own energetic needs before returning to the den. Alternatively, it may have taken several attempts to make a kill,

**24** Post-excursion measurements of 388's movements were made to compare with those of the pre-excursion period. In order to compare, scientists often use *means*, or averages, of a series of measurements— mean distances, mean duration, etc.

**25** In the comparison, authors used statistical calculations (F and df) to determine that the differences between pre- and post-excursion measurements were *statistically insignificant*, or close enough to be considered essentially the same or similar.

**26** As with wolf 388, the investigators measured the movements of caribou during the study period. The areas within which the caribou moved are shown in Figure 2 by shaded polygons mentioned in the second paragraph of this subsection.

**27** This subsection summarizes how distances separating predators and prey varied during the study period.

**28** DISCUSSION: This section is the *interpretation* part of the scientific process.

**29** This subsection reviews observations from other studies and suggests that this study fits with patterns of those observations.

**30** Authors discuss a prevailing *theory* (CBFT) which might explain why a wolf would travel far to meet her own energy needs while taking food caught closer to the den back to her pups. The results of this study seem to fit that pattern.

**31** Here our authors note other possible explanations for wolves' excursions presented by other investigators, but this study does not seem to support those ideas.

**32** Authors discuss possible reasons for why 388 traveled directly to where caribou were located. They take what they learned from earlier studies and apply it to this case, suggesting that the lay of the land played a role. Note that their description paints a clear picture of the landscape.

**33** Authors suggest that 388 may have learned in traveling during previous summers where the caribou were. The last two sentences suggest ideas for future studies.

**34** Or maybe 388 followed the scent of the caribou. Authors acknowledge difficulties of proving this, but they suggest another area where future studies might be done.

**35** Authors suggest that results of this study support previous studies about how fast wolves travel to and from the den. In the last sentence, they speculate on how these observed patterns would fit into the theory of evolution.

**36** Authors also speculate on the fate of 388's pups while she was traveling. This leads to . . .

---

which she then fed on before beginning her return trip. We do not know if she returned food to the pups, but such behavior would be supported by CPFT.

**31** Other workers have reported wolves' making long round trips and referred to them as "extraterritorial" or "pre-dispersal" forays (Fritts and Mech, 1981; Messier, 1985; Ballard et al., 1997; Merrill and Mech, 2000). These movements are most often made by young wolves (1–3 years old), in areas where annual territories are maintained and prey are relatively sedentary (Fritts and Mech, 1981; Messier, 1985). The long excursion of 388 differs in that tundra wolves do not maintain annual territories (Walton et al., 2001), and the main prey migrate over vast areas (Gunn et al., 2001).

Another difference between 388's excursion and those reported earlier is that she is a mature, breeding female. No study of territorial wolves has reported reproductive adults making extraterritorial movements in summer (Fritts and Mech, 1981; Messier, 1985; Ballard et al., 1997; Merrill and Mech, 2001). However, Walton et al. (2001) also report that breeding female tundra wolves made excursions.

*Direction of Movement*

**32** Possible explanations for the relatively direct route 388 took to the caribou include landscape influence and experience. Considering the timing of 388's trip and the locations of caribou, had the wolf moved northwest, she might have missed the caribou entirely, or the encounter might have been delayed.

A reasonable possibility is that the land directed 388's route. The barrens are crisscrossed with trails worn into the tundra over centuries by hundreds of thousands of caribou and other animals (Kelsall, 1968; Thorpe et al., 2001). At river crossings, lakes, or narrow peninsulas, trails converge and funnel towards and away from caribou calving grounds and summer range. Wolves use trails for travel (Paquet et al., 1996; Mech and Boitani, 2003; P. Frame, pers. observation). Thus, the landscape may direct an animal's movements and lead it to where cues, such as the odor of caribou on the wind or scent marks of other wolves, may lead it to caribou.

**33** Another possibility is that 388 knew where to find caribou in summer. Sexually immature tundra wolves sometimes follow caribou to calving grounds (D. Heard, unpubl. data). Possibly, 388 had made such journeys in previous years and killed caribou. If this were the case, then in times of local prey scarcity she might travel to areas where she had hunted successfully before. Continued monitoring of tundra wolves may answer questions about how their food needs are met in times of low caribou abundance near dens.

**34** Caribou often form large groups while moving south to the tree line (Kelsall, 1968). After a large aggregation of caribou moves through an area, its scent can linger for weeks (Thorpe et al., 2001:104). It is conceivable that 388 detected caribou scent on the wind, which was blowing from the northeast on 19–21 July (Environment Canada, 2003), at the same time her excursion began. Many factors, such as odor strength and wind direction and strength, make systematic study of scent detection in wolves difficult under field conditions (Harrington and Asa, 2003). However, humans are able to smell odors such as forest fires or oil refineries more than 100 km away. The olfactory capabilities of dogs, which are similar to wolves, are thought to be 100 to 1 million times that of humans (Harrington and Asa, 2003). Therefore, it is reasonable to think that under the right wind conditions, the scent of many caribou traveling together could be detected by wolves from great distances, thus triggering a long foraging bout.

*Rate of Travel*

**35** Mech (1994) reported the rate of travel of Arctic wolves on barren ground was 8.7 km/h during regular travel and 10.0 km/h when returning to the den, a difference of 1.3 km/h. These rates are based on direct observation and exclude periods when wolves moved slowly or not at all. Our calculated travel rates are assumed to include periods of slow movement or no movement. However, the pattern we report is similar to that reported by Mech (1994), in that homeward travel was faster than regular travel by 1.6 km/h. The faster rate on return may be explained by the need to return food to the den. Pup survival can increase with the number of adults in a pack available to deliver food to pups (Harrington et al., 1983). Therefore, an increased rate of travel on homeward trips could improve a wolf's reproductive fitness by getting food to pups more quickly.

*Fate of 388's Pups*

**36** Wolf 388 was caring for pups during den observations. The pups were estimated to be six weeks old, and were seen ranging as far as 800 m from the den. They received some regurgitated food from two of the females, but were unattended for long periods. The excursion started 16 days after our observations, and it is improbable that the pups could have traveled the distance that 388 moved. If the pups died, this would have removed parental responsibility, allowing the long movement.

Our observations and the locations of radio-collared caribou indicate that prey became scarce in the area of the den as summer progressed. Wolf 388 may have abandoned her pups to seek food for herself. However, she returned to the den after the excursion, where she was seen near pups. In fact, she foraged in a similar pattern before and after the excursion, suggesting that she again was providing for pups after her return to the den.

**(37)** A more likely possibility is that one or both of the other lactating females cared for the pups during 388's absence. The three females at this den were not seen with the pups at the same time. However, two weeks earlier, at a different den, we observed three females cooperatively caring for a group of six pups. At that den, the three lactating females were observed providing food for each other and trading places while nursing pups. Such a situation at the den of 388 could have created conditions that allowed one or more of the lactating females to range far from the den for a period, returning to her parental duties afterwards. However, the pups would have been weaned by eight weeks of age (Packard et al., 1992), so nonlactating adults could also have cared for them, as often happens in wolf packs (Packard et al., 1992; Mech et al., 1999).

Cooperative rearing of multiple litters by a pack could create opportunities for long-distance foraging movements by some reproductive wolves during summer periods of local food scarcity. We have recorded multiple lactating females at one or more tundra wolf dens per year since 1997. This reproductive strategy may be an adaptation to temporally and **(38)** spatially unpredictable food resources. All of these possibilities require further study, but emphasize both the adaptability of wolves living on the barrens and their dependence on caribou.

Long-range wolf movement in response to caribou **(39)** availability has been suggested by other researchers (Kuyt, 1972; Walton et al., 2001) and traditional ecological knowledge (Thorpe et al., 2001). Our report demonstrates the rapid and extreme response of wolves to caribou distribution and movements in summer. Increased human activity on the tundra (mining, road building, pipelines, ecotourism) may influence caribou movement patterns and change the interactions between wolves and caribou in the region. Continued monitoring of both species will help us to assess whether the association is being affected adversely by anthropogenic change.

## **(40)** Acknowledgements

This research was supported by the Department of Resources, Wildlife, and Economic Development, Government of the Northwest Territories; the Department of Biological Sciences at the University of Alberta; the Natural Sciences and Engineering Research Council of Canada; the Department of Indian and Northern Affairs Canada; the Canadian Circumpolar Institute; and DeBeers Canada, Ltd. Lorna Ruechel assisted with den observations. A. Gunn provided caribou location data. We thank Dave Mech for the use of GPS collars. M. Nelson, A. Gunn, and three anonymous reviewers made helpful comments on earlier drafts of the manuscript. This work was done under Wildlife Research Permit – WL002948 issued by the Government of the Northwest Territories, Department of Resources, Wildlife, and Economic Development.

## **(41)** References

BALLARD, W.B., AYRES, L.A., KRAUSMAN, P.R., REED, D.J., and FANCY, S.G. 1997. Ecology of wolves in relation to a migratory caribou herd in northwest Alaska. Wildlife Monographs 135. 47 p.

BROWN, M.B., and FORSYTHE, A.B. 1974. Robust tests for the equality of variances. Journal of the American Statistical Association 69:364–367.

CARLSON, A. 1985. Central place foraging in the red-backed shrike (*Lanius collurio* L.): Allocation of prey between forager and sedentary consumer. Animal Behaviour 33:664–666.

CLARK, K.R.F. 1971. Food habits and behavior of the tundra wolf on central Baffin Island. Ph.D. Thesis, University of Toronto, Ontario, Canada.

ENVIRONMENT CANADA. 2003. National climate data information archive. Available online: http://www.climate.weatheroffice.ec.gc.ca/Welcome_e.html

FOURNIER, B., and GUNN, A. 1998. Musk ox numbers and distribution in the NWT, 1997. File Report No. 121. Yellowknife: Department of Resources, Wildlife, and Economic Development, Government of the Northwest Territories. 55 p.

FRITTS, S.H., and MECH, L.D. 1981. Dynamics, movements, and feeding ecology of a newly protected wolf population in northwestern Minnesota. Wildlife Monographs 80. 79 p.

GUNN, A., DRAGON, J., and BOULANGER, J. 2001. Seasonal movements of satellite-collared caribou from the Bathurst herd. Final Report to the West Kitikmeot Slave Study Society, Yellowknife, NWT. 80 p. Available online: http://www.wkss.nt.ca/HTML/08_ProjectsReports/PDF/SeasonalMovementsFinal.pdf

HARRINGTON, F.H., and ASA, C.S. 2003. Wolf communication. In: Mech, L.D., and Boitani, L., eds. Wolves: Behavior, ecology, and conservation. Chicago: University of Chicago Press. 66–103.

HARRINGTON, F.H., MECH, L.D., and FRITTS, S.H. 1983. Pack size and wolf pup survival: Their relationship under varying ecological conditions. Behavioral Ecology and Sociobiology 13:19–26.

HARRIS, S.A. 1986. Permafrost distribution, zonation and stability along the eastern ranges of the cordillera of North America. Arctic 39(1):29–38.

HEARD, D.C., and WILLIAMS, T.M. 1992. Distribution of wolf dens on migratory caribou ranges in the Northwest

**37** Discussion of cooperative rearing of pups and, in turn, to speculation on how this study and what is known about cooperative rearing might fit into the animal's strategies for survival of the species. Again, the authors approach the broader theory of evolution and how it might explain some of their results.

**38** And again, they suggest that this study points to several areas where further study will shed some light.

**39** In conclusion, the authors suggest that their study supports the hypothesis being tested here. And they touch on the implications of increased human activity on the tundra predicted by their results.

**40** ACKNOWLEDGEMENTS: Authors note the support of institutions, companies and individuals. They thank their reviewers ad list permits under which their research was carried on.

**41** REFERENCES: List of all studies cited in the report. This may seem tedious, but is a vitally important part of scientific reporting. It is a record of the sources of information on which this study is based. It provides readers with a wealth of resources for further reading on this topic. Much of it will form the foundation of future scientific studies like this one.

Territories, Canada. Canadian Journal of Zoology 70:1504–1510.

HEARD, D.C., WILLIAMS, T.M., and MELTON, D.A. 1996. The relationship between food intake and predation risk in migratory caribou and implication to caribou and wolf population dynamics. Rangifer Special Issue No. 2:37–44.

KELSALL, J.P. 1968. The migratory barren-ground caribou of Canada. Canadian Wildlife Service Monograph Series 3. Ottawa: Queen's Printer. 340 p.

KUYT, E. 1962. Movements of young wolves in the Northwest Territories of Canada. Journal of Mammalogy 43:270–271.

———. 1972. Food habits and ecology of wolves on barren-ground caribou range in the Northwest Territories. Canadian Wildlife Service Report Series 21. Ottawa: Information Canada. 36 p.

MECH, L.D. 1994. Regular and homeward travel speeds of Arctic wolves. Journal of Mammalogy 75:741–742.

MECH, L.D., and BOITANI, L. 2003. Wolf social ecology. In: Mech, L.D., and Boitani, L., eds. Wolves: Behavior, ecology, and conservation. Chicago: University of Chicago Press. 1–34.

MECH, L.D., and GESE, E.M. 1992. Field testing the Wildlink capture collar on wolves. Wildlife Society Bulletin 20:249–256.

MECH, L.D., WOLFE, P., and PACKARD, J.M. 1999. Regurgitative food transfer among wild wolves. Canadian Journal of Zoology 77:1192–1195.

MERRILL, S.B., and MECH, L.D. 2000. Details of extensive movements by Minnesota wolves (*Canis lupus*). American Midland Naturalist 144:428–433.

MERRILL, S.B., ADAMS, L.G., NELSON, M.E., and MECH, L.D. 1998. Testing releasable GPS radiocollars on wolves and white-tailed deer. Wildlife Society Bulletin 26:830–835.

MESSIER, F. 1985. Solitary living and extraterritorial movements of wolves in relation to social status and prey abundance. Canadian Journal of Zoology 63:239–245.

MOHR, C.O., and STUMPF, W.A. 1966. Comparison of methods for calculating areas of animal activity. Journal of Wildlife Management 30:293–304.

MUSIANI, M. 2003. Conservation biology and management of wolves and wolf-human conflicts in western North America. Ph.D. Thesis, University of Calgary, Calgary, Alberta, Canada.

ORIANS, G.H., and PEARSON, N.E. 1979. On the theory of central place foraging. In: Mitchell, R.D., and Stairs, G.F., eds. Analysis of ecological systems. Columbus: Ohio State University Press. 154–177.

PACKARD, J.M., MECH, L.D., and REAM, R.R. 1992. Weaning in an arctic wolf pack: Behavioral mechanisms. Canadian Journal of Zoology 70:1269–1275.

PAQUET, P.C., WIERZCHOWSKI, J., and CALLAGHAN, C. 1996. Summary report on the effects of human activity on gray wolves in the Bow River Valley, Banff National Park, Alberta. In: Green, J., Pacas, C., Bayley, S., and Cornwell, L., eds. A cumulative effects assessment and futures outlook for the Banff Bow Valley. Prepared for the Banff Bow Valley Study. Ottawa: Department of Canadian Heritage.

STEPHENSON, R.O., and JAMES, D. 1982. Wolf movements and food habits in northwest Alaska. In: Harrington, F.H., and Paquet, P.C., eds. Wolves of the world. New Jersey: Noyes Publications. 223–237.

THORPE, N., EYEGETOK, S., HAKONGAK, N., and QITIRMIUT ELDERS. 2001. The Tuktu and Nogak Project: A caribou chronicle. Final Report to the West Kitikmeot/Slave Study Society, Ikaluktuuttiak, NWT. 160 p.

TIMONEY, K.P., LA ROI, G.H., ZOLTAI, S.C., and ROBINSON, A.L. 1992. The high subarctic forest-tundra of northwestern Canada: Position, width, and vegetation gradients in relation to climate. Arctic 45(1):1–9.

WALTON, L.R., CLUFF, H.D., PAQUET, P.C., and RAMSAY, M.A. 2001. Movement patterns of barren-ground wolves in the central Canadian Arctic. Journal of Mammalogy 82:867–876.

WILLIAMS, T.M. 1990. Summer diet and behavior of wolves denning on barren-ground caribou range in the Northwest Territories, Canada. M.Sc. Thesis, University of Alberta, Edmonton, Alberta, Canada.

ZAR, J.H. 1999. Biostatistical analysis. 4th ed. New Jersey: Prentice Hall. 663 p.

Appendix III

# Appendix IV

## A Plain English Map of the Human Chromosomes

© 2002 Susan Offner/SK45176-02

Haploid set of human chromosomes. The banding patterns characteristic of each type of chromosome appear after staining with a reagent called Giemsa. The locations of some of the 20,065 known genes (as of November, 2005) are indicated. Also shown are locations that, when mutated, cause some of the genetic diseases discussed in the text.

# Appendix V

## Length

1 kilometer (km) = 0.62 miles (mi)
1 meter (m) = 39.37 inches (in)
1 centimeter (cm) = 0.39 inches

| To convert | multiply by | to obtain |
|------------|-------------|-----------|
| inches | 2.25 | centimeters |
| feet | 30.48 | centimeters |
| centimeters | 0.39 | inches |
| millimeters | 0.039 | inches |

## Area

1 square kilometer = 0.386 square miles
1 square meter = 1.196 square yards
1 square centimeter = 0.155 square inches

## Volume

1 cubic meter = 35.31 cubic feet
1 liter = 1.06 quarts
1 milliliter = 0.034 fluid ounces = 1/5 teaspoon

| To convert | multiply by | to obtain |
|------------|-------------|-----------|
| quarts | 0.95 | liters |
| fluid ounces | 28.41 | milliliters |
| liters | 1.06 | quarts |
| milliliters | 0.03 | fluid ounces |

## Weight

1 metric ton (mt) = 2,205 pounds (lb) = 1.1 tons (t)
1 kilogram (kg) = 2.205 pounds (lb)
1 gram (g) = 0.035 ounces (oz)

| To convert | multiply by | to obtain |
|------------|-------------|-----------|
| pounds | 0.454 | kilograms |
| pounds | 454 | grams |
| ounces | 28.35 | grams |
| kilograms | 2.205 | pounds |
| grams | 0.035 | ounces |

## Temperature

Celcius (°C) to Fahrenheit (°F) :
$$°F = 1.8 \, (°C) + 32$$

Fahrenheit (°F) to Celsius:
$$°C = \frac{(°F - 32)}{1.8}$$

| | °C | °F |
|------------------------|-----|------|
| Water boils | 100 | 212 |
| Human body temperature | 37 | 98.6 |
| Water freezes | 0 | 32 |

# Appendix VI

**Periodic Table of the Elements**

**DNA fingerprint** An individual's unique array of short tandem repeats. **184**

**DNA ligase** Enzyme that seals breaks or gaps in double-stranded DNA. **109**

**DNA polymerase** DNA replication enzyme. Assembles a new strand of DNA based on the sequence of a DNA template. **108**

**DNA repair mechanism** Any of several processes by which enzymes repair damaged DNA. **109**

**DNA replication** Process by which a cell duplicates its DNA before it divides. **108**

**DNA sequence** The order of nucleotide bases in a strand of DNA. **108**

**dominant** Refers to an allele that masks the effect of a recessive allele paired with it. **158**

**dormancy** Period of arrested growth. **568**

**dosage compensation** Theory that X chromosome inactivation equalizes gene expression between males and females. **129**

**double fertilization** In flowering plants, one sperm fertilizes the egg, forming the zygote, and another fertilizes a diploid cell, forming what will become endosperm. **281, 568**

**eardrum** Membrane of middle ear that vibrates in response to sound waves. **498**

**echinoderms** Invertebrates with a water–vascular system and an endoskeleton made of hardened plates and spines. **304**

**ecological restoration** Actively altering an area in an effort to restore or create a functional ecosystem. **381**

**ecological succession** A gradual change in a community in which one array of species replaces another. **347**

**ecology** The study of interactions among organisms, and between organisms and their environment. **322**

**ecosystem** A community interacting with its environment. **5, 340**

**ectoderm** Outermost tissue layer of an animal embryo. **524**

**ectotherm** Animal that gains heat from the environment; commonly called "cold-blooded." **310**

**effector cell** Antigen-sensitized B cell or T cell that forms in an immune response and acts immediately. **446**

**egg** Mature female gamete, or ovum. **148**

**ejaculation** Smooth muscle contractions propel semen through the penis and out of the body. **526**

**electron** Negatively charged subatomic particle that occupies orbitals around the atomic nucleus. **21**

**electron transfer chain** Array of enzymes and other molecules that accept and give up electrons in sequence, thus releasing the energy of the electrons in small, usable increments. **68**

**electron transfer phosphorylation** Metabolic pathway in which electron flow through electron transfer chains sets up a hydrogen ion gradient that drives ATP formation. **85**

**electrophoresis** Technique that separates DNA fragments by size. **184**

**element** A pure substance that consists only of atoms with the same number of protons. **21**

**elimination** Expulsion of unabsorbed material from the digestive tract. **461**

**embolus** Clot that forms in a blood vessel, then breaks loose. **431**

**emergent property** A characteristic of a system that does not appear in any of a system's component parts. **5**

**emigration** Movement of individuals out of a population. **324**

**enamel** Hard material that covers the exposed surface of teeth. **462**

**endangered species** A species that faces extinction in all or part of its range. **370**

**endemic disease** A disease that remains present at low levels in a population. **262**

**endemic species** A species that evolved in one place and is found nowhere else. **370**

**endocrine gland** Ductless gland that secretes hormones into a body fluid. **391**

**endocrine system** Hormone-producing glands and secretory cells of a vertebrate body. **505**

**endocytosis** Process by which a cell takes in a small amount of extracellular fluid by the ballooning inward of its plasma membrane. **74**

**endoderm** Innermost tissue layer of an animal embryo. **524**

**endomembrane system** Series of interacting organelles (endoplasmic reticulum, Golgi bodies, vesicles) between the nucleus and plasma membrane; produces lipids and proteins. **53**

**endoplasmic reticulum (ER)** Organelle that is a continuous system of sacs and tubes; extension of the nuclear envelope. Rough ER is studded with ribosomes; smooth ER is not. **53**

**endorphins** Natural pain-reliever molecules. **494**

**endoskeleton** Hard internal parts that muscles attach to and move. **304, 405**

**endosperm** Nutritive tissue in an angiosperm seed. **281, 568**

**endosperm mother cell** A cell with two nuclei ($n + n$) that is part of the female gametophyte of a flowering plant. **568**

**endosymbiont** A species that lives in the body of another species in a commensal, mutualistic, or parasitic relationship. **342**

**endosymbiosis** One species lives inside another. **245**

**endotherm** Animal that produces its own heat; commonly called "warm-blooded." **310**

**energy** The capacity to do work. **6, 63**

**energy pyramid** Diagram that illustrates the energy flow in an ecosystem. **352**

**enzyme** Protein or RNA that speeds a reaction without being changed by it. **48, 66**

**eosinophil** White blood cell that targets internal parasites. **440**

**epidemic** A disease spreads rapidly through a population. **262**

**epidermis** Outermost tissue layer; in animals, epithelial layer of skin. **394, 551**

**epiglottis** Tissue flap that folds down to prevent food from entering the airways when you swallow. **428**

**epiphyte** Plant that grows on the trunk or branches of another plant but does not harm it. **275**

**epistasis** Effect in which a trait is influenced by the products of multiple genes. **164**

**epithelial tissue** Sheetlike animal tissue that covers outer body surfaces and lines internal tubes and cavities. **390**

**erection** Penis becomes erect as a result of increased fluid pressure inside its spongy tissue. **531**

**esophagus** Muscular tube between the throat and stomach. **463**

**essential amino acid** Amino acid that the body cannot make and must obtain from food. **468**

**essential fatty acid** Fatty acid that the body cannot make and must obtain from the diet. **467**

**estrogens** Sex hormones produced by a female's ovaries. **515**

**estuary** A highly productive ecosystem where nutrient-rich water from a river mixes with seawater. **368**

**ethylene** Gaseous plant hormone that inhibits cell division in stems and roots; also promotes fruit ripening. **577**

**eudicots** Largest lineage of angiosperms; includes herbaceous plants, woody trees, and cacti. **280**

**eugenics** Idea of deliberately improving the genetic qualities of the human race. **190**

**eukaryote** Organism whose cells characteristically have a nucleus; a protist, plant, fungus, or animal. **8, 244**

**eutrophication** Nutrient enrichment of an aquatic ecosystem. **374**

**evaporation** Transition of a liquid to a gas. **27**

**evolution** Change in a line of descent. **199**

**evolutionary tree** Type of diagram that summarizes evolutionary relationships among a group of species. **235**

**exaptation** Adaptation of an existing structure for a completely different purpose; a major evolutionary novelty. **231**

**exocrine gland** Gland that secretes milk, sweat, saliva, or some other substance through a duct. **391**

**exocytosis** Process by which a cell expels a vesicle's contents to extracellular fluid. **74**

**exoskeleton** Hard external parts that muscles attach to and move. **301, 405**

**exotic species** A species that evolved in one community and later became established in a different one. **340**

**experiment** A test to support or falsify a prediction. **12**

**experimental group** A group of objects or individuals that display or are exposed to a variable under investigation; Experimental results for this group are compared with results for a control group. **12**

**exponential growth** A population grows by a fixed percentage in successive time intervals; the size of each increase is determined by the current population size. **324**

**extinct** Refers to a species that has been permanently lost. **231**

**extracellular matrix (ECM)** Complex mixture of secreted substances that supports cells and tissues; also has roles in cell signaling. **56**

**extreme halophile** Organism that lives where the salt concentration is high. **250**

**extreme thermophile** Organism that lives where the temperature is very high. **250**

**fat** Lipid with one, two, or three fatty acid tails. **32**

**fatty acid** Organic compound that consists of a long chain of carbon atoms with an acidic carboxyl group at one end. Carbon chain of saturated types has single bonds only; that of unsaturated types has one or more double bonds. **32**

**feces** Unabsorbed food material and cellular waste that is expelled from the digestive tract. **465**

**feedback inhibition** Mechanism by which a change that results from some activity decreases or stops the activity. **67**

**fermentation** An anaerobic pathway by which cells harvest energy from carbohydrates. **92**

**fertilization** Fusion of a sperm and an egg, the result being a single-celled zygote. **144, 524**

**fetus** Developing human between 9 weeks of age and birth. **539**

**fever** An internally induced rise in core body temperature above the normal set point; response to infection. **443**

**fibroblast** Main cell type in soft connective tissue; secretes collagen and other components of extracellular matrix. **391**

**fibrous joint** Joint where dense connective tissue holds bones firmly in place. **407**

**filtration** Blood pressure forces water and small solutes, but not blood cells or proteins, out across the walls of capillaries. **472**

**first law of thermodynamics** Energy cannot be created or destroyed. **63**

**fish** Aquatic vertebrate of the oldest and most diverse vertebrate group. **307**

**fitness** The degree of adaptation to an environment, as measured by an individual's relative genetic contribution to future generations. **200**

**fixed** Refers to an allele for which all members of a population are homozygous. **225**

**flagellated protozoan** Member of a heterotrophic lineage of protists with one or more flagella. **252**

**flagellum** Long, slender cellular structure used for motility. **50**

**flatworm** Bilaterally symmetrical invertebrate with organs but no body cavity; for example, a planarian or tapeworm. **297**

**flower** Specialized reproductive shoot of a flowering plant. **280**

**fluid mosaic model** Model of a cell membrane as a two-dimensional fluid of mixed composition. **48**

**food chain** Linear description of who eats whom. **350**

**food web** System of cross-connecting food chains. **350**

**foraminiferan** Heterotrophic protist that secretes a calcium carbonate shell. **253**

**fossil** Physical evidence of an organism that lived in the ancient past. **202**

**founder effect** Change in allele frequencies that occurs after a small number of individuals establish a new population. **225**

**fovea** Region of vertebrate eye with densest concentration of photoreceptors. **496**

**fruit** Mature flowering plant ovary, often with accessory parts; encloses a seed or seeds. **280, 570**

**fungus** Type of eukaryotic consumer with cell walls of chitin; obtains nutrients by digestion and absorption outside the body. **8, 283**

**gallbladder** Organ that receives bile from the liver, stores it, and expels it into the small intestine. **464**

**gamete** Mature, haploid reproductive cell; e.g., an egg or a sperm. **144**

**gametophyte** A haploid, multicelled body in which gametes form during the life cycle of plants. **148, 271**

**ganglion** Cluster of nerve cell bodies. **486**

**gap junction** Cell junction that forms a channel across the plasma membranes of adjoining animal cells. **57**

**gastric fluid** Fluid secreted by the stomach lining; contains enzymes, acid, and mucus. **464**

**gastropod** Mollusk that moves about on its enlarged foot. For example, a snail. **298**

**gastrula** Three-layered developmental stage formed by gastrulation in an animal. **524**

**gastrulation** Animal developmental process by which cell movements produce a three-layered gastrula. **524**

**gene** Part of a DNA base sequence; specifies an RNA or protein product. **117**

**gene expression** Process by which the information encoded by a gene becomes converted to an RNA or protein product. **117**

**gene flow** The movement of alleles into and out of a population, as by individuals that immigrate or emigrate. **226**

**gene knockout** A gene that has been inactivated in an organism. **128**

**gene pool** All of the genes in a population; a pool of genetic resources. **217**

**gene therapy** The transfer of a normal or modified gene into an individual with the goal of treating a genetic defect or disorder. **190**

**genetic code** Set of sixty-four mRNA codons, each of which specifies an amino acid or stop signal in translation. **120**

**genetic drift** Change in allele frequencies in a population due to chance alone. **225**

**genetic engineering** Process by which deliberate changes are introduced into an individual's genome. **186**

**genetic equilibrium** Theoretical state in which a population is not evolving. **218**

**genetically modified organism (GMO)** An organism whose genome has been deliberately modified. **180**

**genome** An organism's complete set of genetic material. **182**

**genomics** The study of genomes. **186**

**genotype** The particular alleles carried by an individual. **158**

**genus** Taxonomic group of species that share a unique set of traits. **8**

**geologic time scale** Chronology of Earth history. **204**

**germination** The resumption of growth after a period of dormancy. **574**

**ghrelin** Molecule made in the stomach and brain that increases appetite. **460**

**gibberellin** Plant hormone; induces stem elongation, helps seeds break dormancy. Role in flowering in some species. **576**

**gills** Folds or body extensions that increase the surface area for respiration. **427**

**gland** Cluster of secretory epithelial cells. **391**

**global climate change** Wide-ranging changes in rainfall patterns, average temperature, and other climate factors that are thought to result from rising concentrations of greenhouse gases. **356, 377**

**glottis** Opening formed when the vocal cords relax. **428**

**glucagon** Pancreatic hormone that raises the blood glucose level. **512**

**glycolysis** Set of reactions in which glucose or another sugar is broken down to two pyruvate for a net yield of two ATP. **89**

**Golgi body** Organelle that modifies polypeptides and lipids; also sorts and packages the finished products into vesicles. **53**

**gonads** Ovaries and testes; organs that produce gametes and secrete sex hormones. **515**

**Gondwana** Supercontinent that formed more than 500 million years ago. **207**

**grasslands** Biome in the interior of continents, where grasses and other low-growing plants are adapted to warm summers, cold winters, periodic fires, and grazing animals. **365**

**gravitropism** Plant growth in a direction influenced by gravity. **577**

**gray matter** Tissue in brain and spinal cord that consists of cell bodies, dendrites, and neuroglial cells. **490**

**green alga** Single-celled, colonial, or multicelled photosynthetic protist belonging to the group most closely related to land plants. **257**

**greenhouse effect** Warming of Earth's lower atmosphere and surface as a result of heat trapped by greenhouse gases. **356**

**greenhouse gas** Atmospheric gas such as carbon dioxide that helps keep heat from escaping into space and thus warms the Earth. **356**

**ground tissue system** Tissue system that makes up the bulk of the plant body; includes most photosynthetic cells. **549**

**groundwater** Water between soil particles and in aquifers. **353**

**growth** Increases in the number, size, and volume of cells in multicelled species. **7**

**growth hormone** Anterior pituitary hormone that promotes growth and development throughout the body. **508**

**guard cell** One of a pair of cells that define a stoma across the epidermis of a leaf or stem. **552**

**gymnosperms** Seed plant lineage that does not make flowers or fruits. **272**

**habitat** The type of place a species lives. **341**

**half-life** Characteristic time it takes for half of a quantity of a radioisotope to decay. **203**

**haploid** Having one of each type of chromosome characteristic of the species. **144**

**heart** Muscular organ that pumps fluid through a body. **419**

**heart attack** Heart cells die because of impaired blood flow through cardiac arteries. **431**

**hermaphrodite** Animal that makes both eggs and sperm. **296, 523**

**heterotroph** Organism that obtains energy and carbon from organic compounds assembled by other organisms. **80**

**heterozygous** Having two different alleles of a gene. **158**

**histone** Type of protein that structurally organizes eukaryotic chromosomes. **103**

**homeostasis** Processes by which an organism keeps internal conditions within tolerable ranges. **7, 389**

**homeotic gene** Type of master gene; its expression controls formation of specific body parts during development. **128**

**hominid** Human or extinct humanlike species. **313**

**homologous** Refers to the two members of a pair of chromosomes with the same length, shape, and genes. **139**

**homologous structure** Similar body parts that reflect shared ancestry among lineages. **208**

**homozygous** Having identical alleles of a gene. **157**

**hot spots** Threatened regions with great biodiversity that are considered a high priority for conservation efforts. **380**

**humans** Members of the genus *Homo*. **314**

**human chorionic gonadotropin (HCG)** Hormone produced by the chorion and later by the placenta; encourages maintenance of the uterus thus sustaining a pregnancy. **537**

**humus** Decaying organic matter in soil. **557**

**hybrid** The offspring of a cross between two individuals that breed true for different forms of a trait. **157**

**hydrogen bond** Attraction that forms between a covalently bonded hydrogen atom and another atom taking part in a separate covalent bond. **25**

**hydrolysis** Process by which an enzyme breaks a molecule into smaller subunits by attaching a hydroxyl group to one part and a hydrogen atom to the other. **30**

**hydrophilic** Describes a substance that dissolves easily in water. **26**

**hydrophobic** Describes a substance that resists dissolving in water. **26**

**hydrostatic skeleton** Of soft-bodied invertebrates, a fluid-filled chamber that muscles act on, redistributing the fluid. **405**

**hydrothermal vent** Place where hot, mineral-rich water streams out from an underwater opening in Earth's crust. **242, 369**

**hypertension** Chronically high blood pressure. **431**

**hypertonic** Describes a fluid with a high solute concentration relative to another fluid. **70**

**hypha** A single filament in a fungal mycelium. **283**

**hypothalamus** Forebrain region that controls processes related to homeostasis and has endocrine functions. **491, 508**

**hypothesis** Testable explanation of a natural phenomenon. **10**

**hypotonic** Describes a fluid with a low solute concentration relative to another fluid. **70**

**immigration** Movement of individuals into a population. **324**

**immunity** The body's ability to resist and fight infections. **439**

**immunization** A procedure designed to promote immunity to a disease. **454**

**inbreeding** Nonrandom mating among close relatives. **226**

**incomplete dominance** Condition in which one allele is not fully dominant over another, so the heterozygous phenotype is between the two homozygous phenotypes. **163**

**indicator species** A species that is highly sensitive to environmental changes and can be monitored to assess whether an ecosystem is threatened. **380**

**inflammation** A local response to tissue damage or infection; characterized by redness, warmth, swelling, and pain. **442**

**ingestion** Taking food into the digestive system. **461**

**inheritance** Transmission of DNA from parents to offspring. **7**

**inhibitor** Hypothalamic hormone that acts in the anterior pituitary to slow hormone secretion. **508**

**innate immunity** Set of inborn, fixed general defenses against infection; includes phagocytosis, inflammation, fever, complement activation. **439**

**insects** Land-dwelling arthropods with a pair of antennae, three pairs of legs, and—in the most diverse groups—wings. **303**

**insertion** Mutation in which one or more base pairs become inserted into DNA. **125**

**insulin** Pancreatic hormone that causes cells to take up glucose from the blood, thus lowering blood glucose level. **512**

**integumentary exchange** Gas exchange across the outer body surface. **427**

**intercostal muscles** Muscles between the ribs; help alter the size of the thoracic cavity during breathing. **429**

**intermediate filament** Cytoskeletal element that locks cells and tissues together. **54**

**interneurons** Neurons that receive signals from other neurons and integrate information. **481**

**interphase** In a eukaryotic cell cycle, the interval between mitotic divisions when a cell grows, roughly doubles the number of its cytoplasmic components, and replicates its DNA. **138**

**interspecific competiton** Two species compete for a limited resource and both are harmed by the interaction. **343**

**interstitial fluid** Fluid between cells of a multicelled body. **419**

**intervertebral disk** Cartilage disk between two vertebrae. **405**

**invertebrate** Animal without a backbone. **295**

***in vitro* fertilization** Infertility treatment in which gametes are combined outside the body. **534**

**ion** Atom that carries a charge because it has an unequal number of protons and electrons. **23**

**ionic bond** Type of chemical bond in which a strong mutual attraction forms between ions of opposite charge. **24**

**iris** Ring of smooth muscle with pupil at its center; adjusts how much light enters the eye. **495**

**isotonic** Describes a fluid with the same solute concentration relative to another fluid. **70**

**isotopes** Forms of an element that differ in the number of neutrons their atoms carry. **21**

**jaws** Hinged skeletal elements used in feeding. **306**

**joint** Region where bones meet. **407**

**karyotype** Image of an individual's complement of chromosomes arranged by size, length, shape, and centromere location. **105**

**key innovation** An evolutionary adaptation that gives its bearer the opportunity to exploit a particular environment more efficiently or in a new way. **232**

**keystone species** A species that has a disproportionately large effect on community structure. **348**

**kidney** Organ of the vertebrate urinary system that filters blood, adjusts its composition, and forms urine. **307, 471**

**kidney dialysis** Procedure used to cleanse blood and restore proper solute concentrations in a person with impaired kidney function. **474**

**Krebs cycle** Cyclic pathway that, along with acetyl–CoA formation, breaks down two pyruvate to carbon dioxide for a net yield of two ATP and many reduced coenzymes. Part of aerobic respiration pathway. **90**

**K-selection** Selection favoring individuals that compete well in crowded conditions; selection for offspring quality. **329**

**labor** Expulsion of a placental mammal from its mother's uterus by muscle contractions. **542**

**lactate fermentation** Anaerobic carbohydrate breakdown pathway that produces ATP and lactate. **92**

**lancelets** Invertebrate chordates that have a fishlike shape and retain their defining chordate traits into adulthood. **305**

**large intestine** Organ that receives digestive waste from the small intestine and concentrates it as feces. Also called the colon. **465**

**larva** Preadult stage in some animal life cycles. **296**

**larynx** Short airway containing the vocal cords (voice box). **428**

**lateral meristem** Sheetlike cylinder of meristem inside older stems and roots; vascular cambium or cork cambium. **555**

**law of nature** Generalization that describes a consistent natural phenomenon for which there is incomplete scientific explanation; e.g., first and second laws of thermodynamics. **11**

**lens** Disk-shaped structure that focuses light on an eye's photoreceptors. **495**

**leptin** Molecule made by adipose cells that suppresses appetite. **460**

**lethal mutation** Mutation that drastically alters phenotype; usually causes death. **218**

**leukemia** Cancer that increases white blood cell numbers. **431**

**lichen** Composite organism consisting of a fungus and a single-celled photosynthetic alga or bacterium. **286**

**life history pattern** A set of traits related to growth, survival, and reproduction such as life span, age-specific mortality, age at first reproduction, and number of breeding events. **328**

**ligament** Dense connective tissue that holds bones together at a joint. **407**

**light-dependent reactions** Metabolic pathway of photosynthesis that converts light energy to chemical energy of ATP and NADPH. **84**

**light-independent reactions** Metabolic pathway of photosynthesis that uses ATP and NADPH to assemble sugars from water and $CO_2$. **84**

**lignin** Material that stiffens cell walls of vascular plants. **271**

**limiting factor** A necessary resource, the depletion of which halts population growth. **325**

**lineage** Line of descent. **202**

**lipid** Fatty, oily, or waxy organic compound. **32**

**lipid bilayer** Structural foundation of cell membranes; mainly phospholipids arranged tail-to-tail in two layers. **43**

**liver** Organ that produces bile, stores glycogen, and detoxifies many substances. **464**

**lobe-finned fish** Bony fish with bony supports in its fins. **308**

**logistic growth** A population grows slowly, then increases rapidly until it reaches carrying capacity and levels off. **326**

**loose connective tissue** Connective tissue with relatively few fibroblasts and fibers scattered in its matrix. **392**

**lung** Of most land vertebrates and some fish, saclike organ inside which blood exchanges gases with the air. **306, 427**

**lysis** Breaking of a cell's plasma membrane; results in death of the cell. **260**

**lysogenic pathway** Bacteriophage replication pathway in which the virus becomes integrated into the host's chromosome and is passed to its descendants. **260**

**lysosome** Enzyme-filled vesicle that functions in intracellular digestion. **53**

**lysozyme** Antibacterial enzyme that occurs in body secretions such as mucus. **441**

**lytic pathway** Bacteriophage replication pathway in which the virus replicates in its host and quickly kills it. **260**

**macroevolution** Patterns of evolution that occur above the species level. **231**

**macrophage** Phagocytic white blood cell that patrols tissue fluids; presents antigen to T cells. **440**

**mammal** Vertebrate that nourishes its young with milk from mammary glands. **312**

**mantle** Skirtlike extension of tissue in mollusks; covers the mantle cavity and secretes the shell in species that have a shell. **298**

**marsupial** Mammals in which young complete development in a pouch on the mother's body. **312**

**mass extinction** Simultaneous loss of many lineages from Earth. **196, 231**

**mass number** Total number of protons and neutrons in the nucleus of an element's atoms. **21**

**mast cell** White blood cell that is anchored in many tissues; factor in inflammation. **440**

**master gene** Gene encoding a product that affects the expression of many other genes. **128**

**mechanical digestion** Breaking of food into smaller pieces by mechanical processes such as chewing. **462**

**mechanoreceptor** Sensory receptor that responds to pressure, position, or acceleration. **493**

**medulla oblongata** Hindbrain region that controls breathing rhythm and reflexes such as coughing and vomiting. **491**

**medusa** Bell-shaped, free-swimming cnidarian body form. **297**

**megaspore** Haploid spore that forms in ovary of seed plants; gives rise to a female gametophyte with egg cell. **277, 568**

**meiosis** Nuclear division process that halves the chromosome number. Basis of sexual reproduction. **137**

**melatonin** Hormone produced by pineal gland; affects onset of puberty, sleep–wake cycles. **516**

**membrane potential** Potential energy across the membrane of a resting neuron. **481**

**memory cell** Antigen-sensitized B or T cell that forms in a primary immune response but does not act immediately. Participates in a secondary response if the same antigen returns. **446**

**meninges** Membranes that surround and protect the brain and spinal cord. **490**

**menopause** Of a human female, the end of fertility and of menstrual cycles. **531**

**menstrual cycle** Approximately monthly cycle in which the uterine lining thickens in preparation for pregnancy, then is shed if pregnancy does not occur. **530**

**menstruation** Flow of blood and bits of shed uterine lining out through the vagina. **530**

**meristem** Zone of undifferentiated plant cells that can divide rapidly. **553**

**mesoderm** Middle tissue layer of a three-layered animal embryo. **524**

**messenger RNA (mRNA)** Type of RNA that carries a protein-building message. **117**

**metabolic pathway** Series of enzyme-mediated reactions by which cells build, remodel, or break down an organic molecule. **67**

**metabolism** All the enzyme-mediated chemical reactions by which cells acquire and use energy as they build and break down organic molecules. **30**

**metamorphosis** Dramatic remodeling of body form during the transition from larva to adult. **301**

**metaphase** Stage of mitosis during which the cell's chromosomes align midway between poles of the spindle. **140**

**methanogen** Organism that produces methane gas as a metabolic by-product. **250**

**MHC markers** Self-recognition protein on the surface of body cells. Triggers adaptive immune response when bound to antigen fragments. **445**

**microevolution** Change in allele frequencies in a population or species. **218**

**microfilament** Reinforcing cytoskeletal element; a fiber of actin subunits. **54**

**microspore** Walled haploid spore of seed plants; gives rise to a pollen grain. **277, 568**

**microtubule** Cytoskeletal element involved in movement; hollow filament of tubulin subunits. **54**

**microvilli** Thin projections that increase the surface area of brush border cells. **464**

**migration** Periodic movement of many individuals between one or more regions. **324**

**mimicry** Two or more species come to resemble one another. **345**

**mineral** Inorganic substance that is required in small amounts for normal metabolism. **469**

**mitochondrion** Double-membraned organelle that produces ATP; site of second and third stages of aerobic respiration in eukaryotes. **53**

**mitosis** Nuclear division mechanism that maintains the chromosome number. Basis of body growth, tissue repair and replacement in multicelled eukaryotes; also asexual reproduction in some plants, animals, fungi, and protists. **137**

**model** System similar to an object or event that cannot itself be tested directly. **10**

**molecule** An association of two or more atoms joined by chemical bonds. **5, 24**

**mollusk** Invertebrate with a reduced coelom and a mantle. **298**

**molting** Periodic shedding of an outer body layer or part. **300**

**monocots** Lineage of angiosperms that includes grasses, orchids, and palms. **280**

**monohybrid cross** Cross in which individuals with different alleles of one gene are crossed. **158**

**monomers** Molecules that are subunits of polymers. **30**

**monophyletic group** An ancestor and all of its descendants. **235**

**monotreme** Egg-laying mammal. **312**

**morphological convergence** Evolutionary pattern in which similar body parts evolve separately in different lineages. **209**

**morphological divergence** Evolutionary pattern in which a body part of an ancestor changes in its descendants. **208**

**motor neurons** Neurons that control muscles and glands. **481**

**motor protein** Type of energy-using protein that interacts with cytoskeletal elements to move the cell's parts or the whole cell. **54**

**motor unit** One motor neuron and the muscle fibers it controls. **411**

**multiregional model** Model that postulates *H. sapiens* populations in different regions evolved from *H. erectus* in those regions. **316**

**muscle fatigue** Decrease in a muscle's ability to contract despite ongoing stimulation. **412**

**muscle tension** Force exerted by a contracting muscle. **412**

**muscle twitch** Brief muscle contraction. **411**

**mutation** Permanent change in DNA sequence. Primary source of new alleles. **109**

**mutualism** Species interaction that benefits both species. **286, 342**

**mycelium** Mass of threadlike filaments (hyphae) that make up the body of a multicelled fungus. **283**

**mycorrhiza** Fungus–plant root partnership. **286, 558**

**myelin** Insulating material around most vertebrate axons; increases speed of signal transmission. **487**

**myofibrils** Threadlike, cross-banded skeletal muscle components that consist of sarcomeres arranged end to end. **409**

**myosin** Protein in thick filaments of muscle fibers. **409**

**natural killer cell (NK cell)** White blood cell that kills infected or cancerous cells. **440**

**natural selection** A process of evolution in which individuals of a population who vary in the details of heritable traits survive and reproduce with differing success. **200**

**naturalist** Person who observes life from a scientific perspective. **197**

**nature** Everything in the universe except what humans have manufactured. **5**

**nectar** Sweet fluid exuded by some flowers; attracts pollinators. **581**

**nematocyst** Touch-sensitive stinging organelle unique to cnidarians. **297**

**negative feedback** A change causes a response that reverses the change. **398**

**nephron** Kidney tubule and associated capillaries; filters blood and forms urine. **472**

**nerve net** Mesh of interacting neurons with no central control, as in the nervous system of jellies. **486**

**nerves** Axons bundled in connective tissues. **486**

**nervous tissue** Animal tissue composed of neurons and supporting cells; detects stimuli and controls responses to them. **394**

**neuroglia** Cells that support neurons. **481**

**neuron** One of the cells that make up communication lines of nervous systems; transmits electrical signals along its plasma membrane and communicates with other cells through chemical messages. **394, 481**

**neurotransmitter** Chemical signal released by a neuron's axon endings. **484**

**neutral mutation** A mutation that has no effect on survival or reproduction. **218**

**neutron** Uncharged subatomic particle in the atomic nucleus. **21**

**neutrophil** Circulating phagocytic white blood cell. **440**

**niche** The role of a species in its community. **341**

**nitrogen cycle** Movement of nitrogen among the atmosphere, soil, and water, and into and out of food webs. **354**

**nitrogen fixation** Formation of ammonia from nitrogen gas and hydrogen. **250, 355, 558**

**nitrification** Conversion of ammonium to nitrates. **355**

**nondisjunction** Failure of sister chromatids or homologous chromosomes to separate during meiosis or mitosis. **172**

**nonpolar** Having an even distribution of charge. **25**

**normal flora** Microorganisms that normally live in or on a healthy animal or person. **251, 440**

**notochord** Stiff rod of connective tissue that runs the length of the body in chordate larvae or embryos. **305**

**nuclear envelope** A double membrane that constitutes the outer boundary of the nucleus. **52**

**nucleic acid** Single- or double-stranded chain of nucleotides joined by sugar–phosphate bonds; e.g., DNA, RNA. **37**

**nucleic acid hybridization** Base-pairing between DNA or RNA from different sources. **182**

**nucleoid** Region of cytoplasm where the DNA is concentrated inside a prokaryotic cell. **43**

**nucleosome** A length of DNA wound around a spool of histone proteins. **103**

**nucleotide** Monomer of nucleic acids; has a five-carbon sugar, a nitrogen-containing base, and phosphate groups. **37**

**nucleus** Of an atom, core region occupied by protons and neutrons. Of a eukaryotic cell, organelle with two membranes that holds the cell's DNA. **21, 43**

**nutrient** Substance that an organism needs for growth and survival, but cannot make for itself. **6**

**oocyte** Immature egg. **528**

**open circulatory system** Circulatory system in which blood leaves vessels and flows among tissues. **419**

**organ** Structural unit composed of two or more tissues and adapted to carry out a particular task. **389**

**organ of Corti** Sound-detecting organ in the cochlea. **498**

**organ system** Organs that interact closely in some task. **389**

**organelle** Structure that carries out a specialized metabolic function inside a cell. **43**

**organic** Refers to a molecule that consists primarily of carbon and hydrogen atoms. **29**

**organism** Individual that consists of one or more cells. **5**

**orgasm** Sexual climax during which neurotransmitter release causes smooth muscle contractions accompanied by a feeling of release and pleasure. **532**

**osmosis** The diffusion of water across a selectively permeable membrane. **70**

**osmotic pressure** Amount of turgor that prevents osmosis into a hypertonic fluid. **70**

**osteoporosis** Disorder in which bones weaken. **406**

**ovarian follicle** Immature egg and surrounding cells. **528**

**ovary** In flowering plants, the enlarged base of a carpel, inside which one or more ovules form and eggs are fertilized. In animals, organ in which eggs form. **280, 526, 567**

**oviduct** Ciliated tube connecting an ovary to the uterus. **528**

**ovulation** Release of a secondary oocyte from an ovary. **529**

**ovule** Of seed plants, chamber inside which the female gametophyte forms; after fertilization, matures into a seed. **277, 567**

**ovum** Mature animal egg. **532**

**ozone layer** Atmospheric layer with a high concentration of ozone; prevents much UV radiation from reaching Earth's surface. **244, 376**

**pain** Perception of tissue injury. **493**

**pancreas** Organ that secretes digestive enzymes into the small intestine and hormones into the blood. **464**

**pandemic** A disease that spreads worldwide. **262**

**Pangea** Supercontinent that formed about 237 million years ago and broke up about 152 million years ago. **206**

**parasite** A species that withdraws nutrients from another species (its host), usually without killing it. **346**

**parasitoid** An insect that lays eggs in another insect (the host), and whose young devour their host from the inside. **346**

**parasympathetic neurons** Neurons of the autonomic system that encourage housekeeping tasks. **489**

**parathyroid glands** Four small endocrine glands whose hormone product increases the level of calcium in blood. **511**

**parenchyma** Simple plant tissue made up of living cells; the main component of the ground tissue system. **549**

**parthenogenesis** Process by which individuals develop from unfertilized eggs. **523**

**passive transport** Mechanism by which a concentration gradient drives the movement of a solute across a cell membrane through a transport protein. Requires no energy input. **72**

**pathogen** Organism that infects another organism and causes disease. **251**

**PCR** Polymerase chain reaction. Method that rapidly generates many copies of a specific DNA fragment. **182**

**pedigree** Chart showing the pattern of inheritance of a trait in a family. **167**

**pelagic province** The ocean's open waters. **368**

**pellicle** Layer of proteins that gives shape to many unwalled, single-celled protists. **252**

**peptide bond** A bond between the amine group of one amino acid and the carboxyl group of another. Joins amino acids in proteins. **34**

**per capita growth rate** For some interval, the number of individuals added divided by the initial population size. **324**

**periderm** Plant dermal tissue that replaces epidermis on older stems and roots. **555**

**peripheral nervous system** Nerves that extend through the body and carry signals to and from the central nervous system. **486**

**permafrost** Layer of permanently frozen soil in the Arctic. **367**

**peroxisome** Enzyme-filled vesicle that breaks down amino acids, fatty acids, and toxic substances. **53**

**pH** Measure of the number of hydrogen ions in a fluid. **27**

**phagocytosis** Endocytic pathway by which a cell engulfs particles such as microbes or cellular debris. **74**

**pharynx** Throat; opens to airways and digestive tract. **428**

**phenotype** An individual's observable traits. **157**

**pheromones** Signaling molecules that affect another member of the same species. **494**

**phloem** Complex vascular tissue that distributes sugars through a plant body. **271, 550**

**phospholipid** A lipid with a phosphate group in its hydrophilic head, and two nonpolar fatty acid tails; main constituent of cell membranes. **32**

**phosphorus cycle** Movement of phosphorus among rocks, water, soil, and living organisms. **354**

**phosphorylation** Phosphate-group transfer. **65**

**photoautotroph** Photosynthetic autotroph. **88**

**photoperiodism** Biological response to seasonal changes in the relative lengths of day and night. **579**

**photoreceptor** Light-sensitive sensory receptor. **493**

**photorespiration** Reaction in which rubisco attaches oxygen instead of carbon dioxide to ribulose bisphosphate. **87**

**photosynthesis** Metabolic pathway by which photoautotrophs capture light energy and use it to make sugars from $CO_2$ and water. **80**

**photosystem** Cluster of pigments and proteins that converts light energy to chemical energy in photosynthesis. **83**

**phototropism** Change in the direction of cell movement or growth in response to a light source. **577**

**phylogeny** Evolutionary history of a species or groups of species. **234**

**phytochrome** A light-sensitive pigment that helps set plant circadian rhythms based on length of night. **578**

**pigment** An organic molecule that can absorb light of certain wavelengths. **81**

**pilus** A protein filament that projects from the surface of some bacterial cells. **50**

**pineal gland** Endocrine gland in the forebrain that secretes melatonin; secretion declines when the eye is exposed to light. **516**

**pioneer species** Species that can colonize a new habitat. **347**

**pituitary gland** Pea-sized endocrine gland in the forebrain that interacts closely with the adjacent hypothalamus. **508**

**placenta** Of placental mammals, organ composed of maternal and embryonic tissues that allows the exchange of substances between a developing individual and its mother. **537**

**placental mammal** Mammal in which young are nourished within the mother's body by way of a placenta. **312**

**placozoan** Structurally simplest animal known, with only four types of cells and a small genome. **293**

**plankton** Community of tiny drifting or swimming organisms. **253**

**plant** A multicelled, typically photosynthetic producer, in which embryos form on a parent. **8, 271**

**plaque** On teeth, a thick biofilm composed of bacteria, their extracellular products, and saliva proteins. **444**

**plasma** Fluid portion of blood. **424**

**plasma membrane** A cell's outermost membrane. **43**

**plasmid** Of many prokaryotes, a small ring of non-chromosomal DNA replicated independently of the chromosome. **181, 249**

**plasmodial slime mold** Heterotrophic protist that moves and feeds as a multinucleated mass; forms a fruiting body when conditions are unfavorable. **258**

**plate tectonics** Theory that Earth's outer layer of rock is cracked into plates, the slow movement of which rafts continents to new locations over geologic time. **207**

**platelet** Cell fragment that helps blood clot. **424**

**pleiotropic** Refers to a gene whose product influences multiple traits. **164**

**polar** Having an uneven distribution of charge. **25**

**polarity** Any separation of charge into distinct positive and negative regions. **25**

**pollen grain** Male gametophyte of a seed plant. **272**

**pollination** Delivery of pollen to the female part of a plant. **277, 568**

**pollination vector** Any agent that moves pollen grains from one plant to another. **580**

**pollinator** Animal that moves pollen from one plant to another, thus facilitating pollination. **280, 566**

**pollutant** A natural or man-made substance that is released into the environment in greater than natural amounts and damages the health of organisms. **373**

**polymers** Molecules that consist of multiple monomers. **30**

**polyp** Tubular cnidarian body form that usually attaches to some surface. **297**

**polypeptide** Chain of amino acids linked by peptide bonds. **34**

**polyploid** Having three or more of each type of chromosome characteristic of the species. **172**

**polysome** Cluster of ribosomes that are simultaneously translating an mRNA. **123**

**pons** Hindbrain region between medulla oblongata and midbrain; helps control breathing. **491**

**population** A group of organisms of the same species who live in a specific location and breed with one another more often than they breed with members of other populations. **5, 322**

**population density** The number of organisms of a particular population in a given area. **323**

**population distribution** The way in which members of a population are spread out in their environment. **323**

**population size** Number of individuals in a population. **323**

**predation** One species feeds on another, usually killing it. **344**

**predator** One species that eats and kills another. **344**

**prediction** A statement, based on a hypothesis, about a condition that should exist if the hypothesis is not wrong. **10**

**pressure flow theory** Explanation of how flow of fluid through phloem is driven by differences in pressure and sugar concentration between a source and a sink. **561**

**prey** A species that is eaten by a predator. **344**

**primary growth** Plant growth from apical meristems in root and shoot tips. **553**

**primary production** The energy captured by an ecosystem's producers. **352**

**primary succession** Ecological succession occurs in an area where there was previously no soil. **347**

**primate** Mammalian group that includes tarsiers, monkeys, apes, and humans. **313**

**primer** Short, single strand of DNA designed to hybridize with a DNA fragment. **182**

**prion** Infectious protein. **36**

**probe** Short fragment of DNA labeled with a tracer; designed to hybridize with a nucleotide sequence of interest. **182**

**producers** Organisms that capture energy and make their own food from inorganic materials in the environment. **6, 350**

**product** A molecule remaining at the end of a reaction. **64**

**progesterone** Sex hormone produced by a female's ovaries. **515**

**prokaryote** Single-celled organism in which the DNA resides in the cytoplasm; a bacterium or archaean. **8, 244**

**prokaryotic conjugation** One prokaryotic cell transfers a plasmid to another. **249**

**prokaryotic fission** Method of asexual reproduction in which one prokaryotic cell divides and forms two identical descendant cells. **249**

**promoter** In DNA, a sequence to which RNA polymerase binds. **119**

**prophase** Stage of mitosis in which chromosomes condense and become attached to a newly forming spindle. **140**

**prostate gland** Exocrine gland that encircles a male's urethra; its secretions contribute to semen. **526**

**protein** Organic compound that consists of one or more chains of amino acids. **33**

**protist** A eukaryote that is not a plant, fungus, or animal. **8, 252**

**protocells** Membranous sacs that contain interacting organic molecules; hypothesized to have formed prior to the earliest life forms. **243**

**proton** Positively charged subatomic particle that occurs in the nucleus of all atoms. **21**

**pseudocoel** Body cavity not fully lined with mesoderm. **295**

**pseudopod** Extendable lobe of membrane-enclosed cytoplasm. **55**

**puberty** Period when reproductive organs mature and begin to function. **515**

**pulmonary circuit** Circuit through which blood flows from the heart to the lungs and back. **420**

**pulse** Brief stretching of artery walls that occurs when ventricular contraction forces blood into arteries. **424**

**Punnett square** Diagram used to predict the genetic and phenotypic outcome of a cross. **159**

**pupil** Opening through which light enters the eye. **495**

**pyruvate** Three-carbon end product of glycolysis. **89**

**radial symmetry** Having parts arranged around a central axis, like spokes around a wheel. **294**

**radioactive decay** Process by which atoms of a radioisotope spontaneously emit energy and subatomic particles when their nucleus disintegrates. **21**

**radioisotope** Isotope with an unstable nucleus. **21**

**radiometric dating** Method of estimating the age of a rock or fossil by measuring the content and proportions of a radioisotope and its daughter elements. **203**

**radula** Tonguelike organ of many mollusks. **298**

**rain shadow** Dry region on the downwind side of a coastal mountain range. **363**

**ray-finned fish** Bony fish with fins supported by thin rays derived from skin. **308**

**reabsorption** In the kidney, water and solutes leave the filtrate and enter capillaries. **472**

**reactant** Molecule that enters a reaction. **64**

**reaction** Process of chemical change. **64**

**receptor** Molecule or structure that can respond to a form of stimulation. **6**

**receptor protein** Plasma membrane protein that binds to a particular substance outside of the cell. **49**

**recessive** Refers to an allele with an effect that is masked by a dominant allele on the homologous chromosome. **158**

**recognition protein** Plasma membrane protein that tags a cell as belonging to self (one's own body). **48**

**recombinant DNA** A DNA molecule that contains genetic material from more than one organism. **181**

**rectum** Portion of the large intestine that stores feces until they are expelled. **466**

**red alga** Single-celled or multicelled photosynthetic protist with red accessory pigment. **256**

**red blood cell** Hemoglobin-filled blood cell that transports oxygen. **424**

**red marrow** Bone marrow that makes blood cells. **406**

**reflex** Automatic (involuntary) response to a stimulus. **491**

**releaser** Hormone that is secreted by one endocrine gland and stimulates secretion by another. **508**

**replacement model** Model for origin of *H. sapiens*; humans evolved in Africa, then migrated to different regions and replaced the other hominids that lived there. **317**

**reproduction** Process by which parents produce offspring. **7**

**reproductive cloning** Technology that produces genetically identical individuals. **110**

**reproductive isolation** Absence of gene flow between populations; part of speciation. **227**

**reptile** Amniote subgroup that includes lizards, snakes, turtles, crocodilians, and birds. **310**

**resource partitioning** Use of different portions of a limited resource; allows species with similar needs to coexist. **344**

**respiration** Physiological process by which gases enter and leave an animal body. **426**

**respiratory cycle** One inhalation and one exhalation. **429**

**respiratory surface** Moist surface across which gases are exchanged between animals cells and their environment. **426**

**resting potential** Membrane potential of a neuron that is not being stimulated. **482**

**restriction enzyme** Type of enzyme that cuts specific base sequences in DNA. **181**

**retina** Layer of eye that contains photoreceptors. **495**

**reverse transcriptase** A viral enzyme that uses mRNA as a template to make a strand of cDNA. **182**

**rhizome** Stem that grows horizontally along the ground. **274**

**ribosomal RNA (rRNA)** A type of RNA that becomes part of ribosomes. **121**

**ribosome** Organelle of protein synthesis. **50**

**RNA** Ribonucleic acid. Typically single-stranded nucleic acid; roles in protein synthesis. *See also* ribosomal RNA, transfer RNA, messenger RNA. **37**

**RNA polymerase** Enzyme that carries out transcription. **118**

**RNA world** Hypothetical early interval when RNA served as the material of inheritance. **242**

**rod cell** Photoreceptor active in dim light; provides coarse perception of image and detects motion. **497**

**root hairs** Hairlike, absorptive extensions of a young cell of root epidermis. **554**

**root nodules** Swellings of some plant roots that contain nitrogen-fixing bacteria. **558**

**roundworm** Unsegmented worm with a pseudocoel and a cuticle that is molted as the animal grows. **300**

**r-selection** Selection favoring individuals that produce many offspring fast; selection for offspring quantity. **329**

**rubisco** Ribulose bisphosphate carboxylase. Carbon-fixing enzyme of the Calvin–Benson cycle. **86**

**salivary amylase** Enzyme in saliva that begins carbohydrate digestion by breaking starch into disaccharides. **463**

**salt** Compound that dissolves easily in water and releases ions other than $H^+$ and $OH^-$. **26**

**sampling error** Difference between results derived from testing an entire group of events or individuals, and results derived from testing a subset of the group. **14**

**saprobe** Organism that feeds on wastes and remains. **283**

**sarcomere** Contractile unit of skeletal and cardiac muscle. **409**

**saturated fat** Fatty acid with no double bonds in its carbon tail. **32**

**scales** Hard, flattened elements that cover the skin of some vertebrates. **307**

**science** Systematic study of nature. **9**

**scientific theory** Hypothesis that has not been disproven after many years of rigorous testing, and is useful for making predictions about other phenomena. **10**

**sclera** Protective covering at the sides and back of eyeball. **495**

**sclerenchyma** Simple plant tissue; dead at maturity, its lignin-reinforced cell walls structurally support plant parts. **550**

**scrotum** Pouch that holds the testes. **526**

**seamount** An undersea mountain. **369**

**second law of thermodynamics** Energy tends to disperse. **63**

**second messenger** Molecule that forms inside a cell when a hormone binds at the cell surface; sets in motion reactions that alter enzyme activity inside the cell. **506**

**secondary growth** A thickening of older stems and roots at lateral meristems. **277, 555**

**secondary succession** Ecological succession occurs in an area where a community previously existed and soil remains. **347**

**seed** Embryo sporophyte of a seed plant packaged with nutritive tissue inside a protective coat. **272, 570**

**segmentation** Having a body composed of units that repeat along its length. **295**

**selective permeability** Membrane property that allows some substances, but not others, to cross. **69**

**semen** Sperm mixed with fluid secreted by exocrine glands. **526**

**seminal vesicles** Exocrine glands that secrete fluid into the vas deferentia; main source of semen volume. **526**

**senescence** Phase in a life cycle from maturity until death; also applies to death of parts, such as plant leaves. **579**

**sensory neurons** Neurons that detect specific stimuli such as light, touch, or a particular chemical. **481**

**sensory receptor** Cell or cell part that responds to a particular stimulus. **398**

**sequencing** Method of determining the order of nucleotides in DNA. **185**

**sex chromosome** Member of a pair of chromosomes that differs between males and females. **104**

**sexual reproduction** Reproductive mode by which offspring arise from two parents and inherit genes from both. **144, 523**

**sexual selection** Mode of natural selection in which some individuals outreproduce others of a population because they are better at securing mates. **223**

**sexually transmitted disease** Infectious disease caused by a pathogen that can live in the reproductive tract. **534**

**shell model** Model of electron distribution in an atom; orbitals are shown as nested circles, electrons as dots. **23**

**sister chromatid** One of two attached members of a duplicated eukaryotic chromosome. **103**

**sister groups** The two lineages that emerge from a node on a cladogram. **235**

**skeletal muscle tissue** Striated, voluntary muscle that interacts with bone to move body parts. **393**

**sliding-filament model** Explanation of how interactions among actin and myosin filaments shorten a sarcomere and bring about muscle contraction. **410**

**small intestine** Longest portion of the digestive tract, and the site of most digestion and absorption. **464**

**smooth muscle tissue** Involuntary muscle that lines blood vessels and hollow organs; not striated. **393**

**solute** A dissolved substance. **26**

**solvent** Liquid that can dissolve other substances. **26**

**somatic cell nuclear transfer (SCNT)** Method of reproductive cloning in which genetic material is transferred from an adult somatic cell into an unfertilized, enucleated egg. **111**

**somatic nervous system** Set of nerves that control skeletal muscle and relay signals from joints and skin. **488**

**somatic sensations** Sensations that arise when sensory neurons in skin and near joints and muscle are activated. **493**

**speciation** Process by which new species arise from existing species. **227**

**species** A type of organism. **8**

**sperm** Mature male gamete. **148**

**sphincter** Ring of muscle that controls passage through a tubular organ or body opening. **463**

**spinal cord** Portion of central nervous system that connects peripheral nerves with the brain. **490**

**spindle** Dynamically assembled and disassembled array of microtubules that moves chromosomes during mitosis or meiosis. **140**

**sponge** Aquatic invertebrate that has no tissues or organs and filters food from the water. **296**

**spongy bone** Lightweight bone with many internal spaces. **406**

**sporadic disease** A disease that breaks out occasionally and affects only a small portion of a population. **262**

**sporophyte** Diploid, spore-producing stage of a plant life cycle. **148, 271**

**sprain** Ligaments of a joint are injured. **407**

**stabilizing selection** Mode of natural selection in which intermediate phenotypes are favored over extremes. **221**

**stamen** The male reproductive part of a flowering plant; consists of a pollen-producing anther on a filament. **280, 567**

**stasis** Macroevolutionary pattern in which a lineage persists with little or no change over evolutionary time. **231**

**statistically significant** Refers to a result that is statistically unlikely to have occurred by chance. **14**

**stem cell** A cell that can divide to form more stem cells or differentiate to become a specialized cell type. **388**

**steroid** A type of lipid with four carbon rings and no fatty acid tails. **33**

**steroid hormone** Hormone, such as testosterone, that is derived from cholesterol. **506**

**stomach** Muscular organ that mixes food with gastric fluid that it secretes. **464**

**stomata** Gaps that open between guard cells on plant surfaces; allow water vapor and gases to diffuse across the epidermis. **86, 271**

**strain** A subgroup within a species that has a characteristic trait or traits. **249**

**stroke** Event in which brain cells die because a clot or vessel rupture disrupts blood flow within the brain. **431**

**stroma** Semifluid matrix between the thylakoid membrane and the two outer membranes of a chloroplast; site of light-independent photosynthesis reactions. **83**

**stromatolites** Dome-shaped structures composed of layers of prokaryotic cells and sediments. **244**

**substrate** A reactant molecule that is specifically acted upon by an enzyme. **66**

**surface-to-volume ratio** A relationship in which the volume of an object increases with the cube of the diameter, but the surface area increases with the square. **44**

**survivorship curve** Graph showing the decline in numbers of a cohort over time. **328**

**sustainable development** Using resources to meet current human needs in a way that takes into account the needs of future generations. **382**

**swim bladder** Organ that adjusts buoyancy in bony fishes. **306**

**symbiosis** One species lives in or on another in a commensal, mutualistic, or parasitic relationship. **342**

**sympathetic neurons** Neurons of the autonomic system; their activity prepares the body for danger or excitement. **489**

**sympatric speciation** Pattern in which speciation occurs in the absence of a physical barrier. **229**

**syndrome** The set of symptoms that characterize a genetic disease. **167**

**synovial joint** Joint such as the knees that is lubricated by fluid and allows movement of bones around the joint. **407**

**systemic circuit** Circuit through which blood flows from the heart to the body tissues and back. **420**

**systolic pressure** Blood pressure when ventricles are contracting. **425**

**T cell receptor (TCR)** Antigen-binding receptor on the surface of T cells; also recognizes MHC markers. **445**

**T lymphocyte (T cell)** Circulating white blood cell central to adaptive immunity; some kinds target sick body cells. **440**

**taiga** Extensive northern biome that is dominated by conifers. Also called boreal forest. **366**

**taxon (taxa)** A grouping of organisms. **233**

**taxonomy** Science of naming and classifying species. **233**

**telophase** Stage of mitosis during which chromosomes arrive at the spindle poles and decondense, and new nuclei form. **140**

**temperate deciduous forest** Biome dominated by trees that drop all their leaves in fall and become dormant during a cold winter. **366**

**temperature** Measure of molecular motion. **27**

**tendon** Strap of dense connective tissue that connects a skeletal muscle to bone. **408**

**testes** In animals, organs that produces sperm. **526**

**testosterone** Sex hormone produced by a male's testes. **515**

**tetrapod** Vertebrate with four limbs. **306**

**theory of uniformity** Idea that gradual repetitive processes occurring over long time spans shaped Earth's surface. **199**

**therapeutic cloning** Using somatic cell nuclear transfer to produce human embryos for research. **111**

**thermoreceptor** Temperature-sensitive sensory receptor. **493**

**thigmotropism** Directional growth of a plant in response to contact with a solid object. **578**

**threatened species** A species likely to become endangered in the near future. **370**

**threshold potential** Membrane potential at which voltage-gated sodium channels in a neuron axon open, causing an action potential. **482**

**thrombus** Clot that forms in a vessel and remains in place. **431**

**thylakoid membrane** A chloroplast's highly folded inner membrane system; forms a continuous compartment in the stroma. Site of light-dependent photosynthesis reactions. **83**

**thymus** Endocrine gland beneath breastbone; produces hormones that help T cells mature. **511**

**thyroid gland** Endocrine gland at the base of the neck; produces thyroid hormone, which increases metabolism. **510**

**tight junction** Array of fibrous proteins that joins epithelial cells. Collectively prevent fluids from leaking between cells in tissues. **56**

**tissue** One or more types of cells that are organized in a specific pattern and that carry out a particular task. **294, 389**

**tissue culture propagation** Laboratory method in which body cells are induced to divide and form an embryo. **572**

**total fertility rate** Average number of children born to a woman in a particular population. **333**

**tracer** A molecule with a detectable label. **22**

**trachea** Airway to the lungs; windpipe. **428**

**tracheal system** Tubes that deliver air from body surface to tissues of insects and some other land arthropods. **427**

**transcription** Process by which an RNA is assembled from nucleotides using the base sequence of a gene as a template. **117**

**transcription factor** Protein that influences transcription by binding to DNA. **127**

**transfer RNA (tRNA)** Type of RNA that delivers amino acids to a ribosome during translation. **121**

**transgenic** Refers to an organism that has been genetically modified to carry a gene from a different species. **180**

**translation** Process by which a polypeptide chain is assembled from amino acids in the order specified by an mRNA. **117**

**translocation** Process that moves organic compounds through phloem. **561**

**transpiration** Evaporation of water from plant parts. **560**

**transport protein** Protein that passively or actively assists specific ions or molecules across a membrane. **49**

**transposable element** Small segment of DNA that can spontaneously move to a new location in a chromosome. **126**

**triglyceride** A lipid with three fatty acid tails attached to a glycerol backbone. **32**

**trophic level** Position of an organism in a food chain. **350**

**tropical rain forest** Species-rich tropical biome in which continual warmth and rainfall allows the dominant broadleaf trees to grow all year. **366**

**tropism** In plants, directional growth response to an environmental stimulus. **577**

**tubular secretion** Substances are moved out of capillaries and into filtrate in kidney tubules. **472**

**tumor** Abnormally growing and dividing mass of cells. **130**

**tunicates** Invertebrate chordates that lose their defining chordate traits during the transition to adulthood. **305**

**turgor** Pressure that a fluid exerts against a wall, membrane, or some other structure that contains it. **70**

**unsaturated fat** Lipid with at least one double bond in a fatty acid tail. **32**

**ureter** Tube that carries urine from a kidney to the bladder. **471**

**urethra** Tube through which urine from the bladder flows out of the body. **471**

**urinary bladder** Hollow, muscular organ that stores urine. **471**

**urinary system** Organ system that filters blood, and forms, stores, and expels urine. **471**

**urine** Mix of water and soluble wastes formed and excreted by the urinary system. **471**

**uterus** Muscular chamber where offspring develop; womb. **528**

**vaccine** A preparation introduced into the body in order to elicit immunity to an antigen. **454**

**vacuole** A fluid-filled organelle that isolates or disposes of waste, debris, or toxic materials. **53**

**vagina** Female organ of intercourse and birth canal. **528**

**variable** A characteristic or event that differs among individuals. **12**

**vascular bundle** Multistranded, sheathed cord of primary xylem and phloem in a stem or leaf. **551**

**vascular cambium** Ring of meristematic tissue that produces secondary xylem and phloem. **555**

**vascular cylinder** Sheathed, cylindrical array of primary xylem and phloem in a root. **554**

**vascular plant** A plant that has xylem and phloem. **271**

**vascular tissue system** Tissue system that distributes water and nutrients through a plant body. **549**

**vas deferens** Main duct that conveys mature sperm toward the urethra. **526**

**vector** Animal that transmits a pathogen between its hosts. **251**

**vegetative reproduction** Growth of new roots and shoots from extensions or fragments of a parent plant; form of asexual reproduction in plants. **571**

**vein** Large-diameter vessel that returns blood to the heart. **421**

**ventricle** Heart chamber that pumps blood out of the heart and into an artery. **420**

**venule** Small-diameter blood vessel that carries blood from capillaries to a vein. **421**

**vernalization** Stimulation of flowering in spring by low temperature in winter. **579**

**vertebrae** Bones of the backbone. **405**

**vertebral column** The backbone. **306, 405**

**vertebrate** Animal with a backbone. **295**

**vesicle** Small, membrane-enclosed, saclike organelle; different kinds store, transport, or degrade their contents. **53**

**villi** Multicelled projections from the lining of the small intestine. **464**

**virus** Infectious particle that consists of protein and nucleic acid and replicates only inside a living cell. **259**

**visceral sensations** Sensations that arise when sensory neurons in soft internal organs are stimulated. **493**

**vitamin** Organic substance required in small amounts for normal metabolism. **468**

**warning coloration** Distinctive color or pattern that makes a well-defended prey species easy to recognize. **345**

**water cycle** Water moves from its main reservoir—the ocean—into the air, falls as rain and snow, and flows back to the ocean. **353**

**water mold** Heterotrophic protist that forms a mesh of nutrient-absorbing filaments. **255**

**water–vascular system** Of echinoderms, a system of fluid-filled tubes and tube feet that function in locomotion. **304**

**wavelength** Distance between the crests of two successive waves of light. **81**

**wax** Water-repellent lipid with long fatty acid tails bonded to long-chain alcohols or carbon rings. **32**

**white blood cell** Blood cell with a role in housekeeping and defense. **424**

**white matter** Tissue of brain and spinal cord consisting of myelinated axons. **490**

**wood** Lignin-stiffened secondary xylem of some seed plants. **277, 555**

**xenotransplantation** Transplantation of an organ from one species into another. **189**

**xylem** Plant vascular tissue; distributes water and dissolved mineral ions through tubes that consist of interconnected walls of dead cells. **271, 550**

**yellow marrow** Bone marrow that is mostly fat; fills cavity in most long bones. **406**

**yolk** Nutritious material in many animal eggs. **524**

**zygote** Cell formed by fusion of gametes; first cell of a new individual. **144, 524**

# Art Credits & Acknowledgments

CHAPTER 1: **1.1** Courtesy of Conservation International. **1.3** below, JupiterImages Corporation. **1.4** © Biosphoto/ BIOS, Bios - Auteurs (droits geres), Denis-Huot Michel & Christine/ Peter Arnold Inc. **1.5** clockwise from top left, SciMAT/ Photo Researchers, Inc.; © Dr. Harald Huber, Dr. Michael Hohn, Prof. Dr. K.O.Stetter, University of Regensburg, Germany; JupiterImages Corporation; © Biosphoto/ BIOS, Bios - Auteurs (droits geres), Denis-Huot Michel & Christine/ Peter Arnold Inc.; Courtesy of John S. Russell, Pioneer High School; Astrid Hanns-Frieder michler/ SPL/ Photo Researchers, Inc. **Page 9** JupiterImages Corporation. **1.6** © Raymond Gehman/ Corbis. **1.7** above, © Bob Jacobson/ Corbis; below, © SuperStock. **1.8** (a) © Adrian Vallin; (b), © Antje Schulte. **1.9** © Adrian Vallin. **1.10** Photo courtesy of Dr. Robert Zingg/ Zoo Zurich. **Page 16** Section 1.1, Courtesy of Conservation International; Section 1.3, © Biosphoto/ BIOS, Bios - Auteurs (droits geres), Denis-Huot Michel & Christine/ Peter Arnold Inc; Section 1.4, 1.5, JupiterImages Corporation; Section 1.6, Raymond Gehman/ Corbis; Section 1.7, © Bob Jacobson/ Corbis. **Page 17** Scientific Paper; Adrian Vallin, Sven Jakobsson, Johan Lind and Christer Wiklund, *Proc. R. Soc. B* (2005 272, 1203, 1207). Used with permission of The Royal Society and the author.

CHAPTER 2: **2.1** © ThinkStock/ SuperStock. **2.3** © Michael S. Yamashita/ Corbis. **2.7** (c) © Herbert Schnekenburger. **2.9** © JupiterImages Corporation. **2.10** Michael Grecco/ Picture Group. **Page 30** © JupiterImages Corporation. **2.13** © JupiterImages Corporation. **2.16** Tim Davis/ Photo Researchers, Inc. **Page 35** PDB ID: 1QLX; Zahn, R., Liu, A., Luhrs, T., Reik, R., Von Schroetter, C., Garcia, F.L., Billeter, M., Calzolai, L., Wider, G. Wuthrich, K.: NMR Solution Structure of the Human Prion Protein, *Proc. Nat. Acad. Sci*, USA 97 p. 145 (2000). **2.19** (b) Sherif Zaki, MD PhD, Wun-Ju Shieh, MD PhD; MPH/ CDC; (c) © Lily Echeverria/ Miami Herald. **Page 37** © JupiterImages Corporation. **Page 38** Section 2.1, 2.7, © JupiterImages Corporation; Section 2.4, © Herbert Schnekenburger; Section 2.5, Michael Grecco/ Picture Group. **2.19** This lipoprotein image was made by Amy Shih and John Stone using VMD and is owned by the Theoretical and Computational Biophysics Group, NIH Resource for Macromolecular Modeling and Bioinformatics, at the Beckman Institute, University of Illinois at Urbana-Champaign. Labels added to the original image by book author.

CHAPTER 3: **Page 42** © JupiterImages Corporation. **3.1** From left, Astrid Hanns-Frieder michler/ SPL/ Photo Researchers, Inc.; Courtesy of Allen W. H. Bé and David A. Caron; © Wim van Egmond/ Visuals Unlimited; © Dr. Dennis Kunkel/ Visuals Unlimited; © Stem Jems/

Photo Researchers, Inc. **3.3** Tony Brian, David Parker/ SPL/ Photo Researchers, Inc. **3.4** (a,b; d,e) Jeremy Pickett-Heaps, School of Botany, University of Melbourne; (c) © Prof. Franco Baldi. **3.5** Virus, CDC; Bacteria, Tony Brian, David Parker/ SPL/ Photo Researchers, Inc.; Eukaryotic cells, Jeremy Pickett-Heaps, School of Botany, University of Melbourne; Louse, Edward S. Ross; Ladybug, Image © Dole, Used under license from Shutterstock.com; Goldfish, Image © Ultrashock, Used under license from Shutterstock.com; Butterfly, From Meyer, A., Repeating Patterns of Mimicry. *PLoS Biology* Vol. 4, No. 10, e341 doi:10.1371/journal. pbio.0040341; Guinea pig, Image © Sascha Burkard, Used under license from Shutterstock .com; Dog, Image © Pavel Sazonov, Used under license from Shutterstock.com; Human, JupiterImages Corporation; Giraffe, © Ingram Publishing, SuperStock; Whale, JupiterImages Corporation; Tree, Courtesy of © Billie Chandler. **Page 46** © The Royal Society. **3.7** (a) Rocky Mountain Laboratories, NIAID, NIH; (b) © R. Calentine/ Visuals Unlimited; (c) Archi-MeDes; (d,e) © K.O. Stetter & R. Rachel, Univ. Regensburg. **3.10** © Kenneth Bart. **3.11** (a) Micrograph, Keith R. Porter; (b) Dr. Jeremy Burgess/ SPL/ Photo Researchers, Inc. **3.12** (b) © Dylan T. Burnette and Paul Forscher. **3.15** © ADVANCELL (Advanced In Vitro Cell Technologies; S.L.) www.advancell.com. **Page 57** © Stephanie Schuller/ Photo Researchers, Inc. **Page 58** Section 3.1, 3.2, Astrid Hanns-Frieder michler/ SPL/ Photo Researchers, Inc.; Section 3.3, © The Royal Society; Section 3.5, Archi-MeDes; Section 3.6, © Kenneth Bart. **Page 59** Critical Thinking #2, P.L. Walne and J. H. Arnott, *Planta*, 77:325–354, 1967.

CHAPTER 4: **4.1** above, © BananaStock/ SuperStock. **4.6** (a) right, © Scott McKiernan/ ZUMA Press. **4.8** Lisa Starr, after David S. Goodsell, RCSB, Protein Data Bank. **4.9** (a) © JupiterImages Corporation. **4.12** M. Sheetz, R. Painter, and S. Singer, *Journal of Cell Biology*, 70:193 (1976) by permission, The Rockefeller University Press. **4.13** PDB files from NYU Scientific Visualization Lab. **4.14** After David H. MacLennan, William J. Rice, and N. Michael Green, "The Mechanism of $Ca^{2+}$ Transport by Sarco(Endo)plasmic Reticulum $Ca^{2+}$-ATPases." *J. Biol. Chem.* 1997, 272: 28815–28818. **4.17** Biology Media/ Photo Researchers, Inc. **4.18** (a) Courtesy Dr. Edward C. Klatt; (b) Courtesy of Downstate Medical Center, Department of Pathology, Brooklyn, NY. **Page 76** Section 4.1, © BananaStock/ SuperStock; Section 4.4, © JupiterImages Corporation; Section 4.6, M. Sheetz, R. Painter, and S. Singer, *Journal of Cell Biology*, 70:193 (1976) by permission, The Rockefeller University Press. **4.19** top, JupiterImages Corporation.

CHAPTER 5: **5.1** Photo by Peggy Greb/ USDA. **Page 82** © Larry West/ FPG/ Getty Images. **5.3**

left, JupiterImages Corporation. **5.7** (a) Courtesy of John S. Russell, Pioneer High School; (c) © Bill Boch/ FoodPix/ JupiterImages; (d) Lisa Starr. **5.12** © Ben Fink Photography. **Page 92** JupiterImages Corporation. **5.13** left, © Randy Faris/ Corbis; right, Lilly M/ http://commons .wikimedia.org; below Courtesy of © William MacDonald, M.D. **Page 94** upper, © Lois Ellen Frank/ Corbis; lower, JupiterImages Corporation. **5.15** © JupiterImages Corporation. **Page 96** Photo by Peggy Greb/ USDA. **5.15** JupiterImages Corporation. **5.16** left, © Roger W. Winstead, NC State University; right, Photo by Scott Bauer, USDA/ ARS. **Page 98** Section 5.1, Photo by Peggy Greb/ USDA; Section 5.2, © Larry West/ FPG/ Getty Images; Section 5.5, Lisa Starr; Section 5.7, © Ben Fink Photography; Section 5.8, © Lois Ellen Frank/ Corbis; Section 5.9, © JupiterImages Corporation.

CHAPTER 6: **6.1** Photos by Victor Fisher, courtesy Genetic Savings & Clone. **6.2** left, Andrew Syred/ Photo Researchers, Inc. **6.4** © University of Washington Department of Pathology. **6.6** (d) A. C. Barrington Brown, 1968 J. D. Watson. **6.7** PDB ID: 1BBB; Silva, M.M., Rogers, P.H., Arnone, A.: A third quaternary structure of human hemoglobin at 1.7-A resolution. *J. Biol. Chem* 276 pp. 17248 (1992). **6.10, 6.11** Courtesy of Cyagra, Inc., www.cyagra.com. **Page 111** left upper, © McLeod Murdo/ Corbis Sygma; lower, Photo by Victor Fisher, courtesy Genetic Savings & Clone. **Page 112** Section 6.2, Andrew Syred/ Photo Researchers, Inc.; Section 6.5, © McLeod Murdo/ Corbis Sygma. **6.12** (a) Eye of Science/ Photo Researchers, Inc.

CHAPTER 7: **7.1** Vaughan Fleming/ SPL/ Photo Researchers, Inc. **7.3** © JupiterImages Corporation. **7.4** O. L. Miller. **Page 123** © Kiseleva and Donald Fawcett/ Visuals Unlimited. **7.10** left, Dr. Gopal Murti/ SPL/ Photo Researchers, Inc.; right, © Ben Rose/ WireImage/ Getty Images. **7.11** (a) © John W. Gofman and Arthur R. Tamplin. From *Poisoned Power: The Case Against Nuclear Power Plants Before and After Three Mile Island*, Rodale Press, PA, 1979. **7.12** (a,b) David Scharf/ Photo Researchers, Inc.; (c) Eye of Science/ Photo Researchers, Inc.; (d) Courtesy of the Aniridia Foundation International, www.aniridia.net; (e) M. Bloch. **7.13** © Dr. William Strauss. **7.14** After Patten, Carlson, & others. **7.15** left, Courtesy of Robin Shoulla and Young Survival Coalition; right, From the archives of www.breastpath.com, courtesy of J.B. Askew, Jr., M.D., P.A. Reprinted with permission, copyright 2004 Breastpath .com. **Page 131** © Vaughan Fleming/ SPL/ Photo Researchers, Inc. **Page 132** Section 7.1, Vaughan Fleming/ SPL/ Photo Researchers, Inc.; Section 7.3, © JupiterImages Corporation; Section 7.6, © John W. Gofman and Arthur R. Tamplin. From *Poisoned Power: The Case Against Nuclear Power Plants Before and After Three Mile*

*Island*, Rodale Press, PA, 1979; Section 7.7, © Dr. William Strauss. **Page 133** © Sascha Burkard, Used under license from Shutterstock.com.

CHAPTER 8: **8.1** Micrograph, Dr. Pascal Madaule, France; inset, Courtesy of the family of Henrietta Lacks. **8.2** © Carolina Biological Supply Company/ Phototake. **8.5** left photos, Michael Clayton/ University of Wisconsin, Department of Botany; right photos, Ed Reschke. **8.6** (c) right, © D. M. Phillips/ Visuals Unlimited. **8.7** (c) right, Michael Clayton/ University of Wisconsin, Department of Botany. **8.8** Image courtesy of Carl Zeiss MicroImaging, Thornwood, NY. **8.10** top photos, With thanks to the John Innes Foundation Trustees, computer enhanced by Gary Head. **8.12** right, Courtesy of © Billie Chandler. **8.13** © Phillip B. Carpenter, Department of Biochemistry and Molecular Biology, University of Texas–Houston Medical School. **8.15** (a) © Ken Greer/ Visuals Unlimited; (b) Biophoto Associates/ Photo Researchers, Inc.; (c) James Stevenson/ Photo Researchers, Inc. **Page 151** Courtesy of the family of Henrietta Lacks. **Page 152** Sections 8.1, 8.2, © Carolina Biological Supply Company/ Phototake; Section 8.4, Michael Clayton/ University of Wisconsin, Department of Botany; Section 8.5, © D. M. Phillips/ Visuals Unlimited; Section 8.6, Image courtesy of Carl Zeiss MicroImaging, Thornwood, NY; Section 8.9, James Stevenson/ Photo Researchers, Inc. **8.17** left, SPL/ Photo Researchers, Inc.; right, Courtesy of © Dr. Thomas Ried, NIH and the American Association for Cancer Research.

CHAPTER 9: **9.1** Clockwise from top left, Courtesy of © The Cody Dieruf Benefit Foundation, www.breathinisbelievin.org; Courtesy of © Bobby Brooks and The Family of Jeff Baird; Courtesy of © Steve & Ellison Widener and Breathe Hope, http://breathehope.tamu.edu; Courtesy of © the family of Brandon Herriott; Courtesy of © The Family of Savannah Brooke Snider; Courtesy of The family of Benjamin Hill, reprinted with permission of © Chappell/Marathonfoto. **9.3** top, Jean M. Labat/ Ardea London. **Page 157** The Moravian Museum, Brno. **9.5** white pea plan flower, © George Lepp/ Corbis. **9.8** © Gary Roberts/ worldwidefeatures.com. **9.9** top, © David Scharf/ Peter Arnold, Inc. **9.10** © JupiterImages Corporation. **Page 164** Courtesy of the family of Haris Charalambous and the University of Toledo. **9.12** lower, Courtesy of Ray Carson, University of Florida News and Public Affairs. **9.13** (a) JupiterImages Corporation; (b) © age fotostock/ SuperStock; (c) © Dr. Christian Laforsch. **9.15** Courtesy of Irving Buchbinder, DPM, DABPS, Community Health Services, Hartford CT. **9.16** (b) Eddie Adams/ AP Wide World Photos. **9.17** (b) Rick Guidotti, Positive Exposure. **9.18** (a,b) Photo by Gary L. Friedman, www.Friedman Archives.com. **9.20** (b) Lauren Shear/ Photo Researchers, Inc.; (c) L. Willatt, East Anglian Regional Genetics Service/ Photo Researchers, Inc. **9.21** UNC Medical Illustration and Photography. **9.22** Saturn Stills/ SPL/ Photo

Researchers, Inc. **Page 174** Fran Heyl Associates © Jacques Cohen, computer-enhanced by © Pix Elation. **9.23** © Howard Sochurek/ The Medical File/ Peter Arnold, Inc. **Page 175** © Gary Gaugler/ The Medical File/ Peter Arnold Inc. **Page 176** Section 9.1, Courtesy of © The Cody Dieruf Benefit Foundation, www.breathinisbelievin.org; Section 9.2, © Gary Roberts/ worldwidefeatures.com; Section 9.4, JupiterImages Corporation; Section 9.7, © Lauren Shear/ Photo Researchers, Inc.; Section 9.8, © Howard Sochurek/ The Medical File/ Peter Arnold, Inc.

CHAPTER 10: **10.1** © Courtesy of Golden Rice Humanitarian Board. **10.6** Courtesy of © Genelex Corp. **10.7** Patrick Landmann/ Photo Researchers, Inc. **Page 187** Photo Courtesy of Systems Biodynamics Lab, P.I. Jeff Hasty, UCSD Department of Bioengineering, and Scott Cookson. **10.8** (4) © Lowell Georgis/ Corbis; (5) Keith V. Wood. **10.9** The Bt and Non-Bt corn photos were taken as part of field trial conducted on the main campus of Tennessee State University at the Institute of Agricultural and Environmental Research. The work was supported by a competitive grant from the CSREES, USDA titled "Southern Agricultural Biotechnology Consortium for Underserved Communities," (2000–2005). Dr. Fisseha Tegegne and Dr. Ahmad Aziz served as Principal and Co-principal Investigators respectively to conduct the portion of the study in the State of Tennessee. **10.10** (a) © Adi Nes, Dvir Gallery Ltd.; (b) Transgenic goat produced using nuclear transfer at GTC Biotherapeutics. Photo used with permission; (c) Photo courtesy of MU Extension and Agricultural Infomation. **Page 190** © Jeans for Gene Appeal. **Page 191** © Corbis/ SuperStock; © Courtesy of Golden Rice Humanitarian Board. **Page 192** Section 10.1, © Courtesy of Golden Rice Humanitarian Board; Section 10.3, Patrick Landmann/ Photo Researchers, Inc.; Section 10.4, Keith V. Wood; Section 10.5, © Jeans for Gene Appeal. **10.11** (a) Laboratory of Matthew Shapiro while at McGill University. Courtesy of Eric Hargreaves, www.pageoneuroplasticity.com.

CHAPTER 11: **11.1** © Brad Snowder. **11.2** (a,c) © Wolfgang Kaehler/ Corbis; (b) © Earl & Nazima Kowall/ Corbis; (d,e) Edward S. Ross. **11.3** (a) © Dr. John Cunningham/ Visuals Unlimited; (b) Gary Head. **Page 198** Courtesy of Daniel C. Kelley, Anthony J. Arnold, and William C. Parker, Florida State University Department of Geological Science. **11.4** (a) Courtesy George P. Darwin, Darwin Museum, Down House. **11.5** (a) © John White; (b) 2004 Arent. **11.6** Down House and The Royal College of Surgeons of England. **11.7** (a) W. B. Scott (1894); (b) above, Doug Boyer in P. D. Gingerich et al. (2001) © American Association for Advancement of Science; below, John Klausmeyer, University of Michigan Exhibit of Natural History; inset, © P. D. Gingerich, University of Michigan. Museum of Paleontology; (c) above, © P. D. Gingerich and M. D. Uhen (1996), © University of Michigan. Museum of Paleontology;

inset, Phillip Gingerich, Director, University of Michigan. Museum of Paleontology. **Pages 202, 203** Courtesy of Stan Celestian/ Glendale Comunity College Earth Science Image Archive. **11.8** (b) © PhotoDisc/ Getty Images. **11.9** © JupiterImages Corporation. **11.10** bottom, USGS. **11.11** After A.M. Ziegler, C.R. Scotese, and S.F. Barrett, *Mesozoic and Cenozoic Paleogeographic Maps* and J. Krohn and J. Sundermann (Eds.), *Tidal Frictions and the Earth's Rotation II*, Springer-Verlag, 1983. **11.13** (a) © Taro Taylor, www.flickr.com/photos/tjt195; (b) © JupiterImages Corporation; (c) © Linda Bingham. **11.14** from top, © Lennart Nilsson/ Bonnierforlagen AB; Courtesy of Anna Bigas, IDIBELL-Institut de Recerca Oncologica, Spain; From "Embryonic staging system for the short-tailed fruit bat, *Carollia perspicillata*, a model organism for the mammalian order Chiroptera, based upon timed pregnancies in captive-bred animals," C.J. Cretekos et al., *Developmental Dynamics* Volume 233, Issue 3, July 2005, Pages: 721–738. Reprinted with permission of Wiley-Liss, Inc. a subsidiary of John Wiley & Sons, Inc.; Courtesy of Prof. Dr. G. Elisabeth Pollerberg, Institut für Zoologie, Universität Heidelberg, Germany; USGS. **Page 211** © David A. Kring, NASA/ Univ. Arizona Space Imagery Center. **Page 212** Section 11.2, © Wolfgang Kaehler/ Corbis; Section 11.3, Courtesy George P. Darwin, Darwin Museum, Down House; Section 11.4, Courtesy of Stan Celestian/ Glendale Comunity College Earth Science Image Archive; Section 11.5, USGS; Section 11.6, © Lennart Nilsson/ Bonnierforlagen AB. **11.16** top, Lawrence Berkeley National Laboratory.

CHAPTER 12: **12.1** © Rollin Verlinde/ Vilda. **12.2** third from left, © Roderick Hulsbergen/ http://www.photography.euweb.nl; all others, © JupiterImages Corporation. **12.4** J. A.Bishop, L. M. Cook. **12.7** above, Peter Chadwick/ SPL/ Photo Researchers, Inc. **12.9** Thomas Bates Smith. **12.10** (a) Bruce Beehler; (b) Courtesy of Gerald Wilkinson; (c) © Ingo Arndt/ Nature Picture Library. **12.11** (a,b) After Ayala and others; (c) © Michael Freeman/ Corbis. **12.12** (a,b) Adapted from S.S. Rich, A.E. Bell, and S.P. Wilson, *Genetic drift in small populations of Tribolium* Evolution 33:579–584, Fig. 1, p. 580, 1979. Used by permission of the publisher; below, Photo by Peggy Greb/ USDA. **12.13** Dr. Victor A. McKusick. **12.14** From Meyer, A., Repeating Patterns of Mimicry. *PLoS Biology* Vol. 4, No. 10, e341 doi:10.1371/journal.pbio.0040341. **Page 227** Alvin E. Staffan/ Photo Researchers, Inc. **12.16** (a) Courtesy of Joe Decruyenaere; (b,c) © David Goodin; (d) Courtesy of Dr. James French. **12.17** G. Ziesler/ ZEFA. **12.18** above, Southeastern Regional Taxonomic Center/ South Carolina Department of Natural Resources; below, NASA. **12.20** above, © Michelle Harrington; below, Ole Seehausen and Inke van der Sluijs. **12.21** above, Courtesy of The Virtual Fossil Museum, www.fossilmuseum.net; below, Mark Erdman. **12.22** Photo by © Marcel Lecoufle. **12.23** all, © Jack Jeffrey Photography. **12.24** from left, Joaquim Gaspar; Bogdan; Opiola Jerzy;

Ravedave; Luc Viatour. **Page 235** © Rollin Verlinde/ Vilda. **Page 236** Sections 12.1, 12.2, left and center, © JupiterImages Corporation; right, © Roderick Hulsbergen/ http://www.photography.euweb.nl; Section 12.3, J. A. Bishop, L. M. Cook; Section 12.4, Courtesy of Gerald Wilkinson; Section 12.5, G. Ziesler/ ZEFA; Section 12.6, Photo by © Marcel Lecoufle.

CHAPTER 13: **13.1** © Lowell Tindell; inset, NIBSC/ SPL/ Photo Researchers, Inc. **13.3** (a) Eiichi Kurasawa/ Photo Researchers, Inc.; (b) Courtesy of the University of Washington. **13.4** (a) © Janet Iwasa; (b) Photo by Tony Hoffman, courtesy of David Deamer. **13.5** (a) Chase Studios/ Photo Researchers, Inc.; (b,c) © University of California Museum of Paleontology. **13.7** © N.J. Butterfield, University of Cambridge. **13.10** (a) CNRI/ Photo Researchers, Inc.; (b) © Dr. Dennis Kunkel/ Visuals Unlimited. **13.11** (a) Alan L. Detrick, Science Source/ Photo Researchers, Inc.; (b) © Martin Miller / Visuals Unlimited; (c) Dr. John Brackenbury/ Science Photo Library/ Photo Researchers, Inc. **13.12** (a) © R. Calentine/ Visuals Unlimited; (b) SciMAT / Photo Researchers, Inc.; (c) Stem Jems/ Photo Researchers, Inc.; (d) California Department of Health Services. **13.14** (a) © Dr. Dennis Kunkel/ Visuals Unlimited; (b) Oliver Meckes/ Photo Researchers, Inc. **13.15** Courtesy of Allen W. H. Bé and David A. Caron. **13.16** (a) Gary W. Grimes and Steven L'Hernault; (b) © Dr. David Phillips/ Visuals Unlimited. **13.17** © Frank Borges Llosa/ www.frankley.com. **13.18** Based on Fig. 1 from *Genetic linkage and association analyses for trait mapping in Plasmodium falciparum*, by Xinzhuan Su, Karen Hayton & Thomas E. Wellems, *Nature Reviews Genetics* 8, 497–506 (July 2007). **Page 255** Malaria illustration by Drew Berry, The Walter and Eliza Hall Institute of Medical Research. **13.20** (a,c) © Wim van Egmond/ Visuals Unlimited; (b) Montery Bay Aquarium; (d) © Kim Taylor/ Bruce Coleman, Inc. **13.21** (a) M I Walker/ Photo Researchers, Inc.; (b) Edward S. Ross. **13.22** (b) After Stephen L. Wolfe; (c) Dr. Richard Feldmann/ National Cancer Institute; (d) Russell Knightly/ Photo Researchers, Inc. **13.23** left, Science Photo Library/ Photo Researchers, Inc. **13.24** left, After Stephen Wolfe, *Molecular Biology of the Cell*, Wadsworth, 1993; below, Micrographs Z. Salahuddin, National Institutes of Health. **13.25** © WHO, Pierre-Michel Virot, photographer; inset, Sercomi/ Photo Researchers, Inc. **13.26** CAMR, Barry Dowsett/ Science Photo Library/ Photo Researchers, Inc. **Page 265** Kent Wood/ Photo Researchers, Inc. **Page 266** Section 13.1, NIBSC/ SPL/ Photo Researchers, Inc.; Section 13.3, © University of California Museum of Paleontology; Section 13.5, © Dr. Dennis Kunkel/ Visuals Unlimited.

CHAPTER 14: **14.1** © William Campbell/ TimePix/ Getty Images. **14.4** Courtesy of Christine Evers. **14.5** Art, Raychel Ciemma **14.6** (a) © University of Wisconsin–Madison, Department of Biology, Anthoceros CD; (b) National Park Services, Paul Stehr-Green. **14.7** Art, Raychel Ciemma; photo, A. & E. Bomford/ Ardea, London. **14.8** (a) © S. Navie; (b)

David C. Clegg/ Photo Researchers, Inc.; (c) © Klein Hubert/ Peter Arnold, Inc. **14.9** below, left, © Martin LaBar, www.flickr.com/photos/martinlabar; right, © William Ferguson. **14.11** (a) R. J. Erwin/Photo Researchers, Inc.; (b) © Stan Elems/ Visuals Unlimited; (c) © Dave Cavagnaro/ Peter Arnold, Inc. **14.12** (a) © M. Fagg, Australian National Botanic Gardens; (b) Michael P. Gadomski/ Photo Researchers, Inc.; (c) © E. Webber/ Visuals Unlimited; (d) © Gerald & Buff Corsi/ Visuals Unlimited. **14.13** (b) Courtesy of Christine Evers. **14.15** from left, Photo USDA; Photo by Scott Bauer, USDA/ ARS; Courtesy of Linn County, Oregon Sheriff's Office. **14.16** (a) © Dr. Dennis Kunkel/ Visuals Unlimited; (b) Photo by Scott Bauer/ USDA; (c) Robert C. Simpson/ Nature Stock; (d) Micrograph Garry T. Cole, University of Texas, Austin/ BPS. **14.17** After T. Rost, et al., *Botany*, Wiley, 1979. **14.18** (a) © Micrograph J. D. Cunningham/ Visuals Unlimited; inset, Micrograph Ed Reschke; (b) © age fotostock/ SuperStock; (c) © Bill Beatty/ Visuals Unlimited; (d) © Chris Worden. **14.19** (a) © Gary Braasch; (b) Gary Head; (c) © Mark E. Gibson/ Visuals Unlimited. **14.20** (a) Photo by Yue Jin/ USDA; (b) Dr. P. Marazzi/ SPL/ Photo Researchers, Inc. **Page 287** Gary A. Monroe © USDA-NRCS PLANTS Database. **Page 288** Section 14.1, © William Campbell/ TimePix/ Getty Images; Section 14.6, © Stan Elems/ Visuals Unlimited; Section 14.7, Courtesy of Christine Evers; Section 14.8, Robert C. Simpson/ Nature Stock; Section 14.9, Dr. P. Marazzi/ SPL/ Photo Researchers, Inc. **14.21** After graph from www.pfc.forestry.ca. **Page 289** Jane Burton/ Bruce Coleman, Ltd.

CHAPTER 15: **Page 292** Archaeopteryx, P. Morris/ Ardea London; others, © James Reece, Nature Focus, Australian Museum. **15.1** (a) © Ana Signorovitch; (b) Dr. Chip Clark. **15.4** (b) Image © ultimathule, Used under license from Shutterstock.com. **15.5** (b) © Wim van Egmond/ Visuals Unlimited; (c) © Brandon D. Cole/ Corbis; (d) © Jeffrey L. Rotman/ Corbis. **15.6** right, Andrew Syred/ SPL/ Photo Researchers, Inc. **15.8** Art after from Solomon, 8th edition, p. 624, figure 29-4. **15.9** (a) J. Solliday/ BPS; (b,c) J. A. L. Cooke/ Oxford Scientific Films. **15.10** (a) left, Danielle C. Zacherl with John McNulty; (b) © K.S. Matz; (c) Alex Kirstitch; (d) Frank Park/ ANT Photo Library; (e) © Dave Fleetham/Tom Stack & Associates. **15.11** (b) Courtesy of © Emily Howard Staub and The Carter Center. **15.12** (a) Jane Burton/ Bruce Coleman, Ltd; (b) After D.H. Milne, *Marine Life and the Sea*, Wadsworth, 1995. **15.13** (a) Image © Eric Isselée, Used under license from Shutterstock.com; (b) © Frans Lemmens/ The Image Bank/ Getty Images; (c) Angelo Giampiccolo / FPG / Getty Images. **15.14** (a) © David Tipling/ Photographer's Choice/ Getty Images; (b) © Peter Parks/ Imagequestmarine.com. **15.15** (a) CDC/ Piotr Naskrecki; (b) Photo by Scott Bauer/ USDA; (c) Edward S. Ross; (d) CDC/ Harvard University, Dr. Gary Alpert; (e) Courtesy of Christine Evers. **15.16** (a) © Herve Chaumeton/ Agence Nature; (b) © Fred Bavendam/ Minden Pictures; (c) © George Perina, www.seapix.com.

**15.17** (a) Peter Parks/ Oxford Scientific Films/ Animals Animals; (b) © California Academy of Sciences. **15.18** left, Runk & Schoenberger / Grant Heilman, Inc. **15.20** (a) Heather Angel/ Natural Visions; (b) © Jonathan Bird/ Oceanic Research Group, Inc.; (c) After E. Solomon, L. Berg, and D.W. Martin, *Biology*, Seventh Edition, Brooks/Cole. **15.21** (a) © David Nardini/ Getty Images; (b) © Norbert Wu/ Peter Arnold, Inc.; (c) Wernher Krutein/ photovault.com. **15.22** (a,c) © P. E. Ahlberg; (b) © Alfred Kamajian. **15.23** (a) Bill M. Campbell, MD; (b) Stephen Dalton/ Photo Researchers, Inc.; (c) © David M. Dennis/ Tom Stack & Associates, Inc. **15.25** (a) © S. Blair Hedges, Pennsylvania State University; (b) Z. Leszczynski/ Animals Animals; (c) © Kevin Schafer/ Corbis; (d) © Kevin Schafer/ Tom Stack & Associates. **15.26** © Gerard Lacz/ ANTPhoto.com.au. **15.27** (a) © Sandy Roessler/ FPG/ Getty Images; (b) Jean Phillipe Varin/ Jacana/ Photo Researchers, Inc.; (c) Jack Dermid. **15.28** (a) Larry Burrows/ Aspect Photolibrary; (b) © Art Wolfe/ Photo Researchers, Inc.; (c) © Dallas Zoo, Robert Cabello; (d) © Kenneth Garrett/ National Geographic Image Collection. **15.29** (a,d) Pascal Goetgheluck/ Photo Researchers, Inc.; (e) Dr. Donald Johanson, Institute of Human Origins; (f) Louise M. Robbins; (g) © Kenneth Garrett/ National Geographic Image Collection. **15.31** Jean Paul Tibbles. **15.32** (a) Pascal Goetgheluck/ Photo Researchers, Inc.; (b,c) © Peter Brown. **Page 318** Section 15.2, © Ana Signorovitch; Section 15.3, Courtesy of Christine Evers; Section 15.4, Runk & Schoenberger / Grant Heilman, Inc.; Section 15.5, © Alfred Kamajian; Section 15.6, Z. Leszczynski/ Animals Animals. **15.34** right, Jane Burton/ Bruce Coleman, Ltd.

CHAPTER 16: **16.1** Courtesy of Joel Peter. **16.2** (b) © Steve Bloom/ stevebloom.com; (c) E. R. Degginger; inset, Jeff Fott Productions/ Bruce Coleman, Ltd. **16.4** (a) © G. K. Peck; (b) © Rick Leche, www.flickr.com/photos/rick_leche. **16.6** right, © Jacques Langevin/ Corbis Sygma. **16.7** (a) © Cynthia Bateman, Bateman Photography; (b) © Tom Davis. **16.8** (a) © Joe McDonald/ Corbis; (b) © Wayne Bennett/ Corbis; (c) Estuary to Abyss 2004. NOAA Office of Ocean Exploration. **16.9** (a) David Reznick/ University of California–Riverside; computer enhanced by Lisa Starr; (b,c) Hippocampus Bildarchiv; right, Helen Rodd. **16.10** © Bruce Bornstein, www.captbluefin.com. **16.11** Art by Precision Graphics, photograph, NASA. **16.13** left, © Adrian Arbib/ Corbis; right, © Don Mason/ Corbis. **Page 335** U.S. Department of the Interior, U.S. Geological Survey. **Page 336** Section 16.1, Courtesy of © Joel Peter; Section 16.2, Steve Bloom/ stevebloom.com; Section 16.3, © Jacques Langevin/ Corbis Sygma; Section 16.4, © Bruce Bornstein, www.captbluefin.com. **16.14** © Reinhard Dirscherl/ www.bciusa.com.

CHAPTER 17: **17.1** (a) Photo by Stephen Ausmus, USDA/ARS; (b) Photo by Scott Bauer/ USDA; (c) John Kabashima. **17.2** left, Donna Hutchins; right, upper, © Martin Harvey, Gallo Images/ Corbis; lower, © Len Robinson,

Frank Lane Picture Agency/ Corbis. **17.3** (a) David C. Clegg/ Photo Researchers, Inc.; (b) © Thomas W. Doeppner. **17.4** © Pekka Komi. **17.5** left, Michael Abbey/ Photo Researchers, Inc. **17.6** (a) Geoff Tompkinson/ SPL/ Photo Researchers, Inc.; (b) © Erwin & Peggy Bauer/ www.bciusa.com; (c) Edward S. Ross; (d) © Nigel Jones. **17.7** (a) W. M. Laetsch; (b) © Bob Jensen Photography. **17.8** (a) Bill Hilton, Jr., Hilton Pond Center; (b) © The Samuel Roberts Noble Foundation, Inc. **17.10** (a) R. Barrick/ USGS; (b) USGS; (c) P. Frenzen, USDA Forest Service. **17.11** © Richard W. Halsey, California Chaparral Institute. **17.12** Luther C. Goldman, U.S. Fish and Wildlife Service. **17.13** (a) Angelina Lax/ Photo Researchers, Inc.; (b) Photo by Scott Bauer, USDA/ARS; (c) © Greg Lasley Nature Photography, www .greglasley.net. **17.15** From left, © Van Vives; © D. A. Rintoul; © D. A. Rintoul; © Lloyd Spitalnik/ lloydspitalnikphotos.com. **17.16** from left, top row, © Bryan & Cherry Alexander/ Photo Researchers, Inc.; © Dave Mech; © Tom & Pat Leeson, Ardea London Ltd.; 2nd row, © Tom Wakefield/ Bruce Coleman, Inc.; © Paul J. Fusco/ Photo Researchers, Inc.; © E. R. Degginger/ Photo Researchers, Inc.; 3rd row, © Tom J. Ulrich/ Visuals Unlimited; © Dave Mech; © Tom McHugh/ Photo Researchers, Inc.; mosquito, Photo by James Gathany, Centers for Disease Contro; flea, © Edward S. Ross; 4th row, © Jim Steinborn; © Jim Riley; © Matt Skalitzky; earthworm, © Peter Firus, flagstaffotos .com.au. **17.20** Fisheries & Oceans Canada, Experimental Lakes Area. **17.23** NASA. **Page 358** Section 17.1, John Kabashima; Section 17.2, © Martin Harvey, Gallo Images/ Corbis; Section 17.3, © Thomas W. Doeppner; Section 17.4, USGS.

CHAPTER 18: **18.1** U.S. Navy photo by Chief Yeoman Alphanso Braggs. **18.4** NASA. **18.5** (a) Courtesy of Jim Deacon, The University of Edinburgh; (b) © D. A. Rintoul; (c) Jack Wilburn/ Animals Animals. **18.6** (a) © Franz Lanting/ Minden Pictures; (b) © James Randklev/ Corbis. **18.7** right, Image © Serg Zastavkin, Used under license from Shutter stock.com. **18.8** © Darrell Gulin/ Corbis. **18.9** (a) © John Easley, www.johneasley.com; (b) © Dr. Ray Berkelmans, Australian Institute of Marine Science. **18.10** (b) NOAA; (c) NOAA/ Photo courtesy of Cindy Van Dover, Duke University Marine Lab. **18.11** © George M. Sutton/ Cornell Lab of Ornithology. **18.12** (a) © Dr. John Hilty; (b) Joe Fries, U.S. Fish & Wildlife Service. **18.13** © Orbimage Imagery. **18.14** left, NASA, courtesy the MODIS Rapid Response Team at Goddard Space Flight Center; right, Courtesy of Guido van der Werf, Vrije Universiteit Amsterdam. **18.15** (b) © Ted Spiegel/ Corbis; (c) Frederica Georgia/ Photo Researchers, Inc. **18.16** Claire Fackler/ NOAA. **18.17** Image © Stephen Mcsweeny, Used under license from Shutterstock.com. **18.18** (a) NASA. **18.19** (a) National Snow and Ice Data Center, W. O. Field; (b) National Snow and Ice Data Center, B. F. Molnia; (c-d) NASA. **18.20** From www.esrl.noaa.gov. **18.21** U.S. Department of Transportation, Federal Highway Administration. **18.22** (a) Hans

Renner; (b) © Adolf Schmidecker/ FPG/ Getty Images. **18.23** (a) Diane Borden-Bilot, U.S. Fish and Wildlife Service; (b) U.S. Fish and Wildlife Service. **18.24** Image © Lee Prince, Used under license from Shutterstock.com. **18.25** Mountain Visions/ NOAA. **Page 384** Section 18.1, U.S. Navy photo by Chief Yeoman Alphanso Braggs; Section 18.3, Courtesy of Jim Deacon, The University of Edinburgh; © James Randklev/ Corbis; Section 18.4, © John Easley, www.johneasley.com; NOAA/ Photo courtesy of Cindy Van Dover, Duke University Marine Lab; Section 18.5, NASA; Section 18.6, © Adolf Schmidecker/ FPG/ Getty Images.

CHAPTER 19: **19.1** Courtesy © Bryce Richter/ Courtesy of University of Wisconsin–Madison. **19.2** cardiac muscle, Ed Reschke; heart, C. Yokochi and J. Rohen, *Photographic Anatomy of the Human Body*, 2nd Ed., Igaku-Shoin, Ltd., 1979; human, Image © Yuri Arcurs, Used under license from Shutterstock.com. **Page 391** left, Image © Stuart Miles, Used under license from Shutterstock.com. **19.4** from top, Ray Simmons/ Photo Researchers, Inc.; © Ed Reschke/ Peter Arnold, Inc.; © Don W. Fawcett. **19.5** (a) © John Cunningham/ Visuals Unlimited; (b,c) Ed Reschke; (d,g) Science Photo Library/ Photo Researchers, Inc.; (e) © University of Cincinnati, Raymond Walters College, Biology; (f) Michael Abbey/ Photo Researchers, Inc.; center, Image © Yuri Arcurs, Used under license from Shutterstock.com. **19.6** (a,b) Ed Reschke; (c) Biophoto Associates/ Photo Researchers, Inc. **19.7** © Triarch/ Visuals Unlimited. **Page 399** Courtesy Su-Chun Zhang/ University of Wisconsin–Madison. **Page 400** Section 19.2, from left, Ed Reschke; C. Yokochi and J. Rohen, *Photographic Anatomy of the Human Body*, 2nd Ed., Igaku-Shoin, Ltd., 1979; Section 19.3, from top, © Ed Reschke/ Peter Arnold, Inc.; Michael Abbey/ Photo Researchers, Inc.; Ed Reschke; © Triarch/ Visuals Unlimited. **19.13** Courtesy of © Organogensis, Inc., www.organo.com. **Page 401** Critical Thinking, CNRI/ Photo Researchers, Inc.

CHAPTER 20: **20.1** top, @ Stuart Isett; bottom, Image © Lakatos Sandor, Used under license from Shutterstock.com. **20.3** right, Micrograph Ed Reschke. **20.6** left, Raychel Ciemma; (c) above, © Don Fawcett/ Visuals Unlimited. **20.8** right, Image © Phase4Photography, Used under license from Shutterstock.com. **20.11** Images courtesy of Department of Pathology, The University of Melbourne. **20.12** Painting by Sir Charles Bell, 1809, courtesy of Royal College of Surgeons, Edinburgh. **Page 413** bottom, Se-Jin Lee, Johns Hopkins University School of Medicine. **Page 414** Section 20.1, © Stuart Isett. **Page 415** top, Courtesy of the family of Tiffany Manning.

CHAPTER 21: **Page 418** Image © Timothy Large, Used under license from Shutterstock .com. **21.7** right, National Cancer Institute/ Photo Researchers, Inc. **Page 424** Photograph, Professor P. Motta/ Department of Anatomy/ University La Sapienca, Rome/ Photo Researchers, Inc. **21.14** above, Photographs, Courtesy

of Kay Elemetrics Corporation. **21.17** (a) Ed Reschke; (b) Biophoto Associates/ Photo Researchers, Inc. **21.19** © O. Auerbach/ Visuals Unlimited. **21.20** Courtesy of Dr. Joe Losos. **Page 434** Section 21.5, National Cancer Institute/ Photo Researchers, Inc.; Section 21.8 left, Biophoto Associates/ Photo Researchers, Inc.; right, Courtesy of Dr. Joe Losos.

CHAPTER 22: **22.1** above, National Cancer Institute; below, In memory of Frankie McCullough. **22.2** After *Bloodline Image Atlas*, University of Nebraska–Omaha, and Sherri Wicks, *Human Physiology and Anatomy*, University of Wisconsin Web Education System, and others. **22.3** (a) © David Scharf, 1999. All rights reserved; (b) Juergen Berger/ Photo Researchers, Inc.; (c) © John D. Cunningham/ Visuals Unlimited. **22.4** (a) Biology Media/ Photo Researchers, Inc.; (c) Robert R. Dourmashkin, courtesy of Clinical Research Centre, Harrow, England. **22.6** (a) Kwangshin Kim/ Photo Researchers, Inc.; (b,c) www.zahnarzt stuttgart.com. **22.13** Dr. A. Liepins/ SPL/ Photo Researchers, Inc. **22.14** (a) © David Scharf/ Peter Arnold, Inc.; (b) Kent Wood/ Photo Researchers, Inc.; (c) Hayley Witherell. **22.15** (a) NIBSC/ Photo Researchers, Inc.; (b) © Peter Turnley/ Corbis; (c) © Zeva Oelbaum/ Peter Arnold, Inc. **22.16** above, James Hicks, Centers for Disease Control and Prevention; below, Eye of Science/ Photo Researchers, Inc. **Page 455** CDC. **Page 456** Section 22.3, Juergen Berger/ Photo Researchers, Inc.; Section 22.4, Biology Media/ Photo Researchers, Inc.; Section 22.7, Dr. A. Liepins/ SPL/ Photo Researchers, Inc.; Section 22.8, © Peter Turnley/ Corbis; Section 22.9, James Hicks, Centers for Disease Control and Prevention.

CHAPTER 23: **23.1** Courtesy of Dr. Jeffrey M. Friedman, Rockefeller University. **23.6** After A. Vander et al., *Human Physiology: Mechanisms of Body Function*, Fifth Edition, McGraw-Hill, 1990. **Page 464** Microslide courtesy Mark Nielsen, University of Utah. **23.7** After Sherwood and others; #4, D. W. Fawcett/ Photo Researchers, Inc. **23.9** (b) National Cancer Institute. **23.11** USDA, www.mypyramid.gov. **23.14** left, Evan Cerasoli. **Page 476** Section 23.1, Courtesy of Dr. Jeffrey M. Friedman, Rockefeller University; Sections 23.4, 23.5, USDA, www.mypyramid.gov. **23.16** USDA.

CHAPTER 24: **24.1** above, © EMPICS; below, Manni Mason's Pictures. **24.3** © Micrograph Manfred Kage/ Peter Arnold, Inc. **24.6** (a) AP Images; (b,c) From Neuro Via Clinicall Research Program, Minneapolis VA Medical Center. **24.13** C. Yokochi and J. Rohen, *Photographic Anatomy of the Human Body*, 2nd Ed., Igaku-Shoin, Ltd., 1979. **24.15** (a) © Eric A. Newman; (b) Merlin D. Tuttle, Bat Conservation International. **24.19** Bo Veisland/ Photo Researchers, Inc. **24.20** (a) Will & Deni McIntyre/ Photo Researchers, Inc.; (b) © Ophthalmoscopic image from Webvision http://webvision.med.utah.edu. **24.21** (a) above, Micrograph Lennart Nilsson © Boehringer Ingelheim International GmbH; Art based on www.2.gasou.edu/psychology/

courses/muchinsky and www.occipita.cfa .cmu.edu. **24.22** (1) © Fabian/ Corbis Sygma; (3) Medtronic Xomed. **Page 500** Section 24.1, Manni Mason's Pictures; Section 24.5, C. Yokochi and J. Rohen, *Photographic Anatomy of the Human Body*, 2nd Ed., Igaku-Shoin, Ltd., 1979.

CHAPTER 25: **25.1** (a) © David Ryan/ Super-Stock; (b) © Catherine Ledner Photography. **25.6** (a) China Daily/ Reuters; (b) Courtesy of Dr. William H. Daughaday, Washington University School of Medicine, from A. I. Mendelhoff and D. E. Smith, eds., *American Journal of Medicine*, 1956, 20:133.; (c) Courtesy of G. Baumann, MD, Northwestern University. **25.7** (a) Gary Head; (b) Scott Camazine/ Photo Researchers, Inc. **25.8** Biophoto Associates/ SPL/ Photo Researchers, Inc. **25.10** © Elizabeth Musar; inset, © Manny Hernandez/ Diabetes Hands Foundation, www.tudiabetes .com. **25.12** Photograph by Cecil Stoughton, White House, in the John F. Kennedy Presidential Library and Museum, Boston. **25.14** Dr. Carlos J. Bourdony. **Page 518** Section 25.1, © Catherine Ledner Photography; Section 25.3, China Daily/ Reuters; Section 25.4, Gary Head.

CHAPTER 26: **26.1** © Dana Fineman/ Corbis Sygma. **26.2** (a) Biophoto Associates/ Photo Researchers, Inc.; (b) © Rodger Klein/ Peter Arnold, Inc; (c) © Staebler/ JupiterImages. **26.4** (1–4) Carolina Biological Supply Company; (5) left, center, © David M. Dennis/ Tom Stack & Associates, Inc.; right, © John Shaw/ Tom Stack & Associates. **Page 531** AJPhoto/ Photo Researchers, Inc. **26.11** (a) © Heidi Specht, West Virginia University; (b) Courtesy of Elizabeth Sanders, Women's Specialty Center, Jackson, MS. **26.12** (a) Dr. E. Walker/ Photo Researchers, Inc.; (b) Western Ophthalmic Hospital/ Photo Researchers, Inc.; (c) CNRI/ Photo Researchers, Inc. **Page 537** © iStock

photo.com/ Ronnie Comeau. **26.14** © Lennart Nilsson/ Bonnierforlagen AB. **26.16** James W. Hanson, M.D. **Page 544** Section 26.1, © Dana Fineman/ Corbis Sygma; Section 26.2, © Staebler/ JupiterImages; Section 26.5, Western Ophthalmic Hospital/ Photo Researchers, Inc.

CHAPTER 27: **27.1** (a) © OPSEC Control Number #4 077-A-4; (b) Billy Wrobel, 2004. **27.3** © Donald L. Rubbelke/ Lakeland Community College. **27.4** below, © Andrew Syred/ Photo Researchers, Inc. **27.5** (a) from top, © Bruce Iverson; © Ernest Manewal/ Index Stock Imagery; Courtesy of Dr. Thomas L. Rost; © Franz Holthuysen, Making the invisible visible, Electron Microscopist, Phillips Research; (b) from top, Photo by Mike Clayton/ University of Wisconsin Department of Botany; © Darrell Gulin/ Corbis; Gary Head; Courtesy of Janet Wilmhurst, Landcare Research, New Zealand. **27.6** (a) Photo by Mike Clayton/ University of Wisconsin Botany Department; (b) Carolina Biological Supply Company. **27.9** © Dale M. Benham, Ph.D., Nebraska Wesleyan University. **27.11** (a) After Salisbury and Ross, *Plant Physiology*, Fourth Edition, Wadsworth; (b) © Brad Mogen/ Visuals Unlimited; (c) © Dr. John D. Cunningham/ Visuals Unlimited. **27.13** (b) © Peter Gasson, Royal Botanic Gardens, Kew. **Page 557** © JupiterImages Corporation. **27.14** (a) Courtesy of Mark Holland, Salisbury University; (b) Photo courtesy of Iowa State University Plant and Insect Diagnostic Clinic; (c) © Wally Eberhart/ Visuals Unlimited; (d) NifTAL Project, Univ. of Hawaii, Maui. **27.15** left, Image © Jan Martin Will, Used under license from Shutterstock.com. **27.16** (a) Micrograph by Ken Wagner/ Visuals Unlimited, computer-enhanced by Lisa Starr; (b,c) Courtesy of E. Raveh. **Page 560** Image © Nikolay Okhitin, Used under license from Shutterstock.com. **Page 561** Photo by Keith Weller, ARS, Courtesy of USDA. **Page 562**

Section 27.1, © OPSEC Control Number #4 077-A-4; Section 27.5, Courtesy of Mark Holland, Salisbury University; Section 27.6, upper, Image © Nikolay Okhitin, Used under license from Shutterstock.com; lower, Courtesy of E. Raveh. **Page 563** Edward S. Ross.

CHAPTER 28: **28.1** (a) © Alan McConnaughey, www.flickr.com/photos/engrpiman; (b) Courtesy of James H. Cane, USDA-ARS Bee Biology and Systematics Lab, Utah State University, Logan, UT. **28.2** (b) © Robert Essel NYC/ Corbis. **28.4** (a; c,d) Michael Clayton, University of Wisconsin; (b) Botanical Society of America Image Collection, used with permission. **28.5** (a) © T. M. Jones; (b) R. Carr; (c) © JupiterImages Corporation; (d) © Robert H. Mohlenbrock © USDA-NRCS PLANTS Database; (e) © Trudi Davidoff, www.WinterSown.org; (f) © iStockphoto.com/ Greggory Frieden. **28.6** (a, c) Lisa Starr; (b) Image © Daniel Gale, Used under license from Shutterstock.com. **28.7** (a) © Richard Uhlhorn Photography; (b,c) Photo by Peggy Greb, USDA, ARS. **28.8** (b) left, Barry L. Runk / Grant Heilman, Inc.; right, © James D. Mauseth, MCDB; below, © John D. Cunningham/ Visuals Unlimited. **28.9** (a) above, Herve Chaumeton/ Agence Nature. **28.10** © Sylvan H. Wittwer/ Visuals Unlimited. **28.12** below, © Cathlyn Melloan/ Stone/ Getty Images. **28.14** left, Larry D. Nooden; right, © Adrian Chalkley. **Page 580** © Alan McConnaughey, www.flickr.com/photos/engrpiman. **Page 582** Section 28.1, © Alan McConnaughey, www .flickr.com/photos/engrpiman; Section 28.2, © Robert Essel NYC/ Corbis; Section 28.3, © JupiterImages Corporation; Section 28.4, Image © Daniel Gale, Used under license from Shutterstock.com; Section 28.5, Herve Chaumeton/ Agence Nature; Section 28.6, © Sylvan H. Wittwer/ Visuals Unlimited; Section 28.7, © Adrian Chalkley. **28.16** left, © Mary Sue Ittner/ Pacific Bulb Society; right, © Steven D. Johnson.

# Index

The letter *f* designates figure; *t* designates table; **bold** designates key terms; ■ highlights the location of applications contained in text.

RNA translation to, 122–124
transport, 49, 49f, 71, 72–73
Protein structure, 35–36
Protein synthesis, 34
Protists, **8**, **252**–258
Protocells, **243**, 243f
Protons, **21**
Protozoans, flagellated, 252–253, 253f
Pseudocoel, **295**, 295f
Pseudopod, 54, **55**
Puberty, 514, **515**
Pulmonary circuit, **420**, 420f, 421, 421f
Pulmonary valve, 422f
Pulmonary veins, 422f
Pulp cavity, 463f
Pulse, **424**, 425
Punnett square, **159**, 159f
Pupil, **495**, 495f
Pyruvate, **89**